MOLYBDENUM

ITS BIOLOGICAL AND COORDINATION CHEMISTRY AND INDUSTRIAL APPLICATIONS

CHEMISTRY RESEARCH AND APPLICATIONS

Additional books in this series can be found on Nova's website
under the Series tab.

Additional e-books in this series can be found on Nova's website
under the e-book tab.

MOLYBDENUM

ITS BIOLOGICAL AND COORDINATION CHEMISTRY AND INDUSTRIAL APPLICATIONS

ALVIN A. HOLDER
EDITOR

nova
publishers
New York

NOTICE TO THE READER

The Publisher has taken reasonable care in the preparation of this book, but makes no expressed or implied warranty of any kind and assumes no responsibility for any errors or omissions. No liability is assumed for incidental or consequential damages in connection with or arising out of information contained in this book. The Publisher shall not be liable for any special, consequential, or exemplary damages resulting, in whole or in part, from the readers' use of, or reliance upon, this material. Any parts of this book based on government reports are so indicated and copyright is claimed for those parts to the extent applicable to compilations of such works.

Independent verification should be sought for any data, advice or recommendations contained in this book. In addition, no responsibility is assumed by the publisher for any injury and/or damage to persons or property arising from any methods, products, instructions, ideas or otherwise contained in this publication.

This publication is designed to provide accurate and authoritative information with regard to the subject matter covered herein. It is sold with the clear understanding that the Publisher is not engaged in rendering legal or any other professional services. If legal or any other expert assistance is required, the services of a competent person should be sought. FROM A DECLARATION OF PARTICIPANTS JOINTLY ADOPTED BY A COMMITTEE OF THE AMERICAN BAR ASSOCIATION AND A COMMITTEE OF PUBLISHERS.

Additional color graphics may be available in the e-book version of this book.

Library of Congress Cataloging-in-Publication Data

Molybdenum : its biological and coordination chemistry and industrial applications / editor, Alvin Holder (The University of Southern Mississippi, Department of Chemistry and Biochemistry, Hattiesburg, MS, USA).
     pages cm
 Includes bibliographical references and index.
 ISBN 978-1-62417-272-4 (hardcover)
 1. Molybdenum. I. Holder, Alvin A.
 TA480.M6M665 2013
 669'.734--dc23
                          2012042093

Published by Nova Science Publishers, Inc. ✦ *New York*

CONTENTS

PREFACE

Molybdenum is an essential trace element for virtually all life forms. It functions as a cofactor for a number of enzymes that catalyze important chemical transformations in the global carbon, nitrogen, and sulfur cycles. Thus, molybdenum-dependent enzymes are not only required for human health, but also for the health of our ecosystem. Molybdenum and its compounds are also very important in catalysis and in medicine, so it is not surprising that its biological and coordination chemistry remain very active areas of research. The enormous chemistry of molybdenum, much of which remains untapped, was investigated over many years by two icons: Edward I. Stiefel and A. Geoffrey Sykes. Ed and Geoff, as they were affectionately called by many of their friends and research students, are being honoured for their contributions to research on molybdenum with this textbook.

My goal at the outset was to capture the full vibrancy of the biological and coordination chemistry of this very important element called molybdenum and, in this way, to reflect the insight and enthusiasm of the two honorees. To do so, I divided this textbook into twelve (12) areas and invited experts in each of these areas to complete this project by contributing a chapter. The chapters are as follows: Chapter 1, Dedications and Memories of Two Icons of Moly; Chapter 2, Molybdenum (*Molybdaenum*): Its history, occurrence, brief inorganic and bioinorganic chemistry; Chapter 3, Recent Advances in the Chemistry of Molybdenum–Molybdenum Multiple Bonds; Chapter 4, Molybdenum Aqua Ions; Chapter 5, Incomplete and Complete Cuboidal Clusters of Molybdenum; Chapter 6, Model Studies of Molybdenum Electron Transfer Reactions; Chapter 7, Coordination Chemistry of Molybdenum with Catecholate Ligands; Chapter 8, Molybdenum-based Compounds In Catalysis Reactions; Chapter 9, Molybdenum and Pterins; Chapter 10, Molybdenum-nitrogenase and Related Enzymes; Chapter 11, The Molybdenum Hydroxylases: Xanthine oxidase and related enzymes; and Chapter 12, Organometallic Molybdenum Complexes as Anti-cancer Agents.

It has been my good fortune to work with so many exceptionally talented contributors from all over the world in compiling a textbook that I believe will be a valuable resource for graduate students, young investigators, and more senior scholars in the field of biological and coordination chemistry. I thank all the contributors for their hard work and their willingness to assist me whenever requested.

ACKNOWLEDGMENTS

It all started with my former high school chemistry teacher, Mr. Cornelius O'Shea (R.I.P.), who introduced me to transition metal chemistry at The Lodge School (1721), Barbados, in the 6th form (September 1982-July 1985); then it continued with my former Ph.D. advisor, Prof. Tara P. Dasgupta at The University of the West Indies, Mona Campus, Jamaica (October1990-May 1994). Prof. Dasgupta gave me the confidence and knowledge to conquer a section of molybdenum(VI) chemistry. Mr. O'Shea and Prof. Dasgupta, I thank you dearly!! I also give thanks to everyone in Prof. Dasgupta's research group, inclusive of my buddies, Drs. Richard Kirby, Paul T. Maragh, Kamaluddin Abdur-Rashid, Floyd A. Beckford, Conrad Ingram, Richard Fairman, and Novelette Sadler-McKnight. Nuff respect to my gym training Brethrens, Drs. Paul Aiken and Odelly Henry, who helped me through the stressful period of graduate school. Love to my beloved mother, Agatha Erla Holder (R.I.P.), my wife, Denise, and son, Alvin, Jnr., who believed in me during my stint in Jamaica. Without Mummy, I would not have had the opportunity to edit, and contribute by writing a chapter in this illustrious textbook

I would also like to thank the University of the West Indies and The Leverhulme Trust who gave me a fellowship in June 1995 to pursue research in Geoff's Laboratory in the Department of Chemistry, University of Newcastle, Newcastle upon Tyne, NE1 7RU, U.K., and the Inter-American Development Bank and The University of the West Indies for giving me a fellowship to pursue research in Ed's Laboratory at ExxonMobil Research and Engineering Company, New Jersey 08801, U.S.A. from August 26, 1996 to August 26, 1997. Special thanks to The Prince of Normandy, Norman Walker (R.I.P.), Geoff's Laboratory Technician, and Mrs. Ernestine Hill, Ed's Laboratory Technician, who made many Moly complexes for us.

Now, the task of working with so many gifted authors has been a real treat for me. The project also presented many challenges. I would not have made it to the finish line without the assistance of so many distinguished colleagues. The fall 2011 course CHE 400/500: Chemical Literature students who were led by J. Hugh Broome, a graduate student, and Stuart E. Ramsdale, a CHE 392 Introduction to Research in Chemistry/Biochemistry undergraduate student, I would personally like to thank you are for helping me compile Chapter 2. I would like to thank Jeannette Stiefel and Liz Sykes, the Dearest of those that have left us, for the pictures of Geoff and Ed, and for their encouragement over the years. Jeannette and Liz's dinners were of the highest palatable tastes while they hosted and entertained so many of us from all over the Globe. Finally, this work was also supported in part by an appointment to the Student Research Participation Program at the U.S. Army Engineer Research and Development Center, Construction Engineering Research Laboratory, administered by the Oak Ridge Institute for Science and Education through an interagency agreement between the U.S. Department of Energy and ERDC-CERL. This work was also supported by the Center Directed Research Program at the U.S. Army Corps of Engineers and by the Mississippi INBRE funded by grants from the National Center for Research Resources (5P20RR016476-11) and the National Institute of General Medical Sciences (8 P20 GM103476-11) from the National Institutes of Health. We have not lost any Soldados on this journey. Thank God!! Possunt quia posse videntur!!!

In: Molybdenum
Editor: Alvin A. Holder

ISBN: 978-1-62417-272-4
© 2013 Nova Science Publishers, Inc.

Chapter 1

DEDICATIONS AND MEMORIES OF TWO ICONS OF MOLY

Alvin A. Holder
The University of Southern Mississippi, Hattiesburg, MS, US

A DEDICATION TO DR. EDWARD (ED) I. STIEFEL

Ed Stiefel was a New Yorker through and through. He was raised in Brooklyn, graduated from New York University, and then attended Columbia University, where he earned a Ph.D. in Chemistry in 1967. After spending seven years at SUNY-Stony Brook, where he won the all-university teaching award, Ed moved on to the privately-funded Charles F. Kettering Foundation Research Laboratory in Ohio to continue his studies of molybdenum and tungsten chemistry as it related to biology and medicine. Then, in 1980 and for the next 20 or so years, he worked at Exxon Research on a variety of projects, ranging from ferritins through the development of new oil additives to the cleanup of the Exxon Valdez oil spill – a wide range indeed! After retiring from Exxon, Ed moved to Princeton University, where he was affiliated with both the Chemistry Department and the Princeton Environmental Institute.

This move satisfied both his long-abiding love of teaching and his more recent interest in environmental chemistry. Ed was granted 30 U.S. patents and published numerous scientific articles, reviews and books, most recently 'Biological Inorganic Chemistry', which he co-edited with Ivano Bertini, Harry Gray, and Joan Valentine. Ed earned the American Chemical Society Award in Inorganic Chemistry in 2000, he was a member of the board of reviewing editors of Science, and a Fellow of the American Association for the Advancement of Science.

Ed was an inveterate attendee at scientific meetings, especially the smaller Gordon Conference-style meetings, and it was through this mechanism that most members of the worldwide bioinorganic-chemistry community met Ed. In fact, he was instrumental in founding Gordon Conferences on both 'Molybdenum and Tungsten Enzymes' and 'Environmental Bioinorganic Chemistry'. Ed was always smiling and approachable and was always delighted to engage in (what always turned out to be) animated conversations and discussions about a wide range of topics, particularly those that involved the chemistry of the early transition metals in biological systems, that he or anyone else brought to the table – and at Gordon Conferences, this was literally at the dining table! Anyone who met him benefitted from the encounter. Ed's knowledge of the literature was incredibly wide and, in those areas in which he worked, was truly encyclopedic – just read his review articles and see his thoroughness and depth of thought. Many of us who worked with him benefitted directly because Ed was always willing to share his thoughts, ideas and results quite openly and completely and to comment constructively on those of his colleagues. Ed was a great educator and communicator both in the laboratory and in the classroom. One of his many talents was to see new connections among a mass of data from a variety of sources and to generate fresh ways of looking at a process or system. The scientific world needs intellects like that of Ed Stiefel, but they are very few and far between. Those of us who knew him well miss him and will continue to do so far into the future. He is survived by his wife, Jeannette, daughter Karen and her husband, and his two grandsons.

William E. Newton
Department of Biochemistry
Virginia Polytechnic Institute and State University
Blacksburg
Virginia 24061, U.S.A.
E-mail: wenewton@vt.edu

A DEDICATION TO PROFESSOR A. GEOFFREY (GEOFF) SYKES

It is with great pleasure and honor that I write this dedication to A. Geoffrey (Geoff) Sykes to mark this edited book which summarizes much of the chemistry he loved and for which is was renowned.

Geoff Sykes graduated with B.Sc. (1955) and Ph.D (1958) degrees in Chemistry from the University of Manchester, England. He then embarked on the many travels around the world that would epitomize his professional life and his immense contribution to inorganic chemistry, beginning with postdocs at Princeton (1958–1959) and Adelaide (1959–1960). Geoff began his academic career at the University of Leeds (1961-1980) being promoted to Reader in 1970. His marriage to Elizabeth (Liz) in 1963 produced two sons; Richard and Andrew and a daughter Caroline. Geoff quickly established a considerable reputation with a series of pioneering studies on peroxo-dicobalt species and in 1964 gained considerable recognition for his seminal text; 'Kinetics of Inorganic Reactions'.

Throughout the 1960s and 1970s the Sykes' group thrived as a result of recruiting many of the best Leeds graduates, post-doctoral fellows, and many top visiting scientists. That same year he became a founder member and later Chairman of the first Society discussion group devoted to research in Inorganic Reaction Mechanisms (IMDG). The inaugural inorganic mechanisms meeting was held in Leeds in January 1970 stimulated by the successful international meeting held the previous year at Bedford College, London with a plenary by Fred Basolo. The IMDG still thrives today under the now Royal Society of Chemistry with an annual meeting held either in Europe or in the UK. Throughout the 1970s many now well established scientists spent time at Leeds with Geoff further enhancing his reputation including: Karl Wieghardt (Mulheim, Germany), Yoichi Sasaki (Hokkaido, Japan), Andreja

Bakac (Ames, Iowa), Takashi Shibahara (Okayama, Japan), T. Ramasami (Madras, India), David Weatherburn (Wellington, NZ), Graham Lappin (Notre Dame) and Richard Henderson (Geoff's successor to the Inorganic Chair at Newcastle) along with Ph.D. students: Roger Thorneley (Norwich) and Fraser Armstrong (Oxford). By the end of the 1970s Geoff had developed an interest in the rapidly expanding area of biological inorganic chemistry performing seminal work on the mechanism of action of redox metalloproteins such as plastocyanin (Segal) and the ferredoxins (Armstrong).

In 1980, Geoff was appointed to the Established Chair of Inorganic Chemistry at Newcastle. Mechanistic studies on aqua ion chemistry continued (Richens, Castillo-Blum), which soon became focused almost entirely on Mo and W (Richens, Ooi). This paved the way for extensive work throughout the 1980s and 1990s on the chalcogenide-bridged Mo, W analogues (Ooi, Fedin, Mederos, Holder, Sokolov and Hernandez-Molina). This was a highly productive period. Exchanges with groups at the University of Bloemfontein (Leipoldt, Lamprecht, Roodt, Swarts) and Stellenbosch (Cruywagen, Koch) kept the international flavor going. At Newcastle, the metalloprotein studies also continued to thrive. Work on blue copper proteins (notably Chapman, McGuinnis, Dennison, Kyritsus) and the ferridoxins (Chapman, Im, Worrall) continued, and the attachment of $[Ru(NH_3)_5(H_2O)]^{2+}$ to surface histidine residues provided an opportunity for studying long range intramolecular electron transfer (Jackman, Lloyd-Raven; 1998 JACS paper). Seminal studies on hemerythrin (Armstrong), hemocyanin (Andrew), aconitase (Faridoon, Zhuang), the binuclear iron-enzymes ribonucleotide reductase (Han, Dobbing) and purple acid phosphatase (Holder, Aquino, Twichett) and the multicopper-enzyme galactose oxidase (Knowles, Phillips and McPherson) provided further important insights.

The international multicultural flavor of Geoff's group was reflected by students/visitors from over 40 different nationalities spending time at various stages over the years providing a friendly and productive atmosphere for research. The group produced a total of 53 Ph.D students, and amassed over 500 publications. Geoff was editor of 28 books, including volumes 32–53 of the highly regarded review series; Advances in Inorganic Chemistry.

In 1999, his immense contribution to our understanding of the mechanisms of metalloprotein reactions and inorganic coordination complexes was recognized by his election to a Fellowship of the Royal Society, believed to be the first for contributions to this area of chemistry. Geoff was undoubtedly one of the most influential British inorganic chemists of his generation.

From my own experience he undoubtedly had a unique ability to attract, enthuse, support and inspire young graduates and researchers into the area of Chemistry that he loved. He was appreciated as a good friend by everyone who knew him. He was a loyal supporter, mentor and teacher to all who worked, studied under and collaborated with him over the years, a person who gave of his time generously. We all miss him dearly.

David T. Richens,
Department of Chemistry and Biochemistry
New Mexico State University
Las Cruces
New Mexico 88003-8001
U.S.A.
E-mail: richens@nmsu.edu

MEMORIES OF TWO ICONS OF MOLY

I joined Geoff Sykes's group in Newcastle in August 1995. In fact, from my background in molybdenum chemistry as my Ph.D. research topic I was already familiar with his name, and I clearly regarded him as one of the protagonists in Mo chemistry. I had made extensive use of Geoff's papers in the literature survey for my Thesis, and felt deeply impressed by the awesome quantity and quality of his research on inorganic reaction mechanisms. In 1994 I came to Newcastle to visit my former supervisor, Professor Vladimir Fedin, who was staying with Geoff that time. It was Fedin who had introduced me to Geoff. I was almost immediately captivated by his personality, his intellect and, first and foremost, by his attitude of absolute devotion to the chemistry which he enjoyed doing and talking about so much! So I accepted his offer to spend a postdoctoral year in Newcastle without hesitation.

Looking back, I think that the year 1995-1996 which I spent with Geoff, was one of the most fruitful in my career, and probably one of the most decisive for my research interests. Everyday's interaction with Geoff was very important, and I appreciated very much our long discussions about chemistry, careful planning of the experiments to be done (Geoff was very much fond of going into the smallest details, and, amazingly, he kept all these details in his memory), his excitement about new results (I still remember his anxious questions "Have you tried it already? Any colour changes? Is the reaction fast or slow? Can we get crystals?"), and sometimes also his impatience and irritation when he felt that somebody's enthusiasm for *doing* chemistry was slacking down. I have learned from him how not to be put off by initial negative results, and I often remember his stubborn (yes!) perseverance in pursuing his goal when *my* students try to get rid of (for them) complicated and unfruitful research tasks after a couple of inconclusive experiments. Geoff looked for chemical challenges! It was a fascination to observe him finding simple but very smart ways to overcome experimental difficulties into which his adventurous and inquisitive mind would often lead our research. In brief, Geoff has become, and remains for me, a chemist *par excellence*. My impression of Geoff's personality would remain incomplete and one-sided if I do not mention his high general culture, good English humor, and his elegant use of rich English language.

Sometimes even now, when speaking or writing in English, I catch myself using a word or an expression which I first learned from Geoff (I used to have a small notebook where I use to write down colorful and witty expressions which Geoff used during our group meetings). He had a deep sense of duty and obligation, too. He never did research in order to bury the results for good in a forgotten research report. All the results he treated as important and he has published them *all*, with all the students and postdocs included as co-authors, no matter how modest their contribution could have been.

It was sad news for me when I learned that Geoff passed away, and I feel very honored to participate in a book dedicated to two great scientists - Ed Stiefel and Geoff Sykes.

Professor Maxim Nailyevich Sokolov
Nikolaev Institute of Inorganic Chemistry
Russian Academy of Sciences, Siberian Branch
Prospekt Lavrentyeva 3, Novosibirsk 630090, Russian Federation

I would like to say that when I entered Geoff's research field, I knew little about Mo chemistry. It was all new for me and it got time and hard work to get used to work under rigorously air free conditions. My work with Geoff was important from both personal and scientific point of view. Personally I have had the opportunity to work in a multicultural group with people from different nationalities (Russians, Koreans, Brazilians, Chinese, Japanese, Indonesians, Arabs), which Geoff handled with supreme tact and consummated correctness. It was indeed a rich experience for me. I met there other postdocs, with whom, thank to Geoff, I have started a long and fruitful collaboration which has endured ever since 1996. And I got hooked to the chalcogenide cluster chemistry, research field that I keep going up to now. This is all Geoff's legacy which I value very much. I spent one year (1996) in Geoff's group and I was so satisfied with the results that I came back in 1997 for four months, and again in 1999 for another two months. It was the most fruitful period of my scientific career (I have published 15 papers with Geoff!!). Geoff was sometimes very stubborn with his ideas and it was very difficult to convince him that an experiment would not work but at the end his perseverance and undying optimism won the day and were the key to success!

Later I met Geoff many times in congresses as a good friend, and welcomed him in his visits to La Laguna – he was a keen traveler and a bird-watcher. I enjoyed very much talking to Geoff, he used to spend a lot of time with each of the member of his group giving advices and ideas. He was quite prodigious at that! Geoff and his wife Liz were very hospitable hosts at their home parties where they used to invite the entire group and to make everybody feel welcome and comfortable.

I am pleased to participate in a book dedicated to someone who has contributed enormously to my scientific career.

Dr. Rita Hernandez-Molina
Departamento de Química Inorgánica
Universidad de La Laguna
La Laguna
Spain

It all began on a Monday in June 1995: 06/95-09/95: *Leverhulme Fellow*, Department of Chemistry, University of Newcastle, Newcastle upon Tyne, NE1 7RU, U.K., with Professor A. Geoffrey Sykes. There, I synthesized, characterized, and studied the reactivity of molybdenum and tungsten supramolecular clusters (incomplete and complete cuboidal clusters) in aqueous solution.

I remembered that Monday morning when I entered the Bedson Building in Newcastle upon Tyne and asked this neatly attired Gentleman if he knew where Prof. Sykes' laboratory was located. It was no other than the Prince of Normandy, Norman Walker, Geoff's Laboratory Technician. During the summer, we all began at 0900 hours and worked until 2200 hours!! p-Toluene sulfonic acid (HPTS) was the ACID of choice for all aqueous chemistry!!! I must say that Geoff wanted results every five seconds, and believed that chemists are not supposed to be millionaires.

I was shock to see that Geoff would keep his Sephadex G-256 and Dowex resins in his office, only giving you portions in containers when needed. He was frugal in the way he spent his grant money. He insisted on keeping a well written laboratory notebook, and insisted that all experiments must be reproducible before writing a manuscript for submission to a peer-reviewed journal. He was a perfectionist!!!

Entertainment at Geoff's house was nice; his immaculate green house and garden were of the highest standard!! I met Che-Hun Kwak (South Korea), Keisuke Umakoshi (Japan), Fauziah (Kuwait), Colin and David Saysell, Vladimir Federov (Russia), and Sang-Choul Im (South Korea), the illustrious Profs. William McFarlane, John Errington, William Clegg, and Mark Elsegood, and Geoff's Secretary, Mrs. Isobelle Compson. I must say that Geoff was well versed in sports such as cricket and football!!

One year later, an Inter-American Development Bank and The University of the West Indies provided me with a fellowship to carry out research in Ed's laboratory:

08/96-08/97: *Postdoctoral Fellow/Visiting Professor*, ExxonMobil Research and Engineering Company, New Jersey 08801, U.S.A., with Dr. Edward I. Stiefel. There, I synthesized, characterized, and studied the reactivity of nitrosyl complexes, molybdenum, rhenium, and tungsten supramolecular clusters; then applied such clusters as potential anti-friction agents.

I enjoyed working with NO and other NO_x compounds that were vasodilators. Induced-electron transfer processes were the themes in non-aqueous solvents I met Mrs. Ernestine Hill, Drs. Hal Murray, Jonathan and Christine McConnachie, Ramon Espino, John Robbins, Mark Greaney, Rick Bare, Robert Stibrany, Michael G. Matturro, István Horváth, Veronica Herrera, , Raquel Terroba and Mr. Chuck Pitroski.

Like Geoff, Ed, on the job, insisted on keeping a well written laboratory notebook, and insisted that all experiments must be reproducible before writing a manuscript for submission to a peer-reviewed journal. He was a perfectionist!!!

Off the job, Ed had the other side of him: Ed was so easy going (Caribbean Style), unruffled, and always was an excellent entertainer with Jeannette at his side. Ed would take us to New York and would walk around Manhattan, eat at the finest Brazilian restaurants. He loved his ice cream sorbets!!

One year later, and the subsequent year (1999) back to Geoff's laboratory with money from the U.K.: 06/98-09/98: A Wellcome Research Travel Grant. Research involving the bioinorganic chemistry of purple acid phosphatase isolated from soybeans, sweet potatoes, and the porcine uterine fluids. A collaborative effort with Professor A. Geoffrey Sykes at the Department of Chemistry, University of Newcastle, Newcastle upon Tyne, NE1 7RU, U.K. US$2,800 That summer we wrote a grant proposal and received funding: 10/98-10/00: A Wellcome Trust International Research Development Award. Research involving the bioinorganic chemistry of purple acid phosphatase isolated from soybeans, sweet potatoes, and the porcine uterine fluids. A collaborative effort with Professor A. Geoffrey Sykes at the Department of Chemistry, University of Newcastle, Newcastle upon Tyne, NE1 7RU, U.K. US$62,000.

During 1998 and 1999, I met Rita (Spain), Maxim (Russia), Danil (Russia), Diego, Mauricio Casanova (Chile), and the whole crew from Geoff' laboratory: Craig, Iain, John, Mark, Mark, Dave, Mi-Sook Seo (South Korea), and Jin (South Korea). We had fun!!! The Pub and parties with Geoff. Biggs Market, the Quay Side. The trips to Fife, Edinburgh, London, and Paris, were all great during all visits to Geoff's castle in Newcastle upon Tyne. Gateshead, Tynemouth, North and South Shield, and St. James Park for The Newcastle United Football Club were memories!!

In 2000, I invited Geoff to visit all three campuses of The University of the West Indies, Mona Campus, Jamaica; Cave Hill Campus, Barbados; and St. Augustine Campus, Trinidad and Tobago. While in Barbados and Trinidad and Tobago, he enjoyed his favourite past time: bird watching. He enjoyed my rum punch and coconut bread!!!

In summary, I enjoyed Ed and Geoff's company. I will miss them dearly!! R.I.P.

In: Molybdenum
Editor: Alvin A. Holder

ISBN: 978-1-62417-272-4
© 2013 Nova Science Publishers, Inc.

Chapter 2

MOLYBDENUM (*MOLYBDAENUM*): ITS HISTORY, OCCURRENCE, BRIEF INORGANIC AND BIOINORGANIC CHEMISTRY

J. Hugh Broome[1], Stuart E. Ramsdale[1],
Alvin A. Holder[1]*, Tara P. Dasgupta[2], Daniel Hinton[1],
Aaron Davis[1], Amber W. Gresham[1], Michael Shattles[1],
Yiliyasi Wusimanjiang[1], Bradley Evans[1], Joseph Spangler[1],
Mark Holcomb[1], Tiffany Dobbs[1], Jo T. Burrell[1], Jessa Faye Arca[1],
Mallory Rogers[1] and Nathaniel Satcher[1]

[1]Department of Chemistry and Biochemistry,
The University of Southern Mississippi, Hattiesburg, Mississippi, US
[2]Department of Chemistry, The University of the West Indies,
Mona Campus, Mona, Kingston, Jamaica

ABSTRACT

This chapter describes the history, occurrence, and brief inorganic and bioinorganic chemistry of molybdenum, inclusive of the molybdate(VI) chemistry as researched by Alvin A. Holder and Tara P. Dasgupta. Sections are also dedicated to basic molybdenum chemistry, ^{95}Mo NMR spectroscopy, inorganic reaction mechanisms, catalysis, and medicinal uses of molybdenum compounds.

ABBREVIATIONS

bpy = 2,2'-bipyridine
dien = diethylenetriamine

---

* E-mail: alvin.holder@usm.edu and alvinaholder@yahoo.com.

dipic^{2-} = dipicolinate anion
en = 1,2-diaminoethane
phen = 1,10-phenanthroline
PY5Me$_2$ = 2,6-bis(1,1-bis(2-pyridyl)ethyl)pyridine
sep = sepulchrate = 1,3,6,8,10,13,16,19-octaazabicyclo[6.6.6]ecosane
trans[14]diene = 5,7,7,12,14,14- hexamethyl-1,4,8,11-tetraazacyclodeca-4,11-diene
terpy = = tpy = 2,2';6',2"-terpyridine
tren = 2,2',2"-triaminotriethylamine

HISTORY

Molybdenum is a Group 6 (Group VIA) metal that has the symbol Mo, an atomic number of 42 (electronic configuration = [Kr] $4d^5 5s^1$), and an atomic weight of 95.96 g mol^{-1}. Its name is derived from Neo-Latin *Molybdaenum*, from Ancient Greek Μόλυβδος *molybdos*, which means *lead, as* molybdenum's ores were always confused with lead ores.[1]

Figure 1. A photo of molybdenum as a metal.[4]

In 1778, molybdenum was discovered by the Swedish chemist Carl William Scheele.[1] Scheele first thought he was analyzing a sample of lead, but soon discovered it was a sample of molybdenite.[2] Although Scheele was credited with the discovery of molybdenum in its elemental form, it was Peter Hjelm who first reduced the oxide with carbon in order to produce the gray metallic powder called molybdenum.[3]

OCCURRENCE AND PRODUCTION OF MOLYBDENUM

Molybdenum is the 54th most abundant element in the Earth's crust and the 25th most abundant element in the oceans, with an average concentration of 10 ppb; it is the 42nd most abundant element in the Universe.[5] It was reported that the Russian Luna 24 mission discovered a molybdenum-bearing grain in a pyroxene fragment taken from Mare Crisium on the Moon.[6] Molybdenum never occurs freely in nature as it is always found present in an ore. Molybdenum is mined as a principal ore, and is also recovered as a by-product of copper and tungsten mining.

The world's largest producers of molybdenum materials are the United States, China, Chile, Peru and Canada. Based on the estimated twelve million metric tons of molybdenum in the world, five and a half million metric tons are estimated to be in the U.S.A.[7] Significant amounts of molybdenum are found in mines located in Colorado, New Mexico, and Idaho. Although molybdenum is found in such minerals as wulfenite ($PbMoO_4$) and powellite ($CaMoO_4$), the main commercial source of molybdenum is molybdenite (MoS_2).

The ore, molybdenite, is first processed by heating to a temperature of 700 °C; then the sulfide is oxidized by the air to form molybdenum(VI) oxide:[8]

$$2MoS_2 + 7O_2 \rightarrow 2MoO_3 + 4SO_2 \tag{1}$$

The oxidized ore is then either heated to 1,100 °C in order to sublime the oxide, or leached with aqueous ammonia, which reacts with the molybdenum(VI) oxide to form water soluble molybdates:

$$MoO_3 + 2NH_4OH \rightarrow (NH_4)_2MoO_4 + H_2O \tag{2}$$

Copper-containing compounds, which are impurities in molybdenite, are less soluble in aqueous ammonia. In order to completely remove copper-containing compounds from the solution, these species are precipitated by bubbling hydrogen sulfide through the solution.[5] Pure molybdenum is then produced by reduction of the oxide with hydrogen, while the molybdenum for steel production is reduced by the aluminothermic reaction with the addition of iron to produce ferromolybdenum. A common form of ferromolybdenum contains 60% molybdenum.[5,8]

PHYSICAL PROPERTIES

Molybdenum has one of the highest melting temperatures of all the elements, yet unlike most other high-melting point metals, its density (10.22 g cm^{-3})[9] is only 25% greater than that of iron. Its coefficient of thermal expansion is the lowest of the engineering materials, while its thermal conductivity exceeds all but a handful of elements.[9] In its pure form, molybdenum is a silvery-grey metal with a Mohs hardness of 5.5.[4] It has a melting point of 2,623 °C;[9] of the naturally occurring elements, only tantalum, osmium, rhenium, tungsten, and carbon have higher melting points.[1] Weak oxidation of molybdenum starts at 300 °C. It has one of the lowest coefficients of thermal expansion[9] (4.8×10^{-6} K^{-1} at 25 °C) among commercially used metals.[5] The tensile strength of molybdenum wires increases about three times, from about 10 to 30 GPa, when their diameter decreases from ~50–100 nm to 10 nm.[10] Its thermal conductivity is 138 W m^{-1} K^{-1} at 20 °C.[9]

USES OF MOLYBDENUM AND ITS COMPOUNDS

Due to molybdenum's combined properties of conductivity, strength, and corrosion resistance, molybdenum is unique in its uses.[9] It is used in steel, aircrafts, missiles, filaments in electric heaters, lubricants, and protective coatings in boiler plates.[9] When added to steel and iron, it increases strength, hardness,[9,11,12] its ability to be welded, durability, and corrosion resistance.[13]

In nickel-based alloys, molybdenum improves resistance to both corrosion and high-temperature creep deformation.[9,11,12] Molybdenum-based alloys[9] have a unique combination of properties, including high strength at elevated temperatures, high thermal and electrical conductivity, and low thermal expansion.[9,11,12] Molybdenum metal and its alloys are the first choice in many demanding specialized applications.[9,11,12] Without the use of molybdenum as an alloying agent in the production of ferrous and nonferrous alloys, which contributes to increased strength and corrosion resistance in many commercial products such as jet engines and afterburner parts, the technology of flying and the production of higher grades of steel would not have progressed as much as it has in today's world. The market for molybdenum production is global and has numerous diverse applications, and as such, there are many products that come from the mining and processing of ores containing molybdenite.[9] Molybdenite is the major source for industrial production of molybdenum compounds.[9] Molybdenum and its chemical products are used in catalysts, polymer compounding, corrosion inhibitors, and also high performance lubrication formulas.[9] Molybdenum-99 is a parent radioisotope to the daughter radioisotope technetium-99m, which is used in many medical procedures.[14]

Molybdenum is also used in NO, NO_2, NO_x analyzers in power plants for pollution controls. At 350 °C the element acts as a catalyst for NO_2/NO_x to form only NO molecules for consistent readings by infrared light.[15] Ammonium heptamolybdate is used in biological staining procedures; while phosphomolybdic acid is a stain used in thin layer chromatography. Also, molybdenum coated soda lime glass is used for CIGS solar cell fabrication.

Molybdenum has extensive sulfur chemistry, where one of its important compounds, molybdenum disulfide, is used as a solid lubricant and a high-pressure high-temperature (HPHT) anti-wear agent. Its layer structure confers lubricating properties similar to that of graphite. It forms strong films on metallic surfaces and is a common additive to HPHT greases, where in the event of a catastrophic grease failure, a thin layer of molybdenum prevents contact of the lubricated parts.[16] It also has semiconducting properties with distinct advantages over traditional silicon or graphene in electronics applications.[17] Molybdenum-sulfur chemistry underlines one of the most important industrial catalysts, where the MoS_2-based hydrodesulfurization catalyst [18] is used in removing sulfur compounds from petroleum by reaction with hydrogen and conversion to H_2S.[11] MoS_2 is also used as a catalyst in hydrocracking of petroleum fractions which contain nitrogen, sulfur and oxygen.[19]

Complexes of dithiocarbamates, $R_2NCS_2^-$, and of dithiophosphates, $(RO)_2PS_2^-$, are used as oil-soluble lubricant additives, decomposing at rubbing surfaces to MoS_2.[11,12] Mitchell and his research group developed Mo-S chemistry in contracts with Shell and, later, with Esso, in order to synthesize Mo-S compounds and lubricant additives.[20] The Mo-dithiolate complex was an excellent friction modifier and wear reducer (and the colored oil a beautiful green) but was expensive.[11,12] The water-soluble Mo-cysteine complex has potential in metal work applications.[11,12] Stiefel *et al.*[21-26] have also pioneered the use of molybdenum compounds as anti-friction agents at ExxonMobil Research and Engineering Company.

THE ISOTOPES OF MOLYBDENUM AND THEIR MEDICINAL USES

Molybdenum has 39 isotopes, of which seven of them are naturally occurring, with ^{98}Mo being the most abundant at 24.39% abundance.[1] Only five (^{94}Mo, ^{95}Mo, ^{96}Mo, ^{97}Mo, and ^{98}Mo) of the seven naturally occurring isotopes are not radioactive, leaving the other 34 isotopes of molybdenum as the active emitters in the molybdenum isotope group. The isotopes' radioactive emission includes beta particles, isomeric transitions (IT), and electron capture (EC), with half-lives ranging from slightly greater than 0.15 μs to greater than 6 x 10^{20} years.[1]

The earliest isotopes were discovered in the late 1920s using mass spectroscopy methods.[27] The early isotopes included ^{92}Mo, ^{94}Mo, ^{95}Mo, ^{96}Mo, ^{97}Mo, ^{98}Mo, and ^{100}Mo. In 2010, ^{115}Mo, ^{116}Mo, and ^{117}Mo were discovered via Projectile Fission or Fragmentation (PF). Many other methods such as Fusion Evaporation (FE), Light Particle Reactions (LP), Neutron Fission (NF), and Charged-Particle Fission (CPF) were utilized to discover the other 29 isotopes.

The most recent discovery of ^{115}Mo, ^{116}Mo, and ^{117}Mo in 2010 was at the RI Beam Factory at RIKEN in Japan by the Projectile Fission method.[27] A ^{238}U atom was accelerated and collided with a beryllium target resulting in the formation of 45 new isotopes. Among those 45 new isotopes were ^{115}Mo, ^{116}Mo, and ^{117}Mo. There were 993 counts for ^{115}Mo, 78 counts for ^{116}Mo, and 6 counts for ^{117}Mo, which were determined by a BigRIPS superconducting in-flight separator.[27]

Molybdenum isotopes are in high demand for their applications. ^{99}Mo is the parent isotope of ^{99m}Tc, which is the most widely used radioactive isotope in the medical field. Therefore, the industrial production of ^{99}Mo is of great value. Current production methods are expensive and low yielding. These include neutron induced nuclear fission of ^{235}U and the formation of ^{99}Mo from ^{98}Mo upon the fusion of a neutron.[28] A newer method of synthesis developed in Argentina utilizes a uranium/aluminum alloy that is bombarded with neutrons to promote the fission of the ^{235}U and the production of ^{99}Mo. Morreale, Novog, and Luxat at McMaster University in Ontario, Canada utilized a reactor owned by Atomic Energy of Canada Limited in order to research the viability of producing ^{99}Mo for medical uses.[28] However, economic and design issues must be further investigated to produce practical amounts of ^{99}Mo.[29]

The natural source of the isotopes, specifically ^{92}Mo and ^{94}Mo, has long been disputed among scientists. No one is certain as to the precise origin of the light Mo isotopes, but it is widely accepted that they originate in space. Fisker, Hoffman, and Pruet hypothesize that the lighter naturally occurring isotopes, ^{92}Mo and ^{94}Mo, are potentially products of several astronomical processes. 30] These processes include neutron-rich outflows from blossoming neutron stars, outflows from black hole accretion disks, and extremely neutrino-irradiated neutron-rich outflows from neutron stars.

Since it is accepted that most of the lighter isotopes of molybdenum originate in the galaxy upon the origination of neutron stars or the yields of black holes, many scientists have analyzed meteorites for molybdenum isotopes, which has led to interesting conclusions about the solar system.[31] Molybdenum isotopes have been some of the significant deciding factors in the determination of the chemical composition of our solar system. Wieser at The University of Calgary and De Laeter at Curtin University of Technology analyzed the molybdenum isotopic fractionation in several iron meteorites utilizing Thermal Ionization Mass Spectroscopy.[31] They discovered that the isotopic fractionations for various meteorites were homogeneous, which suggested that in the early solar nebula the galaxy had a homogeneous isotopic composition.

Dauphas, Davis, Marty, and Reisberg have also concluded that there is a correlation with the Earth's formation and the composition of certain meteorites. Molybdenum and ruthenium isotopic analysis of meteorites revealed anomalies in their molybdenum and ruthenium isotopic fractionations that correlated their formation to their origination of the Earth's inner core. This revealed significant insights into the beginnings of the Earth and the Universe.[32]

Geochemically, molybdenum isotopes reveal important data concerning the formation of the Earth's mantle and crust. This has been an area of peak interest for geologists and chemists in recent years. Since molybdenum is the most abundant transition metal in sea water, research concerning the Earth's oceans and the seven naturally occurring isotopes will generally be related. Molybdenum exists in ocean water as the molybdate ion (MoO_4^{2-}).[33] Molybdenum exists in the sediments on the ocean floor due to its rapid aggregation under anoxic conditions. Multiple-collector inductively coupled plasma mass spectrometry (MC-ICP-MS) and other techniques are currently being utilized to analyze the molybdenum isotopic fractionation in the Earth's ocean sediments.[34]

A plethora of molybdenum geochemistry and its research involving isotopes have been reported due to the fact that the radioactive isotopes facilitate easy detection. Siebert et al.[33] at the University of Berne in Switzerland utilized MC-ICP-MS to detect the isotopic fractionation in the crust and black shales.[33] Their study also included an indepth study that analyzed the isotopic fractionation over time. Siebert et al.[33] also attempted to determine the molybdenum cycle in the world's oceans. Their results indicated that the ocean had a much heavier isotopic composition than any other source of molybdenum isotopes. Siebert et al.[33] observed that the concentration of Mo in anoxic conditions, where molybdenum as MoO_4^{2-} readily forms thiomolybdates with the sulfur from the H_2S, was similar to the overall bulk concentration ratios that were observed in the world's oceans. As for their depth study, they found that the overall isotopic composition of molybdenum has not changed over the past 60 million years.[33]

Another geochemical study carried out by Scheiderich et al.[35] focused on the Mediterranean region, which is known for its organic-rich sediment deposits or sapropels. These sapropels formed during depleted oxygen conditions and at high sulfur concentrations, which aided in precipitating many trace metals such as molybdenum. Scheiderich et al.[35] reported that the samples were combusted to destroy organic matter and dissolved in concentrated inorganic acids. Soluble samples were analyzed via Nu Plasma MC-ICP-MS, while uncombusted samples were analyzed via X-ray Diffraction (XRD). Scheidrich et al.[35] concluded that the Mo isotopic composition is believed to be that of the period of the

Messinian Salinity Crisis, in which the oceanic flow in the Mediterranean is hypothesized to have subsided.[35] This would have led to the higher concentrations of Mo isotopes that Schiederich *et al.*[35] observed in their research findings. Due to the lack of oceanic flow, anoxic conditions would have prevailed leading to the aggregation of the thiomolybdates, which have the general formula $MoO_xS_{4-x}^{2-}$ under anoxic conditions.[36]

Isotopic tagging has been a utilized to determine molybdenum's use and mechanisms in the human body. Molybdenum-100 was used by Sievers *et al.*[37] as an extrinsic tag for monitoring Mo levels of absorption and excretion kinetics in the intestines of infants to gain better insight into the dietary necessities of newborns.[37] The researchers analyzed urinary and fecal excretions via Atomic Absorption Spectroscopy (AAS) and Inductively Coupled Plasma Mass Spectroscopy (ICP-MS).[37] They found that the molybdenum-100 median uptake was about 97.5%, which indicated that the newborn had a severe shortage of Mo. They discovered that the peak concentrations of the radioactive nuclides in the urine were about eight and 24 hours in the feces hours after initial ingestion.[37] Sievers *et al.*[37] also discovered that a high molybdenum diet increases copper excretion in the urine, which could lead to copper depletion.

Another study performed by Yoshida *et al.*[38] monitored molybdenum uptake and concentration in 43 young Japanese women for four years utilizing ^{97}Mo and ^{98}Mo radio isotopes.[38] By varying the diets of these women, researchers were able to determine the effect of certain types of foods on molybdenum absorption and concentration in the women's bodies. For example, soybean products made up a majority of the diet for the third year. Soybean products contain high amounts of molybdenum; hence, the urinary and fecal excretion of the women, which is what Yoshida *et al.*[38] monitored via ICP-MS, should have had higher amounts of molybdenum.[38] However, the researchers discovered that higher molybdenum diets results in a higher molybdenum uptake.[38] Higher molybdenum uptake increased the activity of the enzymes that require molybdenum.[38] This phenomenon is rationalized via a common kinetics relationship that directly relates rate and concentration.

For more information on the molybdenum geochemistry, the readers are encouraged to read a nice chapter entitled "*The Biogeochemistry of Molybdenum and Tungsten*", which was written by Edward I. Stiefel, to whom this textbook is dedicated to in his honor.[39]

BASIC CHEMISTRY OF MOLYBDENUM

Molybdenum is an important second-row transition metal. The main oxidation states of molybdenum are -2, -1, 0. +1, +2, +3, +4, +5, and +6.[40] Molybdenum can exhibit several coordination numbers (four to eight), various geometries stereochemistry,[9,40] and the ability to form many compounds with organic and inorganic elements (for example, oxygen, fluorine, chlorine, and sulfur).[40] It can also form bi-nuclear and poly-nuclear compounds containing bridging oxide or chloride ligands and/or molybdenum-molybdenum bonds.[13,40]

The coordination chemistry of molybdenum is largely dominated by Mo(0), Mo(II), Mo(IV), and Mo(VI) species.[40] In its lower oxidation states, molybdenum has extensive organometallic chemistry exemplified by the well-known hexacarbonyl $[Mo^0(CO)_6]$.[9] $Mo(CO)_6$ is an extremely useful reagent in inorganic synthesis.[40,41] A feature of Mo(II) is strong Mo-Mo bonding, as in the acetate, $Mo_2(CH_3CO_2)_4$, the so-called dichloride, Mo_6Cl_{12}., and other Mo(II) compounds as reported in the literature.[9,42-65]

As mentioned earlier, MoS_2 is sought after for its application as a lubricant. MoS_2 crystallizes in a way that effectively forms alternating sheets of sulfur and molybdenum atoms that can slide past each other in a manner analogous to the way sheets of graphite slide past each other.[66] In MoS_2 each molybenum atom is trigonal-prismatically cited inside a coordination sphere of six sulfur atoms (see figure 2).[67] Each sulfur atom is trigonally bound to three molybenum atoms.[67] This pattern extends indefinitely to form the afforementioned layers.

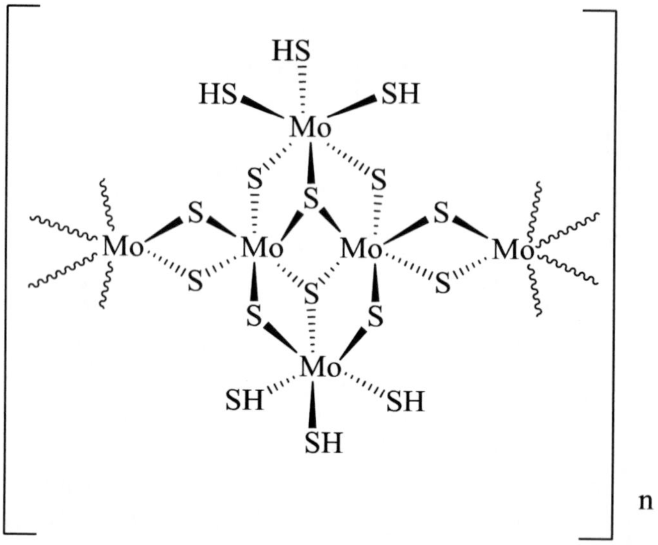

Figure 2. A fragment of the MoS_2 lattice showing the trigonal-prismatic coordination geometry around each molybdenum atom and the trigonal geometry around each sulfur atom.

High purity MoS_2 is normally prepared by heating the elements at 1000 °C for several days.[40] The reaction of anhydrous $MoCl_5$ and Na_2S is a promising alternative reaction.[68] The reaction is so exothermic that it bursts into flames after the mixing of the reactants; it is complete within seconds.

$$2MoCl_5 + 5Na_2S \rightarrow 2MoS_2 + 10NaCl + S \qquad (3)$$

Unlike other metal sulfides, molybdenum disulfide is unreactive to dilute strong acids; it only dissolves in strongly oxidizing acids such as aqua regia and boiling sulfuric acid.[40] However, it has been shown to decompose upon heating in an oxygen rich atmosphere:[40]

$$2MoS_2 + 9O_2 \rightarrow 2MoO_3 + 4SO_3 \qquad (4)$$

At room temperature, molybdenum does not react with air or oxygen, however, at elevated temperatures, MoO_3 is formed:[69]

$$2Mo + 3O_2 \rightarrow 2MoO_3 \qquad (5)$$

Molybdenum also forms MoO (dark brown), MoO_2 (dark brown), and Mo_2O_3 (black).[70] The molybdenum oxides form a series of acids analogous to the sulfur oxoacids upon reaction with water:

$$MoO_3 + H_2O \rightarrow H_2MoO_4 \tag{6}$$

$$H_2MoO_4 + H_2O \rightarrow H_4MoO_5 \tag{7}$$

$$H_4MoO_5 + H_2O \rightarrow H_6MoO_6 \tag{8}$$

For extensive molybdenum chemistry, the reader is encouraged to read the textbook entitled "Advanced Inorganic Chemistry".[40]

A GENERAL SURVEY OF THE GROUP(VI) OXOANIONS

Molybdenum differs from chromium significantly in the richness of its cluster chemistry.[40,67] In this section, we will present a general survey of the Group(VI) oxoanions, then discuss the chemistry of molybdenum in the +6 oxidation state. Group(VI) oxoanions of chromium, molybdenum, and tungsten, namely CrO_4^{2-}, MoO_4^{2-}, and WO_4^{2-}, have found wide application in the field of chemistry and biochemistry. These oxoanions have been used extensively as corrosion inhibitors and oxidants for numerous reactions.[71,72]

The chromate(VI), molybdate(VI), and tungstate(VI) ions are usually tetrahedral in geometry because a coordination number greater than four would create steric hindrance on the central metal atom as result of the number of ligands around the central metal atom. Molybdenum and tungsten, however, being second and third row elements, respectively, can expand their coordination spheres, giving rise to some substituted oxo complexes of higher coordination numbers than their chromium analogues.

In terms of oxidizing ability, chromates are much more powerful in this aspect than molybdates and tungstates. This is the general trend observed for oxoanions of the first row transition metals compared to those of the second and third rows. The E° values are as shown in Table 1.[71,72]

The tendency for these ions to polymerize falls in the reverse sequence, that is, $3^{rd} \gg 2^{nd} > 1^{st}$. There is still some uncertainty surrounding the reason for the polymerization shown with Mo(VI) and W(VI) as compared with Cr(VI). The reason seems to be linked to the size of the atom and the ability of the orbitals to overlap with those of oxygen to give substantial π bonding (M=O).[73] The chromium atom, being smaller, will exhibit multiple bonding to a greater extent than molybdenum and tungsten. Molybdenum forms a large and structurally diverse class of cluster compounds known as the polyoxomolybdates. Polyoxomolybdates are cage-like structures composed of Mo-O-Mo linkages are often highly symmetric. $Mo_6O_{19}^{2-}$, and $Mo_{36}O_{112}(H_2O)_{16}^{8-}$, are representative examples of the class.[70]

Table 1. E° values for various M(VI) species.[71,72]

Process	E°/V
$Cr_2O_7^{2-} + 14H^+ + 6e^- \rightleftharpoons 2Cr^{3+} + 7H_2O$	+1.33
$HCrO_4^- + 7H^+ + 3e^- \rightleftharpoons Cr^{3+} + 4H_2O$	+1.20
$MoO_2^{2+} + 2H^+ + e^- \rightleftharpoons MoO^{3+} + H_2O$	+0.48
$2WO_3 + 2H^+ + 2e^- \rightleftharpoons W_2O_5 + H_2O$	-0.03

The polymerization of MoO_4^{2-} and WO_4^{2-} which is brought about by acidification of their aqueous solution, is a complex subject.[74,75] An excellent review of polytungstate has been written by Keppert.[76] A brief introduction of these species will be discussed below.

Numerous attempts by many researchers[77] have been made to describe the bonding in these tetrahedral MoO_4^{2-} oxoanions on the basis of the MO theory. This would enable one to explain the observed electronic and EPR spectra of these oxoanions. The high oxidation states of these metal centers, in these ions, imply that the M-O bond is likely to have a high degree of covalency with extensive σ and π delocalization of charge (both t_2 and e orbitals on the metal are involved in π bonding in these tetrahedral species) and there is considerable mixing of d and p metal orbitals. The earliest attempt at a semi-empirical MO approach was that of Wolfsberg and Helmholz on the chromate and permanganate ions. The scheme was later criticized by Ballhausen and Liehr,[78] who proposed a somewhat different order of the energy levels. This scheme was found to be consistent by Carrington and Schonland[79] with the electronic spectra of d° tetraoxoanions. Frenske and Sweeny[80,81] suggested that either method is capable of explaining the spectral data depending on the degree of s and p participation in the hybrid ligand orbitals. A very comprehensive molecular orbital scheme for tetraoxo species was proposed by Basch and Gray[77] using a similar treatment as that used by Ballhausen and Liehr,[82,83] but they considered the participation of the oxygen 2s as well as the oxygen 2p orbitals. This scheme was applied to d° systems such as CrO_4^{2-}, MoO_4^{2-}, WO_4^{2-}, MnO_4^{2-}, ReO_4^-, to name a few. The ultraviolet absorption band was found to be interpreted in terms of the $(t_1)3t_2$ electronic transition. Their approach has however received some criticism.[84]

Although the role of the tetrahedral oxoanions of non-metals as ligands on complexes has been extensively studied, that of the corresponding oxoanions of transition metals have received limited attention. This is partially due to the oxidation-reduction reactions often resulting, or because of the formation of insoluble precipitates on mixing. Relative to the oxoanions of non-metals, transition metal oxoanions are surprisingly strong bases, for example, sulfate has a pK value of about 2.5,[85] whereas that of molybdate(VI) is 3.5.[86] Since in all cases, the oxoanion must coordinate through the oxygen lone pair electrons, then it can be anticipated that their relative ligand strengths will parallel approximately to their relative basicities. This would imply that the transition metal oxoanions are likely to be far better ligands than corresponding non-metal ions.[87] If this is the case, then such complexes may play an important role in the redox reactions which frequently occur.

PREPARATION AND CHEMICAL PROPERTIES OF THE MOLYBDATE(VI) ION

The simplest form the molybdenum(VI) exists in basic solution as the tetrahedral MoO_4^{2-}, which is a colorless anion.[40] When the trioxide of molybdenum is dissolved in aqueous alkali, the solution contains the tetrahedral MoO_4^{2-} ion and the simple, or "normal' molybdate such as Na_2MoO_4 can be crystallized from it. Barium salts of the MoO_4^{4+} anions can be obtained from the following reaction:

$$BaMoO_4 + MoO_3 + 3Ba(OH)_2 \rightarrow Ba_2MoO_4 + 3H_2O \qquad (9)$$

Attempts to make these salts directly from their dioxides have not been successful. The "normal" molybdates of many other metals can be prepared by metathetical reactions. The alkali metals, ammonium, magnesium, and thallous salts, are soluble in water, whereas, those of other metals are nearly all insoluble.

When a solution of molybdate(VI) is made weakly acidic,[88,89] polymeric anions are formed, but from more strongly acid solutions, a precipitate of yellow "molybdic acid", $MoO_3 \bullet 2H_2O$, is formed. The monohydrate is obtained rapidly from hot solutions. $MoO_3 \bullet 2H_2O$ contains sheets of MoO_6 octahedra sharing corners, and is best formulated as $[MoO_{4/2}O(H_2O)] \bullet H_2O$ with one H_2O bound to Mo, the other hydrogen bonded to the lattice.

The discrete $[Mo_2O_7]^{2-}$, analogous to the dichromate anion, has been obtained by addition of $[n-Bu_4N]OH$ to a solution of $[n-Bu_4N]Mo_8O_{26}$ in CH_3CN.

The molybdate(VI) anion retains its structure in inorganic solvents, but on addition of small cations, it is converted to $[Mo_6O_{24}]^{6-}$. Other compounds with the composition $M_2^IMo_2O_7$ contain polymeric anions. An example is the commercially important $(NH_4)_2Mo_2O_7$, which has an infinite polymer of linked MoO_6 octahedra and MoO_4 tetrahedra.

ISOPOLYACIDS AND SALTS OF MOLYBDENUM

A prominent feature of the chemistry of molybdenum is the formation of numerous polymolybdate(VI) and their salts.[40] The polymolybdate(VI) chemistry is based upon a polyoxometallate (abbreviated POM) which is a polyatomic ion, usually an anion, that consists of three or more transition metal oxoanions linked together by shared oxygen atoms to form a large, closed 3-D framework. The metal atoms are usually group 5 or group 6 transition metals in their high oxidation states. In this state, their electron configurations are either d^0 or d^1. Examples include vanadium(V), niobium(V), tantalum(V), molybdenum(VI), and tungsten(VI). It has been reported that vanadium(V), niobium(V), tantalum(V), and uranium(VI), all show comparable behavior, but to a more limited extent in some aspects.[73,85] The isopolyacids, in most cases, contain only molybdenum along with oxygen and hydrogen.

The polyanions are built primarily of MoO_6 octahedra, but they are prepared by starting with tetrahedral MoO_4^{2-} ion. It should be noted that W(VI), and not Cr(VI), can form polyanions. As mentioned earlier, in strongly basic solution, Mo(VI) is present only as MoO_4^{2-}. On addition of acid, the protonation equilibria in Table 2 are established.[40,73,85]

The formula of $Mo(OH)_6$ is used for convenience to indicate an octahedral species. From a structural point of view, the alternative proposed formulas, namely, $MoO_2(OH)_2(H_2O)_2$ or $MoO_3(H_2O)_3$, are more acceptable.

One point of interest is that there is an expansion in the coordination number from four to six for the Mo(VI) metal center; these steps are in direct contrast to the protonation of CrO_4^{2-}, where an expansion in the coordination number does not occur.

Table 2. Protonation, equilibria for molybdate(VI).[73,85]

Process	$K/mol^{-1} dm^3$	$\Delta H°/kJ\ mol^{-1}$	$\Delta S°/J\ mol^{-1}\ K^{-1}$
$MoO_4^{2-} + H^+ \xrightarrow{K_1} HMoO_4^-$	$10^{3.5}$	16	123
	$10^{3.7}$	20	140
$HMoO_4^- + H^+ + 2H_2O \xrightarrow{K_2} Mo(OH)_6$	$10^{3.7}$	-45	-76
	$10^{3.7}$	-49	-92

It might be considered surprising that K_2 is as large as K_1 (Table 2),[73,85] especially since the incorporation of two water molecules should cause a very unfavorable entropy change, as indeed, it does.[73,85]

The first example of a polyoxometallate compound was ammonium phosphomolybdate, containing the $[PMo_{12}O_{40}]^{3-}$ anion, discovered in 1826.[90] This anion has the same structure as the phosphotungstate anion, whose structure was determined in 1934.[90] This structure is called the Keggin structure, named after its discoverer.[91,92] Examples of some fundamental polyoxometallate structures are shown in Table 3. The Lindqvist ion is an *iso*-polyoxometallate; the other three are *hetero*-polyoxometallates. The Keggin and Dawson structures have tetrahedrally coordinated hetero-atoms, such as P or Si (see Table 3, where X = P or Si), and the Anderson structure has an octahedral central atom, such as aluminum (see Table 3, where X = Al).

The main chemistry of isopolymolybdates and heteropolymolybdates, their salts, and derivatives are found in the literature.[40,42-48,94-98]

Table 3. Examples of the structures of polyoxomolybdates.[93]

Lindqvist hexamolybdate, $Mo_6O_{19}^{2-}$	Mo$_{36}$-polymolybdate, $Mo_{36}O_{112}(H_2O)_{16}^{8-}$	Strandberg structure, $HP_2Mo_5O_{23}^{4-}$

Keggin structure, $XMo_{12}O_{40}^{n-}$	Dawson structure, $X_2M_{18}O_{62}^{n-}$	Anderson structure, $XM_6O_{24}^{n-}$

THE MOLYBDATE(VI) ANION IN COORDINATION CHEMISTRY

In 1968, a group of novel molybdato complexes were reported by Griffith and Coomber.[99] Forty nine years before those molybdato complexes were discovered, some analogous chromato complexes were also reported.[100] In 1983, and in 1992, $[Co(NH_3)_5CrO_4]^+$, $[Co(en)_2CrO_4]^+$, $[Co(tren)CrO_4]^+$, and $[(trans[14]diene)CoCrO_4]^+$ and their respective chemistries were also reported.[101-103] During that era there was a resurgence of interest in the kinetics reactions governing their formation. Now, an investigation of the rapid complexation between the molybdate(VI) ion and the pentaammineaquacobalt(III) ion was reported by Roger S. Taylor[104] in 1977. It must be stressed that Roger was a former student of Professor A. Geoffrey Sykes (affectionately known as Geoff). The reaction, occurring at stopped-flow rates, indicated that substitution occurred at the Mo(VI) center based on the magnitude of the rate constants.[104] The kinetics of the equilibration[104] of the pentaammineaquacobalt(III) ion with the molybdate(VI) anion

$$[Co(NH_3)_5H_2O]^{3+} + [MoO_4]^{2-} \rightleftharpoons [Co(NH_3)_5MoO_4]^+ + H_2O \qquad (10)$$

were studied at 25 °C and I = 1.0 M ($NaClO_4$) with 7.1 ≤ pH ≤ 8.0 by stopped-flow spectrophotometry. The spectrophotometric equilibrium constant for equation 11, $K = k_f/k_r$ was 475 ± 15 M^{-1}. The kinetics showed a greater than first order dependence on $[MoO_4^{2-}]$ and the second-order formation[104] rate constant, k_f, was expressed as in

$$k_f = k_a + k_b[H^+] = k_c[MoO_4^{2-}] + k_d[H^+][MoO_4^{2-}] \qquad (11)$$

Values of $k_a = 96 \pm 7$ M^{-1} s^{-1}, $k_b = (1.1 \pm 0.2) \times 10^9$ M^{-2} s^{-1}, $k_c = (2.2 \pm 0.2) \times 10^3$ M^{-2} s^{-1}, and $k_d = (1.02 \pm 0.05) \times 10^{11}$ M^{-3} s^{-1} were consistent with substitution at the Mo(VI) metal center, and not the Co(III) metal center. The paths k_a and k_b corresponded to the reaction of $HMoO_4^-$ with $[Co(NH_3)_5OH]^{2+}$ ($k_1 = 6.6 \times 10^4$ M^{-1} s^{-1}) and $[Co(NH_3)_5H_2O]^{3+}$ ($k_2 = 3.2 \times 10^5$ M^{-1} s^{-1}), respectively. The rate constants were much lower than those observed for addition of ligands to the tetrahedral molybdate(VI) anion to give products of increased coordination number. The pathways involving two molybdate ions, k_c and k_d, corresponded to reactions of dimolybdate(VI), a species which had not been previously detected in aqueous solution.[104]

In October 1990, I, Alvin Holder, had the honor of being an M.Phil. student of Professor Tara P. Dasgupta, who was a very close friend of Geoff. It was Professor Dasgupta who gave me the reference that featured the work of Dr. Roger S. Taylor.[104] At that moment in time, Prof. Dasgupta told me that he wanted me to pursue my graduate studies on the synthesis, characterization, acid and base hydrolysis, and electron transfer reactions on mixed-metal binuclear complexes ($[(H_3N)_5CoOMoO_3]ClO_4$ **1**, $[(H_3N)_5CrOMoO_3]ClO_4$ **2**, $[(en)_2CoO_2MoO_2]ClO_4$ **3**, and $[(tren)CoO_2MoO_2]ClO_4$ **4** that contain cobalt(III) and molybdenum(VI) metal centers. The following structures were synthesized and characterized as part of the research project:

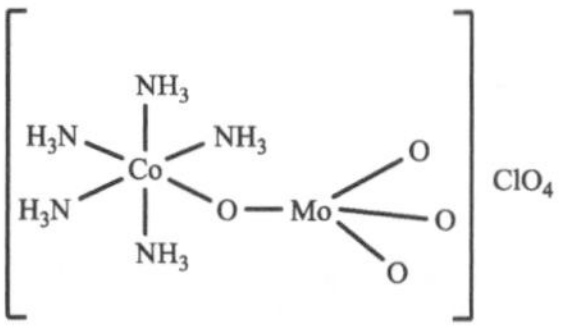

$[(H_3N)_5CoOMoO_3]ClO_4$ **1** 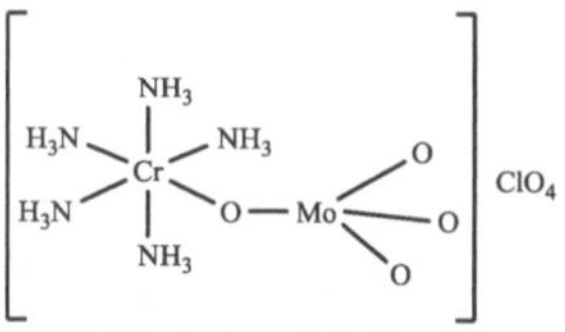 $[(H_3N)_5CrOMoO_3]ClO_4$ **2**

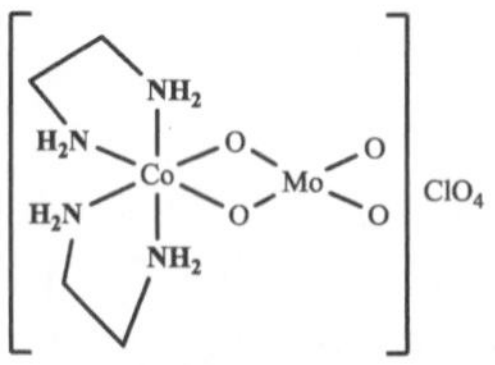

$[(en)_2CoO_2MoO_2]ClO_4$ **3** 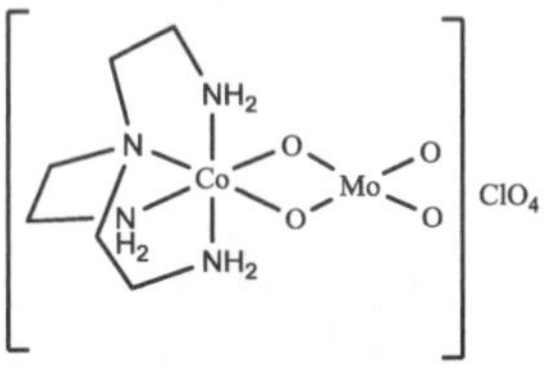 $[(tren)CoO_2MoO_2]ClO_4$ **4**

For a video, please see: http://www.youtube.com/watch?v=k2QAPI8XiLk

I, Alvin Holder, was very fortunate with the fact that by carrying out dedicated research, I was able to upgrade in 1991 from the M.Phil program to the Ph.D. program at The University of the West Indies, Department of Chemistry, Mona Campus, Jamaica.

In 1991, Grace and Tregloan[105] also reported the formation of $[(H_3N)_5CoOMoO_3]^+$ ion in the range pH 7.1-8.0. They suggested that the observed second-order rate dependence upon the concentration of MoO_4^{2-} may be explained by $HMoO_4^-$ acting as proton-donating catalyst. An increase in the rate upon the addition of other protonated anions (HCO_3^- and $H_2PO_4^-$) to the reaction solution, which supported the contention of a general proton-assisted mechanism, was noted.[105] A similar increase in the reaction rate was also noted when $H_2PO_4^-$ was added, and as a result it was concluded that the second-order dependence upon the concentration of MoO_4^{2-} was due to $HMoO_4^-$ acting as a proton-donating catalyst[105] during the course of complexation of MoO_4^{2-}. On submission of my Ph.D. thesis in December 1993, I was called upon to start a faculty position at The University of the West Indies, Department of Chemistry, Cave Hill Campus, Barbados on January 10, 1994. I subsequently successfully defended my Ph.D. thesis in May 1994. After that time, I began writing manuscripts of the work from my Ph.D. thesis, and as such some of the publications that were published will be highlighted in this chapter.

In 1996, Holder and Dasgupta reported the synthesis, acid hydrolysis and formation of compound **1** in aqueous solution.[106] Compound **1** was synthesized and characterized by elemental analysis, UV-visible, and infrared spectroscopy. The kinetics of the acid hydrolysis of compound **1** was studied using the stopped-flow technique over the ranges $0.01 \leq [H^+] \leq 0.45$ M, $24.9 \leq \theta \leq 35.6$ °C, and $0.04 \leq I \leq 1.0$ M ($NaClO_4$). The rate of reaction was inversely dependent on $[H^+]$ due to the expansion of the co-ordination of the molybdenum(VI) metal center from four to six on protonation, along with resonance stabilization.[106] The rate constant ($\mathbf{k_1}$) for the hydrolysis was 5.09 ± 0.02 s^{-1} at 24.9 °C for which $\Delta\mathbf{H}^{\ddagger} = 82 \pm 1$ kJ mol^{-1} and $\Delta\mathbf{S}^{\ddagger} = 43 \pm 5$ J K^{-1} mol^{-1}. The kinetics of formation of compound **1** from pentaammineaquacobalt(III) and molybdate(VI) ions was studied using the stopped-flow method over the range pH 7.13–8.46 and at 25.0–35.9 °C, $I = 1.0$ M. Over this pH range both $[Co(NH_3)_5(OH_2)]^{3+}$ and $[Co(NH_3)_5(OH)]^{2+}$ ion reacted with $HMoO_4^-$ to form $[(H_3N)_5CoOMoO_3]^+$, and the rate constants were $(2.03 \pm 0.05) \times 10^6$ and $(2.73 \pm 0.05) \times 10^5$ M^{-1} s^{-1}, respectively at 25.0 °C. Both acid hydrolysis and complexation were very rapid, suggesting a mechanism involving cleavage of the Mo^{VI}–O not the Co^{III}–O bond.[106]

Complexation between the chromate(VI) anion and $[Co(NH_3)_5H_2O]^{3+}$, *cis*-$[Co(en)_2(H_2O)_2]^{3+}$, and $[Co(tren)(H_2O)_2]^{3+}$ was also reported.[101-103] Also, the complexation between *cis*-$[Co(en)_2(H_2O)_2]^{3+}$ and the tungstate(VI) anion was also reported.[107] These reactions, which occurred at stopped-flow rates, indicated that substitution occurs at the M(VI) centre, that is, via Cr-O and W-O bond breakage.[101-103,107]

The sparse information available on the reactions of aquaamminecobalt(III) complexes with transition metal oxoanions is in direct contrast with the very extensive studies on these groups of aquaamminecobalt(III) with non-metal oxoanions. Reactions between aquaamminecobalt(III) and non-metal oxoanions tend to fall into two categories, one in which very slow complexation and hydrolysis are observed, and is attributed to the breakage of the inert Co-O bond. Oxoanions such as phosphate,[108] dimethylphosphate,[109] oxalate,[110] and sulfate,[111] fall into this category. Rapid complexation and hydrolysis are however observed with oxoanions such as carbonate,[112-119] selenate,[120,121] and arsenate,[122] and also sulfur dioxide.[123-127]

An analogous study was carried by Holder and Dasgupta where the synthesis, acid hydrolysis and formation of the compound **2** in aqueous solution was reported.[128] The complex was synthesized for the first time and characterized by elemental analysis and spectroscopic analyses. The kinetics of the acid hydrolysis and formation of the complex was studied using the stopped-flow technique.[128] The acid hydrolysis experiments were carried out over the ranges, $0.01 \leq [H^+] \leq 0.14$ M, 22.4 °C $\leq \theta \leq 30.1$ °C, and at ionic strength 1.0 M

(NaNO$_3$), whereas the formation kinetics were studied over the ranges $7.22 \leq$ pH ≤ 8.18 and $25.0\ °C \leq \theta \leq 33.9\ °C$, with ionic strength = 1.0 M (NaClO$_4$). The rate of acid hydrolysis was also inversely dependent on [H$^+$] which was ascribed to the expansion of the coordination number of the molybdenum(VI) metal center from four to six on protonation, along with resonance stabilization. The rate constant, k_1, for the hydrolysis was 22.6 ± 0.3 s^{-1} at 25.1 °C for which $\Delta H^{\neq} = 89 \pm 5$ kJ mol^{-1} and $\Delta S^{\neq} = 81 \pm 21$ J mol^{-1} K^{-1}. The rate constants for the reactions of [(NH$_3$)$_5$CrOH$_2$]$^{3+}$ and [(NH$_3$)$_5$CrOH]$^{2+}$ to form the complex were $(1.18 \pm 0.07) \times 10^7$ M^{-1} s^{-1} and $(1.13 \pm 0.05) \times 10^5$ M^{-1} s^{-1}, respectively at 25.0 °C. The results indicate that both processes are occurring via a mechanism involving Mo^{VI}-O bond breakage.[128]

Table 4. Vibrational frequencies and assignments of various molybdato complexes (cm^{-1}) by IR spectroscopy (Reproduced by permission).[129]

Species	ν_1	ν_2	ν_3	ν_4	Ref.
MoO$_4$$^{2-}$.....Raman	897	338	841	338	[99]
[(NH$_3$)$_5$CoOMoO$_3$]ClO$_4$			848.5 vs		[129]
[(NH$_3$)$_5$CrOMoO$_3$]ClO$_4$			856.3 vs		[129]
[(en)$_2$CoO$_2$MoO$_2$]ClO$_4$	940.1 s		859.4 vs		[129]
			839.4 vs		
			794.4 vs		
[(tren)CoO$_2$MoO$_2$]ClO$_4$	932.3 s		860.2 vs		[129]
			837.5 vs		
			792.9 vs		
[(NH$_3$)$_5$CoCl]MoO$_4$	893 w		825 s, b	335 s	[99]
[(NH$_3$)$_5$CoOMoO$_3$]Cl	910 s		877 vs	350 m	[99]
			847 vs		
[(NH$_3$)$_4$CoO$_2$MoO$_2$]NO$_3$	920 s		865 vs	371 m, b	[99]
			845 vs		
			795 vs		

ν(M-Cl) = 278 cm^{-1} (s).
s = sharp and strong, vs = very strong, b = broad, w = weak, and m = medium.
NO$_3$$^-$, NH$_3$, and ClO$_4$$^-$ modes are omitted.

Holder et al.[129] also reported the synthesis and characterization of compounds **3** and **4**, in which the MoO$_4$$^{2-}$ anion was coordinated to a cobalt(III) metal center as a bidentate ligand. In that report, Holder et al.[129] compiled IR vibrational frequencies for various molybdate(VI)-containing species (Table 4).

REDOX CHEMISTRY OF THE "FREE" AND COORDINATED MOLYBDATE(VI) ANION

Mo(VI) is not a good oxidizing agent as the redox reactions are very slow. The E° value of Mo(VI) in acidic media is shown in Table 1. Electrochemical studies were carried out on molybdate(VI) by You et al.;[130] where they found that the redox behavior of molybdate(VI) was complicated and that reduction could be attained more easily if it first polymerizes to form species composed of two or more molybdenum metal centers before reduction takes place.[130] This fact also agreed with the result of Pan *et al.*,[131] so in general, polymerization, protonation or ligation change the coordination number of molybdenum(VI), thereby making the reduction easier.

Mo(VI) can be reduced by $N_2H_5^+$,[132,133] *L*-ascorbic acid,[134] diketosuccinic acid,[135] Sn^{2+},[136] Fe^{2+},[137] *L*-cysteine,[138] reduced glutathione,[138] and thioglycolic acid.[139] The reduction of Mo(VI) with $N_2H_5^+$ in phosphate buffer at pH 1.6 and 60 °C to yield Mo(V) and N_2 is slow, with the rate constant being about 0.5 M^{-1} s^{-1}.[132,133] The detection of N_2H_2 led to the conclusion that the rate determination step of the mechanism was the two electron redox process:

$$N_2H_5^+ + Mo(VI) \xrightarrow{k_1} N_2H_2 + Mo(IV) + 3H^+ \tag{12}$$

followed by the more rapid steps:

$$2N_2H_2 + H^+ \rightarrow N_2 + N_2H_5^+ \tag{13}$$

$$Mo(IV) + Mo(VI) \underset{k_{-3}}{\overset{k_3}{\rightleftarrows}} 2Mo(V) \tag{14}$$

$$2Mo(V) \underset{k_{-4}}{\overset{k_4}{\rightleftarrows}} [Mo(V)]_2 \tag{15}$$

The rate law is as follows: [132,133]

$$-d[N_2H_5^+]/dt = 2k[N_2H_5^+][Mo(VI)] \tag{16}$$

L-ascorbic acid can be oxidized by Mo(VI) as reported by Rudenko,[134] but the details of the mechanism are not known. Diketosuccinic acid can be oxidized by Mo(VI) in $HClO_4$.[135] The rate law is as follows:

$$rate = k[Mo(VI)][substrate][H^+]^n \tag{17}$$

A free radical mechanism was shown by the induced reduction of mercury(II) chloride, indicating that the reaction proceeded by one electron steps.[135] Tin(II) in concentrated HCl can reduce Mo(VI) to give equimolar quantities of Mo(V) and Mo(III) as initial products.[136] This result strongly suggests that the reaction proceeds by the steps:[136]

$$Mo(VI) + Sn(II) \rightarrow Sn(IV) + Mo(IV) \tag{18}$$

$$2Mo(IV) \rightarrow Mo(V) + Mo(III) \tag{19}$$

The rate law is as follows:[136]

$$d[Mo(VI)]/dt = k[Sn(II)[Mo(V)] \tag{20}$$

Mo(VI) can be reduced to Mo(V) by Fe(II) in 8 M HCl.[137] The reaction was followed by means of stopped-flow spectrophotometry. In concentrated HCl, the Mo(VI) species formed appears to be MoO_2Cl_2, which is reduced by Fe(II) to give the emerald green mononuclear species, $[MoOCl_5]^{2-}$. The equilibrium was far to the side of the products, i.e., the back reaction was negligible; the second-order rate constant was 3.6 x 10^3 M^{-1} s^{-1} (20 °C, 8 M HCl).[137] Due to the high rate of ligand substitution in Fe(II), no conclusion could have been made as whether the reaction had proceeded by an inner-sphere or outer-sphere mechanism. However, an inner-sphere mechanism, with Cl⁻ as a bridging ligand, was the most probable.[137]

L-Cysteine (Cys) reduces Mo(VI) to yield L-cystine and a new compound, which was formulated as $[Mo_2O_3(Cys)_4]^{4-}$.[138] It was unfortunate that the latter was converted into $[Mo_2O_4(Cys)_2]^{2-}$.[138] The reaction involving Mo(VI) and thioglycolic acid (TGA) **5** proceeds in two steps: Mo(VI) is first reduced to form a binuclear Mo(V)-TGA compound and to what appears to be a Mo(IV) species of an unknown structure.[139] In both steps, TGA is oxidized to dithiodiglycolic acid (DTDGA) **6**. At pH 6.0 in phosphate buffer, Mo(VI) and Mo(V) form complexes with TGA, both of which oxidize excess TGA to DTDGA. If excess TGA is added to a solution of Mo(VI) (Na_2MoO_4) at this pH value, Mo(V) first increases in concentration; then decreases with time. It was found that by using an NMR technique, the amount of DTDGA formed in the overall reaction was estimated to be equal to the amount of Mo(VI) reacted:[139]

thioglycolic acid **5**   dithiodiglycolic acid **6**

$$2TGA + [Mo^{VI}O_2(TGA)_2]^{2-} \rightarrow Mo(IV) + DTDGA \tag{21}$$

When $[Mo^V_2O_3(TGA)_4]^{4-}$ was added to excess TGA, DTDGA equal in amount to the mo(V) complex reacted is formed:

$$2TGA + [Mo^V_2O_3(TGA)_4]^{4-} \rightarrow 2MoIV + DTDGA \tag{22}$$

The structure of the Mo(IV) species formed is unknown, although it is most likely complexed with TGA.

The mechanism of the oxidation of TGA by $[Mo^{VI}O_2(TGA)_2]^{2-}$ was found to be a straight forward one-electron reaction:[139]

$$TGA + [Mo^{VI}O_2(TGA)_2]^{2-} \rightarrow [Mo^VO_2(TGA)_2]^{3-} + TGA^\bullet \text{ slow} \tag{23}$$

$$2TGA^\bullet \rightarrow DTDGA \qquad\qquad \text{fast} \tag{24}$$

$$H_2O + 2[Mo^VO_2(TGA)_2]^{3-} \rightarrow [Mo^V_2O_3(TGA)_4]^{4-} + 2OH^- \text{ fast} \tag{25}$$

In the oxidation of TGA by $[Mo^V_2O_3(TGA)_4]^{4-}$, the rate was found to be second-order in the compound, and first-order in TGA. There was no satisfactory mechanism to explain these kinetics.[139]

The rate of oxidation of reduced glutathione by Mo(VI) (Na_2MoO_4) at pH 7.50 was found to be independent of Mo(VI) concentration at high Mo(VI) concentrations (≥ 0.02 M) and dependent to the first power on Mo(VI) concentration at low Mo(VI) concentrations (≤ 0.5 mM).[138] In order to explain these results, it was necessary to postulate the existence of an unreactive form of reduced glutathione (GSH") which is in equilibrium with an active form, GSH (glutathione is known to exist in a number of cyclic forms in acid solution,[140] but little is known of its structure in neutral or basic solution).[138]

$$GSH" \xrightleftharpoons[k_{-1}]{k_1} GSH \tag{26}$$

$$MoO_4^{2-} + GSH \xrightarrow{k_2} Mo(V) + GS° \tag{27}$$

$$2Mo(V) \rightleftharpoons [Mo(V)]_2 \tag{28}$$

$$2GS° \rightleftharpoons GSSG \tag{29}$$

(GSH" = inactive, possibly a cyclic form; GSH = active form of reduced glutathione; GS$^\bullet$ = glutathione radical; GSSG = oxidized glutathione). Applying the steady-state assumption to GSH leads to the following rate expression:

$$\frac{-d[Mo(VI)]}{dt} = \frac{k_1 k_2 [Mo(VI)][GSH"]}{k_{-1} + k_2 [Mo(VI)]} \tag{30}$$

In the presence of high Mo(VI) concentrations, $k_2[Mo(VI)] \gg k_{-1}$, which gives the experimental first-order rate law observed under these conditions;

$$-d[Mo(VI)]/dt = k_1[GSH"] \tag{31}$$

At low Mo(VI) concentrations, $k_2[Mo(VI)] \ll k_{-1}$ and the expression is reduced to the observed second-order rate law:[138]

$$-d[Mo(VI)]/dt = k_1 k_2/k_{-1}[Mo(VI)][GSH"] \tag{32}$$

No spectral evidence was found for the existence of either Mo(VI) or Mo(V) complexes with reduced glutathione at this pH value, although subsequent work by Haight and Huang[141] indicated a Mo(V)$_2$-glutathione compound was formed, possibly in small amounts under these conditions.

There has been a report of a controlled, Raman-monitored chemical reduction of a molybdate and vanadate mixture which produced a new type of molybdenum-oxide-based cluster $K_{43}Na_{11}(VO)_4[(Mo^{VI}_{72}V^{IV}_{30}O_{282}(H_2O)_{66}$ $(SO_4)_{12})(Mo^{IV}_{114}Mo^{VI}_{28}O_{432}$ $(OH)_{14}$ $(H_2O)_{58})]\bullet\approx500H_2O$ that shows an unprecedented level of inorganic structural organization.[142] The cluster was found to incorporate two nanosized substructures (a ring and a sphere) in an open clam-like assembly. Multiple methods proved that the nanoring contains delocalized electrons and the nanosphere contains localized but interacting electrons.[142]

The reaction of molybdenum(VI) with $NH_2OH\bullet HCl$ in ^iPrOH solution was reported to lead to the formation of dinitrosyl complexes, whereas that in MeOH produced mononitrosyl complexes.[143] In these reactions complexes of composition cis-dinitrosyl-trans-dichloro-cis-L_2 $Mo(NO)_2L_2Cl_2$ (L = ^iPrOH, py), $(Mo(NO)_2(O^iPr)_2)_n$ and $Mo(NO)_2Cl(OMe)_2L_2$ (L = MeOH, py; L_2 = phen) were isolated.[143] The complexes were characterized by IR, UV-visible, and ^1H NMR spectroscopies. The crystal structure of $[Mo(NO)Cl(OMe)_2$ (phen)]$\bullet$MeOH was determined by X-ray crystallography. The electronic structure of these mono- and dinitrosyl complexes was determined by semi-quantitative Fenske-Hall LCAO MO calculations. Catalytic activity of these complexes in the olefin metathesis reaction was also examined.[143]

A 1,10-phenanthroline chelated molybdenum(VI) compound $[(MoO_2)_2O(H_2cit)(phen)(H_2O)_2]\bullet H_2O$ (H_4cit = citric acid) with citrate as a ligand was synthesized from the reaction of citric acid, ammonium molybdate and phen in acidic media (pH 0.5–1.0).[144] A citrato oxomolybdenum(V) complex, $[(MoO)_2O(H_2cit)_2(bpy)_2]\bullet4H_2O$ **7**, was synthesized by the reduction of citrato molybdate with hydrazine hydrochloride in the presence of bpy, and a mononuclear molybdenum(VI) citrate $[MoO_2(H_2cit)(bpy)]\bullet H_2O$ was also isolated and characterized structurally.[144] The citrate ligand in the three neutral compounds uses the α-alkoxy and α-carboxy groups to chelate as a bidentate leaving the two b-carboxylic acid groups free, that is different from the tridentate chelated mode in the citrato molybdate(VI and V) complexes. $[(MoO_2)_2O(H_2cit)(phen)(H_2O)_2]\bullet H_2O$ and compound **7** in solution show obvious dissociation based on ^{13}C NMR spectroscopic studies.[144]

7

L-Ascorbic acid (H_2A) is a dibasic acid, with a pK_{a1} value of 4.04 (for the hydroxyl group at C(3) of the enol group of H_2A) and a pK_{a2} value of 11.3 (for the hydroxyl group at C(2) of the enol group of HA^-) at an ionic strength of 1.0 M.[145]

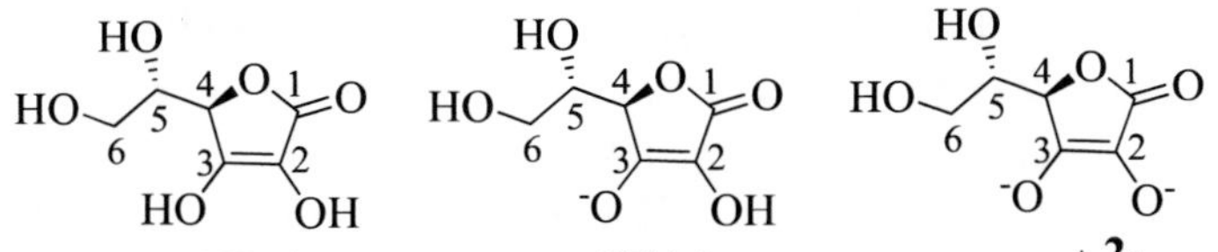

H_2A HA^- A^{2-}

Oxidation of *L*-ascorbic acid is strongly pH dependent, with reactivity increasing with increasing pH. The ascorbate dianion, A^{2-}, is found to be much more readily oxidized than the monoanion, HA^-, which in turn is more reactive than *L*-ascorbic acid. *L*-Ascorbic acid is known to undergo a Michaelis[145] two step redox process with the formation of a transient but stable free radical intermediate as shown below:[145]

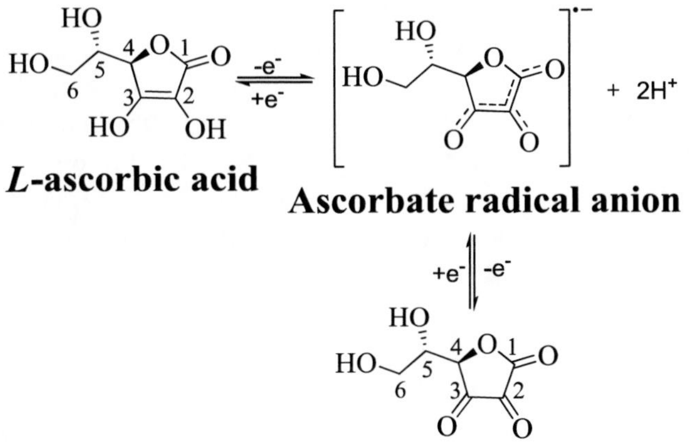

***L*-ascorbic acid**   **Ascorbate radical anion**

Dehydroascorbic acid

The ascorbate anion is a reactive reductant, but its free radical is relatively non-reactive and decays by disproportionation to form *L*-ascorbic acid/ascorbate and dehydroascorbic acid (A):[145]

$$2A^{\bar{\bullet}} + H^+ \rightleftharpoons HA^- + A \tag{33}$$

$$3A^{\bar{\bullet}} + 2H^+ \rightleftharpoons 2HA^{\bullet} + A \tag{34}$$

$$2HA^{\bullet} \rightleftharpoons H_2A + A \tag{35}$$

As "free" molybdate(VI) is reduced to molybdenum(V) by *L*-ascorbic acid (although under very drastic acidic conditions),[134] we found it to be very interesting to determine the fate of the molybdenum(VI) center during the electron transfer between *L*-ascorbic acid and compound **1**. We believed that there could also be some biological relevance of this work in terms of the electron transfer process which has been proposed[146] to occur in the molybdo-enzyme, nitrogenase. In the reaction of *L*-ascorbic acid and the pentaamminecobaltchromato(III) ion, the cobalt(III) center[147] was reduced to cobalt(II), while the chromium(VI) center was reduced to chromium(III).[147] Based on the reports, we reported a detailed kinetic study of the electron transfer process involving compound **1** and *L*-ascorbic acid.[148] A detailed investigation on the oxidation of *L*-ascorbic acid by the compound **1** was carried out using the stopped-flow technique over the ranges, $0.01 \leq$ [ascorbate]$_T \leq 0.10$ M, $6.96 \leq$ pH ≤ 9.05, and $19.6 \leq \theta \leq 30.1$ °C at I = 1.0 M (NaNO$_3$).[148] The main products after the electron transfer reaction were Co(II), molybdate(VI), and *L*-dehydroascorbic acid.[148] The rate of the reaction was dependent on pH and the total ascorbate concentration in a complex manner, that is, k_{obs} = $(k_1 K_1 K_2 + k_2 K_1 [H^+])$[ascorbate]$_T / (K_1 K_2 + K_1 [H^+] + [H^+]^2)$. The second order rate constants at 24.9 °C were: $k_1 = 16 \pm 3$ M^{-1} s^{-1} and $k_2 = (11.30 \pm 0.03)$ x 10^{-2} M^{-1} s^{-1}. $\Delta H^{\neq}_1 = 29 \pm 7$ kJ mol^{-1}, $\Delta H^{\neq}_2 = 99 \pm 9$ kJ mol^{-1}, $\Delta S^{\neq}_1 = -124 \pm 30$ J mol^{-1} K^{-1}, and $\Delta S^{\neq}_2 = 67 \pm 35$ J mol^{-1} K^{-1}. An outer-sphere electron mechanism was proposed for this system.[148] In this study, we determined the redox potentials for compound **1** and for several [(NH$_3$)$_5$CoL]$^{n+}$ complexes (Table 5).[148] All electrochemical studies were acquired by Dr. Sang-Choul Im who was a graduate student of Professor A.Geoffrey Sykes in the year 1995, while I, Alvin Holder, was on a Leverhulme Fellowship for my very first research stint in Professor A.Geoffrey Sykes' laboratory at The University of Newcastle, Newcastle upon Tyne, U.K.[148]

Based on our research findings, we have summarized self-exchange rate constants for various Co^{III}/Co^{II} complexes in Table 6, while in Table 7, we have summarized the rate and activation parameters for the reduction of selected cobalt(III) complexes by *L*-ascorbic acid.[145]

Over the past three decades a number of systems have been studied in our laboratory and by collaborators elsewhere that involve the reactions of various aqua transition metal complex ions with 'free' sulfite in aqueous solution.

Table 5. Reduction potentials, E$_p$ (V *versus* NHE) for [(NH$_3$)$_5$CoL]$^{n+}$ complexes (Reproduced by permission).[148]

L	E$_{p1}$	E$_{p2}$	E$^a_{p3}$	Ref
NH$_3$			-0.16	[155]
OH$_2$			-0.01	[155]
OH$^-$			-0.22	[155]
F$^-$			-0.11	[155]
Cl$^-$			+0.32	[155]
Br$^-$			+0.30	[155]
I$^-$			+0.26	[155]
SCN$^-$			+0.30	[155]
NCS$^-$			+0.46	[155]
CN$^-$			-0.15	[155]
OCO$_2$$^{2-}$			+0.46	[155]
OPO$_3$H^{2-}			+0.45	[155]
OSO$_3$$^{2-}$			-0.04	[155]
OMoO$_3$$^{2-}$	-0.80	-0.09	+0.12	[148]

[a] Irreversible process, Co$^{III/II}$.

Table 6. Self-exchange rate constants for various Co^{III}/Co^{II} complexes at 25 °C (Reproduced by permission).[145]

Reaction	I/M	$k_{ex}/M^{-1} s^{-1}$	Ref.
$[Co(H_2O)_6]^{3+}/[Co(H_2O)_6]^{2+}$	0.5	3	[158]
$[Co(NH_3)_6]^{3+}/[Co(NH_3)_6]^{2+}$	1.0	10^{-7}	[158]
$[Co(NH_3)_4(H_2O)_2]^{3+}/[Co(NH_3)_4(H_2O)_2]^{2+}$	0.1	1.6×10^{-4}	[158]
$[Co(en)_3]^{3+}/[Co(en)_3]^{2+}$	1.0	8×10^{-5}	[158]
$[Co(dien)_2]^{3+}/[Co(dien)_2]^{2+}$	1.0	1.9×10^{-4}	[158]
$[Co(phen)_3]^{3+}/[Co(phen)_3]^{2+}$	1.0	9.5×10^{-2}	[158]
$[Co(bpy)_3]^{3+}/[Co(bpy)_3]^{2+}$	2.0	3.6×10^{-2}	[158]
$[Co(sep)]^{3+}/[Co(sep)]^{2+}$	0.2	5	[158]
$[Co(terpy)_2]^{3+}/[Co(terpy)_2]^{2+}$	1.0	1.7×10^{2}	[158]
$[Co(dipic)_2]^{-}/[Co(dipic)_2]^{2-}$	0.6	1.3×10^{-5}	[145]
$[Co(dipic)_2]^{-}/[Co(dipic)_2]^{2-}$		1.0×10^{-5}	[159]
$[(NH_3)_5CoOMoO_3]^{+}/[(NH_3)_5CoOMoO_3]^{0}$	1.0	2.3×10^{-5}	[148]
$[Co(NH_3)_5OH_2]^{3+}/[Co(NH_3)_5OH]^{+}$	0.5	$\sim 1 \times 10^{-6}$	[160]
$[Co(N_4)(H_2O)_2]^{3+}/[Co(N_4)(H_2O)_2]^{2+}$	0.1	3×10^{-5}	[160][a]
$[Co(N_4)(H_2O)_2]^{3+}/[Co(N_4)(H_2O)_2]^{2+}$	0.1	6×10^{-2}	[160][b]

[a] $N_4 = Me_6[14]4,11$-diene N_4, [b] $N_4 = Me_4[14]$tetraene N_4.

Table 7. Rate and activation parameters for the reduction of some cobalt(III) complexes by *L*-ascorbic acid at 25 °C (Reproduced by permission).[145]

Redox couple	$k/M^{-1} s^{-1}$	$\Delta H^{\neq}/kJ\ mol^{-1}$	$\Delta S^{\neq}/J\ mol^{-1}\ K^{-1}$	Ref.
$[(NH_3)_5CoOCrO_3]^{+}/HA^{-}$	3.5×10^{-2}	20 ± 4	-204 ± 16	[147]
$[(NH_3)_5CoOMoO_3]^{+}/HA^{-}$	1.1×10^{-1}	99 ± 9	67 ± 35	[148]
$[(NH_3)_5CoOMoO_3]^{+}/A^{2-}$	16	29 ± 7	-124 ± 30	[148]
$[(NH_3)_5CoCl]^{2+}/HA^{-}$	9×10^{-4}	81 ± 8	-29 ± 27	[160]
$[Co(dipic)_2]^{-}/HA^{-}$	2.3	30 ± 3	-138 ± 13	[145]
$[Co(C_2O_4)_3]^{3-}/HA^{-}$	4.1×10^{-3}	54 ± 4	-109 ± 5	[148]
$[Co(C_2O_4)_3]^{3-}/A^{2-}$	1.2×10^{-4}	108 ± 22	46 ± 61	[148]

The studies reported include the reactions of the aquapentaammine complexes of cobalt(III),[149-151] rhodium(III),[152] platinum(IV),[153] and chromium(III),[152] along with $[(tren)Co(OH_2)_2]^{3+}$.[149] The kinetic data from those reports show that in each instance the most significant first step in the overall process is very rapid nucleophilic attack by ligand hydroxide on dissolved SO_2 to form an O-bonded sulfito complex, a reaction which is readily reversed by immediate acidification.[149-151,153] Metal-to-oxygen bonding is not involved in this reversible process as confirmed by NMR measurements.[154] As reported, subsequent reactions in the cobalt(III) systems comprise O-bonded to S-bonded isomerisation, internal redox, sulfite ion addition, or a combination of these processes depending on the pH and the nature of the N4 or N5 ligand grouping.[151]

The hexacyanoferrate(II) anion on the other hand, as reported, can reduce some pentaamminecobalt(III) complexes to Co(II) via an outer-sphere electron transfer process.[156] In the past, the reductions of a series of substituted (pyridine) pentaamminecobalt(III) complexes by hexacyanoferrate(II) proceed via the formation of an ion-pair, followed by internal electron transfer within the ion-pair.[157] It is postulated that the ion-pairs feature approach by $Fe(CN)_6^{4-}$ on the ammonia side of the cobalt(III) complexes.[157] The electron transfer process is assumed to be adiabatic and the variations in rate are associated with changes in the reduction potentials and/or rate constants for self-exchange of the cobalt(III) complexes.[157]

Compound **1** is binuclear with a cobalt(III) centre and a molybdenum(VI) centre,[148] so it is possible that one or both metal centers can be reduced by both reductants, that is, Co(III) to Co(II), Mo(VI) to Mo(V) (or even lower oxidation states).[148] We believed that it was possible that there could be anation by the aqueous sulfite followed by internal redox depending on the pH. Clearly both reactions with aqueous sulfite and the hexacyanoferrate(II) (ferrocyanide) anion are of vital importance.

As part of our interest in electron transfer reactions, we carried out a detailed investigation on the oxidation of aqueous sulfite and aqueous potassium hexacyanoferrate(II) by compound **1** using the stopped-flow technique over the ranges, $0.01 \leq [S(IV)]_T \leq 0.05$ M, $4.47 \leq pH \leq 5.12$, and $24.9 \leq \theta \leq 37.6$ °C and at ionic strength 1.0 M ($NaNO_3$) for aqueous sulfite and $0.01 \leq [Fe(CN)_6^{4-}] \leq 0.11$ M, $4.54 \leq pH \leq 5.63$, and $25.0 \leq \theta \leq 35.3$ °C and at ionic strength 1.0 or 3.0 M ($NaNO_3$) for the hexacyanoferrate(II) ion.[161] Both redox processes were dependent on pH and reductant concentration in a complex manner, that is, for the reaction with aqueous sulfite, $k_{obs} = (k_1K_1K_2K_3 + k_2K_1K_4[H^+])[S(IV)]_T/([H^+]^2 + K_1[H^+] + K_1K_2)$ and for the hexacyanoferrate(II) ion, $k_{obs} = (k_1K_3K_4K_5 + k_2K_3K_6[H^+])[Fe(CN)_6^{4-}]_T)/([H^+]^2 + K_3[H^+] + K_3K_4)$.[161] At 25.0 °C, the value of k_1' (the composite of k_1K_3) was 0.77 ± 0.07 M^{-1} s^{-1}, while the value of k_2' (the composite of k_2K_4) was $(3.78 \pm 0.17) \times 10^{-2}$ M^{-1} s^{-1} for aqueous sulfite.

For the hexacyanoferrate(II) ion, k_1' (the composite of k_1K_5) was 1.13 ± 0.01 M^{-1} s^{-1}, while the value of k_2' (the composite of k_2K_6) was 2.36 ± 0.05 M^{-1} s^{-1} at 25.0 °C. In both cases there was reduction of the cobalt(III) metal center to a cobalt(II) metal center, but there was no reduction of the molybdenum(VI) center. The self-exchange rate constant (k_{22}) for aqueous sulfite (as SO_3^{2-}) was calculated to be 5.37×10^{-12} M^{-1} s^{-1}, while for $Fe(CN)_6^{4-}$, it was calculated to be 1.10×10^9 M^{-1} s^{-1} from the Marcus equations.[161]

For further reading in the research area of inorganic reaction mechanisms, the reader is encouraged to read the following textbooks: "*Kinetics of Inorganic Reactions*" by A.G. Sykes, Pergamon Press, 1996, ISBN-10: 0080114415 and "*Specialist Periodical Reports, Inorganic Reaction Mechanisms: Volume 7*", by A.G. Sykes, The Royal Society of Chemistry, 1998, ISBN-13: 9780851863153.

^{95}Mo/^{97}Mo NMR: An Introduction

One incentive for development of the nuclear magnetic resonance (NMR) spectroscopy of molybdenum is the lack of a direct spectroscopic probe for a diamagnetic metal center to complement the role of electron spin resonance as a direct probe for a paramagnetic metal center.

Table 8. Nuclear properties of the isotopes [95]Mo and [97]Mo (Reproduced by permission).[162]

Nucleus	Spin/I	Natural abundance N/atom %	Magnetic moment μ/μ_N	Magnetogyric ratio $\gamma/10^7$ rad T^{-1} s^{-1}	Quadrupole moment $Q/10^{-28}$ m^2	NMR frequency Ξ/MHz	Reference sample	Relative receptivity D^P	Relative receptivity D^C
[95]Mo	5/2	15.72	-1.081	-1.750	-0.015 (4)	6.516926	2 M Na_2MoO_4 in D_2O, apparent pH 11, 20 °C	5.14×10^{-4}	2.92
[97]Mo	5/2	9.46	-1.104	-1787	-0.17 (4)	6.653692	As for [95]Mo	3.29×10^{-4}	1.87

As Mo is a Group VI element, certain aspects of the NMR properties of the Group VI have been reviewed.[162-167] The lack of interest in observation of Group VI nuclei was because they are among the least sensitive of NMR nuclei. The reasons for this low sensitivity include: (a) low receptivities, (b) low resonance frequencies, and (c) nuclear electric quadrupole moments (see Table 8).

^{97}Mo (I = 5/2) has a similar receptivity and resonance frequency to ^{95}Mo, but $Q(^{97}Mo)/Q(^{95}Mo) = 11.4$. Such a large difference between the quadrupole moments of two isotopes of one element with identical spin is exceptional [168] and arises from the fact that ^{95}Mo has an outer half-filled $d_{5/2}$ neutron shell, which makes no contribution to the permanent quadrupole moment. The addition of two neutrons to this shell to create ^{97}Mo results in a relatively large change in Q. The dependence of $W_{1/2}$ on Q^2 means that ^{97}Mo NMR line width are two orders of magnitude greater than those of corresponding ^{95}Mo resonance (Figure 3), and therefore ^{95}Mo is usually the nucleus of choice for chemical studies.

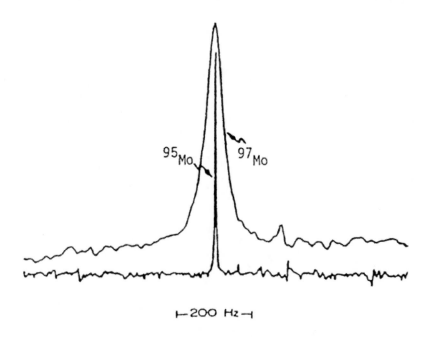

Figure 3. ^{95}Mo and ^{97}Mo NMR spectra of Na$_2$MoO$_4$ (1 M in 3 M NaCl, pH 12) (Reproduced by permission.[162]

The NMR frequencies listed in Table 8 refer to 2 M solutions of Na$_2$MoO$_4$ in D$_2$O at an apparent pH of 11. The standard is easy to observe, indefinitely stable and resonates towards the centre of the known chemical shifts scales. Compounds which resonate at a higher frequency than the MoO$_4$$^{2-}$ reference have positive chemical shifts, and the metal nucleus is deshielded relative to that of the reference complex. Chemical shift changes are described exclusively as shielding changes. Thus a decrease in the metal chemical shift means that the shielding at the metal nucleus has increased.

Prior to 1975, measurements of ^{95,97}Mo NMR concentrated on determination[169-174] of μ, Q, and the Knight shift by observation of the metal or of aqueous molybdate, although ^{95,97}Mo resonances were used to study electronic interactions in cobalt-molybdenum alloys[175] and were detected in solid Na_2MoO_4.[176] Study of chemical phenomena in solution began in 1975 when Vold and Vold[168] nicely exploited the different relaxation times of the ^{95}Mo and the ^{97}Mo nuclei in MoO_4^{2-} to study the protonation and condensation of that anion as a function of pH. In 1976 as part of a series of papers,[177-182] Lutz and co-workers[182,183] started to define a chemical shift by examination of some systems of high symmetry ($Mo(CO)_6$, $Mo(CN)_8^{4-}$ and $[MoO_{4-n}S_n]$ (n = 0 − 4)) for which quadrupolar line-broadening was expected to be minimal. In 1980, the potential of ^{95}Mo NMR for study of organometallic systems was demonstrated,[184] and this area has developed rapidly. Many active research areas in molybdenum chemistry and the role of molybdenum in enzymes[185] have further stimulated the rapid development of ^{95}Mo NMR spectroscopy in the past 33 years.

^{95}Mo NMR Spectroscopy Involving Aqueous Molybdate(VI) and Other Mo(VI) Species

The use of ^{95}Mo NMR as a routine spectroscopic technique in the characterization of molybdenum compounds and as a probe of reactivity patterns is now established. Mononuclear Mo(VI) complexes can have a very large chemical shift range; spectra with ^{95}Mo signals from -500 ppm to as high as 3500 ppm have been reported.[162] The ^{95}Mo NMR scale for Mo(VI) and other species of varying oxidation states are shown in Figure 4. The relaxation rates of molybdate(VI) solutions in water are independent of pH in the range 9-12.[168] The MoO_4^{2-} anion can be examined free of complicating chemical effects because the rate of oxygen exchange is slow (0.02-0.05 s^{-1}) and protonation[186] and condensation processes are unimportant.

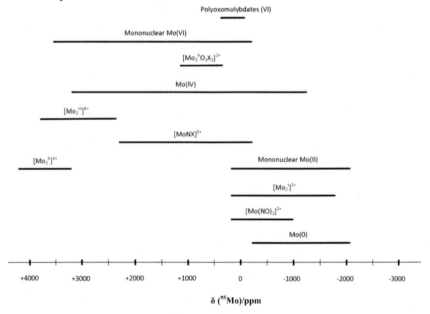

Figure 4. ^{95}Mo NMR chemical shift range for various molybdenum-containing species (Reproduced by permission).[162]

The ^{95}Mo relaxation time of 840 ± 20 ms translates to half-widths of 0.38 Hz for the particular sample (1 M Na_2MoO_4, 3 M NaCl) examined.

Below pH 9, the line-widths of molybdate(VI) solutions increase as chemical exchange processes affect the relaxation rate.[168] Below pH 7.7, protonation of molybdate(VI) dominates the chemistry. As molybdate(VI) solutions are acidified below pH 7.7, the molybdate(VI) signal broadens and a second, broad resonance assigned to $Mo_7O_{24}^{6-}$ appears at about pH 6.5.[178,187,188]

Aqueous solutions of molybdate(VI), which are an important starting point for the preparation of molybdenum catalysts involve a series of equilibria between isomolybdate polymers, and despite many investigations knowledge of the structures concerned is incomplete.[89,189] Studies involving ^{95}Mo NMR[190,191] and Raman[192,193] spectroscopy have shown that the $[MoO_4]^{2-}$ and $[Mo_7O_{24}]^{6-}$ anions coexist in the pH range 4.5 – 6.5. Acidification produces higher polymers, probably $[Mo_8O_{26}]^{4-}$ and $[Mo_{36}O_{112}(H_2O)_{16}]^{8-}$ or protonated forms of these ions.[89]

Molybdenum(VI) equilibria were investigated in $LiClO_4$ (2.0 M) and NaCl (1.0 and 2.0 M) media by potentiometry, ^{95}Mo NMR spectroscopy, and calorimetry.[194] In the case of 2.0 M $Li(ClO_4)$ and 2.0 M $Na(ClO_4)$ media the molybdenum concentration was 1.0 M and the pH range covered was 2–7.5. For the potentiometric measurements in 1.0 M NaCl the molybdenum concentration was varied from $0.1–5.0 \times 10^{-4}$ M, while the pH range covered 1.0–6.5. Reaction models, based on computer treatment of the potentiometric data, were consistent with the NMR data.[194] In 1.0 M NaCl at 25 °C, the formation constants of the polyoxoanions, denoted by βpq, where the subscripts p and q refer to the stoichiometric coefficients of $[MoO_4]^{2-}$ and H^+ in the reactions, were as follows: log β_{78} = 52.86, log β_{79} = 57.25, log β_{68} = 49.53, log $\beta_{8,11}$ = 67.90, log $\beta_{8,12}$ = 71.52, log $\beta_{13,21}$ = 119.49, and log $\beta_{18,32}$ = 171.43. Enthalpy and entropy changes for the formation of the polyions were calculated from the calorimetric data using these constants. The enthalpy values were ΔH_{78} = −258, ΔH_{79} = −248, ΔH_{68} = −218, $\Delta H_{8,11}$ = −275, $\Delta H_{8,12}$ = −285, $\Delta H_{13,21}$ = −508, and $\Delta H_{18,32}$ = −782 kJ mol^{-1}.[194]

^{17}O and ^{95}Mo NMR spectroscopy was used to study aqueous molybdenum(VI) in the pH range 1.2 – 6.[195] Heptamolybdate, $[Mo_7O_{24}]^{6-}$, its monoprotonated form, and β-octamolybdate, $[Mo_8O_{26}]^{4-}$, were clearly identified, and evidence has also been found for an intermediate species $[H_3Mo_8O_{28}]^{5-}$.[195] The protonation site of heptamolybdate was identified, and kinetic and structural data have been correlated to yield a scheme for the transformation of heptamolybdate to octamolybdate upon acidification.[195]

^{95}Mo solid state NMR spectra of a variety of molybdates of alkali metals as well as molybdates of some divalent metals, MoO_3, $Mo(CO)_6$, polyoxo complexes $H_3PMo_{12}O_{40} \cdot \chi H_2O$, and $[(C_4H_9)_4N]_4[Mo_8O_{26}]$ were reported.[196] Alkali-metal molybdates show mainly sharp single resonances. Signals from the molybdates of divalent metals show a splitting due to second-order quadrupole effects.[196] For MoO_3, signals from structurally inequivalent Mo sites seem to be resolved.[196] The ^{95}Mo spectrum of $H_3PMo_{12}O_{40} \cdot \chi H_2O$ exhibited a large chemical shift anisotropy, while for $[(C_4H_9)_4N]_4[Mo_8O_{26}]$ the superposition of a sharp peak from almost regular MoO_4 tetrahedra and a broad line from Mo atoms in distorted octahedra was observed.[196] For molybdates the resonances are shifted upfield with decreasing M=O bond length.[196]

An initial survey of the ^{95}Mo NMR properties of a range of 12 polyoxomolybdates was reported by Gheller *et al.*[197] The species resonate in the range -18 to +140 ppm.[197] The observed line widths generally exceeded 100 Hz for six-coordinate molybdenum sites of low symmetry, but was found to be narrow (< 20 Hz at 20°) for four-coordinate sites.[197] Aqueous solutions of $[Mo_7O_{24}]^{6-}$ at pH 6.1 exhibited exchange between Mo- and Mo_7-based species.[197] Solutions of α-$[Mo_8O_{26}]^{4-}$ in acetonitrile featured a single narrow resonance ($\delta 16$, $W_{h/2}$ 23 Hz at 20°) assigned to the tetrahedral capping sites, while two broad resonances ($\delta 19$, $W_{h/2}$ 240 Hz; $\delta 109$, $W_{h/2}$ C. 270 Hz) are seen in equivalent solutions of β-$[Mo_8O_{26}]^{4-}$.[197] In the study, ^{17}O NMR was used to confirm the integrity of sample solutions and to assist in correction of the ^{95}Mo NMR properties of β-$[Mo_8O_{26}]^{4-}$ [197].

I, Alvin Holder, was very fortunate to have collaborated with Professor William McFarlane, a former collaborator of Professor A. Geoffrey Sykes at The University of Newcastle, who acquired ^{95}Mo NMR spectra of compounds **1**, **2**, **3**, and **4**, with coordinated MoO_4^{2-}. As such, adducts with MoO_4^{2-} tetrahedra coordinated to Cr(III) or Co(III) complexes were studied by high resolution ^{95}Mo NMR spectroscopy.[129] The ^{95}Mo chemical shifts of the adducts with cobalt(III) lie in the range -33.2 to $+ 49.4$ ppm. This may be compared with an overall known chemical shift range in excess of 7000 ppm and implies a similarity in the molybdenum environment in all cases. For adducts with chelated cobalt(III) complexes several rather broad ^{95}Mo signals are obtained with line widths up to 260 Hz. [129] It is interesting to note that compound **2** gave no ^{95}Mo NMR signal, presumably owing to the paramagnetism of the chromium(III) metal center. Table 9 shows the ^{95}Mo NMR spectral data for the respective complexes.

Brito *et al.*[198] reported of the use of ^{95}Mo NMR as a useful tool for structural studies of oxomolybdenum(VI) complexes in solution with the purpose of using this technique as a tool to study their coordination chemistry and reactivity.[198]

Table 9. ^{95}Mo NMR spectral data for the respective complexes (Reproduced by permission)^a [129]

Complex	δ/ppm	Line width/Hz
$[(NH_3)_5CoOMoO_3]ClO_4$ **1**	-5.0^b	30
$[(en)_2CoO_2MoO_2]ClO_4$ **3**	-1.8	260
	$+3.5$	80
	$+27.5$	80
$[(tren)CoO_2MoO_2]ClO_4$ **4**	-33.2	20
	-15.1	140
	$+7.7$	260
	$+31.5$	120
	$+49.4$	90

^{a} pH of solution = 5.87.
^{b} 2.0 mM Na_2MoO_4 gave a chemical shift, δ = -5.0 ppm.

The relationship between the electronic density on the metal tuned by the electron-donor ability of the coordinated ligands and the ^{95}Mo NMR chemical shift was proven for mono- and bimetallic complexes showing a hexa- or hepta-coordination around the metal center.[198] The different origins of the signal broadening (associated either to the symmetry of the metallic polyhedron or to the presence of isomers or to the ligand de-coordination) was also considered in order to rationalize the data.[198] On bioinorganic point of view, the feasibility of using ^{95}Mo NMR spectroscopy to monitor the environment of this nucleus in biochemical systems was established by the observation of the binding of $[MoO_4]^{2-}$ and $[MoS_4]^{2-}$ anions to the protein bovine serum albumin.[199]

Other important uses of ^{95}Mo NMR spectroscopy have been reported in the literature.[200-210]

Catalysis Involving Molybdenum for Hydrogen Production

The production of H_2 by photocatalytic water splitting has attracted attention as a clean and renewable solar H_2 generation system. Despite tremendous efforts, the present great challenge in materials science is to develop highly active photocatalysts for splitting of water at low cost. As mentioned above, molybdenum sulfides are prevalent in both biological enzymes and industrial catalysts. Synthetic molybdenum sulfides can serve as proven electrocatalysts for the hydrogen evolution reaction (HER). MoS_2[211,212] and the incomplete cubane $[Mo_3S_4]^{4+}$ clusters[213,214] have been shown to be active HER catalysts.

Other researchers have been researching on HER catalysts, for example, Xiang *et al.*[215] reported a new composite material consisting of TiO_2 nanocrystals grown in the presence of a layered MoS_2/graphene hybrid as a high-performance photocatalyst for H_2 evolution. The composite material was prepared by a two-step simple hydrothermal process using sodium molybdate, thiourea, and graphene oxide as precursors of the MoS_2/graphene hybrid and tetrabutylorthotitanate as the titanium precursor.[215] Even without a noble-metal cocatalyst, the TiO_2/MoS_2/graphene composite reached a high H_2 production rate of 165.3 μmol h^{-1} when the content of the MoS_2/graphene cocatalyst was 0.5 wt %, and also when the content of graphene in the co-catalyst was 5.0 wt %, with the apparent quantum efficiency reaching 9.7% at 365 nm.[215] The unusual photocatalytic activity is believed to arise from the positive synergetic effect between the MoS_2 and graphene components in the hybrid co-catalyst, which served as an electron collector and a source of active adsorption sites, respectively. The study reported an inexpensive photocatalyst for energy conversion to achieve highly efficient H_2 evolution without the use of any noble metals.[215]

Hydrogen gas as a clean energy resource was found to be produced from a mixture consisting of a H_2O/H_2O_2/$MnMoO_4$ system.[216] The $MnMoO_4$ powder was synthesized by a sol-gel method and was characterized with X-ray diffraction, transmission electron microscopy, and x-ray photoelectron spectrometry. The efficiency of the hydrogen generation increased with increasing H_2O_2 concentration, the quantity of $MnMoO_4$ powder, and intensity of light resource. A mechanism was suggested for hydrogen generation from the H_2O/H_2O_2/$MnMoO_4$ system.[216]

UV light irradiation of TiO_2 in an aqueous ethanol solution of $(NH_4)_2MoS_4$ under air free conditions was reported to yield molybdenum(IV) sulfide nanoparticles on a TiO_2 surface (MoS_2/TiO_2). These species were transformed into molybdenum(VI) oxide species highly dispersed at a molecular level by a subsequent heating at 773 K in air, with the eventual formation of m-MoO_3/TiO_2.[217] In HCOOH aqueous solutions, the MoS_2/TiO_2 system exhibited a high level of photocatalytic activity for H_2 generation, while the m-MoO_3/TiO_2 system showed unique photochromism.[217]

Amorphous molybdenum sulfide films were found to be efficient hydrogen evolution catalysts in water. The films were prepared *via* simple electro-polymerization procedures and are characterized by XPS, electron microscopy, and electronic absorption spectroscopy.[218] Whereas the precatalysts could be MoS_3 or MoS_2, the active form of the catalysts was identified as amorphous MoS_2. Significant geometric current densities were achieved at low overpotentials (*e.g.*, 15 mA cm^{-2} at $\eta = 200$ mV) using the catalysts.[218] The catalysis was compatible with a wide range of pH, 0 to 13. The current efficiency for hydrogen production was quantitative. A 40 mV Tafel slope was observed, suggesting a rate-determining ion plus atom step. The turnover frequency per active site was calculated. The amorphous molybdenum sulfide films were reported to be among the most active non-precious hydrogen evolution catalysts.[218]

There was a report of the light-driven activation of the molybdenum−iron−protein (MoFeP) of nitrogenase for substrate reduction independent of ATP hydrolysis and the iron−protein (FeP), which was believed to be essential for catalytic turnover.[219] A MoFeP variant labeled on its surface with a ruthenium(II) photosensitizer was shown to photocatalytically reduce protons and acetylene, most likely at its active site, FeMoco.[219]

Under visible light irradiation, CdSe-nanoribbons was found to photocatalyze H_2 evolution from aqueous sodium sulfite/sulfide solution with a quantum efficiency of 9.2% at 440 nm, whereas bulk CdSe was not active for the reaction.[220] Photoelectrochemical measurements showed that the activity of nano-CdSe was caused by a raised flat band potential (−0.55 V, NHE) which followed from the increased band gap (2.7 eV) of the quantum confined material. In the presence of a sulfide ion, the flat band potential was fixed to −0.43 V (NHE), slightly below the sulfide redox potential (−0.48 V, NHE).[220] When the nanoribbons were chemically linked to MoS_2 nanoplates that were obtained by exfoliation and ultrasonication of bulk MoS_2, the activity increased almost four times, depending on the mass percentage of MoS_2. Cyclic voltammetry revealed that the enhancement from the MoS_2 nanoplates was due to a reduction of the H_2 evolution overpotential.[220] In contrast, chemical linkage of Pt nanoparticles to the nanoribbons did not affect the photocatalytic activity.[220] Photocatalytic H_2 production on MoS_2/CdS photocatalysts in the presence of different sacrificial reagents under visible light ($\lambda > 420$ nm) was investigated by Zong *et al.*[221] The transformation process of the Mo species loaded on CdS, together with the junctions formed between MoS_2 and CdS, was clearly demonstrated with X-ray photoelectron spectroscopy and transmission electron microscopy.[221] Photocatalytic H_2 evolution was optimized for MoS_2/CdS catalysts. The 0.2 wt % MoS_2/CdS catalyst calcined at 573 K achieved the highest overall activity for H_2 evolution, and the 0.2 wt % MoS_2/CdS catalyst demonstrates even higher activity than the 0.2 wt % Pt/CdS, irrespective of different sacrificial reagents used. The junctions formed between MoS_2 and CdS played an important role in enhancing the photocatalytic activity of MoS_2/CdS catalysts.[221] Electrochemical measurements indicated that MoS_2 was an excellent H_2 evolution catalyst, which was another important factor responsible for the enhancement of the photocatalytic activity of MoS_2/CdS catalysts.[221] It was reported that (CpMoμ-S)$_2$S$_2$CH$_2$ and related derivatives can serve as electrocatalysts for the reduction of protons with current efficiencies near 100%.[222] The kinetics of the electrochemical reduction process was studied, and the effects of varying the proton source, the solvent, the cyclopentadienyl substituents, and the sulfur substituents on the catalyst were reported.[222] The reduction of excess *p*-cyanoanilinium tetrafluoroborate under a hydrogen atmosphere in 0.3 M Et$_4$NBF$_4$/acetonitrile buffered at pH 7.6 was catalyzed by CpMoμ-S)$_2$S$_2$CH$_2$ at −0.64 V versus ferrocene, with an overpotential of 120 mV. Protonation of the sulfido ligand in CpMoμ-S)$_2$S$_2$CH$_2$ was an initial step in the catalytic process, and the rate-determining step at high acid concentrations appears to be the elimination of hydrogen.[222] The elimination was believed to occur either from adjacent hydrosulfido sites or from a hydrosulfido−molybdenum hydride intermediate.[222]

Karunadasa *et al.*[223] recently identified a molybdenum-oxo complex that can catalytically generate gaseous hydrogen either from water at neutral pH or from sea water with a turnover frequency of 2.4 moles of H$_2$ per mole of catalyst per second and a turnover number of 6.1 x 10^5 moles of H$_2$ per mole of catalyst. Water reacted with orange [(PY5Me$_2$)MoI]I$_2$ to release hydrogen and generated a green molybdenum-oxo complex, [(PY5Me$_2$)MoO]I$_2$.[223] The study work shows that high-valency metal-oxo species can be used to create reduction catalysts that are robust and functional in water, a concept that has broad implications for the design of 'green' and sustainable chemistry cycles. Extensive reviews on the coordination chemistry of molybdenum, inclusive of catalysis can be found in the literature.[42-48,65,224,225]

For further reading, the reader is encouraged to read the chapters of Drs. Chakravarthy and Chand; Chisholm and Naseri; Baik, Lord, and Shultz; Hernandez-Molina, Sokolov, and Abramov; Nordlander and Pierpoint; and Richens, which are all featured within this textbook.

BIOLOGICAL ROLE OF MOLYBDENUM

Molybdenum in Enzymes

Molybdenum plays an important role in the Earth's nitrogen cycle. It is essential for biological fixation, participating in a number of biochemical redox reactions; as such molybdenum is an essential micronutrient for most forms of life.[226,227] Molybdenum is essential to life due to its role in the active site of redox enzymes, from which the majority of the free energy available for organisms originates in nature.[228] Molybdenum is a necessary constituent of nitrogenase,[229] the enzyme which catalyses the reduction of N$_2$ to NH$_3$. This large enzyme, which consists of two different proteins, is found in blue-green algae, in free living bacteria, and in bacteria whose symbiotic relationship with legumes (peas, beans, alfalfa, etc.) provides humans and animals with a major source of protein.

While over 50 enzymes containing molybdenum are known, only four have been found to exist in eukaryotes, and most unicellular eukaryotes are excluded from this short list of molybdenum-utilizing organisms.[227] The eukaryotic molybdenum-containing enzymes include nitrate reductase (NAR), sulfite reductase (SO), xanthine dehydrogenase (XOR), and aldehyde oxidase (AO).[226,227] Table 10 lists several of the enzymes that contain molybdenum.

Oxomolybdenum redox chemistry is also exploited in selective oxidation catalysis. In the oxidase enzymes and the heterogeneous catalysts bismuth molybdate and iron molybdate, molybdenum shuttles between oxidation states +6 and +4, while transferring O or OH to substrate molecules.[230]

Table 10. Some enzymes that contain molybdenum

Enzyme	Source	Molecular weight/g mol^{-1}	# of Mo atoms	Fe and S content	Reaction catalyzed
Nitrogenase	Bacteria; blue-green	220,000	2	30 Fe, 30 S	$N_2 + 6H^+ \rightarrow 2NH_3$
	Algae	60,000	0	4 Fe, 4 S	
Nitrate reductase	a	100,000-360,000	1 or 2	Cytochrome b	$NO_3^- + 2H^+ + 2e^- \rightarrow NO_2^- + H_2O$
Xanthine oxidase	Cow's milk	275,000	2	8 Fe, 8 S	Xanthine + $H_2O \rightarrow$ uric acid + $2H^+ + 2e^-$
Xanthine dehydrogenase	Chicken liver	300,000	2	8 Fe, 8 S	Same as above
Aldehyde oxidase	Rabbit liver	270,000	2	8 Fe, 8 S	$RCHO + H_2O \rightarrow RCO_2H + 2H^+ + 2e^-$
Sulfite oxidase	Cow liver	11,000	2	2 Haeme	$SO_3^{2-} + H_2O \rightarrow SO_4^{2-} + 2H^+ + 2e^-$

a Fungi, *E. coli*, spinach, and others.

Molybdenum in Medicine

Molybdenum is an element that is present in very small amounts in the body. It is involved in many important biological processes, and possibly the development of the nervous system, waste processing in the kidneys, and energy production in cells.[231] Molybdenum is an essential element in human nutrition, but its precise functions and interactions with other chemicals in the body are not well understood.[231] There is some evidence that suggest that too little molybdenum in the diet may be responsible for some health problems.[231] Molybdenum is used to treat rare inherited metabolic diseases, such as Wilson's disease in which the body cannot process copper.[231] More research is needed to learn its role in preventing cancer and other diseases. Molybdenum has shown promise in animal studies in reducing the harmful effects of certain cancer drugs on the heart and lungs.[231] Proponents claim that molybdenum is an antioxidant that prevents cancer by protecting cells from free radicals, destructive molecules that may damage cells.[231] Some supporters also claim that molybdenum prevents anemia, gout, dental cavities, and sexual impotence.[231]

The tetrathiomolybdate (MoS_4^{2-}) anion is being tested as a cancer treatment.[231-233] Some studies in mice have shown that tetrathiomolybdate might improve the response to breast cancer drugs, but human studies are required to find out whether this is true.[231] Animal studies also suggest that tetrathiomolybdate might be helpful in reducing the heart and lung damage caused by some chemotherapeutic drugs.[231]

Polyoxometallates, including those that contain molybdenum metal centers have many potential medicinal applications,[234] inclusive of anti-tumoral and anti-viral applications.[235,236]

Four new water soluble molybdenocene complexes were synthesized in aqueous solution at pH 7.0.[237] The new species, $[(\eta^5\text{-}C_5H_5)_2Mo(L)]Cl$ (L = 6-mercaptopurine (for complex

8), 2-amino-6-mercaptopurine, (−)-2-amino-6-mercaptopurine ribose and 6-mercaptopurine ribose), were characterized by spectroscopic methods.[237] The anti-proliferative activities of the new species were investigated in HT-29 colon and MCF-7 breast cancer cell lines. The incorporation of molybdenocene (Cp_2Mo^{2+}) into the thionucleobases/thionucleosides decreased their cytotoxic activities in HT-29 colon cancer cell line. In contrast, in the MCF-7 cell line, [Cp₂Mo(2-amino-6-mercaptopurine)]Cl showed a high cytotoxic activity.[237] This is most likely a consequence of the enhanced lipophilic character on the thionucleobase combined with synergism between Cp_2Mo^{2+} and the thionucleobase ligand.[237] The fine work of Dr. Enrique Meléndez will be featured in chapter 12 of this textbook. Molybdenum as a pharmaceutical is featured in some reviews as published by The Royal Society of Chemistry.[42,43,65,238-242]

8

The Molybdenum Environmental Database for the International Molybdenum Association is a primer for molybdenum biochemistry.[9] As MoS_2, MoO_3, and the molybdates have low toxicity,[9] molybdenum is currently replacing more toxic elements in some applications: chromates in corrosion inhibitors and antimony in polyvinyl chloride smoke suppressants.[9]

On a final note, the reader is encouraged to read the chapters of Drs. Burgmayer, Hille, and Newton; and the textbook entitled *"Biological Inorganic Chemistry: Structure and Reactivity"* by Ivano Bertini, Harry B. Gray, Edward I. Stiefel, and Joan Selverstone Valentine, University Science Books, Sausalito, California, 2007, ISBN-10: 1-891389-43-2, for detailed bioinorganic chemistry of molybdenum.

REFERENCES

[1]   *CRC Handbook of Chemistry and Physics* 89th ed.; Lide, D. R., Ed.; CRC Press: Boca Raton, Fl, 2008.
[2]   Suzuki, K.; Shimizu, H.; Masuda, A. *Geochim. Cosmochim. Acta* 1996, *60*, 3151.
[3]   Konosu, S. *Eng. Fail. Anal.* 1995, *2*, 151.
[4]   http://en.wikipedia.org/wiki/Molybdenum.
[5]   Emsley, J. *Nature's Building Blocks*; Oxford University Press: Oxford, 2001.
[6]   Callaghan, R. *Mineral Commodity Summaries*, U.S. Geological Survey, 2011.
[7]   Oso, P. R. *Molybdenum, Mineral Information Institute* 2011, *2011*.
[8]   Holleman, A. F.; Wiberg, E.; Wiberg, N.; 91–100 ed.; Walter de Gruyter: Berlin, 1985, p 1096–1104.
[9]   http://www.imoa.info.
[10] Shpak, A. P.; Kotrechko, S. O.; Mazilova, T. I.; Mikhailovskij, I. M. *Sci. Technol. Adv. Mater.* 2009, *10*, 045004.
[11] http://pubs.acs.org/cen/80th/molybdenum.html.

[12] Mitchell, P. C. H. *Chem. Eng. News* 2003, *81*, 108.

[13] Hugh, O. P. *Handbook of Refractory Carbides and Nitrides*; William Andrew Publishing: Westwood, NJ, 1996.

[14] Gottschalk, A. *Annu. Rev. Med.* 1969, *20*, 131.

[15] Lal, S.; Patil, R. S. *Environmental Monitoring and Assessment* 2001, *68*, 37.

[16] Winer, W. O. *Wear* 1967, *10*, 422.

[17] Radisavljevic, B.; Radenovic, A.; Brivio, J.; Giacometti, V.; Kis, A. *Nat Nano* 2011, *6*, 147.

[18] Ho, T. C.; McConnachie, J. M. *J. Catal.* 2011, *277*, 117.

[19] Topsøe, H.; Clausen, B. S.; Massoth, F. E. *Hydrotreating Catalysis, Science and Technology.*; Springer-Verlag: Berlin, 1996.

[20] Mitchell, P. C. H. *Wear* 1984, *100*, 281.

[21] McConnachie, J. M.; Bell, I. A. W.; Brown, A. J.; Stiefel, E. I.; Hill, E. W. *US Patent* 2003, *20030224951A1*, 7 pp., Cont.-in-part of U.S. Ser. No. 815,850.

[22] Brown, A. J.; Bell, I. A. W.; McConnachie, J. M.; Stiefel, E. I. *Prepr. - Am. Chem. Soc., Div. Pet. Chem.* 1999, *44*, 326.

[23] McConnachie, J. M.; Stiefel, E. I.; Bell, I. A. W.; Arunasalam, V.-C. *US Patent* 1999, *5906968A*, 3 pp.

[24] Coyle, C. L.; Greaney, M. A.; Stiefel, E. I.; Francis, J. N.; Beltzer, M. *US Patent* 1991, *4995996A*, 4 pp.

[25] Coyle, C. L.; Halbert, T. R.; Stiefel, E. I. *US Patent* 1990, *4978464A*, 5 pp.

[26] Coyle, C. L.; Greaney, M. A.; Stiefel, E. I.; Beltzer, M. *US Patent* 1990, *4966719*, 4 pp.

[27] Parker, A. M.; Thoennessen, M. *Nucl. Exp.* 2011, 1-45, arXiv:1102.2388v1 [nucl-ex].

[28] Morreale, A. C.; Novog, D. R.; Luxat, J. C. *Appl. Radiat. Isot.* 2012, *70*, 20.

[29] Mushtaq, A. *Nucl. Eng. Des.* 2011, *241*, 163.

[30] Fisker, J. L.; Hoffman, R. D.; Pruet, J. *Astrophys. J.* 2009, *690*, 135.

[31] Wieser, M. E.; De Laeter, J. R. *Int. J. Mass spectrom.* 2009, *286*, 98.

[32] Dauphas, N.; Davis, A. M.; Marty, B.; Reisberg, L. *Earth Planet. Sci. Lett.* 2004, *226*, 465.

[33] Siebert, C.; Nägler, T. F.; von Blanckenburg, F.; Kramers, J. D. *Earth Planet. Sc. Lett.* 2003, *211*, 159.

[34] Malinovsky, D.; Rodushkin, I.; Baxter, D. C.; Ingri, J.; Öhlander, B. *Int. J. Mass Spectrom.* 2005, *245*, 94.

[35] Scheiderich, K.; Zerkle, A. L.; Helz, G. R.; Farquhar, J.; Walker, R. J. *Chem. Geo.* 2010, *279*, 134.

[36] Poulson Brucker, R. L.; McManus, J.; Severmann, S.; Berelson, W. M. *Geochem. Geophy. Geosy.* 2009, *10*, Q06010.

[37] Sievers, E.; Dörner, K.; Garbe-Schönberg, D.; Schaub, J. *J. Trace Elem. Med. Biol.* 2001, *15*, 185.

[38] Yoshida, M.; Hattori, H.; Ôta, S.; Yoshihara, K.; Kodama, N.; Yoshitake, Y.; Nishimuta, M. *J. Trace Elem. Med. Biol.* 2006, *20*, 245.

[39] Stiefel, E. I. In *Metals Ions in Biological System*; Sigel, A., Sigel, H., Eds.; CRC Press: New York, 2002.

[40] Cotton, F. A.; Wilkinson, G.; Murillo, C. A.; Bochmann, M. *Advanced Inorganic Chemistry*; 6th ed.; John Wiley and Sons, Inc.: New York, 1999.

[41] Cotton, F. A.; McCleverty, J. A.; White, J. E. *Inorg. Synth.* 1990, *28*, 45.

[42] Holder, A. A. *Annu. Rep. Prog. Chem., Sect. A: Inorg. Chem.* 2006, *102*, 194.

[43] Holder, A. A. *Annu. Rep. Prog. Chem., Sect. A: Inorg. Chem.* 2007, *103*, 159.

[44] Holder, A. A. *Annu. Rep. Prog. Chem., Sect. A: Inorg. Chem.* 2008, *104*, 167.

[45] Holder, A. A. *Annu. Rep. Prog. Chem., Sect. A: Inorg. Chem.* 2009, *105*, 201.

[46] Holder, A. A. *Annu. Rep. Prog. Chem., Sect. A: Inorg. Chem.* 2010, *106*, 176.

[47] Holder, A. A. *Annu. Rep. Prog. Chem., Sect. A: Inorg. Chem.* 2011, *107*, 163.

[48] Holder, A. A. *Annu. Rep. Prog. Chem., Sect. A: Inorg. Chem.* 2012, *108*, DOI:10.1039/C2IC90008D.

[49] Cotton, F. A.; Donahue, J. P.; Murillo, C. A.; Perez, L. M.; Yu, R. *J. Am. Chem. Soc.* 2003, *125*, 8900.

[50] Cotton, F. A.; Eglin, J. L.; James, C. A. *Inorg. Chim. Acta* 1993, *204*, 175.

[51] Cotton, F. A.; Fanwick, P. E.; Niswander, R. H.; Sekutowski, J. C. *Acta Chem. Scand., Ser. A* 1978, *A32*, 663.

[52] Chisholm, M. H. *Macromol. Chem. Phys.* 2012, *213*, 800.

[53] Brown-Xu, S. E.; Chisholm, M. H.; Gallucci, J. C.; Ghosh, Y.; Gustafson, T. L.; Reed, C. R. *Dalton Trans.* 2012, *41*, 2257.

[54] Alberding, B. G.; Chisholm, M. H.; Gustafson, T. L. *Inorg. Chem.* 2012, *51*, 491.

[55] Chisholm, M. H.; Lear, B. J. *Chem. Soc. Rev.* 2011, *40*, 5254.

[56] Alberding, B. G.; Chisholm, M. H.; Lear, B. J.; Naseri, V.; Reed, C. R. *Dalton Trans.* 2011, *40*, 10658.

[57] Chisholm, M. H. *Polym. Prepr. (Am. Chem. Soc., Div. Polym. Chem.)* 2011, *52*, 838.

[58] Alberding, B. G.; Chisholm, M. H.; Gallucci, J. C.; Ghosh, Y.; Gustafson, T. L. *Proc. Natl. Acad. Sci. U. S. A.* 2011, *108*, 8152, S8152/1.

[59] Bunting, P.; Chisholm, M. H.; Gallucci, J. C.; Lear, B. J. *J. Am. Chem. Soc.* 2011, *133*, 5873.

[60] Alberding, B. G.; Chisholm, M. H.; Gustafson, T. L.; Liu, Y.; Reed, C. R.; Turro, C. *J. Phys. Chem. A* 2010, *114*, 12675.

[61] Chisholm, M. H. *Struct. Bonding* 2010, *136*, 29.

[62] Chisholm, M. H.; Patmore, N. J.; Reed, C. R.; Singh, N. *Inorg. Chem.* 2010, *49*, 7116.

[63] Alberding, B. G.; Barybin, M. V.; Chisholm, M. H.; Gustafson, T. L.; Reed, C. R.; Robinson, R. E.; Patmore, N. J.; Singh, N.; Turro, C. *Dalton Trans.* 2010, *39*, 1979.

[64] Lear, B. J.; Chisholm, M. H. *Inorg. Chem.* 2009, *48*, 10954.

[65] Holder, A. A. *Annu. Rep. Prog. Chem., Sect. A: Inorg. Chem.* 2005, *101*, 161.

[66] Hermann, K.; Witko, M. *Chemical Physics of Solid Surfaces*; Elsevier, 2001.

[67] Crichton, R. R. *Biological Inorganic Chemistry*, 2008.

[68] Bonneau, P. R.; Jarvis, R. F.; Kaner, R. B. *Nature* 1991, *349*, 510.

[69] In *Encyclopedia Britannica Academic Edition* Chicago, IL, 2011.

[70] Malito, J. *Annu. Rep. NMR Spectrosc.* 1996, *33*, 151.

[71] Charlot, G. *Oxidation-Reduction Potentials, Tables of Constants and Numerical Data*; Pergamon Press: Oxford, 1958; Vol. 8.

[72] Griffith, W. P. *Coord. Chem. Rev.* 1970, *5*, 459.

[73] Cotton, F. A.; Wilkinson, G. *Advanced Inorganic Chemistry*; 3rd ed.; John Wiley and Sons, Inc.: New York.

[74] Jahr, K. F.; Fuchs, J. *Angew. Chem.* 1966, *5*, 689.

[75] Pope, M. T.; Dale, B. W. *Quart. Rev.* 1968, *22*, 527.

[76] Keppert, D. L. *Prog. Inorg. Chem.* 1962, *4*, 199.

[77] Ballhausen, K.; Liehr, J. *Mol. Spec.* 1958, 342.

[78] Carrington, A.; Schonland, D. S. *Mol. Phys.* 1960, *3*, 331.

[79] Frenske, R. F.; Sweeny, C. C. *Inorg. Chem.* 1964, *3*, 1105.

[80] Basch, H.; Gray, H. B.; Viste, A. *J. Chem. Phys.* 1966, *44*, 10.

[81] Gray, H. B. *Coord. Chem. Rev.* 1966, *1*, 2.

[82] Michelis, G. D.; Oleari, L.; Disipio, L. *Coord. Chem. Rev.* 1966, *1*, 18.

[83] Michelis, G. D.; Oleari, L.; Disipio, L. *Coord. Chem. Rev.* 1966, *1*, 24.

[84] Bailey, N.; Carrington, A.; Lott, K.; Symons, M. *J. Chem. Soc.* 1960, 290.

[85] Cruywagen, J. J.; Heyns, J. B. B. *J. Chem. Educ.* 1989, *66*, 116.

[86] Carrington, A.; Symons, M. C. R. *Chem. Rev.* 1963, *63*, 43.

[87] Richens, D. T.; Sykes, A. G. *Comments Inorg. Chem.* 1981, *1*, 141.

[88] Day, V. W.; Klemperer, W. G. *Science* 1985, *228*, 533.

[89] Pope, M. T. *Heteropoly and Isopoly Oxometalates*; Springer-Verlay: Berlin, 1983.

[90] Keggin, J. F. *Proc. Roy. Soc., A* 1934, *144*, 75.

[91] Song, Y.-F.; Long, D.-L.; Cronin, L. *Angew. Chem. Int. Ed.* 2007, *46*, 3900.

[92] Hong-Xu Guo, H.-X.; Liu, S.-X. *Inorg. Chem. Commun.* 2004, *7*, 1217.

[93] http://en.wikipedia.org/wiki/Polyoxometalate.

[94] Li, F.; Xu, L. *Dalton Trans.* 2011, *40*, 4024.

[95] Krebs, B. *NATO ASI Ser., Ser. C* 1995, *459*, 359.

[96] Misono, M.; Climax Molybdenum Co. Mich.: 1982, p 289-295.

[97] Pope, M. T.; Quicksall, C. O.; Kwak, W.; Rajkovic, L. M.; Stalick, J. K.; Barkigia, K. M.; Scully, T. F. *J. Less-Common Met.* 1977, *54*, 129.

[98] Weakley, T. J. R. *Struct. Bonding* 1974, *18*, 131.

[99] Coomber, R.; Griffith, W. P. *J. Chem. Soc. (A)* 1968, 1128.

[100] Briggs, S. H. C. *J. Chem. Soc.* 1919, 67.

[101] Sadler, N. P.; Dasgupta, T. P. *Transition Met. Chem.* 1992, *17*, 409.

[102] Sadler, N. P.; Dasgupta, T. P. *Transition Met. Chem.* 1992, *17*, 317.

[103] Sadler, N. P. Ph.D., The University of the West Indies, Mona Campus, Jamaica, 1983.

[104] Taylor, R. S. *Inorg. Chem.* 1977, *16*, 116.

[105] Grace, M. R.; Tregloan, P. A. *Polyhedron* 1991, *10*, 2317.

[106] Holder, A. A.; Dasgupta, T. P. *J. Chem. Soc., Dalton Trans.* 1996, 2637.

[107] Gamsjager, H.; Sangmuller, W.; Sykes, A.; Thompson, G. *Inorg. Chem.* 1980, *19*, 997.

[108] Jayne, J.; Lincoln, S. P.; Hunt, J. P. *Inorg. Chem.* 1969, *8*, 2267.

[109] Schmidt, W.; Taube, H. *Inorg. Chem.* 1968, *2*, 698.

[110] Andrade, C.; Jordan, R. B.; Taube, H. *Inorg. Chem.* 1970, *9*, 711.

[111] Harris, G. M.; Eldik, R. V. *Inorg. Chem.* 1975, *14*, 1520.

[112] Chafee, E.; Dasgupta, T. P.; Harris, G. M. *J. Am. Chem. Soc.* 1973, *95*, 4169.

[113] Dasgupta, T. P.; Harris, G. M. *J. Am. Chem. Soc.* 1975, *97*, 1733.

[114] Dasgupta, T. P.; Harris, G. M. *J. Am. Chem. Soc.* 1977, *99*, 2490.

[115] Dasgupta, T. P.; Harris, G. M. *Inorg. Chem.* 1978, *17*, 3123.

[116] Dasgupta, T. P.; Harris, G. M. *Inorg. Chem.* 1978, *17*, 3304.

[117] Harris, G. M.; Palmer, D. A. *Inorg. Chem.* 1974, *13*, 965.

[118] Palmer, D. A.; Van Eldik, R. *Chem. Rev.* 1983, *83*, 651.

[119] Wan, W. K. Ph.D., State University of New York at Buffalo., 1978.

[120] Fowles, A. D.; Stranks, D. R. *Inorg. Chem.* 1977, *16*, 1276.

[121] Fowles, A. D.; Stranks, D. R. *Inorg. Chem.* 1977, *16*, 1282.

[122] Beech, T. A.; Lawrence, N. C.; Lincoln, S. F. *Aust. J. Chem.* 1973, *26*, 1877.

[123] Dasgupta, T. P.; Harris, G. M. *Inorg. Chem.* 1984, *23*, 4399.

[124] El-Awady, A. A.; Dash, A.; Harris, G. M. *Inorg. Chem.* 1981, *20*, 3160.

[125] El-Awady, A. A.; Harris, G. M. *Inorg. Chem.* 1981, *20*, 4251.

[126] Farrell, S. M.; Murray, R. S. *J. Chem. Soc., Dalton Trans.* 1977, 322.

[127] Harris, G. M.; Van Eldick, R. *Inorg. Chem.* 1980, *19*, 880.

[128] Holder, A. A.; Dasgupta, T. P. *Inorg. React. Mech.* 1999, *1*, 177.

[129] Holder, A. A.; Dasgupta, T. P.; McFarlane, W.; Rees, N. H.; Enemark, J. H.; Pacheco, A.; Christensen, K. *Inorg. Chim. Acta* 1997, *260*, 225.

[130] You, J.; Wu, D.; Liu, H. *Polyhedron* 1986, *5*, 535.

[131] Pan, W. H.; Leonowicz, M. E.; Stiefel, E. I. *Inorg. Chem.* 1983, *22*, 672.

[132] Huang, T.; Spence, J. T. *J. Phys. Chem.* 1968, *72*, 4198.

[133] Huang, T.; Spence, J. T. *J. Phys. Chem.* 1968, *72*, 4573.

[134] Rudenko, V. K. *Khim. Kinet. i. Kataliz, M.* 1979, 109.

[135] Verchere, J. F.; Fleury, M. B. *J. Less Common Met.* 1974, *36*, 133.

[136] Bergh, A. A.; Haight, G. P. *Inorg. Chem.* 1962, *1*, 688.

[137] Diebler, H.; Millan, Y. C. *Biol. Soc. Chil. Quim.* 1984, *29*, 277.

[138] Martin, J. F.; Spence, J. T. *J. Phys. Chem.* 1970, *74*, 2863.

[139] Martin, J. F.; Spence, J. T. *J. Phys. Chem.* 1970, *74*, 3589.

[140] Calvin, M.; Colowick, S., Lazarow, A., Racker, E., Schwartz, E., Stadtman, E., Waelsch, H., Eds.; Academic Press: New York, 1964, p 3.

[141] Huang, T. J.; Haight Jr, G. P. *J. Am. Chem. Soc.* 1971, *93*, 611.

[142] Botar, B.; Koegerler, P.; Hill, C. L. *J. Am. Chem. Soc.* 2006, *128*, 5336.

[143] Keller, A.; Szterenberg, L.; Glowiak, T. *Inorg. Chim. Acta* 1992, *202*, 19.

[144] Zhou, Z.-H.; Chen, C.-Y.; Cao, Z.-X.; Tsai, K.-R.; Chow, Y. L. *Dalton Trans.* 2008, 2475.

[145] Holder, A. A.; Brown, R. F. G.; Marshall, S. C.; Payne, V. C. R.; Cozier, M. D.; Alleyne, W. A., Jr.; Bovell, C. O. *Trans. Met. Chem.* 2000, *25*, 605.

[146] Palmer, G.; Massey, V. *J. Biol. Chem.* 1969, *244*, 2614.

[147] Dixon, D. A.; Dasgupta, T. P.; Sadler, N. P. *J. Chem. Soc., Dalton Trans.* 1997, 1903.

[148] Holder, A. A.; Dasgupta, T. P.; Im, S.-C. *Transition Met. Chem.* 1997, *22*, 135.

[149] Dash, A. C.; El-Awady, A. A.; Harris, G. M. *Inorg. Chem.* 1981, *20*, 3160.

[150] El-Awady, A. A.; Harris, G. M. *Inorg. Chem.* 1981, *20*, 1660.

[151] Van Eldik, R.; Harris, G. *Inorg. Chem.* 1980, *19*, 880.

[152] Van Eldik, R. *Inorg. Chim. Acta* 1980, *42*, 49.

[153] Koshy, K. C.; Harris, G. M. *Inorg. Chem.* 1983, *22*, 2947.

[154] Van Eldik, R.; Von Jouanne, J.; Kelm, H. *Inorg. Chem.* 1982, *21*, 2818.

[155] Curtis, N. J.; Lawrence, G. A.; Sargeson, A. M. *Aust. J. Chem.* 1983, *36*, 1327.

[156] Gaswick, D.; Haim, A. *J. Am. Chem. Soc.* 1971, *93*, 7347.

[157] Miralles, A. J.; Szecsy, A. P.; Haim, A. *Inorg. Chem.* 1982, *21*, 697.

[158] Martinez, P.; Zuluaga, J.; Noheda, P.; Van, E. R. *Inorg. Chim. Acta* 1992, *195*, 249.

[159] Dimmock, P. W.; McGinnis, J.; Ooi, B. L.; Sykes, A. G. *Inorg. Chem.* 1990, *29*, 1085.

[160] Dixon, D. A.; Sadler, N. P.; Dasgupta, T. P. *Transition Met. Chem.* 1995, *20*, 295.

[161] Holder, A. A.; Dasgupta, T. P. *Inorg. Chim. Acta* 2002, *331*, 279.

[162] Enemark, J. H.; Minelli, M.; Brownlee, R. T. C.; O'Connor, M. J.; Wedd, A. G. *Coord. Chem. Rev.* 1985, *68*, 169.

[163] Kidd, R. G. *The Multinuclear Approach to NMR Spectroscopy*; Reidel: Dordrecht, 1983.

[164] Kidd, R. G.; Goodfellow, R. J. *NMR and the Periodic Table*; Academic Press: London, 1978.

[165] R.G. Kidd *Annu. Rep., NMR Spectrosc.* 1979, *10A*, 19.

[166] Rinaldi, P. L.; Levy, G. C.; Choppin, G. R. *Rev. Inorg. Chem.* 1980, *2*, 53.

[167] Wehrli, F. W. *Annu. Rep., NMR Spectrosc.* 1979, *9A*, 146.

[168] Vold, R. R.; Vold, R. L. *J. Magn. Reson.* 1975, *19*, 365.

[169] Aksenov, S. I. *Soviet Phys. JETP* 1959, *8*, 207.

[170] Kaufmann, J. *Z. Phys.* 1964, *182*, 217.

[171] Krüger, H.; Lutz, O.; Nolle, A.; Schwenk, A. *Z. Naturforsch., Tiel A* 1973, *28*, 119.

[172] Narath, A.; Alderman, D. W. *Phys. Rev.* 1966, *143*, 328.

[173] Proctor, W. G.; Yu, F. C. *Phys. Rev.* 1951, *81*, 20.

[174] Rowland, T. J. *Prog. Math. Sci.* 1961, *1*, 9.

[175] Narath, A.; Brog, K. C.; Jones, W. H. *Phys. Rev. B* 1970, *2*, 2618.

[176] Lynch, G. F.; Segal, S. L. *Can. J. Phys.* 1972, *50*, 567.

[177] Buckler, K. U.; Haase, A. R.; Lutz, O.; Müller, M.; A. Nolle *Z. Naturforsch., Tiel A* 1977, *32*, 126.

[178] Kautt, W. D.; Krtger, H.; Lutz, O.; Maier, H.; Nolle, A. *Z. Naturforsch., Tiel A* 1976, *31*, 351.

[179] Kroneck, P.; Lutz, O.; Nolle, A. *Z. Naturforsch., Tiel A* 1980, *35*, 226.

[180] Lutz, O.; Nepple, W.; Nolle, A. *Z. Naturforsch., Tiel A* 1976, *31*, 1046.

[181] Lutz, O.; Nolle, A.; Kroneck, P. *Z. Phys. A* 1977, *282*, 157.

[182] Lutz, O.; Nolle, A.; P.Kroneck *Z. Naturforsch., Tiel A* 1976, *31*, 454.

[183] Lutz, O.; Nolle, A.; Kroneck, P. *Z. Naturforsch., Tiel A* 1977, *32*, 505.

[184] Masters, A. F.; Brownlee, R. T. C.; O'Connor, M. J.; Wedd, A. G.; Cotton, J. D. *J. Organomet. Chem.* 1980, *195*, C17.

[185] *Molybdenum and Molybdenum-containing Enzymes*; Coughlan, M., Ed.; Pergamon: Oxford, 1980.

[186] Vold, R. R.; Vold, R. L. *J. Chem. Phys.* 1974, *61*, 4360.

[187] Freeman, M. A.; Schultz, F. A.; Reilley, C. N. *Inorg. Chem.* 1982, *21*, 567.

[188] Gheller, S. F.; Sidney, M.; Masters, A. F.; Brownlee, R. T. C.; O'Connor, M. J.; Wedd, A. G. *Aust. J. Chem.* 1984, *37*, 1825.

[189] Tytko, K.-H.; Glemser, O. *Adv. Inorg. Chem. Radiochem.* 1976, *19*, 239.

[190] Luthra, N. P.; Cheng, W. C. *J. Catal.* 1987, *107*, 154.

[191] Sarrazin, P.; Monchel, B.; Kasztelan, S. *J. Phys. Chem.* 1989, *93*, 904.

[192] Ng, K. Y. S.; Gulari, E. *Polyhedron* 1984, *3*, 1001.

[193] Payen, E.; Grimblot, J.; Kasztelan, S. *J. Phys. Chem.* 1987, *91*, 6642.

[194] Cruywagen, J. J.; Draaijer, A. G.; Heyns, J. B. B.; Rohwer, E. A. *Inorg. Chim. Acta* 2002, *331*, 322.

[195] Howarth, O. W.; Kelly, P.; Pettersson, L. *J. Chem. Soc., Dalton Trans.* 1990, 81.

[196] Mastikhin, V. M.; Lapina, O. B.; Maksimovskaya, R. I. *Chem. Phys. Lett.* 1988, *148*, 413.

[197] Gheller, S. F.; Sidney, M.; Masters, A. F.; Brownlee, R. T. C.; O'Connor, M. J.; Wedd, A. G. *Aust. J. Chem.* 1984, *37*, 1825.

[198] Brito, J. A.; Teruel, H.; Massou, S.; Gómez, M. *Magn. Res. Chem.* 2009, *47*, 573.

[199] Bristow, S.; Garner, C. D.; Hagyard, S. K.; Morris, G. A.; Nicholson, J. R.; Mills, C. F. *J. Chem. Soc., Chem. Commun.* 1985, 479.

[200] Unoura, K.; Kikuchi, R.; Nagasawa, A.; Kato, Y.; Fukuda, Y. *Inorg. Chim. Acta* 1995, *228*, 89.

[201] Bastow, T. J. *Solid State Nucl. Magn. Reson.* 1998, *12*, 191.

[202] Alyea, E. C.; Topich, J. *Inorg. Chim. Acta* 1982, *65*, L95.

[203] Christensen, K. A.; Miller, P. E.; Minelli, M.; Rockway, T. W.; Enemark, J. H. *Inorg. Chim. Acta* 1981, *56*, L27.

[204] Cuny, J.; Furet, E.; Gautier, R.; Le, P. L.; Pickard, C. J.; d'Espinose, d. L. J.-B. *ChemPhysChem* 2009, *10*, 3320.

[205] Sarrazin, P.; Mouchel, B.; Kasztelan, S. *J. Phys. Chem.* 1989, *93*, 904.

[206] Coddington, J. M.; Taylor, M. J. *J. Chem. Soc., Dalton Trans.* 1990, 41.

[207] Lutz, O.; Nolle, A.; Kroneck, P. *Z. Naturforsch., A* 1977, *32A*, 505.

[208] Minelli, M.; Enemark, J. H.; Brownlee, R. T. C.; O'Connor, M. J.; Wedd, A. G. *Coord. Chem. Rev.* 1985, *68*, 169.

[209] Minelli, M.; Enemark, J. H.; Wieghardt, K.; Hahn, M. *Inorg. Chem.* 1983, *22*, 3952.

[210] Minelli, M.; Young, C. G.; Enemark, J. H. *Inorg. Chem.* 1985, *24*, 1111.

[211] Hinnemann, B.; Moses, P. G.; Bonde, J.; Jorgensen, K. P.; Nielsen, J. H.; Horch, S.; Chorkendorff, I.; Norskov, J. K. *J. Am. Chem. Soc.* 2005, *127*, 5308.

[212] Jaramillo, T. F.; Jorgensen, K. P.; Bonde, J.; Nielsen, J. H.; Horch, S.; Chorkendorff, I. *Science* 2007, *317*, 100.

[213] Hou, Y.; Abrams, B. L.; Vesborg, P. C. K.; Bjoerketun, M. E.; Herbst, K.; Bech, L.; Setti, A. M.; Damsgaard, C. D.; Pedersen, T.; Hansen, O.; Rossmeisl, J.; Dahl, S.; Norskov, J. K.; Chorkendorff, I. *Nat. Mater.* 2011, *10*, 434.

[214] Jaramillo, T. F.; Bonde, J.; Zhang, J.; Ooi, B.-L.; Andersson, K.; Ulstrup, J.; Chorkendorff, I. *J. Phys. Chem. C* 2008, *112*, 17492.

[215] Xiang, Q.; Yu, J.; Jaroniec, M. *J. Am. Chem. Soc.* 2012, *134*, 6575.

[216] He, H. Y. *Jom* 2011, *63*, 60.

[217] Kanda, S.; Akita, T.; Fujishima, M.; Tada, H. *J. Colloid Interface Sci.* 2011, *354*, 607.

[218] Merki, D.; Fierro, S.; Vrubel, H.; Hu, X. *Chem. Sci.* 2011, *2*, 1262.

[219] Roth, L. E.; Nguyen, J. C.; Tezcan, F. A. *J. Am. Chem. Soc.* 2010, *132*, 13672.

[220] Frame, F. A.; Osterloh, F. E. *J. Phys. Chem. C* 2010, *114*, 10628.

[221] Zong, X.; Wu, G.; Yan, H.; Ma, G.; Shi, J.; Wen, F.; Wang, L.; Li, C. *J. Phys. Chem. C* 2010, *114*, 1963.

[222] Appel, A. M.; DuBois, D. L.; DuBois, M. R. *J. Am. Chem. Soc.* 2005, *127*, 12717.

[223] Karunadasa, H. I.; Chang, C. J.; Long, J. R. *Nature Lett.* 2010, *464*, 1329.

[224] Tanaka, S.; Annaka, M.; Sakai, K. *Chem. Commun.* 2012, *48*, 1653.

[225] Seino, H.; Hidai, M. *Chem. Sci.* 2011, *2*, 847.

[226] Mendel, R. R. *J. Exp. Bot.* 2007, *58*, 2289.

[227] Mendel, R. R. *Biofactors* 2009, *35*, 429.

[228] Hansch, R.; Mendel, R. R. *Cur. Opin. Plant Biol.* 2009, *12*, 259.

[229] Swedo, K. B.; Enemark, J. H. *J. Chem. Educ.* 1979, *56*, 70.

[230] Mitchell, P. C. H. *J. Inorg. Biochem.* 1986, *28*, 107.

[231] http://www.cancer.org/Treatment/TreatmentsandSideEffects/ComplementaryandAlternativeMedicine/HerbsVitaminsandMinerals/molybdenum.

[232] Redman, B. G.; Esper, P.; Pan, Q.; Dunn, R. L.; Hussain, H. K.; Chenevert, T.; Brewer, G. J.; Merajver, S. D. *Clin. Cancer Res.* 2003, *9*, 1666.

[233] Hassouneh, B.; Islam, M.; Nagel, T.; Pan, Q.; Merajver, S. D.; Teknos, T. N. *Mol. Cancer Ther.* 2007, *6*, 1039.

[234] Hasenknopf, B. *Front. Biosci.* 2005, *10*, 275.

[235] Pope, M. T.; Müller, A. *Angew. Chem., Int. Ed. Engl.* 1991, *30*, 34.

[236] Rhule, J. T.; Hill, C. L.; Judd, D. A. *Chem. Rev.* 1998, *98*, 327.

[237] Acevedo-Acevedo, D.; Matta, J.; Melendez, E. *J. Organomet. Chem.* 2011, *696*, 1032.

[238] Moody, L.; Holder, A. A. *Annu. Rep. Prog. Chem., Sect. A: Inorg. Chem.* 2009, *105*, 505.

[239] Moody, L.; Holder, A. A. *Annu. Rep. Prog. Chem., Sect. A: Inorg. Chem.* 2008, *104*, 477.

[240] Holder, A. A. *Annu. Rep. Prog. Chem., Sect. A: Inorg. Chem.* 2011, *107*, 359.

[241] Holder, A. A. *Annu. Rep. Prog. Chem., Sect. A: Inorg. Chem.* 2010, *106*, 504.

[242] Holder, A. A. *Annu. Rep. Prog. Chem., Sect. A: Inorg. Chem.* 2012, *108*, 350.

In: Molybdenum
Editor: Alvin A. Holder

ISBN: 978-1-62417-272-4
© 2013 Nova Science Publishers, Inc.

Chapter 3

RECENT ADVANCES IN THE CHEMISTRY OF MOLYBDENUM–MOLYBDENUM MULTIPLE BONDS

Malcolm H. Chisholm and Vesal Naseri
Department of Chemistry, The Ohio State University, Columbus, OH, US

ABSTRACT

Molybdenum is known to form arguably the most multiple bonds to itself, as well as with other elements. This chapter will focus on recent developments in the chemistry of Mo–Mo multiple bonds, particularly those that have taken place in the last decade. The most significant of those arise from the discovery of compounds having Mo–Mo quintuple bonds, the formation of Mo_2^{4+} containing polygons, electron delocalization as a result of $M_2\delta$ to ligand interactions and photophysical measurements of quadruply bonded Mo_2 compounds supported by carboxylate ligands.

INTRODUCTION

Of all the elements in the periodic table molybdenum forms arguably the most multiple bonds to itself and to other elements. Molybdenum-carbon [1] and -nitrogen multiple bonds [2,3] and continue to draw interest in metathesis reactions. In this chapter we focus on recent developments in the chemistry of Mo–Mo multiple bonds, particularly those that have taken place in the last decade and those that were not covered in the 3rd edition of Multiple Bonds Between Metal Atoms that was edited by Cotton, Murillo and Walton. [4] The most significant of those arise from the discovery of compounds having Mo–Mo quintuple bonds, the formation of Mo_2^{4+} containing polygons, electron delocalization as result of $M_2\delta$ to ligand interactions and photophysical measurements of quadruply bonded Mo_2 compounds supported by carboxylate ligands.

THE QUINTUPLE BOND

The discovery in 2005 by Power and coworkers [5] of the Cr(I)–Cr(I) dinuclear compound supported by two bulky ligands, namely bis-2,6-(2,6-diisopropylphenyl)phenyl, abbreviated as Ar', Ar'CrCrAr', heralded a new chapter in multiple bonding between metal atoms some 40 years after the discovery of the quadruple bond in the $Re_2Cl_8^{2-}$ anion by Cotton and coworkers. [6] The structure of this Cr_2^{2+} compound had a *trans*-bent geometry depicted schematically by I in Figure 1.

In this geometry the Cr–Cr bonding can be described as a $\sigma^2 \pi^4 \delta^4$. The Cr–Cr distance of 1.855 Å was notably shorter than those observed for Cr_2–quadruply bonded complexes and indeed notably shorter than the Cr–C distance of 2.131 Å. The C–Cr–Cr angle of 109° and the nature of the bulky ligand facilitates the weaker arene–Cr interaction across the Cr–Cr bond such that each Ar' ligand acts as a pseudo bidentate ligand with a Cr···C ipso distance of 2.4 Å indicative of a weak bonding interaction.

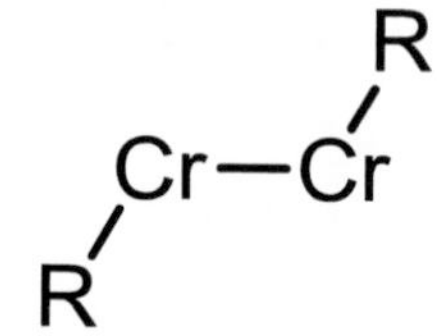

Figure 1. *trans*-Bent geometry of Ar'CrCrAr'.

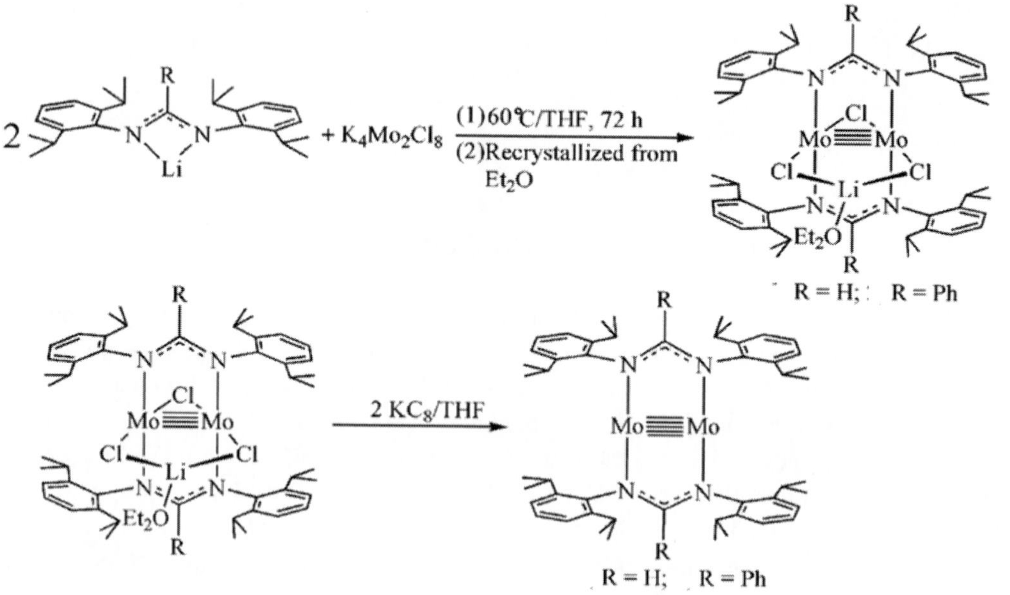

Published in: Yi-Chou Tsai, Hong-Zhang Chen, Chie-Chieh Chang, Jen-Shiang K. Yu, Gene-Hsiang Lee, Yu Wang, Ting-Shen Kuo *J. Am. Chem. Soc.* **2009**, 131, 12534-12535. DOI: 10.1021/ja905035f. Copyright © 2009 American Chemical Society.

Figure 2. Synthesis of the bisamidinate Mo_2^{2+}–containing compounds.

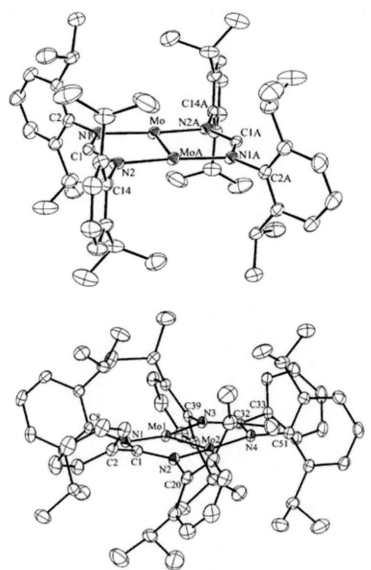

Published in: Yi-Chou Tsai, Hong-Zhang Chen, Chie-Chieh Chang, Jen-Shiang K. Yu, Gene-Hsiang Lee, Yu Wang, Ting-Shen Kuo *J. Am. Chem. Soc.* 2009, 131, 12534-12535. DOI: 10.1021/ja905035f. Copyright © 2009 American Chemical Society.

Figure 3. Structures of the two structurally characterized bisamidinate compounds.

The detailed nature of the bonding in this compound caused considerable interest and Hoffmann and coworkers [7] examined the bonding in an extended series of compounds of the formula RMMR where R = H, F, Cl, Br, CN and CH_3 and M = Cr, Mo and W in a detailed theoretical study.

In these a variety of local minima for various geometries were found including a linear geometry and all could be claimed to generate a quintuple bond with the conformation $\sigma^2 \pi^4 \delta^4$ through a global minima. In a different theoretical study on the structure and bonding in CpMMCp molecules, a similar ground state structure was predicted for M = W having a quintuple bond. [8]

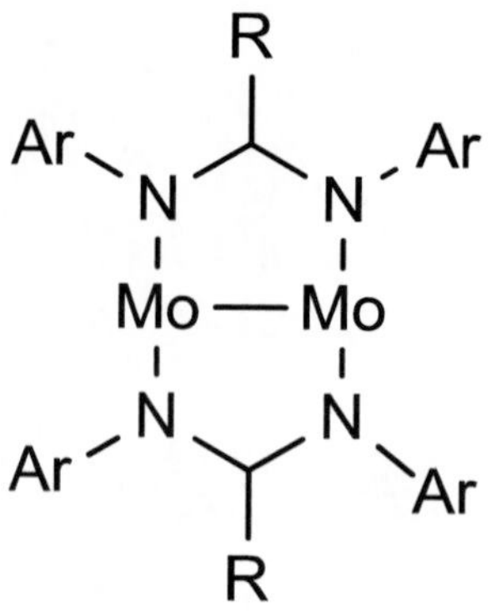

$$\begin{array}{c} R \\ | \\ Ar\!-\!N \quad N\!-\!Ar \\ \diagdown C \diagup \\ N \qquad N \\ | \qquad | \\ Mo\!-\!Mo \\ | \qquad | \\ N \qquad N \\ Ar\!-\!N \quad N\!-\!Ar \\ \diagup C \diagdown \\ | \\ R \end{array} \qquad \mathbf{II}$$

Figure 4. Coordination geometry of the bisamidinate compound.

These calculations were all on hypothetical or at least currently unknown molecules and the realization of the Mo–Mo quintuple bond in a synthesized and structurally characterized molecule fell to Tsai and coworkers from Taiwan. [9] The synthesis of the bisamidinate Mo_2^{2+}–containing compound is shown in Figure 2 and the structures of the two structurally characterized compounds are shown in Figure 3. In both molecules, the use of very bulky ligands is employed and is clearly a requirement to stabilize the low coordination of the metal centers. The essential coordination geometry which is somewhat hard to see in Figure 4 is depicted as II in Figure 4. The formation of a quintuple bond is easy to envisage in this d^5–d^5 dinuclear compound though the two δ bonds are not equivalent. If we envisage that each Mo atom uses sp hybrid orbitals to form two Mo-N bonds one of the d_{xy}, or $d_{x2–y2}$ orbitals can also be employed and mix with the sp hybrids.

The Mo–Mo distances in the two structurally characterized compounds are 2.016(1) and 2.019(1) Å which are notably shorter than most Mo–Mo quadruple bonds. [4]

Mo_2^{4+} IN HIGHER ORDER ASSEMBLIES: POLYGONS

Independently the Chisholm [10,11] and Cotton group [12,13] started to study the linking together of Mo–Mo quadruple bonded units. The Cotton group employed the use of formamidinate ligands, most often p-anisole formamidinates, p-$MeOC_6H_4NCHNC_6H_4$-p-OMe which provided good solubility and crystallinity of products. Metathetic reactions employing $(ArNCHNAr)_3Mo_2^+$ or $(ArNCHNAr)_2Mo_2^{2+}$ salts in [14] acetonitrile with dianionic bridges yielded dimers of dimers, molecular triangles, loops and squares of the type shown in Figure 5. The ability of the Mo_2^{4+} unit to axially coordinate Lewis bases allowed such units to form extended networks in the solid-state with linkers such as 4,4'-bipyridine.

More recently Hong-Cai Zhou and coworkers [15] have employed $Mo_2(O_2CCF_3)_4$ which has the kinetically labile trifluoroacetate ligands in reactions with dicarboxylic acids having fairly rigid bridging angles of 0, 60, 90 and 120°. Examples of these ligands are given in Figure 6 and the polygons derived from reactions with the $Mo_2(O_2CCF_3)_4$ paddle-wheel core are given in Figure 7.

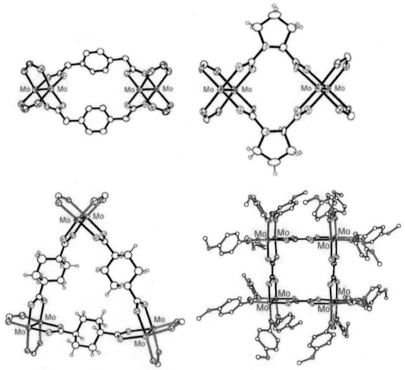

Published in: F. Albert Cotton, Chun Lin, and Carlos A. Murillo *Acc. Chem. Res.* 2001, 34, 759–771. DOI: 10.1021/ar010062+. Copyright © 2001 American Chemical Society.

Figure 5. Structures of dimers of dimers, molecular triangles, loops and squares.

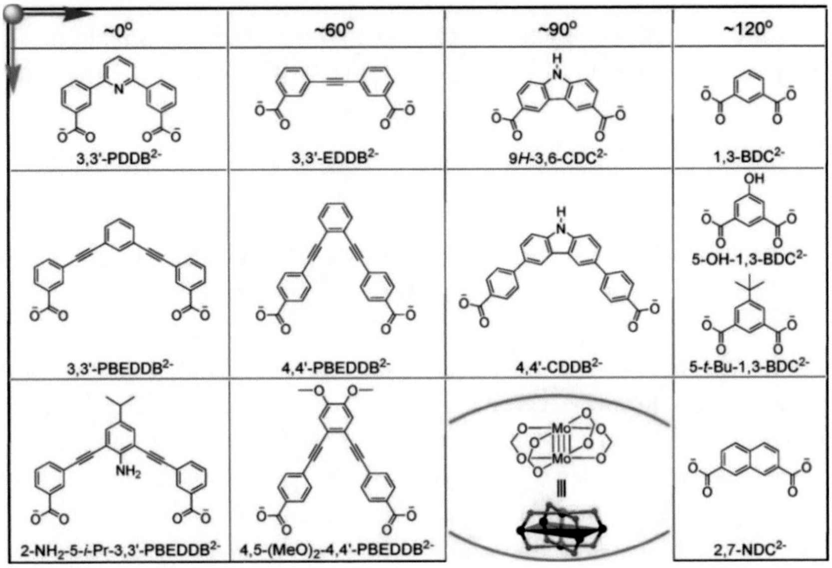

~0°	~60°	~90°	~120°
3,3'-PDDB²⁻	3,3'-EDDB²⁻	9*H*-3,6-CDC²⁻	1,3-BDC²⁻
3,3'-PBEDDB²⁻	4,4'-PBEDDB²⁻	4,4'-CDDB²⁻	5-OH-1,3-BDC²⁻ / 5-*t*-Bu-1,3-BDC²⁻
2-NH₂-5-*i*-Pr-3,3'-PBEDDB²⁻	4,5-(MeO)₂-4,4'-PBEDDB²⁻		2,7-NDC²⁻

Published in: Jian-Rong Li, Andrey A. Yakovenko, Weigang Lu, Daren J. Timmons, Wenjuan Zhuang, Daqiang Yuan, Hong-Cai Zhou *J. Am. Chem. Soc.* 2010, 132, 17599-17610. DOI: 10.1021/ja1080794. Copyright © 2010 American Chemical Society.

Figure 6. Examples of dicarboxylic acids with bridging angles between of 0, 60, 90 and 120°.

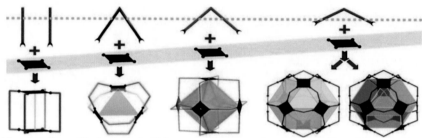

Published in: Jian-Rong Li, Andrey A. Yakovenko, Weigang Lu, Daren J. Timmons, Wenjuan Zhuang, Daqiang Yuan, Hong-Cai Zhou *J. Am. Chem. Soc.* 2010, 132, 17599-17610. DOI: 10.1021/ja1080794. Copyright © 2010 American Chemical Society.

Figure 7. Polygons derived from reactions of a variety of dicarboxylic acids with $Mo_2(O_2CCF_3)_4$.

Two carbazole-based dicarboxylate ligands having nearly 90° bridging angles yielded isostructural polyhedron caged structures involving $[Mo_2]_6$ units that encapsulated an octahedral cavity of cage size 25 and 38 Å with triangular windows of 10.5 and 17.0 Å, respectively.

With 5-hydroxy-1,3-benzene dicarboxylate and 2,7-naphthalene dicarboxylate which have 120° ligand bridge angles $[Mo_2]_{12}$ containing structures were obtained having either cube-octahedral or anti-cube octahedral cages. The bridging alone cannot explain this stereo isomerism. The interest in these kinds of polygons with large cages centers on matters such as gas absorption, gas separation and reactions inside molecular containers. The Mo_2^{4+} centers are also redox active which adds further interest in the properties of the polygons.

Recently, the cationic $Mo_2(CH_3CN)_8^{4+}$ salt with BF_4^- as an anion has been employed in the synthesis of cationic triangles, squares, and loops supported by labile CH_3CN ligands. [16]

Here the bridges were dicarboxylic acids, such as oxalate and terephthalate, and the resulting complexes of the form $[(CH_3CN)_4Mo_2(bridge)^{2+}]_n$ where n = 2 (loop), 3 (triangle), and 4 (square) are promising synthons for the formulation of extended lattice structure *via* the replacement of the acetonitrile ligands.

ELECTRONICALLY COUPLED QUADRUPLY BONDED CENTERS - ELECTROCHEMICAL STUDIES

One of the major research efforts in studying coupled M_2^{4+} units has been the investigation of their redox properties. Each Mo_2^{4+} unit is susceptible to a reversible one electron oxidation that removes an electron from the delta orbital to give a M_2 bonding configuration $\sigma^2 \pi^4 \delta^1$ and when two Mo_2^{4+} units are electronically coupled, one observes two oxidation waves. A measure of the electronic coupling of the two centers is given by the separation of the two redox potentials. The stability of the mixed valence ion represented schematically by $[M_2 \rightsquigarrow M_2]^+$ relative to the neutral and doubly oxidized species as represented by eq.1 in Figure 8 can be determined by the comproportionation constant K_c and this in turn can be related to the electrochemical oxidation waves $\Delta E_{1/2}$ in mV as shown below. [17]

eq.1 $[M_2]\text{\large ⌇}[M_2]$ + $[M_2]\text{\large ⌇}[M_2]^{2+}$ ⇌ $2\ [M_2]\text{\large ⌇}[M_2]^{+}$

$$Kc = \exp(\Delta E_{1/2} / 25.69)$$

Figure 8. Eq.1.

Two very important points must be made in considering the use of electrochemical estimates of the electronic coupling of the two Mo_2^{4+} centers by studies of eq.1 by either cyclic voltammetry of differential pulse voltammetry. (1) The magnitude of K_c is a thermodynamic quantity. It is very dependent on the nature of the solvent and the anion. Thus changing the anion from say BF_4^- to $B(C_6H_3\text{-}3,5\text{-}(CF_3)_2)_4^-$ can dramatically alter the magnitude of $\Delta E_{1/2}$ and hence K_c. [18] Furthermore small values of K_c such as 100 or less may simply reflect electrostatic effects not electronic coupling of two Mo_2^{4+} centers. (2) The magnitude of K_c which can vary between 10 to 10^{12} does not entirely inform one of whether the mixed valence ion $[M_2 \text{\large ⌇} M_2]^+$ is fully delocalized, Class III on the Robin and Day Scheme of mixed valence ions or Class II or I.

However, this relatively routine measurement is very good as a guide toward a classification on the Robin and Day Scheme [19] where large values of $K_c > 10^6$ are suggestive of Class III fully delocalized ions and small values of $K_c \sim 10$ correspond to valence trapped or Class I ions.

As we shall show the classification of Class III, II or I clearly falls to other spectroscopic techniques as even crystallography, which can well define Mo-Mo distances, falls fowl of such matters as disorder or charge pinning in the solid-state.

MOLECULAR ORBITAL CONSIDERATIONS

The electronic coupling of the two Mo_2^{4+} centers rests entirely on the interactions of the Mo_2^{4+} centers and the bridge. Specifically this involves the Mo_2 δ orbital and the bridge π-system and this is well exemplified by the oxalate bridge which is the simplest of dicarboxylate bridges. This system has been studied in great detail by the Chisholm group [20,21] and a schematic frontier molecular orbital diagram for a dicarboxylate bridge $[O_2C \text{\large ⌇} CO_2]$ where $\text{\large ⌇}$ is a conjugated organic group such as 1,4-phenylene [22] or 2,5-thiophene [23] is shown in Figure 9.

In a fully delocalized MV ion the lowest energy electronic transition involves promotion of an electron from the HOMO-1 to the singly occupied HOMO. This is referred to as a charge resonance transition as it is solvent independent. It is not an inter-valence charge transfer transition, a so called IVCT band which, in a Class II ion on the Robin and Day Scheme, moves charge from one redox center to the other and hence is solvent dependent. The magnitude of electronic coupling for a Class III MV ion is just one half of the energy of this transition measured in cm^{-1}. For Mo_2^{4+} centers Class III behavior is rarely observed; most commonly the IVCT band is observed and a measure of the electronic coupling can be determined according to the Hush model. [24]

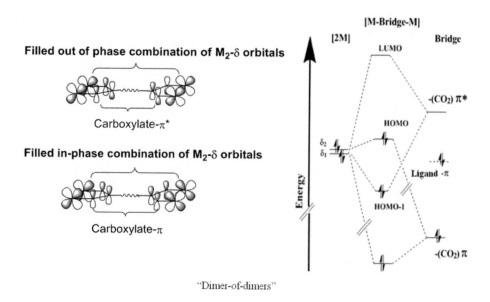

Figure 9. Frontier molecular orbital (FMO) diagram for a dicarboxylate bridge between two dimetal centers.

The magnitude of the electronic coupling falls off with distance as was nicely demonstrated by Cotton, Murillo and Donahue [25] in a series of compounds of the form $[(DANIF)_3Mo_2](\mu\text{-}O_2C\text{-}(CH=CH)_n\text{-}CO_2)$ where $n = 0$-4 and DANIF is dianisole formamidinate. Indeed, for molybdenum compounds of this type only in bridges of ~6 Å or less are the two dimetal centers strongly coupled and fully delocalized, Class III. In this regard a comparison of molybdenum and tungsten dimers of dimers is most interesting since the size of Mo and W are essentially identical due to the lanthanide contraction and solvation effects are very similar.

Thus the comparison between these closely related complexes reveals electronic effects that arise from the relative energies and orbital overlaps of the 4d (Mo) and 5d (W) orbitals and their respective interactions with the bridge π-system. For related complexes such as $Mo_2(O_2C^tBu)_4$ and $W_2(O_2C^tBu)_4$ the oxidation potentials as measured by cyclic voltammetry differ by 0.5 V and by photoelectron spectroscopy by 0.5 eV with the tungsten complexes being easier to oxidize. [4] This effects the ease of removal of an electron from the δ orbital and the influence of the energy of the δ orbital and its coupling *via* a bridge is seen in the series of compounds $(^tBuCO_2)_3MM(\mu\text{-}O_2CCO_2)MM(O_2C^tBu)_3$ in their neutral and oxidized forms, where MM = Mo_2, MoW or W_2. [21] Upon removal of a single electron the MV ions show low energy electronic transitions in the near-IR that are solvent independent. These are shown in Figure 10. Here it is evident with increasing W character the energy of this transition increases and the magnitude of the coupling of the two MM centers is just one half of the energy. The other factor that is immediately apparent from looking at the absorption spectra in Figure 10 is that the shape of the bands differ with the nature of the MM unit. The band for the Mo_2-containing complexes is notably asymmetric with a relatively sharp on-set at low energy and a very broad tail to higher energy.

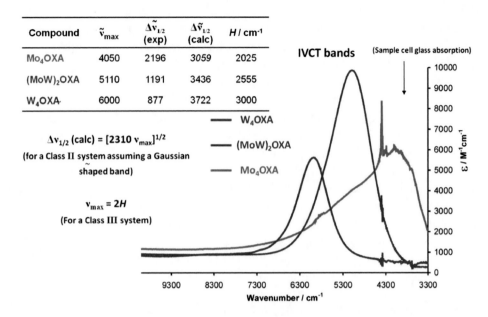

Compound	$\tilde{v}_{max}$	$\Delta\tilde{v}_{1/2}$ (exp)	$\Delta\tilde{v}_{1/2}$ (calc)	H / cm^{-1}
Mo$_4$OXA	4050	2196	3059	2025
(MoW)$_2$OXA	5110	1191	3436	2555
W$_4$OXA	6000	877	3722	3000

$\Delta v_{1/2}$ (calc) = [2310 v_{max}]$^{1/2}$

(for a Class II system assuming a Gaussian shaped band)

v_{max} = 2H

(For a Class III system)

Figure 10. Low energy electronic transitions for the oxidized forms of the compounds (^{t}BuCO$_2$)$_3$MM(μ-O$_2$CCO$_2$)MM(O$_2$C^{t}Bu)$_3$, where MM = Mo$_2$, MoW or W$_2$.

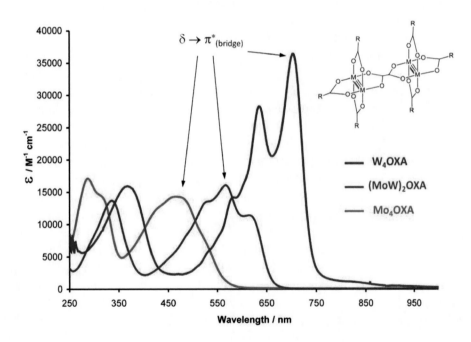

Figure 11. Electronic absorption spectra of [(^{t}BuCO$_2$)$_3$MM]$_2$(μ-O$_2$CCO$_2$).

This is expected based on This type of asymmetric absorption for a MV ion is rather typical of what is considered as an ion that is close to the Class II/III boarder. [26,27] This arises from a rather flat ground state potential energy surface as has been discussed in detail elsewhere. [21]

These bridged compounds also show intense metal-to-ligand charge transfer transitions in both their neutral and oxidized states. This is expected based on the FMO picture presented in Figure 9. The room temperature absorption spectra for the neutral oxalate bridged compounds $[(^tBuCO_2)_3MM]_2(\mu\text{-}O_2CCO_2)$ in THF are shown in Figure 11.

Again two important points can be recognized from an inspection of these spectra. (1) With increasing tungsten content in the MM unit the MLCT bands move to lower energy. This reflects the relative energies of the MM δ orbitals and the HOMO-LUMO gap. (2) Even at room temperature there is a clear evidence of vibronic progressions associated with these bands. At low temperature in the solvent 2-methyl-tetrahydrofuran, which forms a glass below $\sim$ -150°C, the vibronic features become more pronounced as the Boltzmann distribution of molecules adopt the planar ground state bridged structure. With a labeling of the bridge $O_2^{13}C^{13}CO_2$ two progressions can easily be identified based on their isotopic shift as v_1 and v_2 of the totally symmetric modes of the oxalate bridge. [20] However, even at room temperature (see Figure 11) one can see that the (0,0) transition is the most intense for the W_2-containing compound while for the MoW and Mo_2 quadruply bonded bridged complexes the (0,1) transition is the most intense. This reflects the nesting of the ^{1}MLCT state with respect to the ground state. [21] Upon oxidation the MV ions loose much of the vibronic fine structure on the MLCT bands and this is an indication of greater nesting of the two states as the coupling of the two dinuclear centers is increased. [21]

The photo exited states of these bridged compounds can be viewed as mixed valence ions where the positive charge is M_2 centered and the negative charge is localized on the bridge as represented by eq.2 in Figure 12. [28] If the two metal centers are strongly coupled the positive charge can be shared equally by both $[M_2]$ centers.

This would be a Class III MV ion and photoexitation would occur with no change in dipole moment whereas if the charge were localized on one of the $[M_2]$ centers there would be a change in the dipole moment. The oxalate bridged compounds where ^{1}MLCT bands are shown in Figure 11 were examined by electroabsorption spectroscopy, also commonly known as Stark spectroscopy, and were shown to have a negligible change in dipole upon photoexitation. [29] However, with a longer bridge namely 1,4-terephthalate, the complex $[^tBuCO_2)_3Mo_2]_2(\mu\text{-}O_2CC_6H_4CO_2)$ was found to have a significant change in dipole constant with a valence trapped photoexited state. In their oxidized form, terephthalate bridge Mo_2 containing MV ions show EPR spectra comparable to that of $Mo_2(O_2C^tBu)^{4+}$ and broad absorptions, in their NIR spectra are characteristic of Class II ions as predicted by Hush theory. [24]

Cotton and Murillo and their coworkers have made extensive studies of bridged Mo_2-containing compounds and these have been the topic of a recent review. [30] Amongst the most strongly coupled complexes was that having the planar tetraazatetrazene ligand. [31] This gave a splitting of the 1st and 2nd oxidation waves of 416 mV which yields a comproportionation constant for the MV ions of $1.1 \cdot 10^7$.

eq.2 $[M_2]\text{\char`\~\char`\~}[M_2]^+$ $\rightleftharpoons$ $[M_2]^+\text{\char`\~\char`\~}[M_2]$

Figure 12. Eq.2.

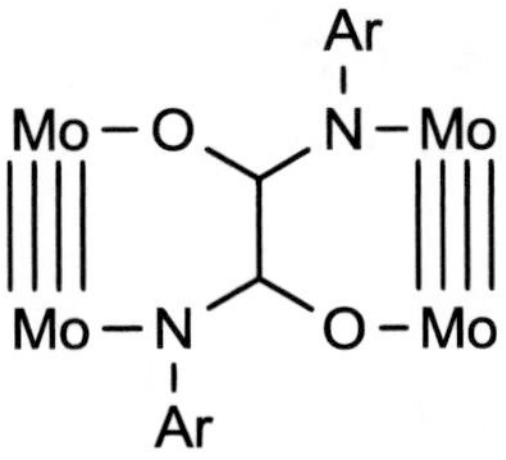

```
        Ar                              Ar
        |                               |
  Mo─O     N─Mo                  Mo─O       N─Mo
  ||||     ||||                  ||||       ||||
  Mo─N     O─Mo                  Mo─N       O─Mo
        |                               |
        Ar                              Ar

         III                             IV
```

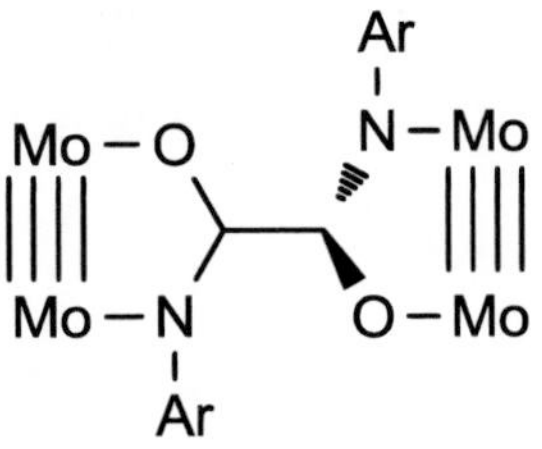

Figure 13. Planar six-membered MoMoOCCN bridge.

This can be compared with the related oxalate bridged anion, which is stereochemically correspondent in placing the two Mo_2 centers 6 Å apart, and has a K_c value of ~10^3. The tetraazatetrazene bridge has two advantages over the oxalate. (1) The four aromatic rings ensure that the planar bridged structure is maintained and (2) the replacement of O by NR increases the mixing of the Mo_2 δ with the filled π-system of the bridge.

Cotton and Murillo [32] also showed that the N,N'-diaryl oxamidinate bridge led to two isomers both of which were isolated and structurally, spectroscopically and electrochemically characterized. [33] The planar bridge involving the six-membered MoMoOCCN rings, depicted as III in Figure 13, showed much stronger electronic coupling than that involving the five-membered MoMoOCN rings, IV which adopted a twisted structure that disrupts the π-conjugation of the bridge: $K_c = 10^3$ and 10^9 for IV and III, respectively.

The importance of π-conjugation in the bridge in leading to electronic coupling was easily seen for complexes having methylene units or 1,4-cyclohexane dicarboxylates. [13] Also in the squarate bridged complexes the inability of the central C_4 unit to facilitate Mo_2 δ-bridge conjugation led to poor electronic coupling of the two M_2 centers. Indeed, in the doubly oxidized squarate bridged compounds the two single electrons on the Mo_2 centers are only weakly antiferromagnetically coupled with $J = -121cm^{-1}$. [33]

PHOTOPHYSICAL STUDIES

Much of the earlier work was devoted to the observation of the δ → δ* electronic transition in metal-metal quadruply bonded complexes which is a relatively weak absorption in complexes/ions of the type $Mo_2Cl_4(PMe_3)_4$ or $Mo_2Cl_8^{4-}$ due to the weak overlap of the d_{xy}-d_{xy} orbitals. [34] Typically this absorption has a molar extinction coefficient of the order of 100 $M^{-1}cm^{-1}$. Emission from this singlet state is similarly weak but shows vibronic fine structure because the δ'δ* state has a MM bond order of 3 and relaxation to the ground state has a MM bond order of 4. [35] Cotton and Nocera [36] noted that studies of the spectroscopic properties of compounds with the δ orbital had led to "The Whole Story of the Two-Electron Bond with the δ Orbital as a Paradigm."

In the case of carboxylate ligands the CO_2 π* orbitals lie close in energy to the δ* orbital and this allows for metal-to-CO_2 π* electronic transitions. These metal to ligand charge transfer transitions are fully allowed and are very intense compared to the $^1δ → {}^1δ*$ transition.

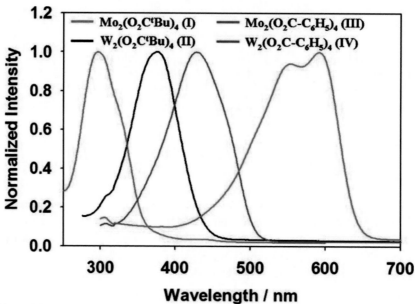

Published in: Brian G. Alberding; Malcolm H. Chisholm; Terry L. Gustafson; Inorg. Chem. 2012, 51, 491-498. DOI: 10.1021/ic201957a Copyright © 2011 American Chemical Society.

Figure 14. Absorption spectra of the compounds $M_2(O_2C^tBu)_4$ and $M_2(O_2C-C_6H_5)_4$.

When the carboxylate group is directly attached to an extended π system the ^{1}MLCT transition is moved to lower energy. This is also the case for MoW or W_2 containing complexes because the $M_2\delta$ orbital moves to higher energy with increasing tungsten content. These effects are nicely demonstrated in the absorption spectra of the compounds $M_2(O_2C^tBu)_4$ and $M_2(O_2C-C_6H_5)_4$ which are shown in Figure 14 where M = Mo or W. [37] Only in the case of $Mo_2(O_2C^tBu)_4$ is the weak $^1\delta \rightarrow {}^1\delta^*$ transition observed at ~450 nm and, in comparison to the intense ^{1}MLCT to the CO_2 π^* orbital, the $^1\delta \rightarrow {}^1\delta^*$ transition is barely visible. In all other cases the $^1\delta \rightarrow {}^1\delta^*$ transition is masked by the intense and broad ^{1}MLCT absorption.

These complexes show relatively weak fluorescence from the ^{1}MLCT S_1 state but for the Mo_2-containing species there is a stronger phosphorescence from the T_1 state which in the majority of cases is the ^{3}MoMo$\delta\delta^*$ state.

This emission occurs at ~1100 nm and at low temperature, 77 K, is more intense, solvent independent and shows striking vibronic features with ν ~400 cm^{-1} characteristic for ν(MoMo) for the quadruple bonded ground state. The solvent independence and the vibronic features associated with ν(MoMo) firmly establish this as emission from the ^{3}MoMo$\delta\delta^*$ state rather than from a ^{3}MLCT state.

As noted previously the energy of the MMδ orbital increases with increasing tungsten content and as a consequence of this the ^{3}MM$\delta\delta^*$ rises in energy. This is nicely seen for the series of compounds MM(T^{i}PB)$_4$ where MM = Mo_2, MoW, W_2 and T^{i}PB = 2,4,6-triisopropylbenzoate. The absorption spectra and phosphorescence from the T_1, ^{3}MM$\delta\delta^*$ states are shown in Figure 15. Here it is clearly seen that the relative energies of the ^{1}MLCT bands follow the order MM = Mo_2 > MoW > W_2 whereas the ^{3}MM$\delta\delta^*$ states are in the order W_2 > MoW > Mo_2.

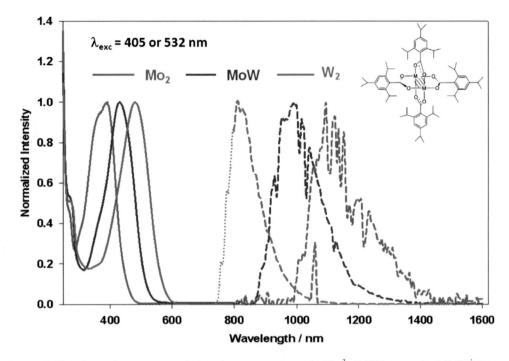

Figure 15. The absorption spectra and phosphorescence from the T_1, $^3MM\delta\delta^*$ states for $MM(T^iPB)_4$.

Because of this ordering of energies most MoW and W_2 complexes do not show phosphorescence from the $^3\delta\delta^*$ state but rather from ^3MLCT states. These are typically solvent dependent and do not show vibronic features assignable to $v(MM)$ but rather $v(CO_2)$ ~1500 cm^{-1}.

Transient absorption spectroscopy has also been employed in examining the S_1 and T_1 states. Typically the S_1 states have lifetimes of 1 - 20 ps and the T_1 states for $^3MoMo\delta\delta^*$ are ~10 - 100 μs. [38]

Aside from the studies of the homoleptic carboxylates described above two other types of compounds have been studied namely the dimers of dimers with thienyl and fused thienyldicarboxylates as bridges [39] and monomeric compounds of the form trans-$MM(T^iPB)_2L_2$ where L = a conjugated carboxylate such as O_2C-2-$(Th)_n$ where n = 1, 2, 3. [40-43]

These complexes show similar photophysical properties involving intense ^1MLCT transitions to either the bridge or the *trans*-L ligands. In complexes of the form *trans*-$MM(T^iPB)_2L_2$, the bulky T^iPB ligands adopt the *trans*-position and the aryl groups are twisted from the plane of the carboxylates which removes or limits the extent of the conjugation. In contrast, the *trans*-L_2 groups enjoy extensive $L\pi$-$M_2\delta$-$L\pi$ conjugation and in the ground state have planar structures as seen, for example, in the molecular structure of *trans*-$Mo_2(T^iPB)_2(O_2C$-CH=CH-Th$)_2$ shown in Figure 16. [43]

In this way the ^1MLCT transitions to the *trans*-L groups occur at lower energy than those to the T^iPB ligands. Compounds of the type *trans*-$Mo_2(T^iPB)_2(O_2CTh_n)_2$ where Th = 2, 2'-thienyl linked groups n = 2 or 3 have similar planar Th_nCO_2-Mo_2-O_2CTh_n structures. [40]

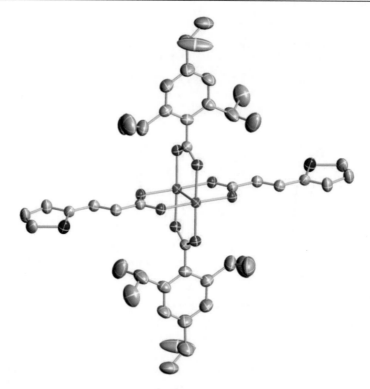

Figure 16. Solid state structure of *trans*-$Mo_2(T^iPB)_2(O_2C\text{-}CH=CH\text{-}Th)_2$. H-atoms and solvent molecules are omitted for clarity. Thermal ellipsoids are drwan at 50% probability level.

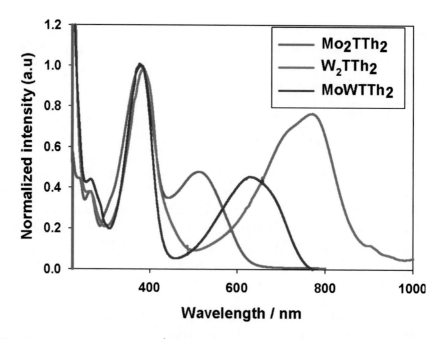

Figure 17. Absorption spectra for $MM(T^iPB)_2(O_2CTh_3)_2$ ($Th_3 = TTh_2$) compounds in THF at room temperature.

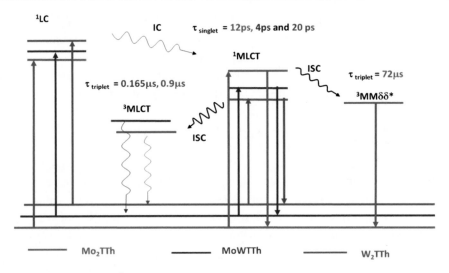

Figure 18. Generalized Jablonski diagram for the compounds *trans*-MM(T^{i}PB)$_2$(O$_2$CTh$_3$)$_2$ were MM = Mo$_2$, MoW and W$_2$.

The absorption spectra of the compounds *trans*-MM(T^{i}PB)$_2$(O$_2$CTh$_3$)$_2$ recorded in THF are shown in Figure 17 which neatly demonstrate three trends. (1) The ^{1}MLCT to the O$_2$CTh$_3$ ligands follow the energy order: Mo$_2$ > MoW > W$_2$. (2) The ^{1}MLCT to the T^{i}PB ligands falls at higher energy and is much weaker and is only clearly seen for MM = W$_2$ and MoW and (3) the intense ^{1}LLCT of the terthienyl carboxylate remains invariant of the MM center at ~400 nm. These observations coupled with transient absorption spectroscopy allow for the formation of the Jablonski diagram shown in Figure 18 together with the half-life times of the respective S$_1$ and T$_1$ states.

TIME RESOLVED INFRARED STUDIES

Aside from the knowledge of the life times and energies of the S$_1$ and T$_1$ states, one would like to know the delocalizations of charge and at this time two related sets of molybdenum and tungsten complexes have been examined, namely *trans*-M$_2$(T^{i}PB)$_2$(O$_2$CC$_6$H$_4$-4-CN)$_2$ and *trans*-M$_2$(O$_2$CMe)$_2$[(^{i}PrN)$_2$CC≡CC$_6$H$_5$]$_2$. Both complexes have IR reporter groups in the C≡N and C≡C bonds. [44]

The time resolved infrared TRIR spectra of the two para-cyanobenzoate complexes are shown in Figure 19 which reveal some interesting similarities and differences as a function of metal.

For M = Mo, there is an intense IR absorption which is shifted ~65 cm^{-1} to lower energy when compared to the ground state. This IR absorption has a lifetime of only a few ps after which there is no transient IR absorption in the region of ν(CN). This is consistent with the S$_1$ state being ^{1}MLCT and the T$_1$ state being ^{3}MoMoδδ* which has no significant influence on the magnitude of ν(CN). However, for M = W the *para*-cyanobenzoate complex shows a similar short lived ps IR band and a longer lived band, >2000 ps, at essentially the same value of ν(CN). From this it is inferred that both the S$_1$ and T$_1$ states are MLCT states for M = W. Moreover the calculated shift ν(CN) for the anions *trans*-M$_2$(O$_2$CH)$_2$(O$_2$CC$_6$H$_4$-4-CN)$_2^-$ are

~65 cm^{-1} which led to the proposal that in these complexes the negative charge in the MLCT state is equally distributed over both *para*-cyanobenzoate ligands. In other words the excited state MV ions are Class III on the Robin and Day Scheme.

The related spectra for the amidinate complexes are shown in Figure 20 and are notably different. At short times, <20 ps, there are two IR bands that can be assigned to $v(C\equiv C)$. One IR absorption is intense and shifted >200 cm^{-1} from the ground state absorption, while the weaker IR band is shifted only ~40 cm^{-1}. The calculated shift in $v(C\equiv C)$ for the anions *trans*-$M_2(O_2CMe)_2[(^iPrN)_2CC\equiv CC_6H_5]_2^-$ is ~140 cm^{-1}.

The MO calculations assume fully delocalized ions and so the observed TRIR at short reaction times are assigned to localized charge MV ions where one amidinate is principally reduced with a small spill over of charge to the other. The use of MO calculations on the anions as a guide to the interpretation of the observed values of $v(C\equiv N)$ and $v(C\equiv C)$ rests on the fact that the spectroscopic features of ligands in MLCT states typically are similar to those of the reduced ligands.

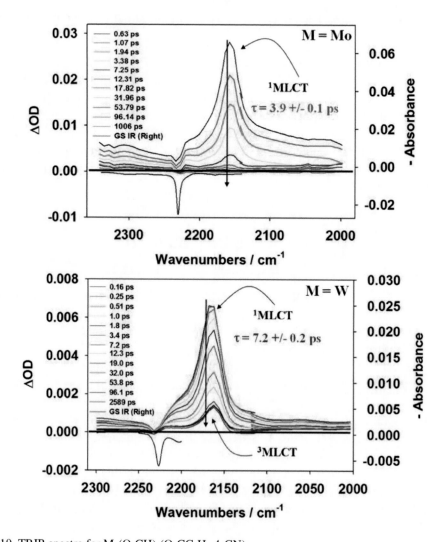

Figure 19. TRIR spectra for $M_2(O_2CH)_2(O_2CC_6H_4\text{-}4\text{-}CN)_2$.

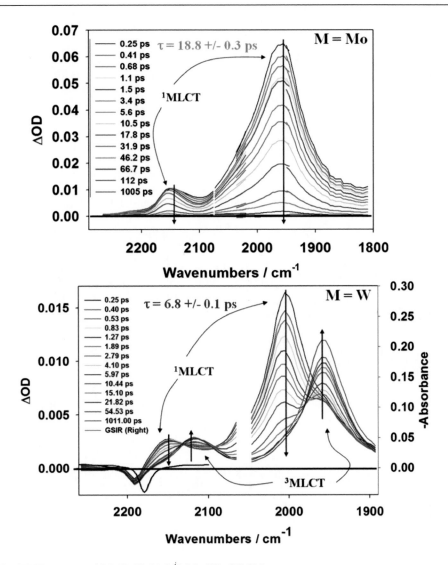

Figure 20. TRIR spectra of $M_2(O_2CMe)_2[(^iPrN)_2CC{\equiv}CC_6H_5]_2$.

REACTIVITY OF MO–MO MULTIPLE BONDS

In this part of the chapter the focus falls on the advances in the chemistry of Mo–Mo multiple bonds that have taken place in the last decade. In particular, we will concentrate on various ligand systems that have been employed to support and couple the quadruply bonded Mo_2^{4+} unit to several metal centers, thus yielding multinuclear homo- or heterometallic compounds. One-dimensional covalently bonded metal strings have been the subject of a great deal of interest regarding their fundamental bonding nature and are envisaged to have promising applications as electronic and optoelectronic materials. [45,46] The arrangement of more than two kinds of transition metals in a linear fashion was successfully demonstrated by employing tridentate mono-anionic ligands (Figure 21).

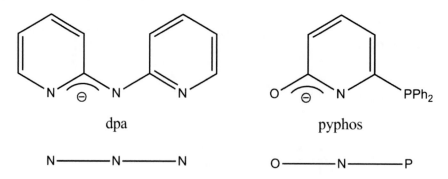

Figure 21. The 2,2'-dipyridylamide (dpa) (left) and the 6-diphenylphosphino-2-pyridonate (pyphos) ligand (right).

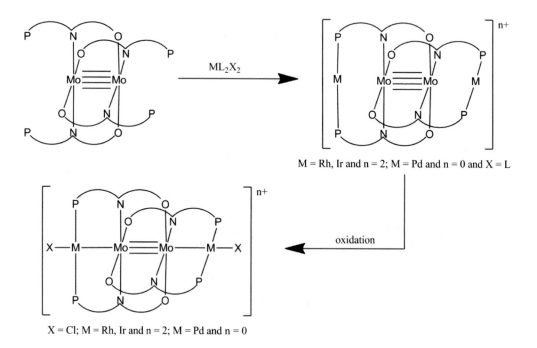

Figure 22. Simplified strategy for the synthesis of linear tetranuclear heterometal arrays.

Mashima *et al.* utilized the 6-diphenylphosphino-2-pyridonate (pyphos) ligand, containing three coordination sites (P, N, and O atoms) in a linear arrangement induced by the rigid pyridone framework, to synthesize and study several M···Mo-Mo···M and M-Mo-Mo-M (M = Pd, Pt, Rh or Ir) tetranuclear bimetalic arrays, with the latter having Mo-Mo triple bonds. A general synthesis of the M···Mo-Mo···M is shown in Figure 22. [47-54]

The quadruply bonded Mo_2^{4+} unit supported by four pyphos ligands, *trans*-Mo_2(pyphos)$_4$, was reacted with the corresponding metal salt (e.g. ML_2X_2) to yield the [M···Mo-Mo···M]$^{n+}$ (M = Rh, Ir and n = 2; M = Pd and n = 0). With subsequent oxidation, the formation of a four metal atom containing string [M-Mo-Mo-M]$^{n+}$ (M = Rh, Ir and n = 4; M = Pd and n = 2) was achieved. Crystal structures of explicit examples for [M···Mo-Mo···M]$^{n+}$, [{(^{t}BuNC)$_4$Rh}Mo$_2$(pyphos)$_4${Rh(^{t}BuNC)$_4$}](BPh$_4$)$_2$, and [M-Mo-Mo-M]$^{n+}$, [(^{t}BuNC)$_4$(Cl)RhMo$_2$(pyphos)$_4$Rh(Cl)(^{t}BuNC)$_4$](PF$_6$)$_2$, are shown in Figure 23. [55]

Berry *et al.* have used dpa as the ligand (Figure 21) to synthesize a series of compounds of the type M-M···M' shown in Figure 24.

The reaction of dpa-H in various high boiling solvents (e.g. naphthalene) with $M(CO)_6$ yields the quadruply bonded dinuclear compounds $M_2(dpa)_4$ (M = Cr, Mo, W) as schematically represented in Figure 25 for molybdenum. The dpa ligands that support the M_2^{4+} units are *trans* with respect to each neighbouring ligand. Subsequent reaction of these compounds with the corresponding metal dichlorides (MCl_2) leads to the formation of trinuclear heterometallic compounds of the type M-M···M'. Interestingly, the dpa ligands now rearrange into an all-*cis* fashion maximizing coordination to the added metal chloride.

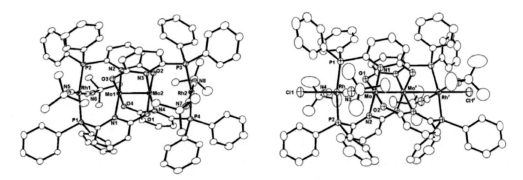

Figure 23. Crystal structures of the compounds [{(${}^tBuNC)_4Rh$}$Mo_2(pyphos)_4${$Rh({}^tBuNC)_4$}](BPh_4)_2 (left) and [(${}^tBuNC)_4(Cl)RhMo_2(pyphos)_4Rh(Cl)({}^tBuNC)_4](PF_6)_2$ (right). Anions and H-Atoms are omitted for clarity.

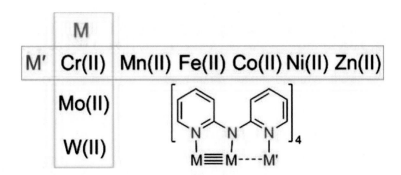

Figure 24. Series of compounds of the type M-M···M' employing the dpa ligand.

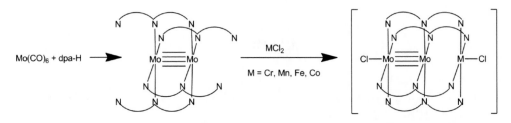

Figure 2. Schematic representation of the synthesis of $Mo_2(dpa)_4$ and $[MoMoM(dpa)_4Cl_2]$ (M = Cr, Mn, Fe, Co).

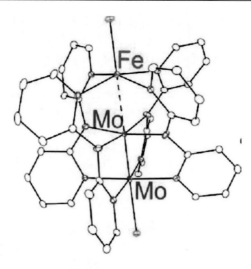

Figure 26. Molecular structure of [MoMoFe(dpa)$_4$Cl$_2$].

The crystal structure of one representative of the compound series of the type [MMM'(dpa)$_4$Cl$_2$], namely [MoMoFe(dpa)$_4$Cl$_2$], is shown in Figure 26. [56] The Mo-Mo distance is common for quadruply bonded molybdenum units. The difference between the Mo-N distances, however, is noteworthy. The Mo-N$_{(amide)}$ bonds are shorter by as much as 0.08 Å compared to the M-N$_{(pyridyl)}$ distances as a result of higher charge localization on N$_{(amide)}$ rather than N$_{(pyridyl)}$ and stronger M-N$_{(amide)}$ bonds. This disparity stands in contrast to the almost identical M-N bond lengths observed in the binuclear precursors Mo$_2$(dpa)$_4$. It is thus apparent that the interaction between the Mo$_2^{4+}$ unit and the equatorial dpa ligand is strongly affected by metalation, and a change in the charge distribution within the dpa ligand takes place, where the strong M-N$_{(amide)}$ bonds dominate over the M-N$_{(pyridyl)}$ and Fe-N$_{(pyridyl)}$ interactions. The extensive study of this series of compounds by various analytical techniques (e.g. Mössbauer spectroscopy, X-ray analysis, cyclic voltammetry) shows that there is only little or no heterometallic bonding in these compounds.

ACKNOWLEDGMENTS

This material is based upon work supported by the National Science Foundation under grant number CHE-0957191. Vesal Naseri thanks the Alexander von Humboldt Foundation for a Feodor Lynen Research Fellowship.

REFERENCES

[1]   R. R. Schrock, *Dalton Trans.* 2011, 7484-7495.

[2]   B. A. Burroughs, B. E. Bursten, M. H. Chisholm and A. R. Kidwell, *Inorg. Chem.* 2008, *47*, 5377-5385.

[3]   E. S. Wiedner, K. J. Gallagher, M. J. A. Johnson and J. W. Kampf, *Inorg. Chem.* 2011, *50*, 5936-5945.

[4]   F. A. Cotton, C. A. Murillo and R. A. Walton, Multiple Bonds Between Metal Atoms, 3rd Ed., *Springer Science and Business Media*, 2005, New York.

[5]   T. Nguyen, A. D. Sutton, M. Brynda, J. C. Fettinger, G. J. Long and P. P. Power, *Science* 2005, *310*, 844-847.

[6]   F. A. Cotton, N. F. Curtis, C. B. Harris, B. F. G. Johnson, S. J. Lippard, T. J. Mague, W. R. Robinson and J. S. Wood, *Science* 1964, *145*, 1305.

[7]   G. Merino, K. J. Donald, J. S. D'Acchioli and R. Hoffmann, *J. Am. Chem. Soc.* 2007, *129*, 15295-15302.

[8]   B. Xu, Q.-S. Li, Y. Xie, R. B. King, H. F. Schaefer III, *J. Chem. Theory Comput.* 2012, *6*, 735-746.

[9]   Y. C. Tsai, H. Z. Chen, C. C. Chang, J. S. K. Yu, G. H. Lee, Y. Wang and T. S. Kuo, *J. Am. Chem. Soc.* 2009, *131*, 12534-12534.

[10] R. H. Cayton and M. H. Chisholm, *J. Am. Chem. Soc.* 1989, *111*, 8924-8923.

[11] R. H. Cayton, M. H. Chisholm, J .C. Huffman and E. B. Lobkovsky, *J. Am. Chem. Soc.* 1991, *113*, 8709-8724.

[12] F. A. Cotton, L. M. Daniels, C. Lin and C. A. Murillo, *J. Am. Chem. Soc.* 1999, *121*, 4538-4539.

[13] F. A. Cotton, C. Lin and C. A. Murillo, *Acc. Chem. Res.* 2001, *34*, 759-771.

[14] M. H. Chisholm, F. A. Cotton, L. M. Daniels, K. Folting, J. C. Huffman, S. S. Iyer, C. Lin, A. M. Macintosh and C. A. Murillo, *Dalton Trans.* 1999, 1387-1392.

[15] J. R. Li, A. A. Yakovenko, W. Lu, D. J. Timmons, W. Zhuang, D. Yuan and H.-C. Tsai, *J. Am. Chem. Soc.* 2010, *132*, 17599-17610.

[16] M. Köberl, M. Cokoja, B. Bechlars, E. Herdtweck and F.E. Kühn, *Dalton Trans.* 2011, *40*, 11490-11496.

[17] H. Taube and D. E. Richardson, *Inorg. Chem.* 1981, *20*, 1278-1285.

[18] F. Barrière and W.E. Geiger, *J. Am. Chem. Soc.* 2006, *128*, 3980-3898.

[19] M. Robin and P. Day, *Adv. Inorg. Radiochem.* 1967, *10*, 247-422.

[20] B. E. Bursten, M. H. Chisholm, R. J. H. Clark, S. Firth, C. M. Hadad, A. M. Macintosh, P. J. Wilson, P. M. Woodward and J. M. Zaleski, *J. Am. Chem. Soc.* 2002, *124*, 3050-3063.

[21] B. J. Lear and M. H. Chisholm, *Inorg. Chem.* 2009, *48*, 10954-10971.

[22] B. E. Bursten, M. H. Chisholm, R. J. H. Clark, S. Firth, C. M. Hadad, P. J. Wilson, P. M. Woodward and J. M. Zaleski, *J. Am. Chem. Soc.* 2002, *124*, 12244-12254.

[23] M. J. Byrnes, M. H. Chisholm, R. J. H. Clark, J. C. Gallucci, C. M. Hadad and N. J. Patmore, *Inorg. Chem.* 2004, *43*, 6334-6344.

[24] N. S. Hush, *Prog. Inorg. Chem.* 1967, *8*, 391-444.

[25] F. A. Cotton, J. P. Donahue and C. A. Murillo, *J. Am. Chem. Soc.* 2003, *125*, 5486-5492.

[26] S. F. Nelson, *Chem. Eur. J.* 2000, *6*, 581-588.

[27] B. S. Brunschwig, C. Creutz and N. Sutin, *Chem. Soc. Rev.* 2002, *31*, 168-184.

[28] M. H. Chisholm and B. J. Lear, *Chem. Soc. Rev.* 2011, *40*, 5254-5265.

[29] M. H. Chisholm, B. J. Lear, A. Moscatelli and L. A. Peteanu, *Inorg. Chem.* 2010, *49*, 1647-1662.

[30] G. Parkin , Structure and Bonding, Chapter 2., *Springer*, 2010, Heidelberger/London, New York.

[31] F. A. Cotton, Z. Li, C. Y. Lin, C. A. Murillo and D. Villagrán, *Inorg. Chem.* 2006, *45*, 767-778.

[32] F. A. Cotton, Z. Li, C. Y. Lin, C. A. Murillo, D. Villagrán and X. Wang, *J. Am. Chem. Soc.* 2003, *125*, 13564-13575.

[33] F. A. Cotton, C. A. Murillo, M. D. Young, R. Yu and Q. Zhao, *Inorg. Chem.* 2008, *47*, 219-229.

[34] M. D. Hopkins, H. B. Gray and V. M. Miskowski, *Polyhedron* 1987, *6*, 705-714.

[35] M. D. Hopkins and H. B. Gray, *J. Am. Chem. Soc.* 1984, *106*, 2468.

[36] F. A. Cotton and D. G. Nocera, *Acc. Chem. Res.* 2000, *33*, 483-490.

[37] B. G. Alberding, M. H. Chisholm and T. L. Gustafson, *Inorg. Chem.* 2012, *51*, 491–498.

[38] G. T. Burdzinski, R. Ramnauth, M. H. Chisholm and T. L. Gustafon, *J. Am. Chem. Soc.* 2006, *128*, 6776-6777.

[39] M. H. Chisholm, P.-T. Chou, Y.-H. Chou, Y. Ghosh, T. L. Gustafson and M.-L. Ho, *Inorg. Chem.* 2008, *47*, 3415-3425.

[40] B. G. Alberding, M. H. Chisholm, Y. Ghosh, T. L. Gustafson, Y. Liu and C. Turro, *Inorg. Chem.* 2009, *48*, 4284-4290.

[41] B. T. Burdzinski, M. H. Chisholm, P.-T. Chou, Y.-H. Chou. F. Feil, J. C. Gallucci, Y. Ghosh, T. L. Gustafson, M.-L. Ho, Y. Liu, R. Ramnauth and C. Turro, *Proc. Natl. Acad. Sci.* 2008, *105*, 15247-15252.

[42] B. G. Alberding, M. H. Chisholm, Y.-H. Chou, Y. Ghosh, T.L. Gustafson, Y. Liu and C. Turro, *Inorg. Chem.* 2009, *48*, 11187-11195.

[43] B. G. Alberding, M. H. Chisholm, B. J. Lear, V. Naseri and C. R. Reed, *Dalton Trans.* 2011, *40*, 10658-10663.

[44] B. G. Alberding, M. H. Chisholm, J. C. Gallucci, Y. Ghosh and T. L. Gustafson, *Proc. Natl. Acad. Sci.* 2011, *108*, 8152-8156.

[45] M. C. Boehn, One-Dimensional Organometallic Materials, Springer, 1987, Berlin.

[46] J. K. Bera, K. R. Dunbar, *Angew. Chem. Int.Ed.* 2002, *41*, 4453.

[47] K. Mashima, H. Nakano, A. Nakamura, *J. Am. Chem. Soc.* 1993, *115*, 11632–11633.

[48] K. Mashima, H. Nakano, A. Nakamura, *J. Am. Chem. Soc.* 1996, *118*, 9083–9095.

[49] H. Nakano, A. Nakamura, K. Mashima, *Inorg. Chem.* 1996, *35*, 4007–4012.

[50] K. Mashima, A. Fukumoto, H. Nakano, Y. Kaneda, K. Tani, A. Nakamura, *J. Am. Chem. Soc.* 1998, *120*, 12151–12152.

[51] T. Ruffer, M. Ohashi, A. Shima, H. Mizomoto, Y. Kaneda, K. Mashima, *J. Am. Chem. Soc.* 2004, *126*, 12244– 12245.

[52] K. Mashima, Y. Shimoyama, Y. Kusumi, A. Fukumoto, T. Yamagata, M. Ohashi, *Eur. J. Inorg. Chem.* 2007, 235– 238.

[53] M. Ohashi, A. Shima, T. Ruffer, H. Mizomoto, Y. Kaneda, K. Mashima, *Inorg. Chem.* 2007, *46*, 6702–6714.

[54] K. Mashima, A. Shima, K. Nakao, A. Fukumoto, Y. Kaneda, Y. Kusumi, *Inorg. Chem.* 2009, *48*, 1879–1886.

[55] T. Ruffer, M. Ohashi, A. Shima, H. Mizomoto, Y. Kaneda, K. Mashima, *J. Am. Chem. Soc.* 2004, *126*, 12244– 12245.

[56] M. Nippe, E. Bill, J. F. Berry, *Inorg. Chem.* 2011, *50*, 7650–7661.

In: Molybdenum
Editor: Alvin A. Holder

ISBN: 978-1-62417-272-4
© 2013 Nova Science Publishers, Inc.

Chapter 4

MOLYBDENUM AQUA IONS

David T. Richens
Department of Chemistry and Biochemistry,
New Mexico State University,
Las Cruces, NM, US

'*Dedicated to the memory of Professor A Geoffrey Sykes who did so much to develop
and systemize this area of Molybdenum chemistry*'

ABSTRACT

Molybdenum has arguably the richest aqueous chemistry of any element with cationic aqua ions representing five oxidation states. A variety of structure types are represented, from multiple metal-metal bonded dinuclear species to M-M bonded clusters, simple homoleptic aqua ions and, finally, a species with terminal and bridging oxo groups. The propensity for molybdenum to form metal-metal bonded species, particularly in the lower oxidation states, is somewhat responsible for the rich diversity of aqueous compounds known. This chapter provides a comprehensive review of the synthesis, structure and spectroscopic properties of the various mononuclear, polynuclear and oxo aqua cations along with a discussion of their aqueous reaction chemistry.

1. INTRODUCTION

Molybdenum has a rich chemistry of aqua ion species, Figure 1, the most of any element typifying the richness of its coordination chemistry overall. [1] There are classical Werner-type complex ions such as $[Mo(OH_2)_6]^{3+}$ and $[Mo(NH_3)_6]^{3+}$, isopolyanion aggregates such as $Mo_8O_{26}^{4-}$, metal-metal bonded clusters such as triangular $[Mo_3(\mu_3\text{-}O)(\mu\text{-}O)_3(OH_2)_9]^{4+}$ representing the 'simplest' aqua ion of molybdenum(IV) and finally multiple metal-metal bonded species such as the quadruply-bonded dimer; $[Mo_2(OH_2)_8]^{4+}$. In total, five oxidation states are represented, having at least one aqua or oxo-aqua cation.

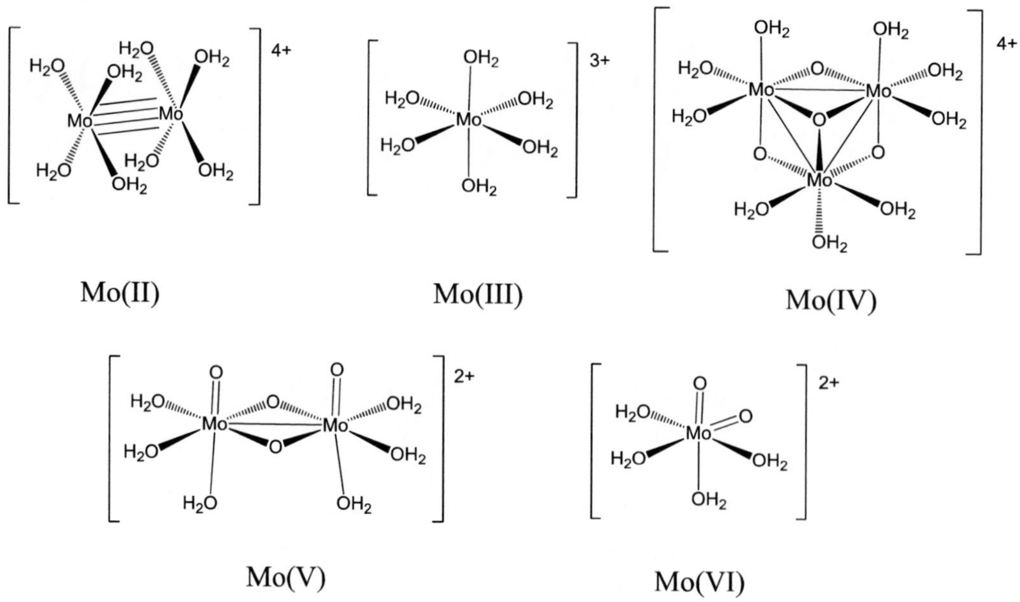

Figure 1. Representative aqua (oxo-aqua) ions of molybdenum.

The propensity for molybdenum to form metal-metal bonded species particularly in the lower oxidation states is somewhat responsible for the rich diversity of aqueous compounds known. Additional factors such as a relatively low electronegativity, particularly in the oxidation states below VI, coupled with an appropriate d-electron count in the various oxidation states results in molybdenum being the only d-block element having cationic oxo-aqua ion species, which characterize five different oxidation states II to VI. [2] Only vanadium in the d-block and the actinide element uranium (each with four states represented by stable oxo-aqua ion species) come anywhere near rivaling molybdenum as an element.

2. MOLYBDENUM(II):
CHEMISTRY OF THE AQUA DIMER: $[Mo_2(OH_2)_8]^{4+}$

The propensity for M-M bond formation in the chemistry of Mo species [3] is exemplified by the aqua ion of Mo(II) which exists not as mononuclear $[Mo(OH_2)_6]^{2+}$ cf. its group partner Chromium, but as the quadruply-bonded dimer $[Mo_2(OH_2)_8]^{4+}$, Figure 2.

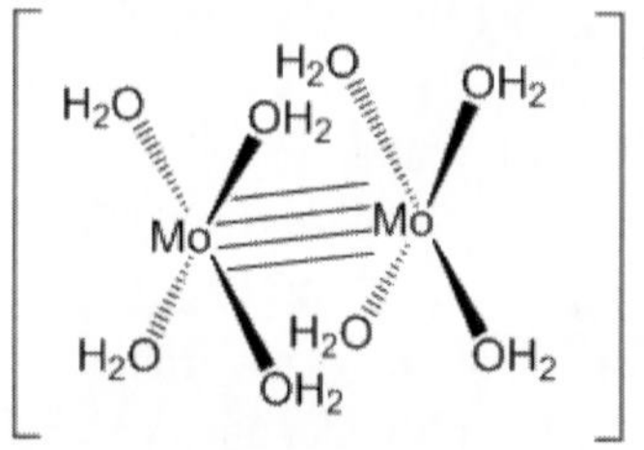

Figure 2. The structure of quadruply-bonded $[Mo_2(OH_2)_8]^{4+}$.

The ion is prepared via Ba^{2+}_{aq} aquation of the tetrasulfate; $[Mo_2(SO_4)_4]^{4-}$ and was first characterised by Bowen and Taube in 1974. [4] It can be viewed as the prototypal quadruply-bonded dimeric Mo(II) species from which all others are derived.

2.1. Synthesis of $[Mo_2(OH_2)_8]^{4+}$

Two preparative routes are established to quadruply-bonded dimeric Mo(II) species. The first and best established route involves the refluxing of $Mo(CO)_6$ in mixtures of ethanoic acid and its anhydride to firstly make the yellow tetraethanoate; $[Mo_2(O_2CCH_3)_4]$. [5] $[Mo_2(O_2CCH_3)_4]$ is then converted firstly to the octachloride $[Mo_2Cl_8]^{4-}$ via treatment with 8.0M aqueous HCl followed by addition of KCl to precipitate red $K_4[Mo_2Cl_8]$ [6] and then to the pinkish-red tetrasulfate; $K_4[Mo_2(SO_4)_4]$ via treatment of $K_4[Mo_2Cl_8]$ with excess K_2SO_4. [7] In the final step, $K_4[Mo_2(SO_4)_4]$ is converted into $[Mo_2(OH_2)_8]^{4+}$ via treatment with acidified solutions of the Ba^{2+} salt of the appropriate non-complexing acid required; usually CF_3SO_3H (triflic acid) or p-$CH_3C_6H_4SO_3H$ (Hpts).

Perchlorate ions cannot be employed due to their rapid oxidation of Mo(II). All of these reactions, Figure 3, are complete within a few minutes at room temperature, although stirring is normally continued for a few hours.

Solutions of the aqua ion have normally been used after filtration of the precipitated $BaSO_4$ but can be further purified by ice-cold air-free ion-exchange chromatography. A second route involving generation of $[Mo_2(O_2CCH_3)_4]$ following direct reduction from Mo(VI) has also been reported, Figure 4. The key step appears to involve the generation of dimeric Mo(III) species such as $[Mo_2Cl_9]^{3-}$ which contain Mo≡Mo bonds.

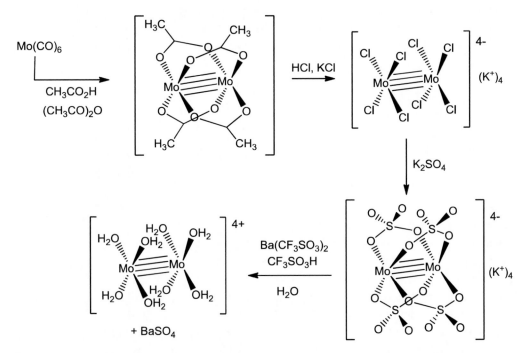

Figure 3. Usual preparative route to $[Mo_2(OH_2)_8]^{4+}$.

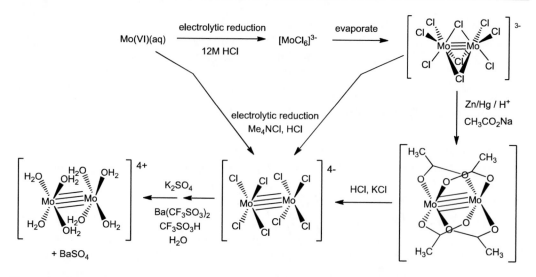

Figure 4. Alternative preparative routes to quadruply–bonded Mo(II) species.

In a procedure reported by Bino in 1980 [8] a solution of molybdenum trioxide (2.0g) in 50 cm^3 of HCl (12.0M) is reduced electrolytically using a platinum or mercury cathode. The initial product is $[MoCl_6]^{3-}$ along with some $[MoCl_5(OH_2)]^{2-}$. [9] Evaporation to near dryness then leads to the formation of dimeric $[Mo_2Cl_9]^{3-}$. [10] Addition of HCl (0.6M) and passage down an ice-cold Jones reductor (Zn/Hg) column into solutions of sodium ethanoate (5.0g in 30cm^3 H_2O) gives 80% yields of the yellow tetraethanoate, far in excess of those normally obtained via $Mo(CO)_6$. $[Mo_2(OH_2)_8]^{4+}$ is then prepared by the Ba^{2+} aquation route, cf. Figure 3.

A 60% yield of dimeric Mo(II) (as a solution of $[Mo_2Cl_8]^{4+}$) has also been reported following mercury pool electrolytic reduction of Mo(VI) in a mixture of HCl (0.5M) and Me_4NCl (3.5M). [11] $[Mo_2Cl_9]^{3-}$ is again presumably formed as an intermediate.

2.2. Properties of $[Mo_2(OH_2)_8]^{4+}$

The most characteristic spectroscopic feature of quadruply-bonded Mo(II) species, including $[Mo_2(OH_2)_8]^{4+}$ is the strong absorption band in the visible electronic spectrum due to the δ-δ* transition. This shifts from 450 nm in the case of $[Mo_2(O_2CCH_3)_4]$ to around 500±10 nm when monodentate ligands such as Cl$^-$ or H_2O are present. Although there is still no crystal structure, the eclipsed arrangement, Figure 2, is assumed as in $[Mo_2Cl_8]^{4-}$ due to the rigidity imparted by the face-on overlap of the d_{xy} (d_{x2-y2}) orbitals in forming the 4th (δ) bond. [3] It is also possible, but not confirmed, that two weakly bonded axial H_2O ligands are present. EXAFS measurements indicate a Mo-Mo separation of 212 pm for $[Mo_2(OH_2)_8]^{4+}$. [12].

The record for the shortest quadruple Mo-Mo bond is held by the bridged bidentate complex with 2-hydroxy-6-methylpyridine (207 pm). Quadruply-bonded dimeric Mo(II) species have characteristic low field ^{95}Mo NMR resonances at ~3000-4000 ppm from MoO_4^{2-}. [13] In 1.0M CF_3SO_3H, $[Mo_2(OH_2)_8]^{4+}$ resonates at 4056 ppm, one of the lowest ^{95}Mo NMR chemical shifts recorded for any Mo compound. As a result the ^{95}Mo NMR chemical shift scale for all Mo compounds covers ~7000 ppm, the highest range for any element. [14]

2.3. Reactions of $[Mo_2(OH_2)_8]^{4+}$

The results of only a few studies in solution on the aqua ion $[Mo_2(OH_2)_8]^{4+}$ have appeared. A kinetic study of substitution at the aqua ligands by NCS⁻ and oxalate was reported by Sykes et al in 1983. [15] Consistent with the evidence of rapid ligand replacement reactions in the steps in Figure 3 the studies required the use of stopped-flow techniques. For NCS⁻ as incoming ligand, $[Mo_2(OH_2)_8]^{4+}$ in 10 fold excess, equilibration kinetics were relevant, rate law $k_{eq} = k_1[Mo_2^{4+}] + k_{-1}$, for reaction studied in I = 0.1M (NaCF₃SO₃). Rate constants (25°C) obtained were $k_1 = 590$ M⁻¹ s⁻¹, $k_{-1} = 0.21$ s⁻¹. Activation parameters for k_1, $\Delta H^{\ne} = 57.6$ kJ mol⁻¹, $\Delta S^{\ne} = +3.0$ J K⁻¹ mol⁻¹ are similar to those characterizing substitution by NCS⁻ on both $[VO(OH_2)_5]^{2+}$ and TiO^{2+}_{aq} suggesting a common mechanism involving initial rapid coordination at the weakly bonded axial position followed by slower movement into the equatorial position, Figure 5. A much slower reaction occurs with $HC_2O_4^-$ as incoming ligand, $k_1 = 0.49$ M⁻¹ s⁻¹, implying here a different rate determining process perhaps involving carboxylate bridge formation. The respective $\Delta H^{\ne}$ values characterizing the dissociation steps (57.2 kJ mol⁻¹, oxalate; 16.3 kJ mol⁻¹, NCS⁻) probably reflects the greater kinetic stability of the μ-carboxylato product. [15] A kinetic study of water exchange on diamagnetic $[Mo_2(OH_2)_8]^{4+}$ using ¹⁷O NMR should be feasible and would be of interest with regard to the differing behaviour observed for NCS⁻ and $HC_2O_4^-$ as substituting ligand.

In H_2SO_4 solution dimeric Mo(II) oxidises in air with effective loss of one δ-bonding electron to give the mixed–valence sulfate; $[Mo_2(SO_4)_4]^{3-}$ which has been isolated as its blue K⁺ salt. [16].

The δ–δ* transition is shifted to lower energy (573 nm) concurrent with an observed increase in Mo-Mo bond length (now 216 pm) and decrease in bond order to 3.5. [17] The corresponding aqua ion has not been characterized. In H_3PO_4 solution oxidation of dimeric Mo(II) to the triply-bonded dimeric Mo(III) complex $[Mo_2(HPO_4)_4]^{2-}$ (Mo-Mo = 223 pm) occurs (loss of the δ-bond). [18].

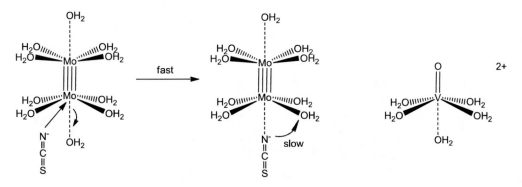

Figure 5. The mechanism of ligand substitution at $[Mo_2(OH_2)_8]^{4+}$ showing its similarity to that at $[VO(OH_2)_5]^{2+}$ [15].

Irradiation of $[Mo_2(OH_2)_8]^{4+}$ at 254 nm results in oxidation to the dimeric Mo(III) aqua ion $[Mo_2(\mu-OH)_2(OH_2)_8]^{4+}$ (section 3.4). [19] In the presence of strong π-accepting ligands (such as CO, RNC and NO) loss of the π-electron density at Mo results in complete fission of the Mo-Mo bond and the formation of mononuclear Mo(II) products.

3. MOLYBDENUM(III)

Various molybdenum(III) aqua ion structure types are known depending upon the method of preparation, ranging from the homoleptic hexaaqua ion A to the hydrolytic dimer B and hydrolytic trimers C and D, Figure 6. Their independent preparation is possible because of the unusually slow rate of hydrolytic polymerization of A to give B - D which reflects a degree of Mo-Mo bonding in the various polynuclear forms.

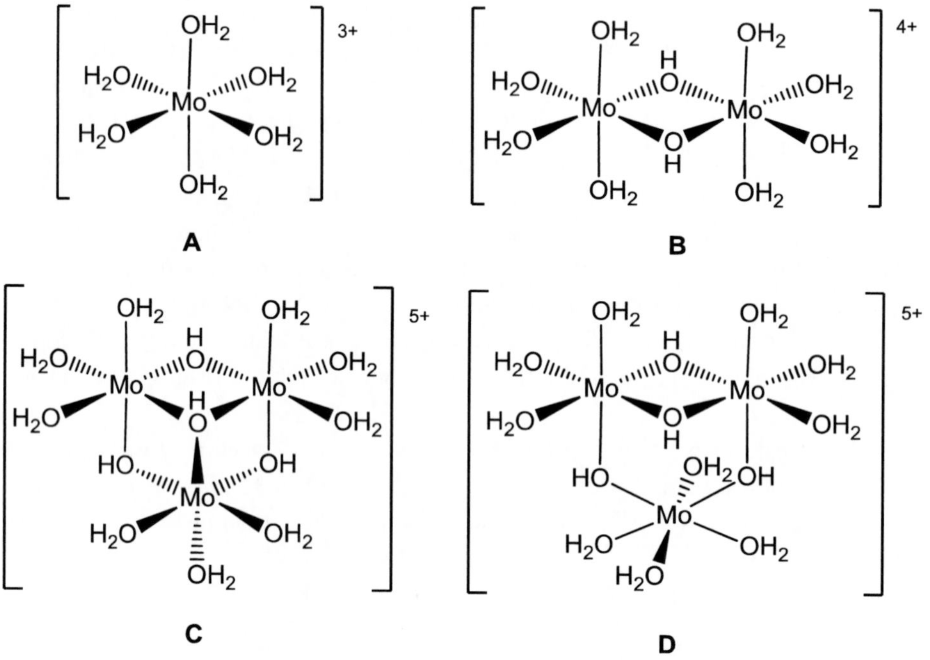

Figure 6. The known aqua and hydroxo-aqua ions of trivalent molybdenum.

3.1. Synthesis and Properties of $[Mo(OH_2)_6]^{3+}$

Pale-yellow $[Mo(OH_2)_6]^{3+}$ represents the only true mononuclear Werner-type homoleptic aqua ion for the element. It was first reported by Bowen and Taube in 1971 [20] and later in more purified form by Sasaki and Sykes in 1975. [21] The earlier samples were contaminated with amounts of the yellow dimeric Mo(V) cation $[Mo=O)_2(\mu-O)_2(OH_2)_6]^{2+}$ (see section 5) to which $[Mo(OH_2)_6]^{3+}$ is readily air-oxidized. Preparations have employed air-free acid-catalyzed aquation of red $[MoCl_6]^{3-}$ or $[MoCl_5(OH_2)]^{2-}$ in non-complexing acidic solution, usually 0.5M Hpts or CF_3SO_3H. The aquation process normally requires a 24 hour period.

However a more convenient lead-in compound has proved to be $Na_3[Mo(HCO_2)_6]$, which aquates to the aqua ion in 0.5M acid over a period of a few minutes. $Na_3[Mo(HCO_2)_6]$ is easily prepared as a pale-yellow air-sensitive solid by dissolving $K_3[MoCl_6]$ in aqueous formic acid followed by treatment with an excess of sodium formate. [22] When dry $Na_3[Mo(HCO_2)_6]$ is only mildly air-sensitive and can be handled for short periods in the air. Following dilution to 0.1M $[H^+]$, separation and purification of $[Mo(OH_2)_6]^{3+}$ can be carried out as in the slower acid-aquation of $K_3[MoCl_6]$ using ice-cold air-free cation-exchange chromatography (usually Dowex 50W X2 resin 200-400 mesh is used). Following washing of the column with 0.5M $[H^+]$, which efficiently removes any Mo(V) as $[Mo=O)_2(\mu-O)_2(OH_2)_6]^{2+}$, the elution of pure solutions of $[Mo(OH_2)_6]^{3+}$ can be carried out using 1.0M or 2.0M solutions of the desired acid (Hpts or CF_3SO_3H). $[Mo(OH_2)_6]^{3+}$ is oxidized by ClO_4^- ions [23] to the extent that $HClO_4$ cannot be employed as supporting medium. Another preparative route involves use of the anhydrous triflate $[Mo(O_3SCF_3)_3]$. This compound is made by refluxing $Mo(CO)_6$ in anhydrous CF_3SO_3H for 3-4 hours according to (1) wherein $[Mo(O_3SCF_3)_3]$ precipitates as an air- sensitive off-white powder which can be removed by filtration and washed with dry diethyl ether and dried under vacuum [24].

$$Mo(CO)_6 + 3\ CF_3SO_3H \quad \rightarrow \quad [Mo(O_3SCF_3)_3] + 6CO + 3/2\ H_2 \qquad (1)$$

$[Mo(O_3SCF_3)_3]$ dissolves readily in air-free aqueous CF_3SO_3H to generate pure solutions of $[Mo(OH_2)_6]^{3+}$. Both $Na_3[Mo(HCO_2)_6]$ and $[Mo(O_3SCF_3)_3]$ are useful for generating high concentrations of $[Mo(OH_2)_6]^{3+}$ (>0.5M) via acid-catalysed aquation before the onset of hydrolytic polymerization (see 3.4). The air-sensitive pale-yellow cesium alum; $Cs[Mo(OH_2)_6](SO_4)_2.6H_2O$, has been prepared by treating aqueous solutions of $Na_3[Mo(HCO_2)_6]$ in H_2SO_4 with CsCl and is structurally characterized. [22, 25] The average $Mo-OH_2$ distance is 209 pm.

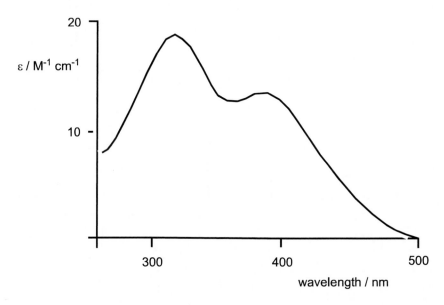

Figure 7. Electronic spectrum of $[Mo(OH_2)_6]^{3+}$ obtained from a solution of $Cs[Mo(OH_2)_6](SO_4)_2.6H_2O$ in 2.0M CF_3SO_3H.

Figure 7 shows the electronic spectrum of a solution of $Cs[Mo(OH_2)_6](SO_4)_2.6H_2O$ (~0.03M) in 2.0M CF_3SO_3H. The spectrum matches well those from freshly generated solutions of $[Mo(OH_2)_6]^{3+}$ following Dowex 50W X2 cation-exchange chromatography. [26] The two bands observed at 386nm (ε = 13.3 M^{-1} cm^{-1}) and 320nm (19.0) are assigned respectively to the transitions from the spin-quartet singlet $^4A_{2g}$ ground state to the excited triplet $^4T_{2g}$ (10Dq) and $^4T_{1g}$(F) states.

The higher energy transition to the $^4T_{1g}$(P) state is obscured by charge transfer absorptions below 250nm. The Racah parameter B for the alum is calculated to be 476cm^{-1}.

As often found in alums involving low d-electron population M^{3+} ions the β structure is adopted with the $M-OH_2$ moiety planar. $Cs[Mo(OH_2)_6](SO_4)_2.6H_2O$ is unstable decomposing under N_2 in a sealed tube at RT within a few weeks due presumably to slow oxidation of Mo(III) by sulfate. The absorption minimum below 300nm, Figure 7, is extremely sensitive to the presence of Mo(V) and a good indicator of purity; the presence of <1% of Mo(V) causing an increase of 10% in the absorption at 350 nm.

3.2. Complex Formation with $[Mo(OH_2)_6]^{3+}$

The rate of water ligand replacement on $[Mo(OH_2)_6]^{3+}$ is unique for a 2nd row transition element in being faster than that on its lighter group partner analogue $[Cr(OH_2)_6]^{3+}$. The reason is largely mechanistic. Biomolecular rate constants for 1:1 substitution by Cl^- and NCS^- on $[Mo(OH_2)_6]^{3+}$ are ~10^5 x larger than found on $[Cr(OH_2)_6]^{3+}$ which have led to the suggestion of a limiting S_N2 or associative (A) mechanism. [21, 27, 28] Strong support comes from the highly negative volume of activation for the 1:1 reaction with NCS^- (-11.4 cm^3 mol^{-1}) [27] and the lack of participation from $[Mo(OH_2)_5(OH)]^{2+}$ cf. substitution on $[Ti(OH_2)_6]^{3+}$ and $[V(OH_2)_6]^{3+}$. The k_{NCS}/k_{Cl} ratio (69) [21] is also the highest seen for a 1:1 substitution reaction on a homoleptic aqua ion indicating a large discrimination between entering ligands. The range of incoming ligands thus far studied is unfortunately limited but measured rate constants, Table 1, already cover ~5 orders of magnitude, the largest spread established so far for a trivalent hexaaqua ion.

Table 1. Kinetic data for 1:1 substitution reactions on $[Mo(OH_2)_6]^{3+}$

Incoming Ligand	k_f /M^{-1} s^{-1}	$\Delta H^{\neq}$ /kJ mol^{-1}	$\Delta S^{\neq}$ /J K^{-1} mol^{-1}	$\Delta V^{\neq}$ /cm^3 mol^{-1}	Ref.
NCS^- [a]	0.317	67.2 ± 2.7	-29.2 ± 9.4	-11.4 ± 0.5	[27]
NCS^- [b]	0.268	68.1 ± 1.7	-26.7 ± 5.4		[21]
Cl^- [b]	0.0046	98.2 ± 2.5	$+40.1 \pm 8.8$	-	[21]
$HC_2O_4^-$ [b]	0.49	-	-	-	[29]
$[Co(C_2O_4)_3]^{3-}$ [c]	0.34	-	-	-	[26]
NO_3^- [c]	0.029	-	-	-	[34]
O_2 [c]	180	-	-	-	[30]
$Mo(O_2)^{3+}$ [c]	42	-	-	-	[30]

a - I = 1.00M ($CF_3SO_3^-$). b - I = 1.00M (pts$^-$). c - I = 2.00M (pts$^-$). The data in c is for the substitution controlled rate determining step of an inner-sphere redox reaction.

It is proposed that the limiting associative S_N2 (A) mechanism is facilitated through a combination of low d-electron population and larger radius of Mo^{3+} readily facilitating formation of a 7-coordinated transition state. Unfortunately the rate constant for the water exchange process itself remains elusive being too slow for line broadening NMR studies and too fast to be followed by conventional oxygen isotopic labeling. It is estimated to lie between 0.1-1.0 s^{-1} at 25°C, around 10^6 x slower than the corresponding rate constant for $[Cr(OH_2)_6]^{3+}$. If one applies the Eigen-Wilkins model (ion-pair pre-association followed by interchange) to the NCS^- anation reaction the volume change to form the outer-sphere pre-association complex (ΔV^o_{os}) can be estimated to be ~ +5.3 cm^3 mol^{-1} from application of the Fuoss equation. [31] From (2), the activation volume for the ligand interchange step ($\Delta V^{\neq}_{I}$) is

$$k_{NCS^-} = k_I. K_{os}; \qquad \Delta V^{\neq}_{NCS} = \Delta V^{\neq}_{I} \qquad + \Delta V^o_{os} \qquad (2)$$

estimated as ~ -17 cm^3 mol^{-1}, which if correlating as expected with $\Delta V^{\neq}_{ex}$ for the water exchange process, would represent the most negative value yet seen for a homoleptic hexaaqua ion. The most negative values of $\Delta V^{\neq}_{ex}$ (cm^3 mol^{-1}) so far determined experimentally for ions having 6 or more coordinated water ligands are for the $3d^1$ ion $[Ti(OH_2)_6]^{3+}$ (-12.1) and the $4f^7$ ion $[Eu(OH_2)_7]^{2+}$ (-11.3) [32] for which limiting A mechanisms have been proposed.

3.3. Redox reactions involving $[Mo(OH_2)_6]^{3+}$

The ready oxidation of $[Mo(OH_2)_6]^{3+}$ to Mo(V) and eventually Mo(VI) has led to a number of kinetic studies with a variety of co-reagents. Both inner-sphere and outer-sphere pathways have been proposed. With $[Mo(OH_2)_6]^{3+}$ in excess the final product is invariably Mo(V) as the dimer $[Mo^V=O)_2(\mu-O)_2(OH_2)_6]^{2+}$. Key studies have been those carried out with the series of oxidants; $[IrCl_6]^{2-}$, $[Fe(OH_2)_6]^{3+}$, $[Co(C_2O_4)_3]^{3-}$ and $[VO(OH_2)_5]^{2+}$ of varying reduction potentials. [26, 33] The reactions were followed by monitoring the appearance of $[Mo^V=O)_2(\mu-O)_2(OH_2)_6]^{2+}$ hence the stoichiometry of the observed rate law (3) for reaction in pts$^-$ media. With the strongest oxidant $[IrCl_6]^{2-}$ (+0.89V) a rapid outer-sphere reaction, $k_{Ox} = k_1 + k_2[H^+]^{-1}$, is observed. At 25°C, $k_1 = 3.4 \times 10^4$ M^{-1} s^{-1} and $k_2 = 2.9 \times 10^4$ s^{-1}. The $[H^+]^{-1}$ path is typical of the involvement of hydrolysis products (here $[Mo(OH_2)_5(OH)]^{2+}$) as resembling more closely the more hydrolyzed nature of the oxidation product, Mo(V) and so more readily oxidized to it. The involvement of $[Mo(OH_2)_5(OH)]^{2+}$ here contrasts with its absence in substitution processes on $[Mo(OH_2)_6]^{3+}$. This behavior parallels that seen for corresponding reactions on $[Ti(OH_2)_6]^{3+}$ and $[V(OH_2)_6]^{3+}$. The two zero order terms; k_d and k_m are also absent in the rate law for the oxidation of $[Mo(OH_2)_6]^{3+}$ by $[Fe(OH_2)_6]^{3+}$ (+0.77V) in 1M Hpts with a simple bimolecular rate law giving $k_{Fe} = (1.30 \pm 0.05) \times 10^3$ M^{-1} s^{-1} [33]. Here the $[H^+]$ dependence was not studied but an outer-sphere reaction is again suspected.

$$d(Mo_2O_4^{2+}{}_{aq})/dt = 2k_{Ox}[Mo^{3+}][Ox] + 4k_d[Mo^{3+}]^2 + 2k_m[Mo^{3+}] \qquad (3)$$

Use of $[Co(C_2O_4)_3]^{3-}$ (+0.58V) as oxidant with the potentially coordinating (bridging) oxalate ligand, $C_2O_4^{2-}$, leads to a much slower oxidant-dependent redox process in addition to the two pathways zero order in oxidant (3). Here the value of k_{Ox} (0.34 M^{-1} s^{-1}) is similar to the rate constant for substitution on $[Mo(OH_2)_6]^{3+}$ by $HC_2O_4^-$ (0.49 M^{-1} s^{-1}) (Table 1) [29] and much slower than that expected for an outer-sphere process on the basis of its redox potential. Therefore in this case a substitution controlled inner-sphere process has been proposed [26].

Finally use of the weak oxidant $[VO(OH_2)_5]^{2+}$ (+0.36V) leads to dominance from the term zero order in oxidant and second order in $[Mo^{3+}]$ (k_d). [26] Here the rate determining step appears to be dimerization (k_d = 1.87 x 10^{-3} M^{-1} s^{-1}) of $[Mo(OH_2)_6]^{3+}$ to $[Mo_2(\mu-OH)_2(OH_2)_8]^{4+}$ (section 3.4) which is then oxidized rapidly by VO^{2+}_{aq} to its dinuclear Mo(V) counterpart $[Mo=O)_2(\mu-O)_2(OH_2)_6]^{2+}$.

Interestingly if the anion is changed to $CF_3SO_3^-$ both k_d and the minor component k_m disappear revealing a first order dependence for each on [pts⁻]. It appears that pts⁻ may promote oxidation of $[Mo(OH_2)_6]^{3+}$ via charge neutralization involving outer-sphere ion association and/or coordination and may also be involved in facilitating hydrolytic polymerization. Air-free solutions (mM) of $[Mo(OH_2)_6]^{3+}$ in 1-2 M Hpts slowly become greenish-brown in color due to the presence of some $[Mo_2(\mu-OH)_2(OH_2)_8]^{4+}$ and higher oligomeric forms. Corresponding solutions in CF_3SO_3H appear far less susceptible. It appears that pts⁻ may not be the innocent non-participating counter anion frequently assumed (see also further evidence below).

The reaction of $[Mo(OH_2)_6]^{3+}$ with dioxygen takes place in three distinct stages, the first two being first order in [Mo(III)] and the last independent of both [Mo(III)] and $[O_2]$. [30] The final product with excess Mo(III) is $[Mo^V=O)_2(\mu-O)_2(OH_2)_6]^{2+}$. A scheme of reactions has been proposed involving successive formation of superoxo-Mo(IV) and peroxo-bridged Mo(IV)$_2$ intermediates prior to eventual formation of $[Mo^V=O)_2(\mu-O)_2(OH_2)_6]^{2+}$.

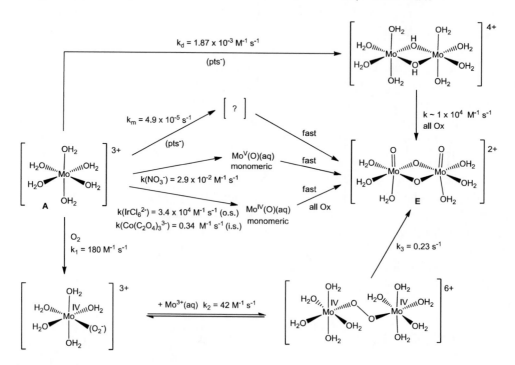

Figure 8. Reaction pathways for oxidation of $[Mo(OH_2)_6]^{3+}$ A to $[Mo^V=O)_2(\mu-O)_2(OH_2)_6]^{2+}$ E in aqueous acidic pts⁻ media.

The reaction of $[Mo(OH_2)_6]^{3+}$ with aqueous HNO_3 in 1M Hpts has also been reported in the context of the involvement of molybdenum in the oxotransferase enzyme *nitrate reductase*. [34].

The final molybdenum product is again $[Mo^V=O)_2(\mu-O)_2(OH_2)_6]^{2+}$. The rate constant, $k_{Ox} = 2.92 \times 10^{-2}$ M^{-1} s^{-1}, suggests an inner-sphere mechanism wherein the rate determining step is initial nitrate complexation to $[Mo(OH_2)_6]^{3+}$ followed by oxygen-atom transfer to give firstly mononuclear $[Mo^V(O)(OH_2)_5]^{3+}$ which then undergoes rapid hydrolytic dimerization to $[Mo^V=O)_2(\mu-O)_2(OH_2)_6]^{2+}$. The detection of significant amounts of NO and N_2O as nitrogen products along with NO_2^- suggests that NO_2^- competes for oxidation of Mo(III). $[Mo(OH_2)_6]^{3+}$ also reacts with DMSO in aqueous Hpts solution abstracting the oxygen atom from it to give Me_2S and $[Mo^V=O)_2(\mu-O)_2(OH_2)_6]^{2+}$ again presumably via initial formation of mononuclear $[Mo^V(O)(OH_2)_5]^{3+}$. Figure 8 summarizes the various pathways for oxidation of $[Mo(OH_2)_6]^{3+}$ to $[Mo^V=O)_2(\mu-O)_2(OH_2)_6]^{2+}$.

3.4. Hydrolytic Polymerized Ions of Mo(III)

Two other forms of aqueous Mo(III) have been characterized analogous to those established for Cr(III); the hydroxy-bridged dimer, $[Mo_2(\mu-OH)_2(OH_2)_8]^{4+}$ B and two forms of hydroxy-bridged trimer; $[Mo_3(\mu_3-OH)(\mu-OH)_3(OH_2)_9]^{5+}$ C and $[Mo_3(\mu-OH)_4(OH_2)_{10}]^{5+}$ D, Figure 6. $[Mo_2(\mu-OH)_2(OH_2)_8]^{4+}$ can be obtained directly by reduction of acidified solutions of Mo(VI) with e.g. zinc amalgam (batch reaction or in the form of a column (Jones reductor)) or electrochemically (Hg pool). This is because $[Mo^V=O)_2(\mu-O)_2(OH_2)_6]^{2+}$ is first generated as an intermediate which then undergoes reduction to its dinuclear Mo(III) counterpart. As a result corresponding reduction of freshly purified $[Mo^V=O)_2(\mu-O)_2(OH_2)_6]^{2+}$ (section 6) can also be employed. The trinuclear forms however can *only* be obtained via reduction from their trinuclear Mo(IV) counterpart; $[Mo_3(\mu_3-O)(\mu-O)_3(OH_2)_9]^{4+}$ (section 4). Pure samples of diamagnetic blue-green $[Mo_2(\mu-OH)_2(OH_2)_8]^{4+}$ were first reported by Ardon and Pernick, [35] and are best obtained using ice-cold air-free Dowex X2 chromatography of solutions of sodium molybdate(VI) (0.01 M) in 1.0M HCl ($100cm^3$) that have been passed slowly down a Jones reductor (Zn/Hg) column (25 x 1cm). Amounts of $[Mo^V=O)_2(\mu-O)_2(OH_2)_6]^{2+}$ (the principal contaminant) are easily removed by washing the column with air-free 0.5M Hpts. Pure solutions of $[Mo_2(\mu-OH)_2(OH_2)_8]^{4+}$ can then be obtained by elution with 2.0M Hpts and, for concentrations > 0.01M, require use within 24 hours to avoid the onset of further hydrolytic polymerization which gives amounts of the trinuclear and higher oligonuclear forms. Freshly prepared solutions are characterized by absorption maxima at 360nm ($\varepsilon = 455$ M^{-1} cm^{-1} per Mo), 572nm (96) and 624nm (110).

Electronic spectra for mononuclear, dinuclear and trinuclear forms of aqueous Mo(III) are shown in Figure 9. Concentrations of Mo(III) are normally determined by adding an excess of Fe(III) under air-free conditions and titrating the Fe(II) generated with aqueous Ce(IV) in 1.0M H_2SO_4 using $[Fe(phen)_3]^{2+}$ as redox indicator. The di-μ-hydroxy $[Mo_2(\mu-OH)_2(OH_2)_8]^{4+}$ structure has been verified by ^{17}O-labelling NMR studies, Figure 10. [36]

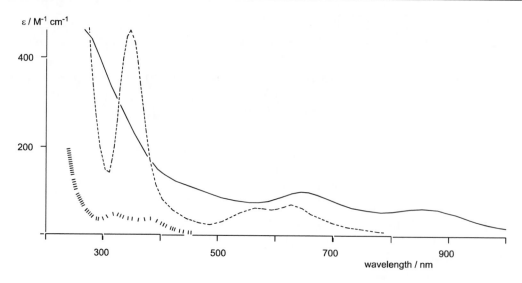

Figure 9. Electronic spectra for mononuclear (|||||||||||||), dinuclear (------) and trinuclear (——) forms of trivalent aqueous molybdenum in 2.0M Hpts.

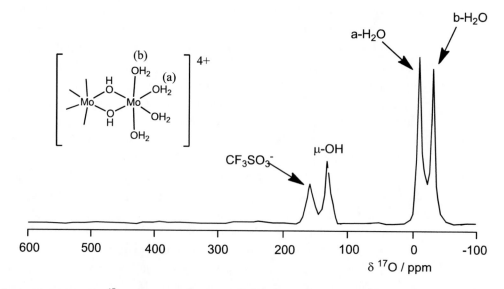

Figure 10. 54.24 MHz ^{17}O NMR spectrum for a 0.01M solution (5 atom % ^{17}O enriched) of $[Mo_2(\mu-OH)_2(OH_2)_8]^{4+}$ in 1.0M CF_3SO_3H (contains 0.1M Mn^{2+} as bulk water relaxant).

The diamagnetism could conceivably arise from efficient superexchange via the μ-OH groups or from a degree of M-M bonding. The M-M bond energy has been estimated from a calorimetric study of the oxidation of both $[Mo(H_2O)_6]^{3+}$ and $[Mo_2(\mu-OH)_2(OH_2)_8]^{4+}$ [37].

Consistent with the scheme of Figure 8 a kinetic study of the oxidation of excess $[Mo_2(\mu-OH)_2(OH_2)_8]^{4+}$ to $[Mo^V=O)_2(\mu-O)_2(OH_2)_6]^{2+}$ by $[Co(C_2O_4)_3]^{3-}$ requires stopped-flow monitoring at 25°C. [38] The rate law, $k_{obs} = Kk_{et}[Mo(III)_2] / (1 + K[Mo(III)_2])$ is relevant with K and k_{et} (25°C) respectively 5090 M^{-1} and 1.8 s^{-1} for reaction in 2.0M Hpts. It is assumed that K represents initial reactant pair formation in a classic outer-sphere redox process. The reaction of $[Mo_2(\mu-OH)_2(OH_2)_8]^{4+}$ with dioxygen, giving

$[Mo^V=O)_2(\mu-O)_2(OH_2)_6]^{2+}$, also occurs much faster (factor of $\sim 10^2$) than the corresponding reaction with $[Mo(OH_2)_6]^{3+}$.

The facile redox interconversion between Mo(III) and Mo(V) here stems from their similar dinuclear structures. Indeed polarograms obtained from solutions of $[Mo_2(\mu-OH)_2(OH_2)_8]^{4+}$ exhibit a 4e$^-$ oxidation wave to Mo(V) (E^o -0.35V). [39] The rate of electrochemical oxidation has been found to correlate with the rate of deprotonation of a water molecule on each Mo center. [40] In contrast, freshly prepared solutions of $[Mo(OH_2)_6]^{3+}$ (at mM concentrations) exhibit no such oxidation wave to Mo(V) on the same polarographic timescale reflecting the need for a structural change. As will prove apparent the rates governing redox interconversions within the various Mo^{n+}_{aq} species are often governed by the structural changes involved (see sections 4 and 5).

The yellow triple-bonded chloro-aqua ion dimer; $[Mo_2Cl_4(OH_2)_4]^{2+}$ (λ_{max} at 430 nm) can be obtained following electrochemical oxidation of solutions of $[Mo_2(OH_2)_8]^{4+}$ in aqueous HCl. [18] It can also be obtained from reaction of aqueous HCl with $[Mo_2(HPO_4)_4]^{2-}$.

Further aspects of the chemistry of the trinuclear forms of aqua molybdenum(III) are discussed in section 4 in the context of their generation via reduction of trinuclear aqua molybdenum(IV).

4. MOLYBDENUM(IV):
CHEMISTRY OF THE TRIANGULAR CLUSTER ION;
$[Mo_3(\mu_3-O)(\mu-O)_3(OH_2)_9]^{4+}$

The existence of an aqua ion representing Mo(IV) was first demonstrated by Souchay in 1966. [41] Efforts to establish the nuclearity of the aqua ion led later to proposals of both mononuclear and dinuclear structures. These early conclusions were based upon electrochemical, kinetic, [42] chromatographic [43] and cryoscopic [44] measurements. As time went by a number of Mo(IV) complexes containing the triangular $Mo_3(\mu_3-O)(\mu-O)_3^{4+}$ core unit with various monodentate and bidentate ligands were identified, many obtained via simple treatment of the 'aqua ion' with the ligand under mild conditions. [45] Finally in 1980 Murmann and co-workers showed conclusively with ^{18}O isotope labeling that the aqua ion was the triangular species $[Mo_3(\mu_3-O)(\mu-O)_3(OH_2)_9]^{4+}$. [46] The success of the isotope labeling method reflected the extreme inertness of the μ-oxo groups within the $Mo_3(\mu_3-O)(\mu-O)_3^{4+}$ core towards exchange. The trinuclear structure has since been verified in solution by ^{17}O NMR using a ^{17}O-labelled sample [36] and finally by an X-ray crystal structure of the salt $[Mo_3(\mu_3-O)(\mu-O)_3(OH_2)_9](pts)_4.13H_2O$. [47] A side view of the $[Mo_3(\mu_3-O)(\mu-O)_3(OH_2)_9]^{4+}$ ion is shown in Figure 11.

The Mo-Mo (248 pm) and Mo-O (core O and OH$_2$) distances are in close agreement with predictions by EXAFS[12] and with those found in other complexes containing the $Mo_3(\mu_3-O)(\mu-O)_3^{4+}$ core. [45] The burgundy-red color of the aqua ion is distinctive and stems from a band in the visible spectrum at 505nm (ϵ = 217 M^{-1} cm^{-1} per Mo$_3$ unit) assigned to a transition within the MO's of the triangular M-M and Mo-O-Mo bonded framework. [48, 49] A further maximum appears in the UV region at 300nm (890 M^{-1} cm^{-1}).

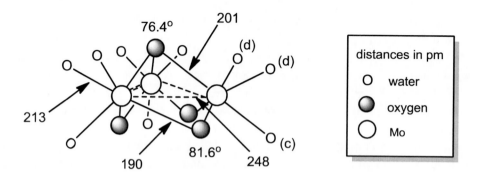

Figure 11. The dimensions of the $[Mo_3(\mu_3\text{-}O)(\mu\text{-}O)_3(OH_2)_9]^{4+}$ ion (ppm) from the X-ray structure of $[Mo_3(\mu_3\text{-}O)(\mu\text{-}O)_3(OH_2)_9](pts)_4.13H_2O$ [47].

The construction of the triangular M_3 unit is easily appreciated on the basis of a total of 6 d electrons forming three M-M bonds. $[Mo_3(\mu_3\text{-}O)(\mu\text{-}O)_3(OH_2)_9]^{4+}$ is now known to be merely the all μ-oxo bridged Mo(IV) species (X=Y=O) within an extensive family of 'incomplete cuboidal' M-M bonded cluster aqua complexes containing the triangular core unit; $[M_3(\mu_3\text{-}X)(\mu\text{-}Y)_3]^{n+}$ (M = Nb, Mo, W; X = O, S, Se, Te, Cl; Y = O, S, Se, Te, Cl; n = 3 or 4). The chemistry of the complete series of molybdenum oxo-chalcogenide and chalcogenide clusters is described in detail in the next chapter.

4.1. Synthesis of the $[Mo_3(\mu_3\text{-}O)(\mu\text{-}O)_3(OH_2)_9]^{4+}$ Ion

The most widely used method of choice involves thermal comproportionation between aqueous Mo(VI) (added as either MoO_3 or $Na_2[MoO_4]$) or aqueous Mo(V) e.g. $[Mo^V=O)_2(\mu\text{-}O)_2(OH_2)_6]^{2+}$ and a source of Mo(III) in 2M acid, usually HCl. The maximum total Mo concentration is usually kept around ~3 x 10^{-2}M with heating at ~90°C sustained for 2 hours to allow assembly of the trinuclear core. In principle any form of aqueous Mo(III) will suffice and in the early preparations the air-stable salt $K_3[MoCl_6]$ was the reactant of choice if available. [2, 42, 47] Other methods have involved heating samples of more reactive forms of Mo(III) such as $[Mo_2(\mu\text{-}OH)_2(OH_2)_8]^{4+}$ with a further equivalent of Mo(VI) (4). This method has the virtue of requiring only Na_2MoO_4 as the lead-in Mo reagent [50].

$$Mo(VI)_{aq} + Mo(III)_{2\ aq} \quad \rightarrow \quad Mo(IV)_{3\ aq} \qquad\qquad (4)$$

$[Mo_2(OH_2)_8]^{4+}$ has also been used as reductant. The synthesis of ^{17}O enriched samples for NMR measurements required the use of ^{17}O-labelled precursors assembled in ^{17}O-enriched acidified water because of the inertness of the core μ-O groups towards exchange. The precursors used were $[Mo^V=^{17}O)_2(\mu\text{-}^{17}O)_2(^{17}OH_2)_6]^{2+}$ and $[Mo(^{17}OH_2)_6]^{3+}$ prepared by treatment with $^{17}OH_2$ in acidified Hpts solution prior to mixing. [36] Following the 2 hour heating period the crude Mo(IV) solution is cooled and diluted to 0.5M [H⁺] with $H_2^{17}O$, allowed to stand at RT for 24 hours to allow aquation of coordinated Cl⁻ ions (if relevant), and then loaded onto a column of Dowex 50W X2 resin in the H⁺ form. Assembly of the various μ-sulfido analogues of $[Mo_3(\mu_3\text{-}O)(\mu\text{-}O)_3(OH_2)_9]^{4+}$ has provided clues to the mechanism of assembly from its Mo(V) precursor, Figure 12. A simpler method for obtaining fully ^{17}O-enriched samples of $[Mo_3(\mu_3\text{-}O)(\mu\text{-}O)_3(OH_2)_9]^{4+}$ analogous to that developed for the tungsten counterpart involves acid hydrolysis (Hpts or HCl) of the air-sensitive green Mo(IV) salt; $K_2[MoCl_6]$.

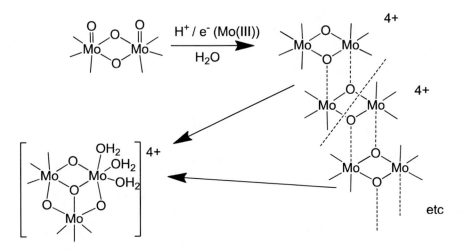

Figure 12. Mechanism of assembly of $[Mo_3(\mu_3\text{-}O)(\mu\text{-}O)_3(OH_2)_9]^{4+}$ from Mo(V)(aq).

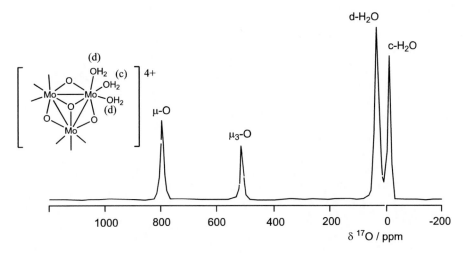

Figure 13. ^{17}O NMR spectrum of a 5 atom % ^{17}O-enriched sample of $[Mo_3(\mu_3\text{-}O)(\mu\text{-}O)_3(OH_2)_9]^{4+}$ in aqueous 2M Hpts (contains 0.1M Mn^{2+} as bulk water relaxant).

Here $[Mo_3(\mu_3\text{-}O)(\mu\text{-}O)_3(OH_2)_9]^{4+}$ assembles from its mononuclear precursor as H$_2$O replaces coordinated Cl$^-$ allowing ready introduction of the ^{17}O label at all the oxygen sites. Samples of $K_2[MoCl_6]$ are conveniently prepared *in situ* by simple treatment of powdered solid $K_3[MoCl_6]$ with elemental Br$_2$. The ^{17}O NMR spectrum from a 5 atom % enriched sample of $[Mo_3(\mu_3\text{-}O)(\mu\text{-}O)_3(OH_2)_9]^{4+}$ is shown in Figure 13.

The single ^{95}Mo NMR resonance of $[Mo_3(\mu_3\text{-} O)(\mu\text{-}O)_3(OH_2)_9]^{4+}$ comes at 1003 ppm downfield from aqueous MoO$_4^{2-}$. [13, 14, 51]

The coordinated waters of $[Mo_3(\mu_3\text{-}O)(\mu\text{-}O)_3(OH_2)_9]^{4+}$ are highly acidic. The K_{aM} value for the first proton dissociation has been determined directly by visible spectrophotometry in 2M Hpts solution to be 0.43 ± 0.04 M. [2a] Kinetic values of K_{aM} have been obtained from the involvement of the monohydroxo species in complex formation (0.39 M) [52] and water exchange (0.24 M), [47] both in 2M Hpts. As a result aqueous solutions $[Mo_3(\mu_3\text{-}O)(\mu\text{-}O)_3(OH_2)_9]^{4+}$ in 1-2M Hpts slowly become brownish-red over time as they age to give amounts of hydrolytically-polymerized products. Solutions in HCl are more stable due to coordination by Cl⁻ which reduces both the cationic charge and the sites available for hydrolysis and are recommended for long term storage of $Mo(IV)_{aq}$ [2].

4.2. Water Exchange and Complex Formation on $[Mo_3(\mu_3\text{-}O)(\mu\text{-}O)_3(OH_2)_9]^{4+}$

There are two distinctly different water ligands on each Mo centre; those approximately opposite the capping oxo group (c) and those opposite the bridging oxo groups (d), Figures 11 and 13. Distinctly different rates of exchange are relevant at the two water sites with the c-waters significantly more inert by factor of $\sim 10^5$. This has been traced from kinetic studies on the more thermally-stable sulfido analogues; $[Mo_3(\mu_3\text{-}S)(\mu\text{-}O)_3(OH_2)_9]^{4+}$ and $[Mo_3(\mu_3\text{-}S)(\mu\text{-}S)_3(OH_2)_9]^{4+}$ [51, 53] to a conjugate-base labilization of the d-waters via the monohydroxy ion in a dissociative mechanism. Exchange at the d-waters follows pathways (5-7) and rate law (8):

$$[Mo_3O_4(c\text{-}OH_2)_3(d\text{-}OH_2)_6]^{4+} + H_2O \underset{}{\overset{K_{aM}}{\rightleftharpoons}} [Mo_3O_4(c\text{-}OH_2)_3(d\text{-}OH_2)_5(d\text{-}OH)]^{3+} + H_3O^+$$

$$(5)$$

$$[Mo_3O_4(c\text{-}OH_2)_3(d\text{-}OH_2)_6]^{4+} + H_2{}^{17}O \underset{}{\overset{k_1}{\rightleftharpoons}} [Mo_3O_4(c\text{-}OH_2)_3(d\text{-}OH_2)_5(d\text{-}H_2{}^{17}O)]^{4+} + H_2O$$

$$(6)$$

$$[Mo_3O_4(c\text{-}OH_2)_3(d\text{-}OH_2)_5(d\text{-}OH)]^{3+} + H_2{}^{17}O \underset{}{\overset{k_{OH}}{\rightleftharpoons}} [Mo_3O_4(c\text{-}OH_2)_3(d\text{-}OH_2)_4(d\text{-}H_2{}^{17}O)(d\text{-}OH)]^{3+} + H_2O$$

$$(7)$$

$$k_{ex}(d) = \frac{k_1[H^+] + k_{OH}K_{aM}}{(H^+ + K_{aM})}$$

$$(8)$$

The kinetic data are shown in table 2. At 25°C k_1 (the pathway via the aqua ion) accounts for less than 1% of the reaction, the dominant pathway for exchange being via the monohydroxo ion (k_{OH}). The relatively high values of $\Delta H^{\neq}$ and, more important, positive $\Delta S^{\neq}$ values for all three trinuclear ions are consistent with a dissociative mechanism for the k_{OH} pathway mediated through the monohydroxo ion.

**Table 2. Kinetic data for water exchange at the d-H$_2$O ligands
on [Mo$_3$(μ_3-X)(μ-Y)$_3$(OH$_2$)$_9$]$^{4+}$ (X, Y = O or S)**

Mo(IV) ion	k_1 /s^{-1}	k_{OH} /s^{-1}	K_{aM} /M	$\Delta H^{\neq}_{OH}$ /kJ mol^{-1}	$\Delta S^{\neq}_{OH}$ /J K^{-1} mol^{-1}	Ref.
X = O, Y = O ^{b}	negl.	160	0.24	71.0 ± 8.5	+35 ± 25	[47]
X = S, Y = O ^{a}	negl.	45	0.58	81.0 ± 8.0	+57 ± 14	[51]
X = S, Y = S ^{a}	<10	7500	0.18	83.0 ± 4.0	+107 ± 15	[53]

a - I = 2.00M (LiClO$_4$). b - I = 2.00M (Lipts).

No variable pressure kinetic studies have been so far been reported to probe the mechanistic pathways relevant to the [H$^+$] independent c-H$_2$O exchange for which an associative mechanism is suspected. If proven this would be the first case of different water exchange mechanistic paths operating on adjacent waters on the same metal center.

It is not yet known why the c-water ligands are not similarly conjugate-base labilized towards exchange. Measurement of the ^{17}O chemical shift of the two water ligands as a function of pH indicates that formation of the monohydroxo ion involves deprotonation at a d-H$_2$O site which might explain the selective labilization of the remaining d-site rather if both d-sites are connected through a common MO. The structure of a hydrolytic dodecamer; [{(Mo$_3$(μ_3-O)(μ-O)$_3$(H$_2$O)$_5$)(μ-OH)$_2$}$_4$](pts)$_8$·41H$_2$O has been reported following crystallization of Mo(IV)$_{aq}$ from 3M Hpts solution. [54] Within the total of eight terminal sites used to link the four trimers together via OH bridges six are from d-sites. The crystallization of the dodecamer from more concentrated (3M) Hpts solution is probably related to the ability of pts$^-$ at high concentrations to stabilize higher charged hydrolytic oligomers through effective ion-pair neutralization as was observed in the promotion both of [Mo(OH$_2$)$_6$]$^{3+}$ oxidation and its hydrolysis to [Mo$_2$(μ−OH)$_2$(OH$_2$)$_8$]$^{4+}$.

Detailed kinetic studies of the 1:1 complexation of oxalate (HC$_2$O$_4^-$) and NCS$^-$ to [Mo$_3$(μ_3-O)(μ-O)$_3$(OH$_2$)$_9$]$^{4+}$ have been reported. Equilibration kinetics is observed under pseudo first order conditions and the rate law (9) is relevant with k_f and k_b representing the forward and backward rate constants respectively. A feature of (9) is the statistical factor of 3 detected

$$k_{obs} = k_f ([L] / 3) \text{ or } [Mo_3O_4^{4+}]) + k_b \qquad (9)$$

from comparisons of pseudo first order kinetics conducted with either L or [Mo$_3$(μ_3-O)(μ-O)$_3$(OH$_2$)$_9$]$^{4+}$ in excess. [53, 55] Rate constants, k_f, obtained from studies with L in excess require to be divided by 3 in order to match those obtained with [Mo$_3$(μ_3-O)(μ-O)$_3$(OH$_2$)$_9$]$^{4+}$ in excess and arise due to the presence of three identical and independantly reacting metal centers which become statistically relevant with excess L present. As in the water exchange study, the ligand complexation process is activated through the monohydroxo ion with k_f increasing with decreasing [H$^+$]. Plots of k_f versus [H$^+$]$^{-1}$ show downward curvature consistent with the high acidity of the aqua ion. The [H$^+$] dependence of k_f and k_b are both of the form (10), identical to that found for k_{ex}(d) (8) and are thought to represent 1:1 complex formation at a d-H$_2$O, (11-14).

$$k_f = \frac{k_1 [H^+] + k_{OH} K_{aM}}{(H^+ + K_{aM})} \qquad k_b = \frac{k_{-1} [H^+] + k_{-OH} K_{aML}}{(H^+ + K_{aML})} \qquad (10)$$

$$[Mo_3O_4(c\text{-}OH_2)_3(d\text{-}OH_2)_6]^{4+} + H_2O \xrightleftharpoons{K_{aM}} [Mo_3O_4(c\text{-}OH_2)_3(d\text{-}OH_2)_5(d\text{-}OH)]^{3+} + H_3O^+ \qquad (11)$$

$$[Mo_3O_4(c\text{-}OH_2)_3(d\text{-}OH_2)_6]^{4+} + L \underset{k_{-1}}{\overset{k_1}{\rightleftharpoons}} [Mo_3O_4(c\text{-}OH_2)_3(d\text{-}OH_2)_5L]^{3+} + H_2O \qquad (12)$$

$$[Mo_3O_4(c\text{-}OH_2)_3(d\text{-}OH_2)_5(d\text{-}OH)]^{3+} + L \underset{k_{-OH}}{\overset{k_{OH}}{\rightleftharpoons}} [Mo_3O_4(c\text{-}OH_2)_3(d\text{-}OH_2)_4(d\text{-}OH)L]^{3+} + H_2O \qquad (13)$$

$$[Mo_3O_4(c\text{-}OH_2)_3(d\text{-}OH_2)_5L]^{3+} + H_2O \xrightleftharpoons{K_{aML}} [Mo_3O_4(c\text{-}OH_2)_3(d\text{-}OH_2)_4(d\text{-}OH)L]^{2+} + H_3O^+ \qquad (14)$$

In discussing the mechanism of substitution on aqua metal ions a fairly reliable indicator has proved to be the ratio of anation rate constants k_{NCS}/k_{Cl^-}. [21] For reaction on the conjugate base form of $[Mo_3(\mu_3\text{-}S)(\mu\text{-}S)_3(OH_2)_9]^{4+}$ for which data is available for both anions, the ratio is close to unity (1.4) in support of the dissociative mechanism (no discrimination between incoming ligands) for water ligand replacement at the d-sites. [53].

This is further supported by computed Eigen-Wilkins interchange rate constants k_I for Cl^- and NCS^- being largely similar to (within a factor of 2 of) the rate constant for water exchange at a d-H_2O.

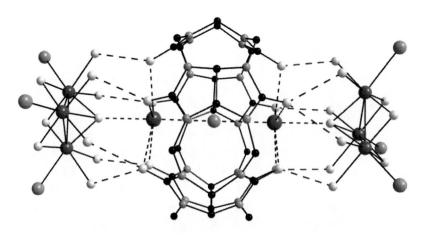

Figure 14. Structure of the cationic supramolecular complex $[\{Mo(\mu_3\text{-}O)(\mu\text{-}O)_3(d\text{-}OH_2)_6 Cl_3\}_2 (Na_2Cl \subset C_{30}H_{30}N_{20}O_{10})]^{3+}$ (Na...Cl and Na...O contacts and hydrogen bonds are indicated by dashed lines). [56] Reproduced with permission from the Russian Chemical Society.

For the fully protonated aqua ion, significant values of k_1 (factor of only 10x smaller than k_{OH}) were found for both Cl^- and NCS^- ($\sim$100 M^{-1} s^{-1}) far in excess (>10x) of the estimated value for water exchange on $[Mo_3(\mu_3-O)(\mu-O)_3(OH_2)_9]^{4+}$.

Such data is consistent with an associative process on the aqua ion (greater nucleophilicity of anionic Cl^- and NCS^- versus H_2O) but further evidence is required. Similar changeovers in substitution mechanism between aqua and monohydroxo forms are well established elsewhere such as in the case of substitution on Fe^{3+}_{aq} ($\Delta V^{\neq}_{ex}$ = -5.4 cm^3 mol^{-1}, I_A path) and $FeOH^{2+}_{aq}$ ($\Delta V^{\neq}_{ex}$ = +7.0 cm^3 mol^{-1}, I_D path). [2a, 2b]

Interesting supramolecular adducts between cucurbit[5]uril and chloro-aqua derivatives of $[Mo_3(\mu_3-X)(\mu-X)_3(OH_2)_9]^{4+}$ ions (M = Mo, W; X = O, S, Se) have been structurally characterized by Fedin and co-workers following crystallization from aqueous HCl in the presence of NaCl. The structure of the adduct derived from $[Mo_3(\mu_3-O)(\mu-O)_3(OH_2)_9]^{4+}$ is shown in Figure 14. [56] Replacement of the three c-H_2Os by Cl^- from the HCl is a common structural feature allowing favorable hydrogen bonding from the six remaining d-H_2Os and single μ_3-O group, positioned on the same side of the cluster, to intercalated Na^+ ions which are themselves hydrogen-bonded to the urea oxygens of curcubit[5]uril and a single Cl^- ion. The stoichiometry is two M_3 clusters, two Na^+ ions and four Cl^- ions per molecule of curcubit[5]uril.

4.3. Redox Processes Involving $[Mo_3(\mu_3-O)(\mu-O)_3(OH_2)_9]^{4+}$

4.3.1. Reduction

A third form of aqua trivalent molybdenum (green) can be obtained following reduction of $[Mo_3(\mu_3-O)(\mu-O)_3(OH_2)_9]^{4+}$ either electrochemically (Hg pool cathode) [57] or chemically with Zn/Hg, [57] $[Cr(OH_2)_6]^{2+}$ [58] or $[Eu(OH_2)_7]^{2+}$. [59] The reversibility of the Mo(IV)/Mo(III) redox reaction implies a cyclic trinuclear Mo(III) product, confirmed later by both ^{17}O and ^{18}O labeling studies [59, 60] which showed retention of the four oxygens of the trinuclear core during the redox cycle. Protonation of all four oxo groups during the reduction has been verified by electrochemical measurements and structure $Mo_3(OH)_4^{5+}$(aq) is relevant. [57] From studies in 2.0M CF_3SO_3H, Paffett and Anson obtained electrochemical evidence for two forms of green trinuclear aqua Mo(III) following rapid reduction of $[Mo_3(\mu_3-O)(\mu-O)_3(OH_2)_9]^{4+}$ via passage down a column of zinc amalgam (Jones reductor), the second form building up over a period of $\sim$30 hours. [57c] Each had different formal potentials for oxidation back to $[Mo_3(\mu_3-O)(\mu-O)_3(OH_2)_9]^{4+}$. Subsequent ^{17}O NMR monitoring of solutions of ^{17}O-enriched $[Mo_3(\mu_3-O)(\mu-O)_3(OH_2)_9]^{4+}$ following treatment with $[Eu(OH_2)_7]^{2+}$ also revealed evidence for two NMR distinct forms of green trinuclear aqua Mo(III) labeled $Mo_3^{IIIA}_{aq}$ and $Mo_3^{IIIB}_{aq}$.[59] The spectra are shown in Figure 15. $Mo_3^{IIIA}_{aq}$ appears to retain the incomplete cuboidal 'Mo_3X_4' core with resonances observed assignable to the capping μ_3-OH group ($\delta^{17}O$ = 209 ppm) and the three bridging μ-OH groups ($\delta^{17}O$ = 355 ppm), formula; $[Mo_3(\mu_3-OH)(\mu-OH)_3(OH_2)_9]^{5+}$. The $Mo^{IIIB}_{3\,aq}$ form however only has a single ^{17}O assignable to μ-OH at 232 ppm and no capping OH group consistent with the formula; $[Mo_3(\mu-OH)_4(OH_2)_{10}]^{5+}$. Both forms oxidize back to $[Mo_3(\mu_3-O)(\mu-O)_3(OH_2)_9]^{4+}$ at the same rate indicating an equilibrium between the two forms on the redox timescale. A cyclic voltammogram obtained from a 5 mM solution of green trivalent aqua molybdenum(III) generated in 2.0M Hpts [57b] is also shown for comparison (Figure 15 inset). It appears that both $Mo_3^{IIIA}{}_{aq}$ and $Mo_3^{IIIB}{}_{aq}$ are produced within minutes in Hpts solution whereas in CF_3SO_3H media $Mo_3^{IIIA}{}_{aq}$ forms first and then slowly converts to an equilibrium mixture of the two forms. [57] Formation of $Mo_3^{IIIB}{}_{aq}$ appears to be promoted by pts⁻ as counter anion and may be related to stabilization (neutralization) of the high 6+ charge of an intermediate mixed-valence $Mo_3^{III,III,IV}{}_{aq}$ form in this medium from which it forms via reduction.

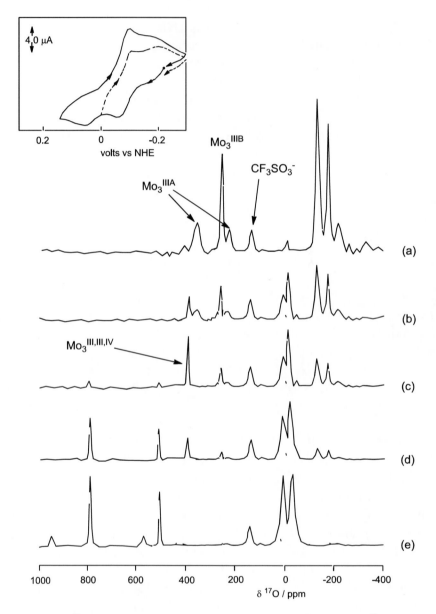

Figure 15. 54.24 MHz ^{17}O NMR spectra following the air oxidation of a 5 atom % ^{17}O-enriched solution of green trivalent aqua molybdenum(III) (10mM) (a) to $[Mo_3(\mu_3\text{-}O)(\mu\text{-}O)_3(OH_2)_9]^{4+}$ (e) in 1.2M Hpts, I = 2.0M ($CF_3SO_3^-$) (contains 0.1M Mn^{2+}). Inset: Cyclic voltammogram of a 5 mM solution of green trivalent aqua molybdenum(III) in 2.0M Hpts (HMDE, 0.1 V s⁻¹) [57b, 59].

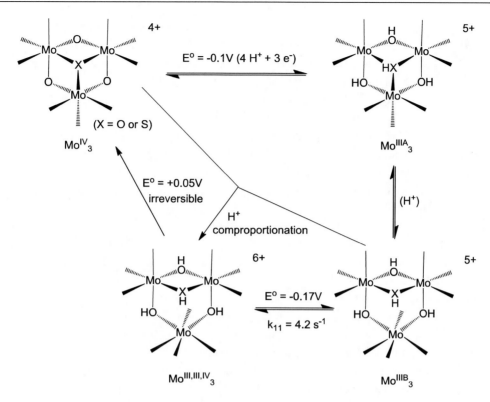

Figure 16. Redox interconversions involving trinuclear aqua ions of Mo(IV) and Mo(III).

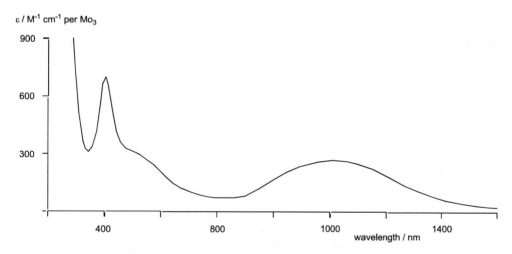

Figure 17. Electronic spectrum of mixed-valence $[Mo_3^{III,III,IV}(\mu\text{-}OH)_4(OH_2)_{10}]^{6+}$.

Consistent with the similar core structures $Mo_3^{IIIA}{}_{aq}$ is oxidized in a single 3e⁻ step to $[Mo_3(\mu_3\text{-}O)(\mu\text{-}O)_3(OH_2)_9]^{4+}$ ($E^\varphi \sim -0.1V$). However $Mo_3^{IIIB}{}_{aq}$ is oxidized in two steps, firstly in a reversible step to the mixed-valence $Mo_3^{III,III,IV}{}_{aq}$ intermediate ($E^\varphi = -0.17V$, 2.0M Hpts) and then irreversibly to $[Mo_3(\mu_3\text{-}O)(\mu\text{-}O)_3(OH_2)_9]^{4+}$ ($E^\varphi = +0.05V$). The redox behavior suggests similar μ-OH bridged structures for $Mo_3^{IIIB}{}_{aq}$ and mixed-valence $Mo_3^{III,III,IV}{}_{aq}$ with the latter having formula; $[Mo_3(\mu\text{-}OH)_4(OH_2)_{10}]^{6+}$. The appearance of only a single resonance for μ–OH at 403 ppm, Figure 15, suggests that $Mo_3{}^{III,III,IV}{}_{aq}$ is valence-delocalized on the NMR timescale. A Marcus-derived self-exchange rate constant for the facile reversible $Mo_3{}^{III,III,IV}{}_{aq}$ / $Mo_3{}^{IIIB}{}_{aq}$ redox process has been measured in 2M Hpts solution as $10^{4.2 \pm 0.6}$ M^{-1} s^{-1} based on a study of the oxidation of $Mo_3{}^{IIIB}{}_{aq}$ to $[Mo_3(\mu_3\text{-}O)(\mu\text{-}O)_3(OH_2)_9]^{4+}$ via $Mo_3{}^{III,III,IV}{}_{aq}$ with a series of Co(III) pentaammine/amine oxidants. [61] The interconversion between $[Mo_3(\mu_3\text{-}O)(\mu\text{-}O)_3(OH_2)_9]^{4+}$ and its various reduced forms is illustrated in Figure 16.

Solutions containing $[Mo_3{}^{III,III,IV}(\mu\text{-}OH)_4(OH_2)_{10}]^{6+}$ possess a characteristic broad maximum at 1050nm ($\varepsilon = 300$ M^{-1} cm^{-1} per Mo_3), Figure 17. Band profile analysis indicates assignment to an intervalence charge-transfer transition within a class IIA mixed-valence system. [57, 59] Small but significant solvent shifts in the band maximum have been detected consistent with this assignment. The existence of stable 8 e^- mixed-valence $Mo_3{}^{III,III,IV}{}_{aq}$ forms in this family of clusters has been rationalized on the basis of Fenske-Hall type calculations which predict an available low lying empty M.O. largely non-bonding in character with respect to the M_3X_4 framework [62].

Studies carried out on the series of Mo(IV) clusters; $[Mo_3(\mu_3\text{-}X)(\mu\text{-}X)_3(OH_2)_9]^{4+}$ (X = O or S) have shown that for ready reduction a protonatable μ-O group is required, the ease of reduction decreasing with the introduction of μ-S for μ-O. In the case of $[Mo_3(\mu_3\text{-}S)(\mu\text{-}O)_3(OH_2)_9]^{4+}$ formation of the equivalent mixed valence $Mo_3{}^{III,III,IV}{}_{aq}$ ion requires reduction in 8.0M HCl, the more negative E^φ values and higher acidity required reflecting the reluctance of the capping μ_3-S group to protonate, Figure 16.

4.3.2. Oxidation

A number of kinetic studies have appeared describing oxidation of $[Mo_3(\mu_3\text{-}O)(\mu\text{-}O)_3(OH_2)_9]^{4+}$ to both Mo(V) and Mo(VI) aqua forms. Depending upon the oxidant either oxidation state can be the major product. Even with strong oxidants ($E^\varphi > 0.9V$) reactions are slow (s timescale) reflective of the mismatch between the structures of the aqua species of Mo(IV), Mo(V) and Mo(VI).

Table 3. Kinetic data for oxidation of $[Mo_3(\mu_3\text{-}O)(\mu\text{-}O)_3(OH_2)_9]^{4+}$
by various reagents[a]

Oxidant rate law[b]	parameters	Ref.
$[IrCl_6]^{2-}$ [f] kK_{aM} [Red] [Ox] / ($[H^+] + K_{aM}$)	$k = 4.5$ M^{-1} s^{-1}, $K_{aM}{}^d = 0.42$ M.	[63]
$VO^{2+}{}_{aq}$ [g] $(kK_{aM} + k'K_{aM}[H^+]^{-1})$ [Red] $[Ox]^2$ / ($[H^+] + K_{aM}$)	$k = 2.6 \times 10^3$ M^{-2} s^{-1}, $k' = 830$ M^{-1} s^{-1}, $K_{aM} = 0.19$ M.	[64]
$BrO_3{}^-$ [h] kKK_{aM} [Red] [Ox] / ($K_{aM} + [H^+] + KK_{aM}[Ox]$)	$k = 0.29$ s^{-1}, $K = 150$ M^{-1}, $K_{aM} = 0.18$ M	[64]
H_5IO_6 [i] same	$k = 44$ s^{-1}, $K = 70$ M^{-1}, $K_{aM} = 0.19$ M	[64]
$Fe(NCS)^{2+}$ [j] $(k_1 + k_2K_{Mo}[NCS^-])$ [Red] [Ox] /$(1 + K_{Fe}[NCS^-])(1 + K_{Mo}[NCS^-])[H^+]^2$	$k_1 = 0.19$ M^2 s^{-1}, $k_2 = 0.14$ M^2 s^{-1} $K_{Mo} = 300$ [e], $K_{Fe} = 138$ [e].	[64]

a - Reactions monitored at 25°C at 505nm except in the case of $Fe(NCS)^{2+}$ (460nm) and $[IrCl_6]^{2-}$ (300nm). b - Rate laws describe $-d(\ln[Mo_3O_4{}^{4+}{}_{aq}])/dt$. c - K values pertain to the $Mo_3O_4{}^{4+}{}_{aq}$-Ox association quotient. d – K_{aM} is the acid dissociation constant for $[Mo_3(\mu_3\text{-}O)(\mu\text{-}O)_3(OH_2)_9]^{4+}$. e - K values reported in ref. 65. f - I = 2.0M (Lipts). g - I = 1.2M (Napts). h - I = 2.0M (Napts). i - I = 1.2M (Napts). j - I = 0.1M (Napts).

In each case the rate laws possess strong $[H^+]^{-1}$ dependances implying involvement of the conjugate base form of $[Mo_3(\mu_3\text{-}O)(\mu\text{-}O)_3(OH_2)_9]^{4+}$ (K_{aM} values from $0.18 - 0.42$ M). Inner-sphere redox pathways are seem to predominate but one reaction with $[Fe(phen)_3]^{3+}$ appears to be outer-sphere. [63] The oxidation by aqueous Fe(III) is promoted by the addition of NCS⁻ and is presumed to involve an NCS⁻ bridged inner-sphere intermediate [64]. The rate constant for oxidation by $[IrCl_6]^{2-}$ (k $(25^\circ C) = 4.5$ M⁻¹ s⁻¹) is very close to typical values for ligand substitution on the conjugate base of $[Mo_3(\mu_3\text{-}O)(\mu\text{-}O)_3(OH_2)_9]^{4+}$ (e.g. NCS⁻; k_{OH} $(25^\circ C) = 4.8$ M⁻¹ s⁻¹) implying an inner-sphere process. [63] Table 3 summarizes some of the relevant kinetic data.

5. MOLYBDENUM(V)

5.1. Preparation and Properties of the Dimeric Ion: $[(Mo=O)_2(\mu\text{-}O)_2(OH_2)_6]^{2+}$

The yellow-orange oxo dimer $[(Mo=O)_2(\mu\text{-}O)_2(OH_2)_6]^{2+}$ was first reported by Ardon and Pernick in 1973. [66] The first preparations involved reactions of Klason's salt; $(NH_4)_2[Mo(=O)Cl_5]$, prepared by mild reduction of aqueous Mo(VI) in 12M HCl followed by addition of solid NH₄Cl. The salt retains its green color and paramagnetism when dissolved in 12M HCl. However on dilution to <2M $[H^+]$ a change to yellow-orange occurs with loss of the paramagnetism, from which a yellow-orange cation can be separated and purified by Dowex cation-exchange chromatography. Retention on the column required loading at $[H^+] <$ 0.2M suggesting a charge < 3+. Elution of the ion can be carried out with a >0.5M solution of any strong acid, including HClO₄. The dinuclear $(Mo=O)_2(\mu\text{-}O)_2^{2+}$ core structure was implied on the basis of redox and cryoscopic behavior and charge/Mo determinations. The reversible formation of the green color of $[Mo(=O)Cl_5]^{2-}$ upon saturating a solution of $[(Mo=O)_2(\mu\text{-}O)_2(OH_2)_6]^{2+}$ with HCl gas suggested retention of the Mo=O group in the dimer. Finally the $[(Mo=O)_2(\mu\text{-}O)_2(OH_2)_6]^{2+}$ formulation, Figure 18, was indicated via the ready formation of structural characterized derivatives with the same $(Mo=O)_2(\mu\text{-}O)_2^{2+}$ core upon simple treatment of the aqua ion with complexing ligands such as e.g. EDTA, $C_2O_4^{2-}$ and cysteinate under mild conditions.

In solutions ~6M in HCl a paramagnetic single-bridged chloro derivative $[(Mo=O)_2(\mu\text{-}O)Cl_8]^{4-}$, Figure 18, is also believed to exist. A convenient method for the direct synthesis of the $[(Mo=O)_2(\mu\text{-}O)_2(OH_2)_6]^{2+}$ is via reduction of solutions of aqueous Mo(VI) (e.g. Na₂MoO₄) in 2.0M HCl with hydrazine for 2 hours at 50°C followed by filtration, dilution to 0.1M $[H^+]$ and Dowex 50W X2 ion-exchange purification. Similarly, solutions $[(Mo=O)_2(\mu\text{-}O)_2(OH_2)_6]^{2+}$ can be readily prepared in high yield by aquation of the formato complex $[(Mo=O)_2(\mu\text{-}O)_2(\mu\text{-}HCO_2)(HCO_2)_4]^{3-}$ in a non-complexing acid followed by Dowex cation-exchange as described [67].

$[(Mo=O)_2(\mu\text{-}O)_2(\mu\text{-}HCO_2)(HCO_2)_4]^{3-}$ is itself made by treating a solution of $[Mo(=O)Cl_5]^{2-}$ with a mixture of ammonium formate and formic acid. [67] From a saturated Dowex 50W X2 column, elution of the ion with 2.0M $[H^+]$ can give solutions of $[(Mo=O)_2(\mu\text{-}O)_2(OH_2)_6]^{2+}$ up to ~ 0.2M.

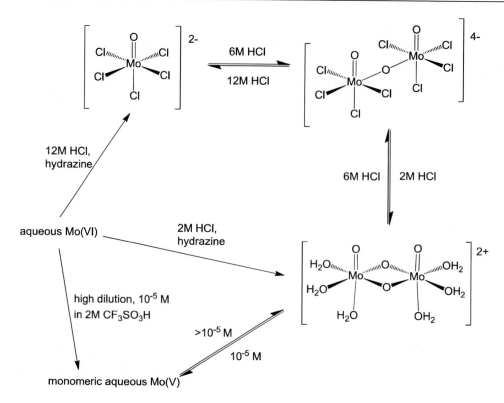

Figure 18. Scheme of reactions involving Mo(V)(aq) species.

Solutions of $[(Mo=O)_2(\mu-O)_2(OH_2)_6]^{2+}$ possess peak maxima at 384nm ($\varepsilon = 103$ M^{-1} cm^{-1} per Mo$_2$), 295 (3550) and 254 (4120). No crystal structure exists for the aqua ion itself although the crystal structure of $(pyH)_4[(Mo=O)_2(\mu-O)_2(NCS)_6].H_2O$ (N-bonded NCS$^-$) indicates non-equivalent isothiocyanate ligands, those Mo-NCS bonds *trans* to the Mo=O groups being longer (230pm) than those *trans* to μ-O (215pm). [68] As with $[Mo_3(\mu_3-O)(\mu-O)_3(OH_2)_9]^{4+}$ the diamagnetism within $[(Mo=O)_2(\mu-O)_2(OH_2)_6]^{2+}$ is presumed to arise through super exchange coupling of the Mo centers through the μ-O groups and/or direct Mo-Mo interaction (Mo-Mo = 256 pm, from EXAFS[12]). A pK_{aM} of >2 is implied by lack of changes to the electronic spectrum of $[(Mo=O)_2(\mu-O)_2(OH_2)_6]^{2+}$ in the [H$^+$] range 0.01-1.0 M. Above pH 2 a change to deeper orange is noticed prior to precipitation of the brown hydrous 'Mo(OH)$_5$'. A soluble polymeric form of aqueous Mo(V) has been reported. [69]

Monomeric aqueous Mo(V) exists under conditions of high dilution (1 x 10^{-5} M) from reversible cyclic voltammograms obtained from solutions of monomeric aqueous Mo(VI) ($[cis-Mo(=O)_2(OH_2)_4]^{2+}$ (section 6)) in 2.0M CF$_3$SO$_3$H. [70] The structure of the ion is presumed to be $[cis-Mo(=O)_2(OH_2)_4]^+$ (cf. structure of VO$_2^+$$_{aq}$). At higher concentrations rapid dimerization to $[(Mo=O)_2(\mu-O)_2(OH_2)_6]^{2+}$ occurs (k ~ 10^3 M^{-1} s^{-1}). The hydrolysis of mononuclear aqueous Mo(V) at high dilution in ClO$_4^-$ media has also been studied. [71] A green monooxo form of mononuclear Mo(V), Mo(=O)$^{3+}$$_{aq}$, is reported to be present in highly concentrated 16M MeSO$_3$H. [72] Dilution to 10M in MeSO$_3$H forms a darker green color assigned to a protonated form of dinuclear Mo(V)$_{aq}$; $[(Mo=O)_2(\mu-OH)_2(OH_2)_6]^{4+}$. Deprotonation of the μ-OH groups is anion dependent, occurring at <10M in MeSO$_3$H but only at <6M in Hpts. Here, as with the studies described above on $Mo(III)_{aq}$ and $Mo(IV)_{aq}$ species, pts⁻ shows itself as a non-innocent counter anion by being better than $MeSO_3^-$ at stabilizing the higher charge of the diprotonated $[(Mo^V=O)_2(\mu\text{-}OH)_2(OH_2)_6]^{4+}$ ion towards deprotonation through extensive ion-pair charge neutralization.

5.2. Complex Formation and Water Exchange on $[(Mo=O)_2(\mu\text{-}O)_2(OH_2)_6]^{2+}$

An ^{18}O labelling study by Murman [73] revealed fast exchange at the Mo=O groups ($t_{1/2}$ 4 mins, $0°C$) but much slower exchange at the μ-O groups ($t_{1/2}$ 100 hours, $40°C$, confirmed by Raman analysis). Further analysis of the μ-O exchange revealed a dependance of the form, k_{ex} = k $[H^+]^2$ implying a mechanism wherein double protonation of a μ-O group breaks the Mo-O-Mo bridge giving a fast exchanging water molecule. Aqueous Mo(VI), added as $Na_2[MoO_4]$, also promotes exchange at the μ-O atoms. The dependence is: k_{ex} = k_o + $k_1[Mo(VI)]$. In 0.3M HCl, $40°C$, k_o = 4.0 x 10^{-6} s^{-1}, $\Delta H_o^{\neq}$ = (108.3±6.6) kJ mol^{-1}, $\Delta S_o^{\neq}$ = (1.7±0.8) J K^{-1} mol^{-1} and k_1 = 4.6 x 10^{-2} M^{-1} s^{-1}. [73] The large value of $\Delta H_o^{\neq}$ reflects the Mo-O bond breaking process. The exchange process has also been studied by ^{17}O NMR. [36] ^{17}O NMR spectra obtained ($25°C$) following treatment of a solution of $[(Mo=O)_2(\mu\text{-}O)_2(OH_2)_6]^{2+}$ in 1.0M CF_3SO_3H with $H_2^{17}O$ (to a final ^{17}O enrichment of 5 atom %) are shown in Figure 18. Rapid appearance of a peak at 964 ppm (Mo=O), within the time taken to mix and recording one spectrum (5 mins), is followed by the slow appearance of a second peak at 582 ppm (μ-O) which reaches maximum height after 10 days. The $t_{1/2}$ of ~ 2 days under these conditions is consistent with that predicted by Murmann. [73]

The H_2O ligands exchange on the fast timescale ($k_{ex} > 10^3$ s^{-1}, $25°C$) and thus their ^{17}O resonances (expected ± 50 ppm from bulk H_2O) are unobservable (broadened into the baseline). The broad resonance at 159 ppm, Figure 19, is from the natural abundance non-exchanging $CF_3SO_3^-$ anion. Fast exchange of the H_2O ligands was predicted from complex formation studies which indicated fast equilibration requiring the use of relaxation techniques.

A T-jump kinetic study of the 1:1 equilibration of NCS⁻ with $[(Mo=O)_2(\mu\text{-}O)_2(OH_2)_6]^{2+}$ revealed an $[H^+]$ independent process with k_f = (2.9 ± 0.1) x 10^4 M^{-1} s^{-1}, $\Delta H_f^{\neq}$ = (47.2 ± 3.8) kJ mol^{-1}, $\Delta S_f^{\neq}$ = (-1.25 ± 13.0) J K^{-1} mol^{-1} and k_b = (120 ± 10) s^{-1}, $\Delta H_b^{\neq}$ = (57.3 ± 10.5) kJ mol^{-1}, $\Delta S_b^{\neq}$ = (-12.5 ± 33.4) J K^{-1} mol^{-1}, I = 2.0M, $LiClO_4$. [74] The kinetically determined K_{eq} (240 M^{-1}) compared well with the value obtained spectrophotometrically (250 ± 25 M^{-1}). A stopped-flow study has also been carried out. [75] The rate constants and activation parameters for the 1:1 NCS⁻ equilibration process support a mechanism similar to that occurring on $[Mo_2(OH_2)_8]^{4+}$ and VO^{2+}aq) wherein initial rapid complexation at the position trans to the Mo=O group is followed by slower isomerization to the equatorial positions. Rate constants are however somewhat faster than those occurring on VO^{2+}(aq) implying additional μ-O labilization of the equatorial positions. The faster exchange occurring at the M=O groups vs that on VO^{2+}(aq) also implies a labilization from the μ-O groups in the dimer structure. In the biological context, the interaction of $[(Mo=O)_2(\mu\text{-}O)_2(OH_2)_6]^{2+}$ with several nucleotides has been studied. [76] The terminal hydroxo derivative $(N_2H_5)_2[(Mo=O)_2(\mu\text{-}O)_2(OH)_4(OH_2)_2]$ has been used in the synthesis of carboxylate complexes of the $(Mo=O)_2(\mu\text{-}O)_2^{2+}$ core [77].

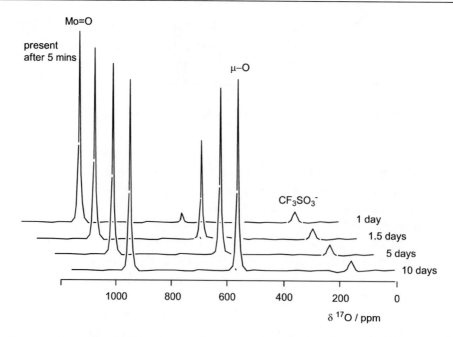

Figure 19. Stacked 54.24 MHz ^{17}O NMR spectra for a solution of [(Mo=O)$_2$(μ-O)$_2$(OH$_2$)$_6$]$^{2+}$ (0.05M) in 1.0M CF$_3$SO$_3$H / 0.1M Mn(CF$_3$SO$_3$)$_2$, 25°C, equilibrated with 5 atom % H$_2$^{17}O over a period of 10 days.

		X = S	X = S, Se
δ^{95}Mo /ppm from MoO$_4$$^{2-}$	544	722	974 (S)
Mo-Mo distance / pm	255	272	281 (S) 283 (Se)

Figure 20. Known dimeric units for Mo(V)(aq).

Substitution by S and Se occurs readily into the bridging μ-O positions of [(Mo=O)$_2$(μ-O)$_2$(OH$_2$)$_6$]$^{2+}$ with both (Mo=O)$_2$(μ-O)(μ-X)$^{2+}$ and (Mo=O)$_2$(μ-X)$_2$$^{2+}$ units structurally characterized in complexes, see next chapter.

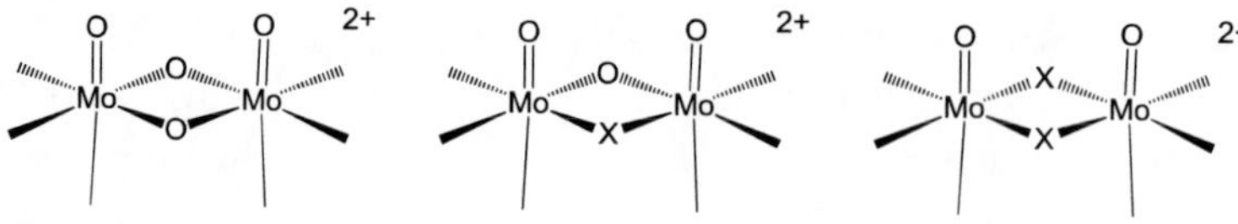

Substitution of μ-O by μ-S results in a downfield shift of 170 ppm in the ^{95}Mo NMR resonance per μ-O substituted, Figure 20, implying effective donation of σ-electron density from μ-S. [51] Each dimeric unit can be conveniently isolated as its respective l-cysteinato complex; [(Mo=O)$_2$(μ-X)$_2$(cysteinate)$_2$]$^{2-}$, either by reduction of aqueous Mo(VI) in HCl with hydrazine followed by the addition of either Na$_2$S.9H$_2$O (acidic pH) (mixed μ-O, μ-S) or H$_2$S (neutral pH) (all μ-S) [78] and then addition of l-cysteine, or alternatively, in the case of Se, reduction of aqueous Mo(VI) directly with HSe$^-$ (both μ-Se) and then addition of l-cysteine. Acid catalysed aquation of the appropriate l-cysteinate complex then gives the corresponding μ-X substituted Mo(V) aqua dimer. These species have proved useful 'lead-ins' to the synthesis of a range of incomplete cuboidal mixed O,S(Se)-bridged Mo(IV) trimers and some cuboidal tetramers, see next chapter. Although a number of Mo(V) species are known containing Mo=S groups, including some complexes of the $(Mo=S)_2(\mu-S)_2^{2+}$ core, no aqua ions exist with terminal Mo=S groups due to rapid replacement of Mo=S by Mo=O in the presence of H_3O^+.

5.3. Redox Reactions Involving $[(Mo=O)_2(\mu-O)_2(OH_2)_6]^{2+}$ and Related Species

Replacement of μ-O by μ-S above introduces a degree of stability towards oxidation to Mo(VI). The μ-Se analogues are intrinsically unstable thermodynamically due to ready loss of Se. Solutions of $[(Mo=O)_2(\mu-O)_2(OH_2)_6]^{2+}$ oxidise only slowly in the air but eventually colorless Mo(VI) is produced sometimes contaminated with an insoluble blue Mo(V,VI) mixed-valence polymer.

Reduction of $[(Mo=O)_2(\mu-O)_2(OH_2)_6]^{2+}$ yields the blue-green $[Mo_2(\mu-OH)_2(OH_2)_8]^{4+}$ in a $4e^-$ step and is a convenient route to its preparation. [35] $[Eu(OH_2)_7]^{2+}$ can also be used as a chemical reductant. [36, 67] The dimeric Mo(III) species resulting from reduction of the $[(Mo=O)_2(\mu-O,X)_2(OH_2)_6]^{2+}$ ions (X = S, Se) however seem not to have been fully characterized. Most kinetic studies have however concentrated on the Mo(V)-Mo(VI) oxidation process. Consistent with the structural mismatch, and the need for bond breaking, oxidation of aqueous Mo(V) is rather sluggish and requires quite powerful reagents for study.

The kinetics of oxidation of $[(Mo=O)_2(\mu-O)_2(OH_2)_6]^{2+}$ with MnO_4^-, [78] $[IrCl_6]^{2-}$, $[Fe(phen)_3]^{3+}$, [79] $VO_2^+(aq)$ [80] and various oxyhalogens [81] have been reported. Use of the strong oxidant MnO_4^- leads to the oxidant dependent rate law: $(k_1 + k_2K_p[H^+])[Mo(V)_2]$ $[MnO_4^-]$. [78] At 25°C, $k_1 = (5.4 \pm 0.4) \times 10^3$ M^{-1} s^{-1} and $k_2 = (2.4 \pm 0.2) \times 10^2$ M^{-1} s^{-1}. The $[H^+]$ dependence implies two parallel oxidation pathways for $[(Mo=O)_2(\mu-O)_2(OH_2)_6]^{2+}$ involving MnO_4^- and $HMnO_4$, $(K_p (MnO_4^- + H^+ \leftrightarrow HMnO_4) = 2.99 \times 10^3$ $M^{-1})$. With $[IrCl_6]^{2-}$ conventional monitoring at 487nm (loss of $[IrCl_6]^{2-}$) with $Mo(V)_2$ in excess leads to the rate law (15) containing a term zero order in oxidant (k_1). At 25°C, I = 2M, $LiClO_4$, $k_1 = (7.95 \pm$

$$-d([IrCl_6]^{2-})/2dt = k_1[Mo(V)_2][H^+]^{-1} + (k_2 + k_3[H^+]^{-1})[Mo(V)_2][IrCl_6]^{2-}] \qquad (15)$$

$0.13) \times 10^{-6}$ M s^{-1}, $k_2 = (0.114 \pm 0.012)$ M^{-1} s^{-1} and $k_3 = (0.052 \pm 0.003)$ s^{-1}. [79] A feature of both pathways is the strong $[H^+]^{-1}$ dependance. A similar rate law was found in the case of oxidation by $[Fe(phen)_3]^{3+}$, $k_1 = 3.09 \times 10^{-6}$ M s^{-1}, $k_2 = 31$ M^{-1} s^{-1} and $k_3 = 6$ s^{-1}. The similar k_1 values support a common oxidant independent process. [79] Both oxidant dependent processes are probably outer-sphere. With weaker oxidants such as the μ-superoxo complex $[Co_2(NH_3)_{10}(\mu-O_2^-)]^{5+}$ only the k_1 pathway $(k_1 = 4.3 \times 10^{-6}$ M $s^{-1})$ is observed. The oxidant independent process is believed to involve cleavage of one μ-O bridge to give the single μ-oxo ion $[(Mo=O)_2(\mu-O)(OH_2)_8]^{4+}$ which is then rapidly oxidized. Total bridge cleavage to give monomeric Mo(V)(aq) is not suggested on the basis of the slow rate of oxidation of the dimer by NO_3^-. The $[H^+]^{-1}$ dependence for k_1 is a surprising observation in view of the $[H^+]^2$ dependence observed for water exchange on the μ-O groups. [73].

Kinetic studies of the reduction of a number of oxyhalide species by $[(Mo=O)_2(\mu\text{-}O)_2(OH_2)_6]^{4+}$ have been reported. [81] The reactions of BrO_3^-, $HBrO_2$, $HClO_2$, and $HOCl$ with excess $Mo(V)_2$ yield the corresponding halide ions whereas the reduction of ClO_3^- yields Cl^-, even when the oxidant is in large excess. The reduction of excess H_5IO_6 rapidly generates IO_3^- which then undergoes further slow reduction to I_2. The reductions of BrO_3^- and ClO_3^- are independent of $[H^+]$ whereas the reduction of $HBrO_2$, $HClO_2$ and H_5IO_6 carry an $[H^+]^{-1}$ term. The $[H^+]$ independent reactions are believed to pass through $Mo(V)_2\text{-}XO_3$ intermediates. A similar intermediate $Mo(V)_2\text{-}ClOH$ is believed relevant to the hypochlorous acid reaction which then deprotonates prior to redox. A 1:1 complex between $[(Mo=O)_2(\mu\text{-}O)_2(OH_2)_6]^{4+}$ and VO^{2+}aq has been detected in aqueous $HClO_4$ media (I = 2M). For the observed stoichiometry $\frac{1}{2}[(Mo=O)_2(\mu\text{-}O)_2(OH_2)_6]^{2+}$ + VO^{2+}_{aq}, K_{eq} = 33 $M^{1/2}$. [82] A number of oxidations are catalyzed by $[(Mo=O)_2(\mu\text{-}O)_2(OH_2)_6]^{2+}$. The oxidation of excess Br^- to Br_3^- by ClO_3^- in the presence of $[(Mo=O)_2(\mu\text{-}O)_2(OH_2)_6]^{2+}$ is said to involve formation of a reactive Mo(VI) dimer in the rate determining step [83].

Flash photolysis of $[(Mo=O)_2(\mu\text{-}O)_2(OH_2)_6]^{2+}$ in aqueous $HClO_4$ / HCl media in the pH range 0.5 – 2.0 leads to disproportionation to give mononuclear Mo(VI) and hydrogen. [84] The single μ-oxo bridged Mo(V) dihydroxo ion $[(Mo=O)_2(OH)_2(\mu\text{-}O)(OH_2)_6]^{2+}$ has been suggested as the species that undergoes the disproportionation process (16).

$$\text{(16)}$$

6. CATIONIC MOLYBDENUM(VI) AQUA IONS

A number of cationic Mo(VI) aqua ions exist in non-complexing strongly acidic aqueous solution. In $\geq$6M aqueous $HClO_4$ the principal species is believed to be mononuclear cis-$[(Mo=O)_2(OH_2)_4]^{2+}$. [85] Between 0.2M and 3M $[H^+]$ a monomer-dimer equilibrium exists and the kinetics of this process have been investigated by Sykes and co-workers in I = 3.0M, $LiClO_4$ solution using the temperature-jump technique. [86] In this range of acidity, a singly positive cationic monomer is relevant which can be written as $HMoO_3^+$(aq) but most likely exists as cis-$[(Mo=O)_2(OH)(OH_2)_3]^+$. The principal pathway for the monomer-dimer equilibrium appears to be (17) with a minor contribution from (18). At 25°C, k_1 = (1.71 ± 0.1) x 10^5 M^{-1} s^{-1}, k_{-1} = (3.2 ± 0.2) x 10^3 s^{-1}, k_2 = (0.3 ± 0.3) x 10^5 M^{-1} s^{-1} and k_{-2} = (30 ± 20) s^{-1}. Krumenacker had earlier obtained independent evidence for dinuclear 2+ and 3+ cationic species in this acidity range. [87] Three dinuclear species were proposed following spectrophotometric studies by Cruywagen and co-workers in $HClO_4$ solution (0.5M - 3M) [88]. Evidence for dinuclear Mo(VI)(aq) species (Mo-O-Mo bridge) has also been obtained from Raman studies in 3M $HClO_4$. Bands were assigned respectively as 953 and 920 cm^{-1} (ν of cis-$(Mo=O)_2$), 825 (ν Mo-O-Mo) and 378 ($\delta(Mo=O)_2$). [89] The principal species under these conditions was deduced to be $[(cis\text{-}(Mo=O)_2)_2(\mu\text{-}O)(OH_2)_6]^{2+}$, Figure 21. Additional evidence for dinuclear $[(cis\text{-}(Mo=O)_2)_2(\mu\text{-}O)(OH_2)_6]^{2+}$ and mononuclear $[cis\text{-}(Mo=O)_2X_2(H_2O)_2]$ (X = Cl or Br) and [cis-$(Mo=O)_2Cl_4]^{2-}$ has been gained from ^{95}Mo NMR and vibrational spectra from solutions of Mo(VI) in aqueous HX. [90] $[(cis\text{-}(Mo=O)_2)_2(\mu\text{-}O)(OH_2)_6]^{2+}$ resonates at -63 ppm from $[MoO_4]^{2-}$ and appears to predominate in solutions up to 6M [H$^+$]. The $(cis\text{-}(Mo=O)_2)_2(\mu\text{-}O)^{2+}$ core is established in the complex $[(cis\text{-}(Mo=O)_2)_2(\mu\text{-}O)(C_2O_4)_2(OH_2)_2]^{2-}$.

$$2 \; cis\text{-}[(Mo=O)_2(OH)(OH_2)_3]^+ \; \underset{k_{-1}}{\overset{k_1}{\rightleftharpoons}} \; [(cis\text{-}(Mo=O)_2)_2(\mu\text{-}O)(OH_2)_6]^{2+} + H_2O$$

(17)

$$\begin{array}{c} cis\text{-}[(Mo=O)_2(OH)(OH_2)_3]^+ \\ + \\ cis\text{-}[(Mo=O)_2(OH_2)_4]^{2+} \end{array} \underset{k_{-2}}{\overset{k_2}{\rightleftharpoons}} [(cis\text{-}(Mo=O)_2)_2(\mu\text{-}OH)(OH_2)_6]^{3+} + H_2O$$

(18)

At pH 2 the principal species appears to be mononuclear. It is often written as 'Mo(OH)$_6$' (cf. 16) but is more probably the complex; $[cis\text{-}(Mo=O)_2(OH)_2(OH_2)_2]$.

The reduction of aqueous Mo(VI) with a number of metal reductants has been studied in detail in acidic media. [91] In each case the final product in weakly acidic solution is $[(Mo=O)_2(\mu\text{-}O)_2(OH_2)_6]^{2+}$. Mononuclear aqueous Mo(V) is said to be formed in some cases as a strongly absorbing intermediate as a result of dissociation from an initially formed Mo(VI)-O(H)-red. precursor species.

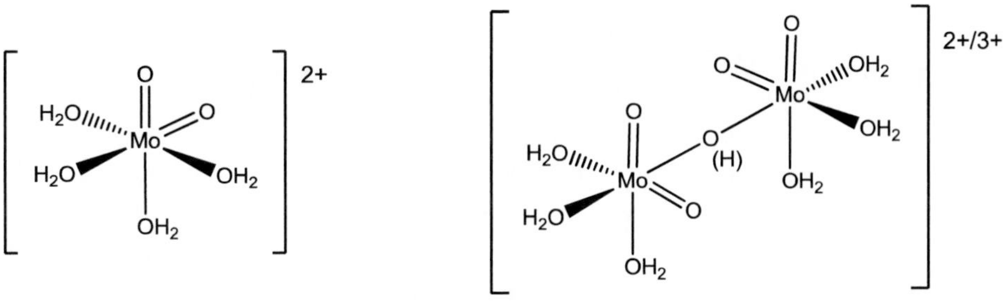

Figure 21. Structures of Mo(VI) cations in strongly acidic solution.

REFERENCES

[1]   Sykes, A. G. in *Comprehensive Coordination Chemistry*, Wilkinson, G.; Gillard, R. D.; McCleverty, J. A.; Eds.; Pergamon, London, 1987, *5*, 1229.

[2]   (a) Richens, D. T. *The Chemistry of Aqua Ions*, Wiley, New York, NY, 1997, Chp. 6. (b) Richens, D. T.; Lincoln, S. F.; Sykes, A. G. in *Comprehensive Coordination Chemistry II,* McCleverty, J. A.; Meyer, T. J.; Eds.; Elsevier-Pergamon, London, 2004, *1.25*, 524. (c) Richens, D. T.; Sykes, A. G. *Comm. Inorg. Chem.* 1981, *1*, 141. (d) Richens, D. T.; Sykes, A. G. *Inorg. Synth.* 1985, *23*, 130. (e) Finholt, J. E.; Leupin, P.; Richens, D. T.; Sykes, A. G. in *Proceedings of the 4th International Conference on the*

Chemistry and Uses of Molybdenum, Barry, H. F.; Mitchell, P. C. H.; Eds.; Amax Corporation, 1982, 98.

[3]   Cotton, F. A.; Walton, R. A. *Multiple Bonds between Metal Atoms;* Wiley, New York, NY, 1982.

[4]   Bowen, A. R.; Taube, H. *Inorg. Chem.* 1974, *13*, 2245.

[5]   Brignole, A. B.; Cotton, F. A. *Inorg. Synth.* 1972, *13*, 88.

[6]   Brencic, J. V.; Cotton, F. A. *Inorg. Chem.* 1970, *9*, 351.

[7]   Cotton, F. A.; Bertram, F. A.; Pedersen, E.; Webb, T. E. *Inorg. Chem.* 1975, *14*, 391.

[8]   Bino, A.; Gibson, D. *J. Am. Chem. Soc.* 1980, *102*, 4277.

[9]   Lohmann, K. H.; Young, R. C. *Inorg. Synth.* 1953, *4*, 97.

[10]   Lewis, J.; Nyholm, R. S.; Smith, P. W. *J. Chem. Soc. A,* 1969, 57.

[11]   Richens, D. T. *unpublished results;* 1985.

[12]   Cramer, S. P.; Eidem, P. K.; Paffett, M. T.; Winkler, J. R.; Dori, Z.; Gray, H. B. *J. Am. Chem. Soc.* 1983, *105*, 799.

[13]   Gheller, S. F.; Hambley, T. W.; Brownlee, R. C.; O'Connor, M. J.; Snow, M. R.; Wedd, A. G. *J. Am. Chem. Soc.* 1983, *105*, 1527.

[14]   Minelli, M.; Enemark, J. H.; Brownlee, R. C.; O'Connor, M. J.; Wedd, A. G. *Coord. Chem. Revs.* 1985, *68*, 169.

[15]   Finholt, J. E.; Leupin, P.; Sykes, A. G. *Inorg. Chem.* 1983, *22*, 3315.

[16]   Cotton, F. A.; Frenz, B. A.; Webb, T. R. *J. Am. Chem. Soc.* 1973, *95,* 4431.

[17]   Pernick, A.; Ardon, M. *J. Am. Chem. Soc.* 1975, *97*, 1255.

[18]   Bino, A. *Inorg. Chem.* 1981, *20*, 623.

[19]   Trogler, W. R.; Erwin, D. K.; Geoffroy, G. L.; Gray, H. B. *J. Am. Chem. Soc.* 1978, *100*, 1160.

[20]   Bowen, A. R.; Taube, H. *J. Am. Chem. Soc.* 1971, *93*, 3287.

[21]   Sasaki, Y.; Sykes, A. G. *Dalton Trans.* 1975, 1048.

[22]   Brorson, M.; Schaffer, C. *Acta. Chem. Scand. A.* 1986, *40*, 358.

[23]   Hills, E. F.; Sykes, A. G. *Polyhedron* 1986, *5*, 511.

[24]   Mayer, J. M.; Abbott, E. H. *Inorg. Chem.* 1983, *22*, 2774.

[25]   Brorson, M.; Gajhede, M. *Inorg. Chem.* 1987, *26,* 2109.

[26]   Richens, D. T.; Harmer, M. A.; Sykes, A. G. *Dalton Trans.* 1984, 2099.

[27]   Richens, D. T.; Ducommun, Y.; Merbach, A. E. *J. Am. Chem. Soc.* 1987, *109*, 603.

[28]   Verma, V. K.; Prasad, K. M. *Aryabhata Res. J. Phys. Sci.* 2004, *7*, 65.

[29]   Kelly, H. M.; Richens, D. T; Sykes, A. G. *Dalton Trans.* 1984, 1229.

[30]   Hills, E. F.; Norman, P. R.; Ramasami, T.; Richens, D. T.; Sykes, A. G. *Dalton Trans.* 1986, 157.

[31]   (a) Eigen M. *Z. Electrochem.* 1960, *64*, 115. (b) Fuoss, R. M. *J. Am. Chem. Soc.* 1958, *80*, 5059.

[32]   Helm, L.; Merbach, A. E. *Chem. Revs.* 2005, *105*, 1923.

[33]   (a) Millan, C.; Diebler, H. *Dalton Trans.* 1988, 2397. (b) Diebler, H.; Millan, C. *Polyhedron* 1986, *5*, 539.

[34]   Ketchum, P. A.; Taylor, R. C.; Young, D. C. *Nature, London* 1976, *259*, 202.

[35]   Ardon, M.; Pernick, A. *Inorg. Chem.* 1974, *13*, 2276.

[36]   Richens, D. T.; Helm, L.; Pittet, P. -A.; Merbach, A. E. *Inorg. Chim. Acta* 1987, *132*, 85.

[37] Proyavkin, A. A.; Dementiev, I. A.; Kozin, A. O.; Kondratiev, Y. V.; Korolkov, D. V. *Mend. Comm.* 2003, *6*, 252.

[38] Harmer, M. A.; Sykes, A. G. *Inorg. Chem.* 1981, *20*, 3963.

[39] Chalilpoyil, P.; Anson, F. C. *Inorg. Chem.* 1978, *17*, 2418.

[40] Paffett, M. T.; Anson, F. C. *Inorg. Chem.* 1984, *23*, 1996.

[41] Souchay, P.; Cadiot, M.; Duhameaux, M. *C. R. Hebd. Seances Acad. Sci.* 1966, *262*, 1524.

[42] Ojo, J. F.; Sasaki, Y.; Taylor, R. S.; Sykes, A. G. *Inorg. Chem.* 1976, *15*, 1006.

[43] Ardon, M.; Bino, A.; Yahaw, G. *J. Am. Chem. Soc.* 1976, *98*, 2338.

[44] Cramer, S. P.; Gray, H. B. *J. Am. Chem. Soc.* 1979, *101*, 2770.

[45] see e.g. Bino, A.; Cotton, F. A.; Dori, Z. *J. Am. Chem. Soc.* 1979, *101*, 3842.

[46] (a) Murmann, R. K.; Shelton, M. E. *J. Am. Chem. Soc.* 1980, *102*, 3984. (b) Schlemper, E. O.; Hussain, M. S.; Murmann, R. K. *Cryst. Struct. Comm.* 1982, *11*, 89.

[47] Richens, D. T.; Helm, L.; Pittet, P. -A.; Merbach, A. E.; Nicolo, F.; Chapuis, G. *Inorg. Chem.* 1989, *28*, 1394.

[48] (a) Bursten, B. E.; Cotton, F. A.; Hall, M. B.; Najjar, R. C. *Inorg. Chem.* 1982, *21*, 302. (b) Cotton, F. A; Fang, X. *Inorg. Chem.* 1991, *30*, 3666. (c) Cotton, F. A. *Polyhedron* 1986, *5*, 3.

[49] (a) Wendan, C.; Qianer, Z.; Jinshun, H.; Jia-xi, L. *Polyhedron* 1989, *8*, 2785. (b) Li, J.; Liu, C. -W.; Jia-xi, L. *Polyhedron* 1994, *13*, 1841.

[50] Cotton, F. A.; Marler, D. O.; Schwotzer, W. *Inorg. Chem.* 1984, *23*, 3671.

[51] Lente, G.; Dobbing, A. M.; Richens, D. T. *Inorg. React. Mech.* 1998, *1*, 3.

[52] Ooi, B. -L.; Sykes, A. G. *Inorg. Chem.* 1988, *27*, 310.

[53] Richens, D. T.; Pittet, P. -A.; Merbach, A. E.; Humanes, M.; Lamprecht, G. J.; Ooi, B. -L.; Sykes, A. G. *Dalton Trans.* 1993, 2305.

[54] Shibahara, T.; Sasaki, M.; Sakane, G. *Inorg. Chim. Acta* 1995, *237*, 1.

[55] Kathirgamanathan, P.; Soares, A. B.; Richens, D. T.; Sykes, A. G. *Inorg. Chem.* 1985, *24*, 2950.

[56] Samsonenko, D. G.; Gerasko, O. A.; Virovets, A. V.; Fedin, V. P. *Russ. Chem. Bull.* 2005, *54*, 1557.

[57] (a) Richens, D. T.; Sykes, A. G. *Inorg. Chim. Acta* 1981, *54*, L3. (b) Richens, D. T.; Sykes, A. G. *Inorg. Chem.* 1982, *21*, 418. (c) Paffett, M. T.; Anson, F. C. *Inorg. Chem.* 1983, *22*, 1347.

[58] Hills, E. F.; Sykes, A. G. *Dalton Trans.* 1987, 1397.

[59] Richens, D. T.; Guille-Photin, C. G. *Dalton Trans.* 1990, 407.

[60] Rodgers, K. R.; Murmann, R. K.; Schlemper, E. O.; Shelton, M. E. *Inorg. Chem.* 1985, *24*, 1313.

[61] Ghosh, S. P.; Gould, E. S. *Inorg. Chem.* 1993, *32*, 864.

[62] (a) Muller, A.; Jostes, R.; Cotton, F. A. *Angew. Chem. Intl. Ed. Eng.* 1980, *19*, 875. (b) Cotton, F. A.; Shang, M.; Sun, Z. S. *J. Am. Chem. Soc.* 1991, *113*, 3007.

[63] Harmer, M. A.; Richens, D. T.; Soares, A. B.; Thornton, A. T.; Sykes, A. G. *Inorg. Chem.* 1981, *20*, 4155.

[64] Ghosh, S. P.; Gould, E. S. *Inorg. Chem.* 1991, *30*, 3662.

[65] Carlyle, D. W.; Espenson, J. H. *J. Am. Chem. Soc.* 1969, *91*, 599.

[66] Ardon, M.; Pernick, A. *Inorg. Chem.* 1973, *12*, 2484.

[67] Brorson, M.; Hazell, A. *Acta Chem. Scand.* 1991, *45*, 758.

[68] Cayley, G. R.; Sykes, A. G. *Inorg. Chem.* 1976, *15*, 2882.

[69] Armstrong, F. A.; Sykes, A. G. *Polyhedron* 1982, *1*, 109.

[70] Paffett, M. T.; Anson, F. C. *Inorg. Chem.* 1981, *20*, 3967.

[71] Nabivanets, B. I.; Gorina, D. O. *Zh. Neorg. Khim.* 1984, *29*, 1738.

[72] Kim, C. S.; Kim, C. W.; Kwon, C. Y.; Yi, M. P. *Taehan Hwahakhoe Chi.* 1985, *29*, 510.

[73] Murmann, R. K. *Inorg. Chem.* 1980, *19*, 1765.

[74] Sasaki, Y.; Taylor, R. S.; Sykes, A. G. *Dalton Trans.* 1975, 396.

[75] Kim, C. S.; Lee, J. H. *Taehan Hwahakhoe Chi.* 1987, *31*, 344.

[76] Iwata, R.; Nagasawa, A.; Sasaki, Y. *Nippon Kagaku Kaishi* 1988, 604.

[77] Klimov, O. V.; Fedotov, M. A.; Kochubei, D. I.; Degtyarev, S. P.; Startsev, A. N. *Russ. J. Coord. Chem.* 1995, *21*, 678.

[78] McAllister, R.; Hicks, K. W.; Hurless, M. A.; Thurston Pittenger, S.; Gedridge, R. W. *Inorg. Chem.* 1982, *21*, 4098.

[79] Cayley, G. R.; Taylor, R. S.; Wharton, R. K.; Sykes, A. G. *Inorg. Chem.* 1977, *16*, 1377.

[80] (a) Martire, D. O.; Feliz, M. R.; Capparelli, A. L. *Polyhedron* 1991, *10*, 359. (b) Kim, C. S.; Yi, M. P. *Bull. Kor. Chem. Soc.* 1986, *7*, 483.

[81] Linn, Jr., D. E.; Ghosh, K.; Gould, E. S. *Inorg. Chem.* 1989, *28*, 3225.

[82] Martire, D. O.; Feliz, M. R.; Capparelli, A. L. *Trans. Met. Chem.* 1994, 19, 154.

[83] Villata, L. S.; Martire, D. O.; Capparelli, A. L. *J. Mol. Catal. A: Chem.* 1995, *99*, 143.

[84] Gonzalez, M. C.; Feliz, M. R.; San Roman, E.; Capparelli, A. L. *J. Photochem. Photobiol. A.: Chem.* 1989, *48*, 69.

[85] Burclova, J.; Prasilova, J.; Bines, P. *J. Inorg. Nucl. Chem.* 1973, *35*, 909.

[86] Ojo, J. F.; Taylor, R. S.; Sykes, A. G. *Dalton Trans.* 1975, 500.

[87] Krumenacker, L. *Ann. Chim.* 1972, *7*, 425.

[88] Cruywagen, J. J.; Heyns, J. B. B.; Rohwer, E. F. C. H. *J. Inorg. Nucl. Chem.* 1978, *40*, 53.

[89] Himeno, S.; Hasegawa, M. *Inorg. Chim. Acta* 1984, *83*, L5.

[90] Coddington, J. M.; Taylor, M. J. *Dalton Trans.* 1990, 41.

[91] Yang, Z.; Gould, E. S. *Dalton Trans.* 2006, 3427.

In: Molybdenum
Editor: Alvin A. Holder

ISBN: 978-1-62417-272-4
© 2013 Nova Science Publishers, Inc.

Chapter 5

INCOMPLETE AND COMPLETE CUBOIDAL CLUSTERS OF MOLYBDENUM

Rita Hernández-Molina[1], Maxim N. Sokolov[2,3] and Pavel A. Abramov[2,3]

[1]Departamento de Química Inorgánica, Facultad de Farmacia, La Laguna, Tenerife, Spain
[2]Nikolaev Institute of Inorganic Chemistry, Russian Academy of Sciences, Novosibirsk, Russia
[3]Novosibirsk State University, Novosibirsk, Russia

ABSTRACT

Numerous studies on metal-chalcogenide cluster complexes have provided exciting developments which relate to many fields of chemical research. Fe_4S_4 was the first cluster to be identified in the proteins, and Fe–S clusters constitute major components of biological electron transport chains. It is remarkable that alongside Fe only Mo provide a similar range of robust cuboidal clusters $\{Mo_4Q_4\}$. What is much more important is the existence of the so-called incomplete cuboidal clusters $\{Mo_3Q_4\}$, first isolated by controlled oxidation of cuboidal clusters with the loss of one of the metal sites, and which are now available by various synthetic routes in high yields. These incomplete cuboidal clusters can incorporate more than twenty chalcophilic transition and post-transition metals in low oxidation states giving rise to unique family of heterometal clusters $\{Mo_3M'Q_4\}$. This review summarizes synthesis, chemical properties and possible application of these clusters.

LIST OF ABBREVIATIONS

Cp = cyclopentadienyl,
Cp* = pentamethylcyclopentadienyl;
MeCp = methylcyclopentadienyl
cys = cysteinate (2-)
pts = p-toluenesulfonate

Hnta = nitrilotriacetate (2-)

H$_2$ida = iminodiacetate

dien = diethylenetriamine

taci = 1,3,5-triamino-1,3,5-tri-deoxy-cis-inositol

tacn = triazacyclononane

pz = pyrazolyl (1-)

Acac = acetylacetonate

ox = oxalate

py = pyridine

dmpe = 1, 2-bis(dimethylphosphine)ethane

dppe = 1,2 –bis(diphenylphosphine)ethane

diphosph = 1,2 – diphosphine (any bidentate)

dtp = dithiophosphate (RO)$_2$PS$_2^-$

lac = lactate (1-)

AcO = acetate

edta = ethylendiaminetetracetate (4-)

NCS = isothiocyanate

TCNQ = 7,7',8,8'-tetracyanoquinodimethane

Dba = dibenzylideneacetone

cod = 1,5- cyclooctadiene

POM = polyoxometalate

OTf = triflate, CF$_3$SO$_3$

1. INTRODUCTION

This chapter is devoted to incomplete and complete cuboidal clusters of molybdenum with chalcogens (Q = S, Se, Te) in the cluster core. Most of the research in this area has been performed since the mid-1980s and has been the subject of numerous reviews. [1-9]. This chapter covers new developments in the field of the last 10 years with emphasis in the synthesis, structure, stability, reactivity, core rearrangements and interconversions.

2. TRINUCLEAR CLUSTERS WITH MO$_3$Q$_4^{4+}$ CORE

This is the most studied single family of clusters of all the early transition metals. The first cluster reported as having this core was the cyclopentadienyl derivative [η^5-(C$_5$H$_5$)$_3$Mo$_3$S$_4$][Me$_3$SnCl$_2$] serendipitously obtained. [10] The field laid dormant for the next ten years, until aqua complex [Mo$_3$S$_4$(H$_2$O)$_9$]$^{4+}$ was reported independently by Shibahara and Cotton groups. In subsequent works by Shibahara, Cotton, Llusar, Sykes, Hernandez-Molina, Fedin, Sokolov, Lu, and other groups a vast number of clusters based on the {Mo$_3$S$_4$}$^{4+}$ core with various ligands have been prepared. The Mo$_3$S$_4^{4+}$ cluster core belongs to the M$_3$(μ$_3$-Q)(μ$_2$-Q)$_3$ type, which contains a triangular metal cluster M$_3$ and four chalcogenide ligands (one μ$_3$-Q and three μ$_2$-Q). Numerous examples of sulfide and selenide clusters of molybdenum are known, but only one Mo$_3$Te$_4^{4+}$ cluster has been reported so far. [11] The number of valence electrons available for metal - metal bonding is 6 (i.e., there are *formally* three two-electron bonds), which are supplied by three Mo^{IV} centers (d^2 configuration). If the M-M bonds are ignored, the metal coordination polyhedron is a distorted octahedron. Alternatively, this cluster core can be referred to as one-metal depleted or incomplete cube. The most up-to-date treatment of the bonding in the Mo$_3$S$_4$$^{4+}$ cluster has unambiguously identified the {Mo$_3$S$_4$} unit as a chemical entity in the first ELF bifurcation diagram. Increasing the Z(r) value separates the Mo–S and S valence domains from that of the {Mo$_3$} core, which further splits into three disynaptic V(Mo, Mo) basins and one trisynaptic V(Mo, Mo, Mo) basin. Calculations of the basin populations and their covariances suggest the existence of a delocalized Mo-(μ_2-S)-Mo bond. [12, 13] This delocalization was hinted at by earlier semiempirical calculations which show extensively delocalized Mo(d)–S(p$_\pi$) bonding, which results in a continuous closed d–p$_\pi$ system, Mo$_3$(μ_2-S)$_3$, with strong interactions between the localized Mo–(μ_2-S)–Mo three-center-two-electron bonds. This delocalization has been referred to as "quasi-aromaticity". This idea has also been supported by Hartree–Fock *ab initio* calculations. [14-18] An explanation of main features of the reactivity pattern of the {Mo$_3$S$_4$}$^{4+}$ clusters based on the application of this "quasi-aromaticity" concept of the {Mo$_3$S$_3$} "heterocycle" was put forward in [19]. Already the simplified MO picture of the Mo-Mo bonding assigns the three Mo–Mo bonds to the occupation of three molecular orbitals of symmetry a$_1$ (HOMO-1) and e (HOMO) which gives the 6 e count. The large energy gap between the bonding e "HOMO" and "LUMO" (2a$_1$ non-bonding or weakly (anti)bonding) orbitals strongly disfavors a seven- or eight-electron population for the {Mo$_3$S$_4$} core, [23] but these states, and even most reduced nine-electron states, can be achieved electrochemically in many real complexes. As for stable reduced species, only few examples have been reported – the seven-electron [Cp*$_3$Mo$_3$S$_4$] [24] and [Mo$_3$S$_4$Cl$_3$(dppe)$_2$(PEt$_3$)] [25]. In a more general context the clusters with the {Mo$_3$Q$_4$} cluster core belong to the family of [M$_3$X$_{13}$] as represented in Scheme 1, and the structure can be described as consisting of three MX$_6$ octahedra, fused together so that each octahedron shares one vertex (μ_3-X) and two edges (the μ_2-X) ligands. In this way each metal atom has three terminal ligands which are easily exchangeable. This type of clusterization is common for early transition metals and does not necessary involve M-M bonding, as it occurs in polyoxometalates and ultimately can be reduced to fragments of one layer in CdX$_2$ (X = Cl, I) structural type. [26] (Scheme 1).

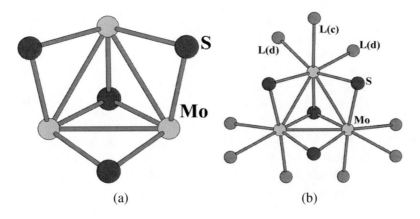

(a)   (b)

Scheme 1. (Continued).

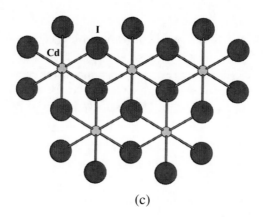

(c)

Scheme 1. a) The {Mo₃S₄} cluster core; b) The same cluster core with its coordination sphere; L(d) are the ligands trans to μ_2-S and L(c) are the ligands trans to μ_3-S; c) a fragment of a layer in the CdI₂ structure type.

2.1. Aqua Complexes [Mo₃Q₄(H₂O)₉]⁴⁺

The aqua complexes $[Mo_3Q_4(H_2O)_9]^{4+}$ are convenient starting materials for preparation of other $\{Mo_3Q_4\}^{4+}$ derivatives with almost any desired ligand. Several efficient methods for the preparation of green $[Mo_3S_4(H_2O)_9]^{4+}$ and brown $[Mo_3Se_4(H_2O)_9]^{4+}$ have been developed. The most efficient synthetic protocol involves sulfur abstraction from the Q_2 bridges in the chalcogen-rich clusters $[Mo_3(\mu_3\text{-}Q)(\mu\text{-}Q_2)_3X_6]^{2-}$ (X = Cl, Br) with PPh₃. [27] These salts in turn can be accessed from polymeric chalcohalides $Mo_3Q_7X_4$ which are made from the elements at 350°. Conversion into the anionic clusters is achieved under harsh conditions (PPh₄Br melt, mechanochemical activation, microwave activation). [28] The X⁻ in $[Mo_3(\mu_3\text{-}Q)(\mu\text{-}Q_2)_3X_6]^{2-}$ can be aquated in 4 M Hpts (pts⁻ = p-toluenesulphonate), and the resulting aqua complex $[Mo_3Q_7(H_2O)_6]^{4+}$ can be converted into $[Mo_3Q_4(H_2O)_9]^{4+}$ by chalcogen abstraction with PPh₃ (Scheme 2) followed by purification of the resulting aqua complex by cation-exchange chromatography. Relevant equations are as follows:

$$Mo_3Q_7Br_4 + 2\ PPh_4Br = (Ph_4P)_2[Mo_3Q_7Br_6]\ (300°\ C)$$

$$(Ph_4P)_2[Mo_3Q_7Br_6] + 6\ H_2O = [Mo_3Q_7(H_2O)_6]^{4+} + 2\ Ph_4P^+ + 6\ Br^-$$

$$[Mo_3Q_7(H_2O)_6]^{4+} + 3PPh_3 + 3\ H_2O = [Mo_3Q_4(H_2O)_9]^{4+} + 3\ SPPh_3$$

The yields are almost quantitative. If Q = S, the sulfur abstraction with PPh₃ can be carried out without aquation in conc. HCl or HBr. Alternatively, the $[Mo_3S_7X_6]^{2-}$ complexes can be made from $(NH_4)_2[Mo_3S_7(S_2)_3]$, directly available from ammonium molybdate and polysulfide [29] in a one-pot self-assembly reaction in high yield. [30] Aqua complex $[Mo_3S_4(H_2O)_9]^{4+}$ can be stored over long periods (years!) in air, the only prerequisite being that [H⁺] should be above 0.3 M lest the conjugate-base forms and irreversible oligomerization becomes relevant. The selenide cluster $[Mo_3Se_4(H_2O)_9]^{4+}$ is less stable and slowly deposits red selenium. The aqua complexes can be isolated as para-toluenesulfonate salts, and crystal structures were reported for $[Mo_3S_4(H_2O)_9](pts)_4 \cdot 9H_2O$ and $[Mo_3Se_4(H_2O)_9](pts)_4 \cdot 10H_2O$. [31,32] Recently a mixed sulfide/selenide aqua complex, $[Mo_3(\mu_3\text{-}S)(\mu_2\text{-}Se)_3(H_2O)_9]^{4+}$, was isolated by treatment of a 4 M Hpts solution of $[Mo_3SSe_6Br_6]^{2-}$ with PPh$_3$ followed by cation-exchange chromatography [33].

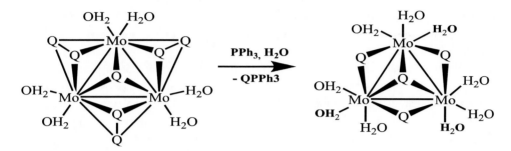

Scheme 2. Transformation of $[Mo_3Q_7(H_2O)_6]^{4+}$ into $[Mo_3Q_4(H_2O)_9]^{4+}$ [27].

The complete range of mixed $[Mo_3O_nQ_{4-n}(H_2O)_9]^{4+}$ (n = 0-4) aqua ions is also known. In all known mixed O/Q clusters the capping position is always occupied by the chalcogen atom. DFT calculations show that for the $[Mo_3S_2O_2(H_2O)_9]^{4+}$ species the $[Mo_3(\mu_3\text{-}S)(\mu\text{-}O)_2(\mu\text{-}S)(H_2O)_9]^{4+}$ isomer is more stable than the hypothetical $[Mo_3(\mu_3\text{-}O)(\mu\text{-}O)(\mu\text{-}S)_2(H_2O)_9]^{4+}$ isomer. [34] These species were initially obtained as by-products from the preparations of $[Mo_3Q_4(H_2O)_9]^{4+}$ by reduction of $[Mo_2O_2Q_2(cys)_2]^{2-}$ in low yields. [35,36] Later, more efficient and selective methods have been developed for preparations of individual members of this series. The most easily accessible member of the family is $[Mo_3S_2O_2(H_2O)_9]^{4+}$ which can be obtained from $[Mo_2S_2O_2(H_2O)_6]^{2+}$ and Mo(CO)$_6$ at 140 °C in 2 M HCl.[34] Replacing Mo(CO)$_6$ with [Re(CO)$_5$Cl] or/and rising temperature to 160° C cleanly gives $[Mo_3SO_3(H_2O)_9]^{4+}$. [37] Good yields of $[Mo_3S_2O_2(H_2O)_9]^{4+}$ and $[Mo_3SO_3(H_2O)_9]^{4+}$ can be obtained by reaction of respectively $[Mo_2S_2O_2(cys)_2]^{2-}$ or $[Mo_2SO_3(cys)_2]^{2-}$ with $[MoCl_6]^{3-}$. [35] $[Mo_3S_4(H_2O)_9]^{4+}$ itself can be a source of the mixed O/S bridged species since it reacts with a large excess of NaBH$_4$ to give predominantly $[Mo_3OS_3(H_2O)_9]^{4+}$ together with only a small amount of other species. [38] Crystal structure of $[Mo_3OS_3(H_2O)_9](pts)_4 \cdot 7H_2O$ has been determined. [39] Among the selenide species, $[Mo_3SeO_3(H_2O)_9]^{4+}$ is selectively obtained from $[MoOCl_5]^{2-}$ and H$_2$Se (generated $in\ situ$ from ZnSe and HCl) at 140°C in 4M HCl in 40% yield. [40] Other oxo selenide clusters can be prepared similarly to their sulfide analogues.

Substitution of water molecules in aqua complexes $[M_3Q_4(H_2O)_9]^{4+}$ has been studied in detail by the Sykes group. [41] The exchange of the coordinated water in $[Mo_3S_4(H_2O)_9]^{4+}$ was studied by ^{17}O NMR technique. Different exchange rates were observed for the ligands in non-equivalent positions. The exchange rate of the molecules in trans-positions relatively to the μ_3-sulfur atom (c-H$_2$O) is two orders of magnitude slower than that for the water molecules in the cis-position relatively to μ_3-S (d-H$_2$O). It was suggested that the conjugated base $[Mo_3S_4(H_2O)_8(OH)]^{3+}$ (K_a 0.18 mol·l^{-1}, 25 °C, I = 2.00 mol·l^{-1}) is formed in which the positions d rather than c are activated.[41] In hydrochloric acid, and depending on the concentration of HCl in the solution, equilibrium mixtures of aqua chloride complexes $[M_3Q_4(H_2O)_{9-x}Cl_x]^{(4-x)+}$ are produced up to $[Mo_3S_4(H_2O)_2Cl_7]^{3-}$. Despite the proven existence of $[Mo_3S_4F_9]^{5-}$ [42] attempts to isolate complexes with completely substituted anions

$[Mo_3S_4Cl_9]^{5-}$ have remained unsuccessful. The small value of the formation constant for the complex $[Mo_3S_4(H_2O)_8Cl]^{3+}$ (3.0) indicates low competitiveness of the chloride ligands in aqueous solutions. [43] At each given value of x, there is a set of isomers differing in the location of Cl$^-$ ligands with respect to the capping chalcogen. One of the three ligands occupies the *trans*-position (*c*) to μ_3-S, and the other two are in the *cis*-position (*d*). Experimental information on the extent of substitution of coordinated water with chloride ligands remained unavailable for a long time, for the attempts to isolate solid cluster complexes from hydrochloric acid solutions yielded only amorphous products. Application of a supramolecular approach based on the formation of complementary bonds between carbonyl groups of a macrocyclic cavitand cucurbit[6]uril (CB[6], $C_{36}H_{36}N_{24}O_{12}$) with water molecules of the aquachloro complexes has made it possible to isolate *individual* cluster complexes of the $[Mo_3S_4(H_2O)_{9-x}Cl_x]^{(4-x)+}$ family from HCl solutions as supramolecular adducts, and structurally characterize them. [44] Cucurbit[6]uril with its D_{6h} symmetry and two identical C=O fringed portals with six oxygen atoms in each is almost ideally suited for the role of second-sphere ligand for these species.

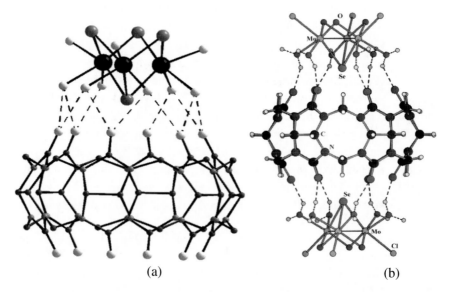

(a)   (b)

Figure 1. (a) 1:1 supramolecular adduct (b) 2:1 supramolecular adduct in the structure of {[Mo$_3$(μ_3-Se)(μ-O)$_3$(H$_2$O)$_6$Cl$_3$]$_2$CB[6]}Cl$_2\cdot$15H$_2$O [40].

If there are at least six water ligands of the *d*-type (e.g. $x \leq 3$), they can form twelve hydrogen bonds, the water ligands acting as hydrogen bond donors and the carbonyl oxygen atoms of the CB[6] molecule as acceptors. In spite of the fact that the energy of each individual hydrogen bond is low, extensive complementary hydrogen bonding is responsible for formation of very stable supramolecular associates.

These compounds are insoluble in aqueous solutions of HCl and crystallize from dilute (10^{-3}-10^{-4} M) solutions of the clusters, the property which greatly facilitates characterization of species, obtained in low yield and/or present in low concentrations.

The cluster-to-CB[6] ratio in the resulting supramolecules can be either 1 : 1 or 2 : 1 (Figure 1); in the latter case the cavity in the cucurbit[6]uril molecule is effectively closed by cluster "lids", and small molecules or ions (Cl$^-$, H$_2$O, PyH$^+$) can be trapped inside. The size of supramolecules closed by two cluster "lids" is 25-30 Å. Use of larger and less soluble cucurbit[8]uril ($C_{48}H_{48}N_{32}O_{16}$, CB[8]) enabled isolation of other aquachloro complexes even when the complementarity is broken, because the inclusion of cluster aquachloro complexes in the large voids between closely packed large molecules of cucurbit[8]uril takes place, assisted by the additional stabilization by various hydrogen bonds [45-53] as outlined in Table 1.

Table 1.

Compound	Isomer	References
$\{[Mo_3S_4(H_2O)_7Cl_2]_2(CB[6])\}Cl_4 \cdot 13H_2O$	$1c2c$	45
$\{[Mo_3S_4(H_2O)_7Cl_2](CB[6])\}Cl_2 \cdot 10H_2O$	$1c2c$	46
$(H_3O)_2\{[Mo_3S_4(H_2O)_6Cl_3](CB[6])\}Cl_3 \cdot 9H_2O$	$1c2c3c$	47
$\{[Mo_3S_4(H_2O)_7Cl_2][Mo_3S_4(H_2O)_6Cl_3](pyH \subset CB[6])\}Cl_4 \cdot 17H_2O$	$1c2c, 1c2c3c$	48
$(H_3O)_4\{[Mo_3S_4(H_2O)_4Cl_5]_2(2C_6H_5PO(OH)_2 \subset CB[8])\}Cl_2 \cdot 8H_2O$	$1c2d^23cd$	49
$(H_3O)_2\{[Mo_3S_4(H_2O)_4Cl_5](CB[8])\}Cl \cdot 14H_2O$	$1c2cd3cd$	45
$(H_3O)_4\{[Mo_3S_4(H_2O)_3Cl_6]_2(8H_2O \subset CB[8])_3\} \cdot 44H_2O$	$1cd2cd3cd$	50
$(H_3O)_6\{[Mo_3S_4(H_2O)_3Cl_6]_2(CB[8])\}Cl_2 \cdot 12H_2O$	$1c2d^23cd^2$	50
$(H_3O)_8\{[Mo_3S_4(H_2O)_3Cl_6][Mo_3S_4(H_2O)_2Cl_7]$ $(CB[8])\}Cl[PdCl_4] \cdot 29H_2O$	$1cd2cd3d^2,$ $1cd2cd3cd^2$	50
$\{[Mo_3Se_4(H_2O)_8Cl]_2(CB[6])\}Cl_6 \cdot 16H_2O$	$1c$	51
$(H_3O)_2\{[Mo_3Se_4(H_2O)_6Cl_3](CB[6])\}Cl_3 \cdot 3.5H_2O$	$1c2c3c$	45
$(H_3O)_2\{[Mo_3Se_4(H_2O)_4Cl_5]_2(CB[6])\} \cdot 15H_2O$	$1d2cd3cd,$ $1d2cd3d^2$	51
$\{[Mo_3SSe_3(H_2O)_{7.5}Cl_{1.5}]_2(CB[6])\}Cl_5 \cdot 11H_2O$	$1c, 1c2c$	52
$(H_7O_3)_2(H_5O_2)[Mo_3S_4Cl_{6.25}Br_{0.25}(H_2O)_2](CB[6]) \cdot$ $CH_2Cl_2 \cdot 6H_2O$	$1cd2cd3d^2,$ $1cd2cd3cd^2$	53
$[(Ca(H_2O)_5)_2(CB[6])][Mo_3O_2S_2Cl_6(H_2O)_3]_2 \cdot 13H_2O$		53
$\{[Mo_3O_2S_2(H_2O)_6Cl_3]_2CB[6]\}Cl_2 \cdot 18H_2O$	$1c2c3c$	34
$\{[Mo_3(\mu_3-S)(\mu_2-O)_3(H_2O)_6Cl_3]_2CB[6]\}Cl_2 \cdot 10.88H_2O$	$1c2c3c$	37
$\{[Mo_3(\mu_3-Se)(\mu-O)_3(H_2O)_6Cl_3]_2CB[6]\}Cl_2 \cdot 15H_2O$	$1c2c3c$	40

2.2. Derivatization of $[Mo_3Q_4(H_2O)_9]^{4+}$

Anionic complexes with single-charged unidentate acido ligands $[Mo_3Q_4L_9]^{5-}$, where L is cyanide, thiocyanate, formate (in $K_4[Mo_3S_4(HCO_2)_8(H_2O)]$) [54] etc., are easily obtained from the aqua complexes by ligand substitution. The cyanide complexes can be also obtained from other sources, for example from $Mo_3Q_7Br_4$ and KCN or from MoS_3 and KCN by sulfur abstraction. Cyanide has high affinity for the M_3Q_4 core, and the $[Mo_3Q_4(CN)_9]^{5-}$ complexes are very stable [55-58].

The substitution of thiocyanate for coordinated water was studied in detail and following regularities were found: the substitution of μ_3-S and of μ_3-Se for μ_3-O on going from $[Mo_3O_4(H_2O)_9]^{4+}$ to $[Mo_3Se_4(H_2O)_9]^{4+}$ decreases the rate substitution in d-positions by 6 (S) and 11 (Se) orders of magnitude. The substitution in μ_2-bridging positions increases the substitution rate by 10 (for S) and 20 (for Se) orders of magnitude per each bridging atom. [36] The thiocyanates $[Mo_3Q_4(NCS)_9]^{5-}$ were obtained from the aqua complexes and in all cases N-coordination of potentially ambidentate NCS ligand was proven by X-ray crystallography [59-61].

The complexes with chelate O-, N-, P- and S-donor ligands are the most abundant. The complexes with oxalate, [62] iminodiacetate, [63-65,111,112] nitrilotriacetate, [66] belong to this family. Polyaminocarboxylates were the subject of fairly detailed studies.

A series of iminodiacetate (H_2ida) and nitrilotriacetate (H_3nta) complexes $[Mo_3S_xO_{4-x}(ida)_3]^{2-}$ and $[Mo_3S_xO_{4-x}(Hnta)_3]^{2-}$ was synthesised. The nitrilotriacetate is a tridentate ligand leaving one of its $-CH_2COOH$ arms free (Figure 2). In all isolated complexes with $Hnta^{2-}$ the nitrogen atoms occupy the *c*-positions respective to the capping sulfur. [63-66] Complex $[Mo_3S_4(Hnta)_3]^{2-}$ reacts with $LaCl_3$ to form a hybrid layered compound $La_{0.75}$ $[Mo_3S_4(Hnta)_3]Cl_{0.25} \cdot 18H_2O$.

The $[Mo_3S_4(Hnta)_3]^{2-}$ anions are directly connected to the La^{3+} cations and resulting hexagonal network possesses large channels (about 12 Å in diameter), filled by uncoordinated $[Mo_3S_4(Hnta)_3]^{2-}$ as "guest". [107] Hydrothermal synthesis from the same components affords $La_2Cl[Mo_3S_4(nta)_3] \cdot 17H_2O$ with a new 3D-network from $[Mo_3S_4(nta)_3]^{5-}$ anion and La^{3+} ions [108].

Complex $[Mo_3S_4(Hnta)_3]^{2-}$ acts as structuring agent steering the self-condensation process of the $[Mo_2O_2S_2(H_2O)_6]^{2+}$ cations to the largest oxothiomolybdenum ring $\{Mo_{18}O_{18}S_{18}(OH)_{18}\}$ so far known. In the crystal structure of $Cs_{4.7}(NMe_4)_{0.3}[Mo_{18}O_{18}S_{18}$ $(OH)_{18}(H_2O)_9(Mo_3S_4(nta)_3)] \cdot 36H_2O$ the ring $\{Mo_{18}O_{18}S_{18}(OH)_{18}\}$ acts as host templated by the $[Mo_3S_4(nta)_3]^{5-}$ guest [109].

Complexes with 1,3,5-triamino-1,3,5-tri-deoxy-cis-inositol (taci) and its hexa-N-methyl derivative were synthesised. Three linkage isomers with ligands coordinated in the N,N,N-, N,N,O-, and N,O,O-mode were identified in aqueous solution of $[Mo_3S_4(taci)_3]^{4+}$. [67] The tridentate ligand diethylenetriamine (dien) reacts with $[Mo_3S_4(H_2O)_9]^{4+}$ and $[Mo_3OS_3(H_2O)_9]^{4+}$ yielding $[Mo_3S_4(dien-H)(dien)_2]Cl_3 \cdot 4H_2O$ and $[Mo_3OS_3(dien-H)(dien)_2]Cl_3 \cdot 3H_2O$ where one of three dien ligands is deprotonated (dien-H). [68] Triazacyclononane yields $[Mo_3S_4(tacn)_3]^{4+}$. [69] Reactions of $[Mo_3S_4(H_2O)_9]^{4+}$ and $[Mo_3OS_3(H_2O)_9]^{4+}$ with $KHB(pz)_3$ result in the pyrazolylborate complexes $[Mo_3Q_4(HB(pz)_3)_3]^+$. [70] Due to partial hydrolysis of the ligand, oxo-bridged complex $[((HB(pz)_3)_2Mo_3S_4)_2(\mu-O)(\mu-pz)_2]$ is also formed. In this compound two cluster moieties are linked by an oxo-bridge, and by two pyrazolate ligands. [71] Complex of $\{Mo_3S_4\}^{4+}$ with a tridentate coordinated L-histidinate was reported. [72] Substituting acetylacetonate for coordinated water molecules in the presence of pyridine yields $[Mo_3Q_4(acac)_3py_3]^+$. [34,37,40,73] Oxalate and acetylacetonate complexes contain both bidentate ($C_2O_4^{2-}$ or acac) and monodentate (H_2O or py) ligands (Figure 3); the latter occupy only the *c*-positions. Solvent extraction technique allowed preparation of complexes of $\{Mo_3S_4\}^{4+}$, $\{Mo_3OS_3\}^{4+}$, $\{Mo_3O_2S_2\}^{4+}$ and $\{Mo_3O_3S\}^{4+}$ with 8-quinolinol and 5-chloro-8-quinolinol ligands from the auqa complexes, of general formula $[Mo_3Q_4(C_9H_6NO)_3(H_2O)_3]^+$ and $[Mo_3Q_4(C_9H_5ClNO)_3(H_2O)_3]^+$.

The nitrogen atom of the quinoline ring occupies the c-position *trans* to the μ_3-S. The d positions are occupied with H_2O and O from deprotonated quinolinol. In DMSO the coordinated water is replaced by the solvent and rotation of the ligand around the Mo-N bond leads to interchange between the pair of *d*-positions at each Mo site [81].

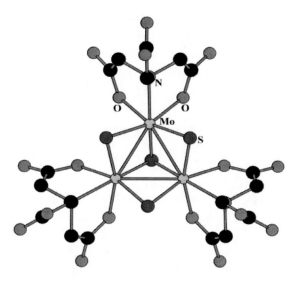

Figure 2. The structure of nitrilotriacetate complex $[Mo_3S_4(Hnta)_3]^{2-}$ [66].

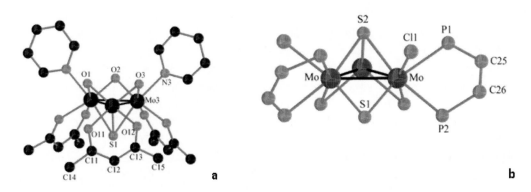

Figure 3. (a) The structure of $[Mo_3SO_3(acac)_3(py)_3]^+$ [37]; (b) $[Mo_3S_4(dppen)_3Cl_3]^+$.

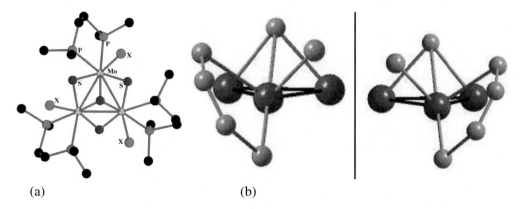

(a) (b)

Figure 4. (a) The structure of the $[Mo_3S_4(P-P)_3X_3]^+$ complexes; P-P a bidentate phosphine; b) origin of chirality on the diphosphine complexes.

A number of complexes with phosphine ligands have been prepared. Reaction of the polymeric $\{Mo_3Q_7X_4\}_x$ (Q = S, Se; X = Cl, Br) with mono- and bidentate phosphines is the standard way to access phosphine complexes with the $M_3Q_4^{4+}$ cores. In the complexes with bidentate phosphines one phosphorus atom always is in the *trans*-position and another in a *cis*-position relatively to the chalcogenide μ_3-ligand (*c,d*-type of coordination of a bidentate ligand) (Figure 3, 4).

This results in chirality of the cluster cations such as $[Mo_3S_4X_3(dmpe)_3]^+$ and $[Mo_3S_4X_3(dppe)_3]^+$ (X = Cl, Br; dmpe is 1,2-bis(dimethylphosphino)ethane, dppe is 1,2-bis(diphenylphosphino)ethane). [76-78] $[Mo_3S_4Cl_3(dppe)_3]^+$ is configurationally stable up to 70°C in solutions, becoming labile only above this temperature due to reversible de-coordination of dppe ligands, as suggested by quantum chemical calculations. [79] Reactions of $Mo_3Q_7X_4$ with achiral diphosphines will obviously produce racemic mixtures. By the contrary, use of chiral diphosphine (+)-1,2-bis[(2R,5R)-2,5-(dimethylphospholane-1-yl)]ethane (or its (S,S)-enantiomer) allowed preparation of *enantiomerically pure* cluster complexes $[Mo_3S_4((R,R)\text{-Me-BPE})_3Cl_3]PF_6$ and $[Mo_3S_4((S,S)\text{-Me-BPE})_3Cl_3]PF_6$ which crystallize in chiral space group R3. [80] Recent developments also involve preparation of water-soluble complexes with hydroxylated phosphines, such as $(OHCH_2P)_2CH_2CH_2P(CH_2OH)_2$, [82] and with other functionally-substituted phosphines, like a diphosphine-substituted tetrathiofulvalene (TTF). In the latter case complex with neutral ligand $[Mo_3Q_4L_3Cl_3]PF_6$ can be stepwise oxidized with up to 4 eq. of $NOPF_6$, the TTF moieties of the phosphine ligands being converted into radical-cations. [83] The diphosphine coordination to $Mo_3S_4^{4+}$ core is a prerequisite for successful synthesis of the hydride complexes. Thus, $[Mo_3S_4(diphos)_3Cl_3]^+$ (diphos is dmpe, R,R-Me-BPE) react with $NaBH_4$ or $LiBH_4$ with the formation of stable cluster hydrides $[Mo_3S_4(diphos)_3H_3]^+$. [84] Methathesis of $[Mo_3S_4(dmpe)_3Cl_3]PF_6$ with KCN produces $[Mo_3S_4(dmpe)_3(CN)_3]PF_6$; the bidentate phosphine ligands are not substituted even under harsh conditions (excess KCN, reflux in CH_3OH). Reaction of $[Mo_3S_4(dmpe)_3(CN)_3]BPh_4$ with $[Mo(CO)_5(THF)]$ gives rise to $[Mo_3S_4(dmpe)_3(\mu\text{-CNMo}(CO)_5)_3]BPh_4$ [85].

There is a significant number of compounds with S-donor ligands, including bidentate dithiophosphate, dithiolate, dithiophosphinate and dithiocarbamate complexes with the *c,d*-coordination mode of the dithioacidic ligands. The dithiophosphates are particularly numerous. Among these, an extensive series of dithiophosphate ester complexes (dtp, $(EtO)_2PS_2$) have been prepared. $[Mo_3S_4(dtp)_3(\mu\text{-dtp})(H_2O)]$, obtainable from the aqua complex and dithiophosphate, is a valuable starting material for the preparation of other derivatives. [86] The water ligand is only weakly bound and undergoes easy substitution with other bidentate ligands such as CH_3CN, py, oxazole, bpy, imidazole, PPh_3, thiourea, $PhCH_2CN$ etc. to give the corresponding $[Mo_3S_4(dtp)_4L]$ complexes. [86,87] The unique bridging dtp ligand is also liable to substitution by other bidentate ligands, in particular with carboxylates, such as formate, acetate, propionate, salicylate, phthalate, lactate and nitrobenzoate. [88-91].

Quite complicated molecules can be obtained on the basis of polynuclear carboxylates, such as the complexes $[(Mo_3S_4(dtp)_3L)_2(\mu\text{-COO}(CH_2)_nCOO)]$ (n is 3 or 4) containing two cluster units linked by bridging glutarate or adipinate ligands [92-94].

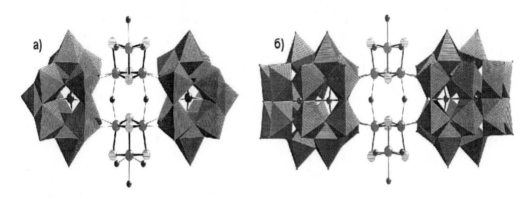

Figure 5. (a) Structure of $[\{(SiW_{11}O_{39})Mo_3S_4(H_2O)_3(\mu\text{-OH})\}_2]^{10-}$; (b) structure of $[\{(P_2W_{17}O_{61})Mo_3S_4(H_2O)_3(\mu\text{-OH})\}_2]^{14-}$ [97].

For chiral lactate complex $[Mo_3S_4(dtp)_3(\mu\text{-lac})(py)]$ (lac is lactate) a number of dynamic processes were identified involving the Mo-py site that include configuration (P to M) inversion, hindered Mo-N rotation and pyridine exchange from temperature-dependent ^{31}P and ^{1}H NMR experiments. Experiments using deuterated pyridine revealed greater substitutional lability of the Mo-py over Ni-py coordinates. [95] The only selenide, $[Mo_3Se_4(dtp)_3(\mu\text{-AcO})(py)]$, was prepared from the aqua complex $[Mo_3Se_4(H_2O)_9]^{4+}$. [96] Reaction of $[Mo_3Te_7(^iPrO)_2PS_2)_3]I$ with Bu_3P in the presence of benzoate or o-aminobenzoate gave the first Mo_3Te_4 cluster, which was isolated and structurally characterized as $[Mo_3Te_4((^iPrO)_2PS_2)_3(\mu\text{-}RC_6H_4CO_2)(PBu_3)]$. [11]. Dithiophosphinates (R_2PS_2) and dithiocarbamates (R_2NCS_2) have been less extensively studied [9].

An interesting aggregation resulting from the combination of trinuclear clusters $[Mo_3S_4(H_2O)_9]^{4+}$ with monovacant Keggin and Dawson-type lacunary anions $[SiW_{11}O_{39}]^{8-}$ and $[P_2W_{17}O_{61}]^{10-}$ to yield nanosized hybrid cluster species $[(SiW_{11}O_{39})Mo_3S_4(H_2O)_3(\mu\text{-OH}))_2]^{10-}$ and $[(P_2W_{17}O_{61})Mo_3S_4(H_2O)_3(\mu\text{-OH}))_2]^{14-}$ isolated and structurally characterized as $Me_2NH_2^+$ salts, was reported. The central core is built by two $\{Mo_3S_4(H_2O)_3\}^{4+}$ fragments, connected through two bridging OH^- groups (cis to μ_3-S) (Figure 5).

These large clusters are stable in solutions at pH between 1 and 7 and are quantitatively converted into $[Mo_3S_4(H_2O)_9]^{4+}$ in more acidic media [97].

Reaction of $[Mo_3S_4(H_2O)_9]^{4+}$ with arsenitotungstate $[AsW_9O_{33}]^{9-}$ gives a hybrid POM-cluster supramolecular complex $\{[(H_4AsW_9O_{33})_2(Mo_3S_4(H_2O)_5)]_2\}^{12-}$. In its structure two $\{H_4AsW_9O_{33}\}^{5-}$ subunits sandwich a $\{Mo_3S_4(H_2O)_5\}^{4+}$ moiety to give a complex $\{[(H_4AsW_9O_{33})_2(Mo_3S_4(H_2O)_5)]\}^{6-}$.

The supramolecular dimeric complex consists of two such units held together by hydrogen bonding between terminal hydroxo groups of the $[H_4AsW_9O_{33}]^{5-}$ subunits and coordinated water molecules and by S•••S contacts between two Mo_3S_4 cluster cores. Complex $\{[(H_4AsW_9O_{33})_2(Mo_3S_4(H_2O)_5)]_2\}^{12-}$ reacts with arsenite to give a closely related anion $\{[(H_2As_2W_9O_{34})(H_4AsW_9O_{33})(Mo_3S_4(H_2O)_5)]_2\}^{14-}$ through a formal coordination of one $\{AsOH\}^{2+}$ group. Electronic spectra of the latter show that in solution, a dissociation equilibrium exists between the dimeric and the monomeric species with $Kd(2) \sim 800$. Ag^+ and Cu^+ react with $\{[(H_2As_2W_9O_{34})(H_4AsW_9O_{33})(Mo_3S_4(H_2O)_5)]_2\}^{14-}$, (Figure 6) leading to complexes $\{[Ag_2(H_2As_2W_9O_{34})(H_2AsW_9O_{33})(Mo_3S_4(H_2O)_5)]_2\}^{16-}$ and $\{[Cu(H_2As_2W_9O_{34})$

$(H_4AsW_9O_{33})(Mo_3S_4(H_2O)_5)]_2\}^{13-}$, respectively, which were isolated as potassium salts and structurally characterized (Figure).

The silver complex has Ag^+ in a unique coordination environment of two sulfur atoms from both $\{Mo_3S_4\}$ units, two oxygen atoms and one central arsenic atom of the $\{AsW_9O_{33}\}$ subunits. UV-vis and potentiometric titration show that incorporation of Ag^+ ions into $\{[(H_2As_2W_9O_{34})(H_4AsW_9O_{33})(Mo_3S_4(H_2O)_5)]_2\}^{14-}$ is quantitative and proceeds in two successive steps with $K_1 = 4.1 \cdot 10^6$ and $K_2 = 2.3 \cdot 10^5$. For the Ag- and Cu-containing complexes observed [183]W NMR pattern agrees with a dynamic hopping of the heterometal cations between equivalent coordination sites [98].

A brown "porphirine"-like complex $[\{Mo_3S_4(H_2O)_5\}_4(\gamma\text{-}SiW_{10}O_{36})_4]^{16-}$ was obtained from equimolar amounts $[Mo_3S_4(H_2O)_9]^{4+}$ and $[\gamma\text{-}SiW_{10}O_{36}]^{8-}$ at pH $1-5$ and isolated as $(Me_2NH_2)_{16}[\{Mo_3S_4(H_2O)_5\}_4(SiW_{10}O_{36})_4]\cdot20H_2O$ (Figure 7). According to X-ray data the size of the cyclic anion is 16 x 30 Å, and there is inner cavity of 4.4 Å in diameter defined by 12 μ_2-S atoms [99].

A unique family of hybrid chalcogenide cluster-incorporated polyoxometalates has been prepared, in which a POM standard building block $\{W_3O_4\}^{10+}$ is replaced by the topologically similar chalcogenide cluster fragments $\{Mo_3S_4\}^{4+}$ and $\{Mo_3S_2O_2\}^{4+}$. This family includes complexes $[EW_{15}Mo_3S_4(H_2O)_3O_{53}]^{9-}$ (E = As, Sb) (Figure 8a); $[TeW_{15}Mo_3S_4(H_2O)_3O_{53}]^{8-}$, and $[AsW_{15}Mo_3O_2S_2(H_2O)_3O_{53}]^{9-}$.

The built-in sulfide ligands provide a new center of coordination for "soft" metal ions: it was shown that $[AsW_{15}Mo_3S_4(H_2O)_3O_{53}]^{9-}$ reacts with Cu^+ with the formation of a new heterometal cluster $[AsW_{15}Mo_3(CuCl)S_4(H_2O)_3O_{53}]^{9-}$ (fig 8b) which contains metals in localized high (W^{+6}), middle (Mo^{4+}) and low (Cu^+) oxidation states [100,101].

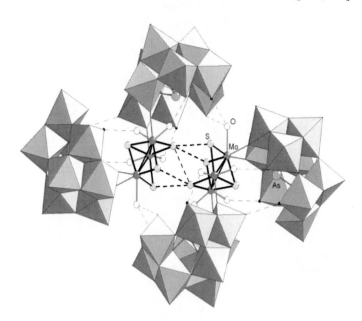

Figure 6. Supramolecular assembly in $[(H_4AsW_9O_{33})_2(Mo_3S_4(H_2O)_5)]_2\}^{12-}$ [98].

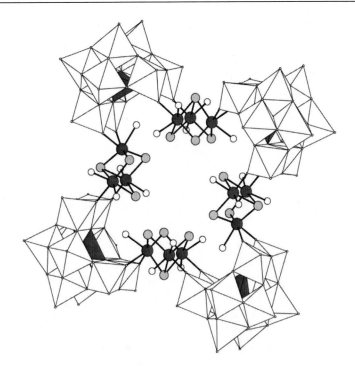

Figure 7. The porphirine-like complex $[(Mo_3S_4(H_2O)_5)_4(\gamma\text{-}SiW_{10}O_{36})_4]^{16-}$ [99].

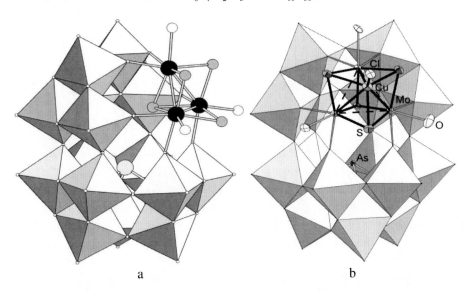

a   b

Figure 8. (a) The structure of $[AsW_{15}Mo_3S_4(H_2O)_3O_{53}]^{9-}$ in polyhedral representation. (b) The structure of $[AsW_{15}Mo_3(CuCl)S_4(H_2O)_3O_{53}]^{9-}$ with cluster fragment $\{Mo_3S_4(H_2O)_3CuCl\}$ shown in ellipsoids of 50% probability. Dashed lines show Mo-Mo bond s in the cluster core [100, 101].

High yield conversion of $[Mo_3S_4(H_2O)_9](pts)_4$ into $[(\eta^5\text{-}C_5H_5)_3Mo_3S_4](pts)$ and $[(\eta^5\text{-}CH_3C_5H_4)_3Mo_3S_4](pts)$ has been reported. It involves THF for water substitution in $[Mo_3S_4(H_2O)_9](pts)_4$ in the presence of $HC(COOEt)_3$ followed by metathesis with CpTl or MeCpTl. [102,103] Historically, $[Mo_3S_4Cp_3][Me_3SnCl_2]$ was the first $\{Mo_3S_4\}^{4+}$ cluster and was obtained by sulfidation of $[CpMo(CO)_3Cl]$ with $(Me_3Sn)_2S.$[10] Soon after, neutral complex [Mo₃S₄Cp₃] (Figure 9) was obtained by reaction of propylenesulfide with [HMo(CO)₂LCp] (L = CO, P(OPh)₃). [104] The permethylated analogue [Mo₃S₄Cp*₃] was obtained by reduction of [Cp*Mo(S^{t}Bu)₃] with Na amalgam. Oxidation of this complex with FcPF₆ produces [Mo₃S₄Cp*₃]PF₆. [105] The reduced species are paramagnetic. Selenidation of [Cp*MoO₂Cl] with H₂Se in situ allowed preparation of [Mo₃Se₄Cp*₃]⁺, isolated as [Zn(H₂O)Cl₃]⁻ salt [106].

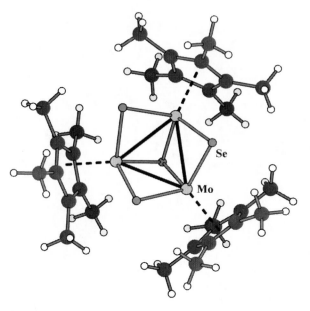

Figure 9. The [Cp*₃Mo₃Se₄]⁺ cluster [106].

2.3. {Mo₃Q₄} Core Reduction and Transformations

Typically, cyclic voltammetry of the {Mo₃Q₄}⁴⁺ clusters shows two or three (quasi)reversible waves which correspond to sequential reduction from Mo^{IV}₃Q₄ through Mo^{III}₃Q₄. [110-112,73,78] The reduction potential becomes more negative in the case of selenide clusters. Only one-electron reduction products could be isolated. Similar reduction processes have been reported for mixed oxo-chalcogenide clusters {Mo₃OQ₃}⁴⁺ and {Mo₃O₂S₂}⁴⁺ clusters [34,37]. Incomplete cubes {Mo₃Q₄}⁴⁺ suffer core transformation by a number of reagents. They may add sulfur from various sources, such as propylenesulfide, to give the chalcogen-rich clusters {Mo₃Q₄S₃}⁴⁺. [96] By reduction (Al, Zn, Mg, V, H₃PO₂) of the aqua complex [Mo₃Q₄(H₂O)₉]⁴⁺ cuboidal clusters [Mo₄Q₄(H₂O)₁₂]⁴⁺ and [Mo₇Q₈(H₂O)₁₈]⁸⁺ are obtained. [113,114] These reactions must involve cluster degradation and re-assembly, but the precise mechanism is not known. Reduction of the phosphine complexes takes a different turn and leads to [Mo₆Q₈(PEt₃)₆] in the case of monodentate, [115] and to [Mo₃Q₅(dppe)₃] in the case of bidentate phosphines. [116] In the first case, reduction of phosphine complexes [Mo₃Q₄(PEt₃)₃₋₄X₄(MeOH)₁₋₂] with magnesium results in the reductive fusion of two metal triangles into an octahedron and the formation of phosphine cluster complexes [Mo₆Q₈(PEt₃)₆], which constitute molecular analogues of the Chevrel phases.[115] Formally the octahedral clusters M₆Q₈ can be regarded as dimerization products of reduced triangular clusters $\{M_3Q_4\}^0$. If the reduction is carried out at low temperatures, the dimerization happens already at the stage of one-electron reduction, affording raft-type clusters $[Mo_6Q_8Cl_6(PEt_3)_6]$ in which two metal triangles are linked by one Mo-Mo bond. [117,118]. Cluster $[Mo_6S_{10}(SH)_2(PEt_3)_6]$ of a similar structure was obtained from $(NH_4)_2[Mo_3S_7(S_2)_3]$ and triethylphosphine [119].

Paramagnetic clusters $[Mo_3S_4(dppe)_3X_3]$ are also produced by reduction of the cationic complexes $[Mo_3S_4(dppe)_3X_3]^+$ with $K[Cp^*(CO)_3Mo]$ or metallic Ga.[116b]

The bicapped triangular clusters $[Mo_3Q_5(dppe)_3]$ can be accessed by various ways including reductions of $[Mo_3Q_4(dppe)_3Br_3]X$ (X = PF_6, Br) with ^tBuSNa, $EuCp^*_2$ or $Zn_2Cp^*_2$.[116a,b] Trinuclear and hexanuclear clusters Mo_3Q_5 and Mo_6Q_8 can be regarded as the first members of a homological cluster $Mo_{3n}Q_{3n+2}$ series built from triangular Mo_3 building blocks. Incorporation of various heterometals into $\{Mo_3Q_4\}^{4+}$ derivatives gives rise to heterometallic clusters of cuboidal structure of the type $\{Mo_3(M'L_n)Q_4(H_2O)_9\}$.

This is the most explored side of the $[Mo_3Q_4(H_2O)_9]^{4+}$ reactivity which implies a core transformation, and altogether some 25 chalcophilic middle, late and post-transition metals have been incorporated. The chemistry of the heterometallic clusters with $\{M_3M'Q_4\}$ cores was initially developed predominantly in aqueous media, and major advances have been made in the field of molybdenum clusters, where the heterometals incorporated into the incomplete cuboidal $[Mo_3S_4(H_2O)_9]^{4+}$ aqua ion according to [3 + 1] synthetic strategy range from Group 6 to Group 15 elements. [7,9] The first example of this type was reported by Shibahara group in 1986 for the reaction of the molybdenum aqua complex $[Mo_3S_4(H_2O)_9]^{4+}$ with iron metal to give the molybdenum-iron mixed-metal cluster $[Mo_3FeS_4(H_2O)_{10}]^{4+}$. [120] Incorporation into $[Mo_3Se_4(H_2O)_9]^{4+}$ has been less studied. [121] Various transformations of the $\{Mo_3S_4\}$ clusters are summarized in the Scheme 3.

Shibahara group reported unexpected carbon-sulfur bond formation through the reaction of $[Mo_3(\mu_3-S)(\mu-O)(\mu-S)_2(H_2O)_9]^{4+}$ and $[Mo_3(\mu_3-S)(\mu-S)_3(H_2O)_9]^{4+}$ with acetylene to afford clusters with alkenedithiolate ligands $[Mo_3(\mu_3-S)(\mu-O)(\mu_3-SCH=CHS)(H_2O)_9]^{4+}$ and $[Mo_3(\mu_3-S)(\mu-S)(\mu_3-SCH=CHS(H_2O)_9]^{4+}$, respectively. [122] Simliar reaction of the nitrilotriacetate complex $[Mo_3(\mu_3-S)(\mu-S)_3(Hnta)_3]^{2-}$ with acetylene and acetylenecarboxylic acid has been reported. [123] (Figure 10).

The reaction of $[Mo_3OS_3(qn)_3(H_2O)_3]^+$ (Hqn = 8-quinolinolato) with equimolar amounts of acetylene carboxylic acid, 4-pentynoic acid, 5-hexynoic acid, acetic acid, and with pimelic acid all gave clusters with μ-carboxylato groups without C-S bond formation. However, reaction with a large excess of acetylene carboxylic acid gave $[Mo_3OS(\mu_3-SCH=C(COOH)S(qn)_3(H_2O)](\mu-HC\equiv CCOO)]$. [124] Reaction of $[Mo_3S_4(dtp)_3(\mu-CH_3COO)(CH_3CN)]$ with alkynes was also reported [125,126].

2.4. Cuboidal Clusters $\{Mo_4Q_4\}$

Each face of the Mo_4 tetrahedron in the clusters with the $\{Mo_4(\mu_3-Q)_4\}$ core coordinates μ_3-chalcogen atoms in such a way that metal and chalcogen atoms form a distorted cubane structure. These cubane clusters are topologically and genetically related to the $\{M_3(\mu_3-Q)(\mu_2-Q)_3\}$ type clusters, which may be regarded as incomplete cubanes, the only difference

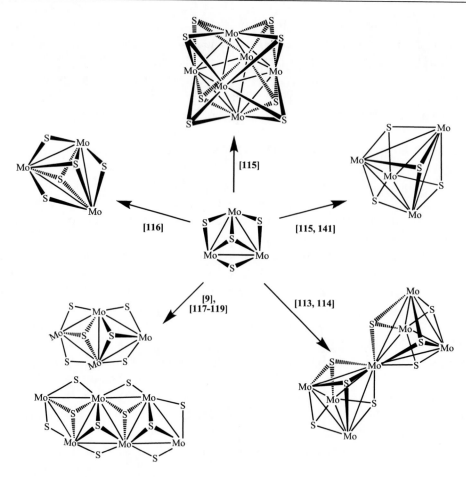

Scheme 3. {Mo$_3$Q$_4$} Cluster core transformations.

Figure 10. [Mo$_3$(μ_3-S)(μ-S)(μ-SCHCHS)(Hnta)$_3$]$^{2-}$ [123].

being one missing M atom. Such cluster type is common almost for all transition metals. Twelve valence electrons are required for the formation of six two-electron two-centre covalent metal - metal bonds in a tetrahedral cluster M_4. [127] The stoichiometry of most of the stable complexes with d^3 electronic configuration of metal ions supports this rule. These clusters are found in the chalcohalides $Mo_4S_4X_4$ (X = Cl, Br, I) [128,129] and in MMo_4Q_8 (M = Al, Ga) [130,131], where the cuboidal clusters are linked into a three-dimensional framework by bridging halides or chalcogenides chalcogen atoms according to the $^3_\infty[Mo_4Q_4X_{12/3}]$ type.

Aqua complexes $[Mo_4Q_4(H_2O)_{12}]^{n+}$ exist in three oxidation states where n is 4, 5 (paramagnetic [136]; the most stable state) and 6.[6] The 4+ species must be kept under nitrogen to avoid oxidation. Preparative routes to ~~for~~ the 5+ species include reduction (e.g. with $NaBH_4$) of Mo_2^V complexes $[Mo_2Q_2S_2(edta)]^{2-}$ or $[Mo_2O_2Q_2(cys)_2]^{2-}$. [35,132,133] The initially formed cuboidal 4+ species are air-oxidized into the 5+ species. The mechanism involves reductive condensation of two $\{Mo(\mu-Q)_2Mo\}$ rhombic moieties into cubane. Another route yielding moderate yields of $[Mo_4S_4(H_2O)_{12}]^{5+}$ together with $[Mo_3S_4(H_2O)_9]^{4+}$ involves refluxing a mixture of $[Mo(CO)_6]$ and Na_2S in acetic anhydride. [134] Other methods for the preparation of $[Mo_4S_4(H_2O)_{12}]^{5+}$ alongside $[Mo_7S_8(H_2O)_{18}]^{8+}$ involve the reaction of $[Mo_3S_4(H_2O)_9]^{4+}$ with various reductants, such as H_3PO_2. However none of the procedures described gives $[Mo_4S_4(H_2O)_{12}]^{5+}$ as the sole product. [113,114] Reactions of the quadruply bonded $[Mo_2Cl_8]^{4-}$ with $[Mo_3S_4(H_2O)_9]^{4+}$ or with $[Mo_2(\mu-S_2)_2Cl_8]^{2-}$ give moderate yields of the cuboidal aqua ion, in the latter case together with $[Mo_3S_4(H_2O)_{12}]^{4+}$. [114] Another efficient access route to $[Mo_4Q_4(H_2O)_{12}]^{5+}$ is provided by reactions of the triangular clusters $[Mo_3Q_4(H_2O)_9]^{4+}$ with $Mo(CO)_6$ under hydrothermal conditions. [141] Similarly, mixed S/Se cluster $[Mo_3SSe_3(H_2O)_9]^{4+}$ can be converted by reaction with $Mo(CO)_6$ into $[Mo_4SSe_3(H_2O)_{12}]^{5+}$.[33] Green $[Mo_4Se_4(H_2O)_{12}]^{5+}$ is made in low yield by $NaBH_4$ reduction of $[Mo_2O_2Se_2(cys)_2]^{2-}$. The crystal structures of $[Mo_4Q_4(H_2O)_{12}](pts)_5 \cdot 14\ H_2O$ (Q = S, Se) have been determined. [133,135] Both aqua ions can be reversibly reduced from 5+ to 4+ state and reversibly oxidized to the 6+ state. [60,133] $[Mo_4Q_4(H_2O)_{12}]^{5+}$ are stable for weeks when stored O_2-free at 4°C in 2 M Hpts, but heating it in air regenerates $[Mo_3Q_4(H_2O)_9]^{4+}$, the stability order being S > Se[6] Air oxidation of $[Mo_4SSe_3(H_2O)_{12}]^{5+}$ is regioselective and regenerates $[Mo_3SSe_3(H_2O)_9]^{4+}$. [33] Orange air sensitive $[Mo_4S_4(H_2O)_{12}]^{4+}$ can be prepared by reduction of the 5+ cluster electrochemically or with $NaBH_4$, $[V(H_2O)_6]^{2+}$, and $[Cr(H_2O)_6]^{2+}$. [137] Red $[Mo_4S_4(H_2O)_{12}]^{6+}$ is generated by a controlled oxidation of $[Mo_4S_4(H_2O)_{12}]^{5+}$ with the stoichiometric amount of $[VO_2(H_2O)_4]^+$. It gradually decays with the formation of $[Mo_3S_4(H_2O)_9]^{4+}$. [138] Mixed oxo-sulfido cube $[Mo_4OS_3(H_2O)_{12}]^{5+}$ was unexpectedly prepared by reduction of $[Mo_3OS_3(H_2O)_9]^{4+}$ with Fe wire. X-ray structure of $[Mo_4OS_3(H_2O)_{12}](pts)_5 \cdot 14\ H_2O$ has been reported [139].

Cyclic voltammetry revealed the possibility of reversible one-electron reduction and oxidation of the clusters $[Mo_xW_{4-x}Q_4(H_2O)_{12}]^{n+}$ (x = 0 - 4). For both ~~for~~ 5+/4+ and 6+/5+ couples the half-wave potential ($E_{1/2}$) almost linearly decreases with the increase in the number of tungsten atoms in the cluster: each additional tungsten atom causes a negative potential shift of approximately 0.2 V. It reflects the predisposition of tungsten to higher oxidation states. The effect of the selenium for sulfur substitution is less pronounced: even complete substitution decreases the potential by less than 0.1 V [6,141].

The chloride ion is weakly coordinated to $[Mo_4S_4(H_2O)_{12}]^{5+}$ (K_1 is 1.98, which is approximately 1000 times less than the corresponding value for thiocyanate). [141]

According to the kinetic data the substitution rate of thiocyanate for water increases by several orders of magnitude in the series 5+ < 4+ < 6+. The final products are N-bonded complexes, though the kinetic data indicate intermediate formation of the S-coordinated isomer. The Se for S substitution increases the substitution rate by one order of magnitude. In all cases full substitution is accompanied by oxidation of the cluster core to the 6+ state [6].

Organometallic clusters $[(\eta^5-C_5H_4R)_4Mo_4S_4]$ have been known for a long time. $[(\eta^5-C_5H_4Pr^i)MoCl_2]_2$ reacts with LiHS or LiHSe producing $[(\eta^5-C_5H_4Pr^i)_4Mo_4Q_4]$ (Q=S, Se) in high yield. Reversible two-electron oxidation was observed for $[(\eta^5-C_5H_4Pr^i)_4Mo_4Q_4]$; the selenium clusters undergoing oxidation more easily [143-145].

A large family of cyanide cluster complexes $[Mo_4Q_4(CN)_{12}]^{n-}$, where Q is S, Se, or Te was studied in detail. The cyanide clusters are prepared by high-temperature reactions of polymeric $\{M_3Q_7Br_4\}_x$ (M = Mo, W; Q = S, Se) or $[Mo_3Te_7I_4]$ with KCN affording cyano complexes $[Mo_4Q_4(CN)_{12}]^{6-}$ (M = Mo; Q = S, Se) or $[Mo_4Te_4(CN)_{12}]^{7-}$ in high yields. [146] Reaction of these cyanides with transition metals ions give extended solids of variable dimensionality. [147-149] The coordinated CN ligands are very robust and do not undergo substitution. Two waves of consecutive one-electron reduction are observed by CVA of the cyanide clusters $[M_4Q_4(CN)_{12}]^{6-}$ (M = Mo, W; Q = S, Se, Te). Substitution of the cyanide for water results in a significant positive shift of the potentials (up to 0.7 V). The cyanide ligands damp the effect of the metal change on the electrode potential. Presumably, this is caused by the participation of the CN-π^*-orbitals in the charge redistribution within the cluster core. Transition from S to Se and Te regularly (by approximately 100 mV) decreases the redox potential, progressively stabilizing the 6+ state [146].

Various salts of $[Mo_4S_4(NCS)_{12}]^{6-}$ and $[Mo_4Se_4(NCS)_{12}]^{6-}$ were prepared. [134,141] Treatment of the aqua complex $[Mo_4S_4(H_2O)_{12}]^{5+}$ with concentrated aqueous ammonia results in the reduction of the cluster core and formation of the complex $[Mo_4S_4(NH_3)_{12}]^{4+}$. [150] Sulfur-containing ligands stabilize the electron deficient state in $Mo_4Q_4^{6+}$: this cluster core was found in dithiophosphates $[M_4Q_4(dtp)_6]$ which result upon addition of the dithiophosphates $(RO)_2PS_2^-$ (R is Et, ^{i}Pr) to the aqua complexes. They can exist in the form of two isomers, namely $[M_4Q_4(\mu-dtp)_2(dtp)_4]$ and $[M_4Q_4(\mu-dtp)_3(dtp)_3]$. The μ_2-dtp ligand is labile enough to be substituted by acetate or benzoate generating $[Mo_4S_4(\mu-O_2CMe)_2(dtp)_4]$. [141,151,152] Similarly built xanthates and dithiocarbamates have been prepared but remain little studied. The bridging dithiocarbamate ligands can be selectively substituted by xanthate producing $[Mo_4S_4(\mu-Et_2NCS_2)(\mu-EtOCS_2)(Et_2NCS_2)_4]$ together with $[Mo_4S_4(\mu-EtOCS_2)_2(Et_2NCS_2)_4]$. [152] Reaction of the aqua complex $[Mo_4S_4(H_2O)_{12}]^{5+}$ with potassium tris(pyrazolyl)borate proceeds without any redox processes and yields $[Mo_4S_4(HB(pz)_3)_4(pz)]$. [153] $[Mo_4Q_4(edta)_2]^{n-}$ (n = 2-, 3-, 4-; Q = S, Se) have been reported. The CVA data show that the substitution of Se for S does not tangibly affect the $E_{1/2}$ value [154,155].

2.5. Heterometallic Derivatives of $[Mo_3Q_4(H_2O)_9]^{4+}$

The driving force for incorporation of heteroatoms into the $M_3Q_4^{4+}$ cores stems from two sources. Obviously, some affinity of the heterometal M´ for the μ_2-S chalcogen atoms (chalcophilicity) is required. In addition, the heterometal must also serve as an electron donor, which is why incorporation requires M' being either in zero or in a low oxidation state (0, groups 6-11, +1 for Rh(I), Ir(I), Cu(I), Ag(I), Au(I); + III for Rh(III)). In many cases incorporation of M' can be regarded as accompanied with two-electron reduction of the $\{M_3Q_4\}$ cluster core. In the case of transition metals, the clusters in which the total number of cluster valence electrons is equal to 60 are the most stable, in accordance with the classical MO scheme for tetrahedral clusters. The derivatives of $Mo_3CuQ_4^{4+}$ (61 e), $Mo_3CoQ_4^{3/4+}$ (58/59 e), $Mo_3FeS_4^{4+}$ (58 e) are exceptions from the rule. When a post-transition element is incorporated, the heterometallic clusters are formed only if it is in the formally zero oxidation state (Zn, Cd, Hg, In, Tl, Ge, Sn, Pb, As, Sb, Bi) or possesses a lone pair of electrons (Ga^I, In^I, Ge^{II}, Sn^{II}, Pb^{II}, Sb^{III}, Bi^{III}). With M^{II} transition metals (M'= V, Mn, Fe, Co, Ni, Cu, Zn, Cd, Pd, Pt), or with post-transition metals in their higher oxidation states, e.g. Ga^{III}, In^{III}, Ge^{IV} and Sn^{IV}, no heterometallic cube formation is observed [7].

The $\{Mo_3M'Q_4\}$ clusters exhibit single, edge linked double-cube and corner shared double cube structures (Scheme 4), represented by the structure types A, B, and C. The heteroatoms M' can simply occupy the vacant single cube site of $[Mo_3S_4(H_2O)_9]^{4+}$ to give A. Edge-linked double cube B can form which may exist in equilibrium with A. Type B structures were found for M'= Co, Ni, Pd, Cu). The conversion A→B occurs when the accompanying anions are non-complexing, e.g. pts⁻, ClO_4^-, and M' is weakly coordinated by H_2O.

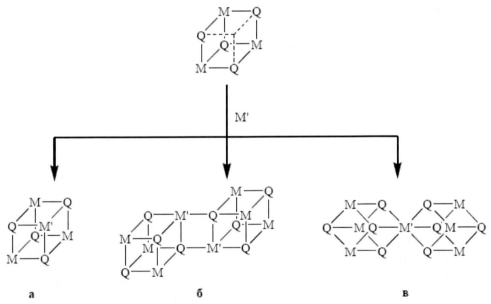

Scheme 4. Types of the cuboidal clusters [7, 9].

The cleavage of B to A occurs upon addition of CO, PR_3, Cl⁻, NCS⁻ which coordinate at M'. When M' is octahedral a corner-shared double cube C is redox accessible. An excess of $[Mo_3S_4(H_2O)_9]^{4+}$, M'^{n+} and a reducing agent (BH_4^- or H_3PO_2) are required for the conversion A → C, while with oxidants, e. g. $[Fe(H_2O)_6]^{3+}$ and $[Co(dipic)_2]^-$, the reverse action is observed (scheme 5).

Whereas Mo-M' bonds of about 2.7-2.8 Å form if M' is a transition metal belonging to groups 6-11, long non-bonding > 3.5 Å Mo…M' separations are a feature when M' is from Groups 12-15. The p-toluenesulphonic acid has been widely used for isolation of the aqua complexes, as well as supramolecular approach based upon formation of complementary hydrogen-bonded associates between CB[6] and the aqua complexes.

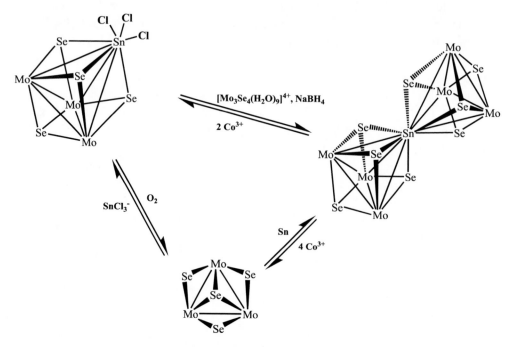

Scheme 5. Interconversions between $[Mo_3Se_4(H_2O)_9]^{4+}$, single $[Mo_3(SnCl_3)Se_4(H_2O)_9]^{3+}$ and corner-shared double $[Mo_6SnSe_8(H_2O)_{18}]^{8+}$ cuboidal cluster.

Almost all heterometallic cubes are air-sensitive, and restore $\{Mo_3Q_4\}$ upon air oxidation. The work on the cuboidal cluster aqua complexes has been exhaustively summarized in several reviews [7,9,156].

The cluster core $\{Mo_3PdS_4\}^{4+}$ is one of the most stable of all the $M_3M'Q_4^{4+}$ clusters, which property has made it a good object for reactivity studies. [157] The heterometal incorporation is achieved by reacting Pd black with $[Mo_3S_4(H_2O)_9]^{4+}$. In HCl solution the chloro-complex $[Mo_3(PdCl)S_4(H_2O)_9]^{3+}$ forms first, followed by much weaker Cl coordination at the Mo sites to give an equilibrium mixture of Cl-substituted species $[Mo_3(PdCl)S_4Cl_x(H_2O)_{9-x}]^{(3-x)+}$ (x = 0-3). Changing from HCl to the non-complexing p-toluenesulfonic acid (Hpts) leads to condensation to give the edge-linked double cuboidal cluster $[(Mo_3PdS_4(H_2O)_9)_2]^{8+}$. [158] Both monocuboidal (Type A) and bis-cuboidal (Type B) species were isolated and structurally characterised as $\{[Mo_3(PdCl)S_4(H_2O)_6Cl_3]$ $(PyH \subset C_{36}H_{36}N_{24}O_{12})\}Cl\cdot14H_2O$ [159] and $[\{Mo_3PdS_4(H_2O)_9\}_2](pts)_8\cdot24H_2O$, [159] respectively. Similar behavior was observed for the selenium analogues and the structures of $[\{Mo_3PdSe_4(H_2O)_9\}_2](pts)_8\cdot18H_2O$ [160] and of $\{[Mo_3(PdCl)Se_4(H_2O)_6Cl_2] (C_{36}H_{36}N_{24}O_{12})\}$ $Cl\cdot7H_2O$ [161] have been determined. The cuboidal clusters $\{M_3M'Q_4\}$ with M' = Ni and Pd are quite robust to the loss of the heterometal, which make them good candidates to explore the unique reactivity at the heterometal. The assignment of zero formal oxidation state of the Pd atom is based upon Fenske-Hall MO calculations. [127] For Ni the situation is more complicated with alternative descriptions as Ni(0) and Ni(II). [162] Taking into account that so far zero oxidation state for Ni and Pd was restricted to the complexes with π-acceptors

(CO, PR_3, alkenes), cuboidal clusters offer unique possibility to study chemistry of Ni(0) and Pd(0) in a sulfide (or selenide) environment. Various ligands L, including phosphines, alkenes, alkynes, CO, etc. bind to the Pd or Ni site to give the corresponding cluster complexes $[M_3(M'L)Q_4(H_2O)_9]^{4+}$ (M = Ni, Pd) (Scheme 6) [158,159,163].

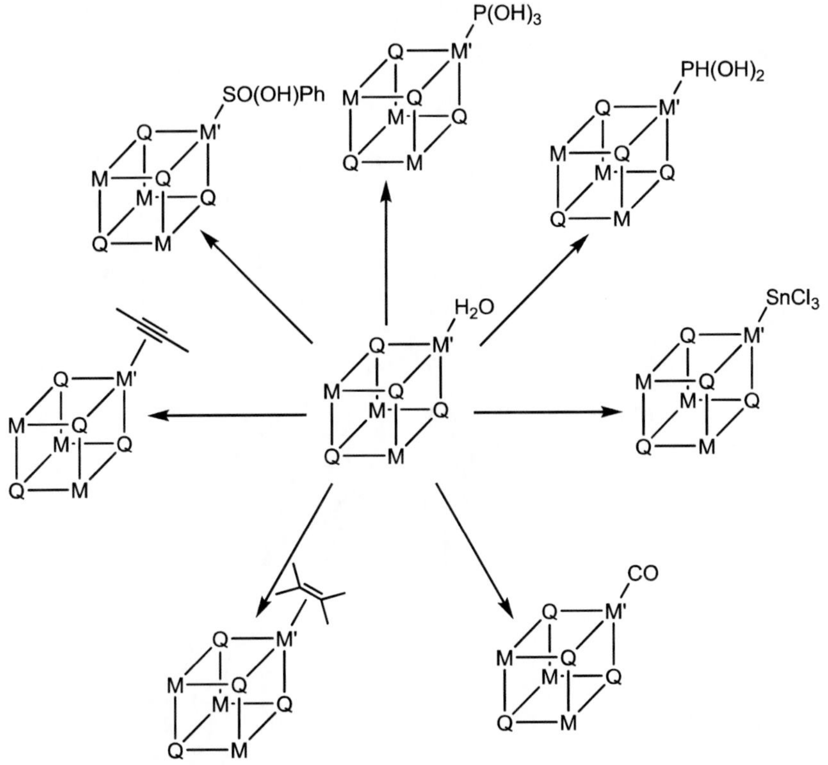

Scheme 6. Reactiviy of the $\{Mo_3M'Q_4\}^{4+}$ clusters (M' is Ni, Pd; Q is S, Se) [156].

The reason for this affinity to the π-acceptor ligands is that the Ni AO component of the HOMO is $3d_{yz}$ orbital, whose symmetry matches well the LUMO of the π-acceptors such as CO or alkenes. By contrary, the corresponding Fe AO ($3d_{z2}$, $3d_{xz}$) in $[Mo_3FeS_4(H_2O)_{10}]^{4+}$ do not match [5] the LUMO of CO and other π-acceptors, and no reaction of this cluster with CO was detected. [170] The most intriguing aspect of the reactivity of these aqua complexes is their reactions with hydrophosphoryl compounds (*i.e.*, compounds containing the O=P-H group). The $\{Mo_3NiS_4\}$ and $\{Mo_3PdS_4\}$ clusters induce their isomerization into the tautomeric P-OH species, (Scheme 1) and phosphorus atom uses the lone pair released after isomerization for coordination at Ni or Pd. In this way phosphorous acid H_3PO_3 $((HO)_2P(O)H)$, hypophosphorous acid H_3PO_2 $((HO)P(O)H_2)$, and their phenyl-substituted derivatives ($Ph_2P(O)H$ and $Ph(OH)P(O)(H)$) isomerize into the hydroxo tautomers $P(OH)_3$, $HP(OH)_2$, $PhP(OH)_2$, and Ph_2POH. The high affinity of the Ni and Pd sites in the clusters for P-donors constitutes the main driving force for these reactions. The ^{31}P NMR spectra provide unambiguous evidence that coordination causes isomerization of the ligands.

The P-H bond cleavage results in the disappearance of the doublet in the case of H_3PO_3 and $Ph(OH)P(O)(H)$ (P-H bonds are absent in $P(OH)_3$ and $PhP(OH)_2$), or in the transformation of the triplet into the doublet (only one P-H bond remains in $HP(OH)_2$). The reactivity decreases in the following order: $Ph_2P(O)H > PhP(OH)(H)(O) >> H_3PO_3$. Both $P(OH)_3$ and $HP(OH)_2$ are the simplest water-soluble phosphine ligands and may be of interest as a cheaper alternative to usual water-soluble organic phosphines in two-phase catalytic systems. The formation of the complexes was confirmed by X-ray analysis of supramolecular adducts with cucurbit[6]uril, which crystallize even from dilute solutions: $\{[Mo_3PdP(OH)_3S_4Cl_3 (H_2O)_6]_2CB[6]\}Cl_2 \cdot 20H_2O$ and $\{[Mo_3(Ni(P(OH)_3)S_4(H_2O)_8Cl]CB[6]\}$ $Cl_3 \cdot 14H_2O$ (Figure 11) [164,165].

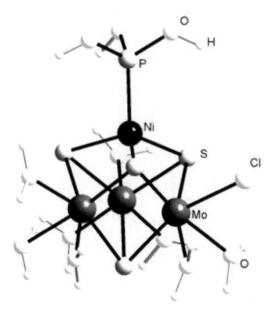

Figure 11. The $[Mo_3(Ni(P(OH)_3)S_4(H_2O)_8Cl]^+$ complex [165].

Kinetic studies were carried out for the reaction between $[Mo_3PdS_4(H_2O)_{10}]^{4+}$ and H_3PO_2 to give a complex in which initial coordination pyr-H_3PO_2 (e.g., the hydrophosphoryl tautomer) (Scheme 7) was detected.

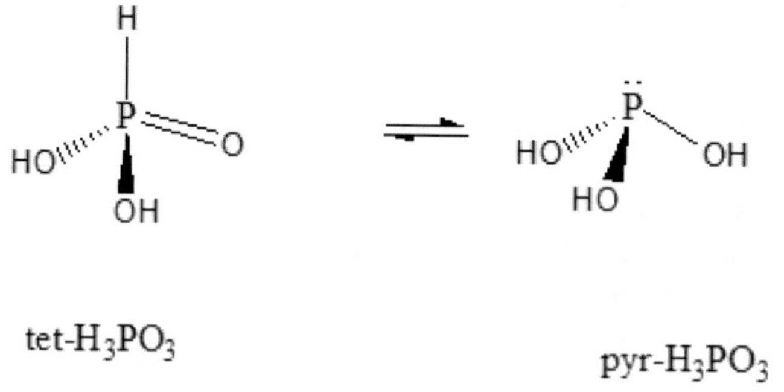

tet-H_3PO_3 pyr-H_3PO_3

Scheme 7. Tautomeric equilibrium between $HP(O)(OH)2$ and $P(OH)3$

This reaction occurs with biphasic kinetics, which indicates the existence of a Pd-O coordinated intermediate. The rate constants for both steps show first order dependence on C_{H3PO2}, thus indicating that both the coordination of a pyr-H_3PO_2 molecule and its isomerization require the participation of another H_3PO_2 molecule, one for each kinetic step.

The second order rate constants derived for both steps are $k_1 = (12.5 \pm 0.3) \times 10^{-2}$ M^{-1}s^{-1} and $k_2 = (2.6 \pm 0.1) \times 10^{-2}$ M^{-1}s^{-1}. For a better understanding of the mechanism DFT calculations were carried out. [166] Coordination of H_3PO_3 to $[Mo_3(PdCl)Q_4(H_2O)_9]^{3+}$ (Q = S, Se) in 4 M HCl is biphasic. The first, very rapid, step corresponds to coordination of the HP(O)(OH)$_2$ through an oxygen atom, and the second step, which is slow and reversible, corresponds to isomerization into P(OH)$_3$ complex with the following parameters: k_f $(1.18\pm0.05)\cdot10^{-4}$ M^{-1}s^{-1}, k_b $(2.3\pm0.25)\cdot10^{-5}$ s^{-1} (Q = S); k_f $(3.0\pm0.1)\cdot10^{-3}$ M^{-1}s^{-1}, k_b $(4.5\pm0.2)\cdot10^{-3}$ s^{-1} (Q = Se). [166] Typical order of reactivity in these reactions is Ni<Pd, S≈Se, and correlates with the relative stability of the M(0) oxidation state. The nickel cluster $[Mo_3(NiCl)S_4(H_2O)_9]^{3+}$ is the least reactive and does not react with hydrophosphoryl compounds in hydrochloric acidic solutions at room temperature, only heating over a long period of time afforded the complexes with HP(OH)$_2$, P(OH)$_3$, Ph$_2$P(OH), and PhP(OH)$_2$, as was proved by ^{31}P NMR [166].

Clusters $[Mo_3S_4(dmpe)_3X_3]^+$ were widely used for preparation of heterometallic cubanes. Reactions of $[Mo_3S_4(dmpe)_3X_3]PF_6$ with $[Cu(CH_3CN)_4]PF_6$ in the presence of Bu$_4$NX give rise to $[Mo_3(CuX)S_4(dmpe)_3X_3]PF_6$ (Figure 12) [167,168]. The corresponding selenides are also known. [169]

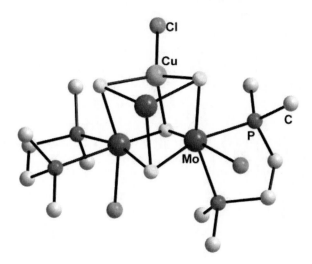

Figure 12. Structure of $[Mo_3(CuCl)S_4(dmpe)_3Cl_3]^+$ [167, 168].

With CuCN, $[Mo_3(CuCN)S_4(dmpe)_3Cl_3]PF_6$ was obtained. [85] Enantiomerically pure $[Mo_3S_4((R,R)$-Me-BPE)$_3Cl_3]PF_6$ and $[Mo_3S_4((S,S)$-Me-BPE)$_3Cl_3]PF_6$ can be converted into the corresponding cuboidal clusters with the retention of chirality [80].

Incorporation of Ni(0) is achieved by reaction of $[Mo_3S_4(dmpe)_3Cl_3]PF_6$ with $[Ni(cod)_2]$. In CH$_3$CN this reaction leads to $[Mo_3(NiCH_3CN)S_4(dmpe)_3Cl_3]PF_6$, while in the presence of Bu$_4$NCl the product is neutral $[Mo_3(NiCl)S_4(dmpe)_3Cl_3]$. The corresponding dppe complex was also reported. The reactivity order toward Ni incorporation is Cl > Br and dmpe > dppe. Reaction of $[Mo_3(NiCH_3CN)S_4(dmpe)_3Cl_3]PF_6$ with CuCl$_2$ leads to transmetallation with the formation of $[Mo_3(CuCl)S_4(dmpe)_3Cl_3]PF_6$. The observation that Cu$^+$, unlike Cu^{2+}, does not replace Ni^0, rules out a dissociative equilibrium previous to oxidation. The MeCN ligand in $[Mo_3(NiCH_3CN)S_4(dmpe)_3Cl_3]^+$ is exchangeable with py, THF, CO, but not with water, alcohols and thiophene. Addition of PPh$_3$ or dmpe causes Ni excision and restoration of [Mo$_3$S$_4$(dmpe)$_3$Cl$_3$]$^+$. [171].

From [Mo$_3$S$_4$(H$_2$O)$_9$]Cl$_4$, dppe and Pt(dba)$_2$, {Mo$_3$PtS$_4$} cubanes [Mo$_3$(PtCl)S$_4$(dppe)$_3$Cl$_3$] and [Mo$_3$(Ptη^1-dppe)(dppe)$_3$Cl$_3$]Cl were prepared. With Pd$_2$(dba)$_3$, [Mo$_3$(Pdη^1-dppe)(dppe)$_3$Cl$_3$]Cl was the product.[172] Reaction of [Mo$_3$S$_4$(dmpe)$_3$Cl$_3$]PF$_6$ with CoCl$_2$ and NaBH$_4$ allows incorporation of Co with the formation of [Mo$_3$(CoCl)S$_4$(dmpe)$_3$Cl$_3$]. This cluster can be reversibly oxidized (in air) into [Mo$_3$(CoCl)S$_4$(dmpe)$_3$Cl$_3$]$^+$; the latter can be reduced back to the neutral cluster with NaBH$_4$. Oxidation of [Mo$_3$(CoCl)S$_4$(dmpe)$_3$Cl$_3$] with TCNQ leads to the radical-anion salt [Mo$_3$(CoCl)S$_4$(dmpe)$_3$Cl$_3$](TCNQ). If the reaction between [Mo$_3$S$_4$(dmpe)$_3$Cl$_3$]PF$_6$, CoCl$_2$ and NaBH$_4$ is carried out under CO, the product is [Mo$_3$(Co(CO))S$_4$(dmpe)$_3$Cl$_3$]. [173] The corresponding selenide series has been prepared likewise. [174] Incorporation of iron into the cluster is achieved in reaction of [Mo$_3$S$_4$(dmpe)$_3$Cl$_3$]BPh$_4$ with FeCl$_2$ and NaBH$_4$. This reaction leads to [Mo$_3$(FeCl)S$_4$(dmpe)$_3$Cl$_3$], which can be converted with NaSPh into [Mo$_3$(FeSPh)S$_4$(dmpe)$_3$(SPh)$_3$] via [Mo$_3$(FeSPh)S$_4$(dmpe)$_3$Cl$_3$] intermediate [175].

The [Mo$_3$S$_4$Cp$_3$]$^+$ clusters (Cp is C$_5$H$_5$, Cp', Cp*) proved excellent starting materials for preparation of the heterocuboidal clusters. Treatment of [Mo$_3$S$_4$Cp*$_3$]PF$_6$ with suitable M(0) sources (M = Ni, Pd) allowed preparation of a series [Mo$_3$(ML)S$_4$Cp*$_3$]PF$_6$ (ML is NiPPh$_3$, NiCO, Pd(dba), PdPPh$_3$, Pdma (ma is maleinic anhydride), Nicod, Nidmad (dmad is MeOOCC≡CCOOMe). By reaction of [Mo$_3$(Pd(dba))S$_4$Cp*$_3$]PF$_6$ with CO a bis-cuboidal cluster [(Mo$_3$PdS$_4$Cp*$_3$)$_2$(μ-CO)](PF$_6$)$_2$ was produced where two cuboidal subunits are linked via a Pd-Pd bond and a bridging CO ligand. Remarkably, the reduced complex [Mo$_3$S$_4$Cp$_3$] does not yield cuboidal clusters. [176-178] Ruthenium clusters [Mo$_3$(RuH$_2$(PR$_3$))S$_4$Cp*$_3$]PF$_6$ (R = Ph, Cy) are obtainable from [Mo$_3$S$_4$Cp*$_3$]PF$_6$ and [RuH$_4$(PPh$_3$)$_3$] or [RuH$_2$(H$_2$)$_2$(PCy$_3$)$_2$], respectively. Both clusters catalyze disproportionation of N$_2$H$_4$ into ammonia and N$_2$ at room temperature. PhNHNH$_2$ was converted into a mixture of PhNH$_2$, N$_2$, C$_6$H$_6$ and NH$_3$. A complex with ammonia [Mo$_3$(Ru(NH$_3$)(PR$_3$))S$_4$Cp*]PF$_6$, and a hydrazide [{Mo$_3$RuS$_4$Cp*}$_2$ (μ-NH$_2$)(μ-NHNH$_2$)](PF$_6$)$_2$ were detected as by-products in these interconversions. Reaction of [Mo$_3$(RuH$_2$(PPh$_3$))S$_4$Cp*]PF$_6$ with sulfur allowed preparation of a bis-cuboidal cluster [{Mo$_3$S$_4$Cp*$_3$}$_2$(μ$_2$-η^1,η^2-S$_2$)](PF$_6$)$_2$. This cluster was used for preparation of trimetallic Mo-Ru-Pd and Mo-Ru-Pt clusters (Figure 13) [179,180].

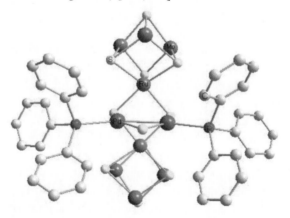

Figure 13. Structure of [(Cp*$_3$Mo$_3$RuS$_4$)$_2$((PdPPh$_3$)$_2$S$_3$)](PF$_6$)$_2$ [180]. Cp* ligands have been omitted for clarity.

[Mo$_3$S$_4$Cp'$_3$](pts) were reacted with [M(CO)$_3$(CH$_3$CN)$_3$] at room temperature to yield the expected cuboidal clusters [Mo$_3$(M(CO)$_3$)S$_4$Cp'$_3$](pts) (M = Cr, Mo, W). [181] Reaction with Co$_2$(CO)$_8$ or CpCo(CO)$_2$ yields [Mo$_3$(Co(CO))S$_4$Cp'$_3$](pts). The coordinated carbonyl in this cluster can be replaced with PPh$_3$, but not with AsPh$_3$. Reactions of [Mo$_3$(Co(CO))S$_4$Cp'$_3$](pts) with I$_2$ or NO give rise to [Mo$_3$(CoI)S$_4$Cp'$_3$] and [Mo$_3$(Co(NO))S$_4$Cp'$_3$], respectively. [182].

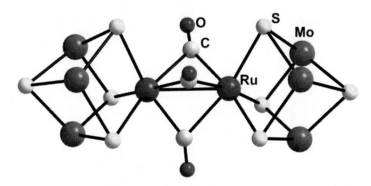

Figure 14. [(Cp'$_3$Mo$_3$S$_4$)(Ru$_2$(CO)$_3$)](pts)$_2$ [183]. Cp´ ligands have been omitted for clarity.

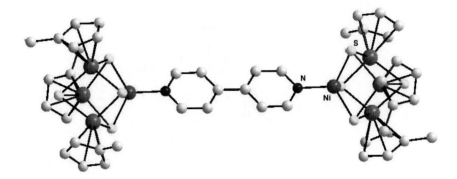

Figure 15. Structure of [(Mo$_3$NiS$_4$Cp'$_3$)(μ-C$_4$H$_8$S$_2$)](pts)$_2$ [195].

A large family of heterometallic cubanes {Mo$_3$(ML)S$_4$Cp'$_3$} was obtained by reaction of [Mo$_3$S$_4$Cp'$_3$](pts) with suitable ML precursors (ML = Ru(CO)$_2$, Os(CO)$_2$, RhCl(PPh$_3$), IrCl(PPh$_3$), Rh(cod), Rh(dppp), NiPPh$_3$, PdPPh$_3$, PtPPh$_3$ (Figure 14) [183] Using ditopic ligands, such as 4,4'-bipy or 1,4-dithiane, allows preparation of bis(cuboidal) clusters, e.g., [(Mo$_3$NiS$_4$Cp'$_3$)(μ-C$_4$H$_8$S$_2$)]$^{2+}$ (Figure 15) [184,185].

Treatment of [Cp*$_3$Mo$_3$S$_4$]PF$_6$ with CuI in CH$_2$Cl$_2$ produces [Cp*$_3$Mo$_3$(CuI)S$_4$]PF$_6$. [Cp*$_3$Mo$_3$S$_4$]PF$_6$ also reacts with Ph$_3$PAgOTf to give [Cp*$_3$Mo$_3$(AgPPh$_3$)S$_4$](OTf)(PF$_6$). The incorporation[10] of Au$^+$ was achieved by reaction with [(R$_3$P)Au]X R = Ph, Cy, ^{t}Bu; X = BF$_4^-$, PF$_6^-$, which afford corresponding complexes [Cp*$_3$Mo$_3$(AuPR$_3$)S$_4$]$^{2+}$. The Mo...Ag and Mo...Au distances appear non-bonding [186].

Heterometal cuboidal clusters with ligands other than H$_2$O, Cp or phosphines, are rare. Earlier works on the clusters with dtp ligands have been reviewed. [9] These clusters are mainly cubes without Mo-M' bonds with non-transition metals as heterometals, though several derivatives of {Mo$_3$CuS$_4$} clusters we also reported. [9] Recently [Mo$_3$(Nipy)S$_4$

(py)(μ-OAc)(dtp)$_3$(py)] was reported. [95] Nitrylotriacetate and dithiophosphate complexes were successfully used for isolation and structural characterization of the double cuboidal clusters (type C) with {Mo$_6$ZnS$_8$}$^{8+}$ and {Mo$_6$CdS$_8$}$^{8+}$ cluster cores. [187,188] Corner shared double cubes such as [CdMo$_6$S$_8$(Hnta)$_6$]$^{4-}$ and [CdMo$_6$S$_8$(dtp)$_8$(CH$_3$CN)$_2$] are obtained by reacting metallic Cd (or Zn) with [Mo$_3$S$_4$(Hnta)]$_3^-$ or [Mo$_3$S$_4$(dtp)$_4$(CH$_3$CN)], respectively, [187] whereas with [Mo$_3$S$_4$(H$_2$O)$_9$]$^{4+}$ single cuboidal cluster [Mo$_3$CdS$_4$(H$_2$O)$_{12}$]$^{4+}$ (type A) was produced. [189] Zn...Mo or Cd....Mo bonding is lacking in these species. [187-188] Reported oxalate complexes include [Mo$_3$(PdPPh$_3$)(μ$_3$-S)$_4$(C$_2$O$_4$)$_3$(H$_2$O)$_3$]$^{2-}$, obtained by reaction of [Mo$_3$S$_4$(C$_2$O$_4$)$_3$(H$_2$O)$_3$]$^{2-}$, PdCl$_2$ and NH$_4$H$_2$PO$_2$, [190] and a series of Cu(I) complexes [Mo$_3$(CuX)(μ$_3$-S)$_4$(C$_2$O$_4$)$_3$(H$_2$O)$_3$]$^{2-}$ (X = Cl, Br, I, NCS) [191]. Cuboidal clusters [Mo$_3$(MCl)(H$_2$O)$_9$]$^{3+}$ (M = Pd or Ni) react with the trivacant [AsW$_9$O$_{33}$]$^{9-}$ Keggin-type anion to give nanosized complexes [(H$_2$AsW$_9$O$_{33}$)$_4${Mo$_3$S$_4$M(H$_2$O)$_5$}$_2$]$^{20-}$ (Figure 16), isolated and structurally characterized as potassium salts.

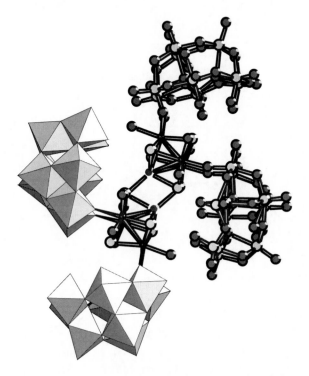

Figure 16. Structure of [(H$_2$AsW$_9$O$_{33}$)$_4${Mo$_3$S$_4$M(H$_2$O)$_5$}$_2$]$^{20-}$ (M = Ni, Pd) [192].

Studies in solution reveal that the structure with double cuboidal core (type B) is maintained in solution. In the presence of exogeneous ligands, such as iodide or pyridine, dissociation of the double cubane into single cubanes (type A) is observed, through a M–L coordination bond (L = I$^-$ or Py) [192].

The reactions between [Mo$_3$(μ$_3$-S)(μ$_2$-S)$_3$(acac)$_3$(py)$_3$]PF$_6$ and CuX (X = Cl, I, SCN) afford heterometallic cubane clusters [Mo$_3$(CuX)(μ$_3$-S)$_4$(acac)$_3$(py)$_3$]PF$_6$. According to the vibrational spectra, the thiocyanate complex in the solid state is a mixture of the linkage isomers [Mo$_3$(CuNCS)S$_4$(acac)$_3$(py)$_3$]PF$_6$ and [Mo$_3$(CuSCN)S$_4$(acac)$_3$(py)$_3$]PF$_6$ whereas in solution only the isothiocyanate form was detected [193].

Reactions of the incomplete cuboidal clusters $[M_3Q_4(acac)_3(py)_3]^+$ (M = Mo, W; Q = S, Se) with group 14 and 15 metal complexes with s^2p^0 electronic configuration ($AsPh_3$, $SbPh_3$, $SbCl_3$, SbI_3, PbI_3^-, $SnCl_3^-$) lead to heterometal incorporation with the formation of cuboidal clusters of the type $[M_3(EX_3)Q_4(acac)_3(py)_3]^{n+}$ (n = 0 for Sn, Pb; n = 1 for As, Sb). Analysis based on the bond distances between E and Q gives the following sequence of affinity: As < Sb; Pb < Sn ≈ Sb; $SbPh_3$ < SbI_3 ≈ $SbCl_3$ [194].

Several {Mo_3FeS_4} clusters have been prepared as complexes with NH_3 and pyrazolylborate, $[Mo_3(FeH_2O)S_4(NH_3)_9]Cl_4$[120] and $[Mo_3(FeX)S_4Tp_3]$ (X = Cl, Br; Tp = hydrotris(pyrazolyl)borate) [70].

2.6. Use of the {Mo₃Q₄} Clusters

Supported transition metal sulfides are catalysts for hydrorefining of crude oil. Co/MoS_2 and Ni/MoS_2 supported onto alumina are widely used in industry for desulfurization. The metal ratio in the clusters {M_3NiS_4} and {M_3CoS_4} corresponds to the composition of the best hydrorefining catalysts and the coordination of heterometal is thought to be similar to that of cobalt or nickel atom in the active centre of such catalysts. [171,195] The triangular and heterometallic cubane-type cationic aqua complexes $[Mo_3S_4(H_2O)_9]^{4+}$ and $[Mo_3NiS_4(H_2O)_{10}]^{4+}$ have been incorporated into zeolites. It was shown that the activity of such catalysts in hydrogenation of thiophene strongly depends on the zeolite type. The complex $[Mo_3NiS_4(H_2O)_{10}]^{4+}$ incorporated into the zeolite cavity catalyses also the synthesis of ethane and ethylene in the hydrogenation of CO [196-198].

The triangular pentamethylcyclopentadienyl cluster $[Cp*_3Mo_3S_4]$ reacts with $[Ni(cod)_2]$ yielding $[(Cp*_3Mo_3NiS_4)_2(cod)]^{2+}$, which is a highly effective catalyst of intramolecular cyclization of alkynoic acids into the enollactones (Scheme 8). [178] The 1,4,7-triazacyclononane (tacn) heterometallic cluster $[Mo_3(PdCl)S_4(tacn)]^3$ catalyzes selective nucleophilic addition of methanol to methyl propiolate resulting in (Z)-MeOCH=CHCO$_2$Me in quantitative yield. It is important that this reaction is more effective than the catalytic reactions of mononuclear palladium complexes. [199] The chloride $[Mo_3(CuCl)S_4$ $(dmpe)_3Cl_3]PF_6$ proved catalytically active in cyclizations of alkenes with diazoacetate, and in intramolecular cyclization of 1-diazo-5-hexene-2-on. Unique catalysts possessing chiral metal chalcogenide backbones can be obtained from chalcogenide clusters [80,200].

All triangular clusters $[Mo_3Q_4L_3X_4]^+$ (Q = S, Se; L = dmpe, dppe) and their copper derivatives $[M_3CuQ_4L_3X_4]^+$ turned out to be promising optical limiters and the value of threshold limiting flux decreases on going from the cubane-type clusters to triangular ones [168].

Finally, and what is perhaps the most important finding, the {Mo_3S_4} clusters taken as $[Mo_3S_4Cp'_3]^+$, when coupled to a p-type silicon semiconductor, efficiently catalyze the evolution of dihydrogen when they are activated by red photons from the solar spectrum. The achieved current densities already match the requirement for a H_2-production system with solar-to hydrogen above 10 % [201].

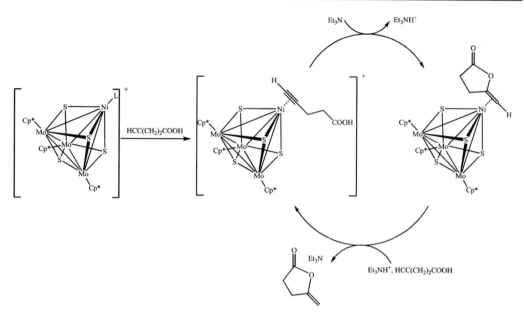

Scheme 8. Proposed mechanism for intramolecular cyclization of alkynoic acids into the enollactones in the presence of $[(Cp^*{}_3Mo_3NiS_4)_2(cod)]^{2+}$ [178].

REFERENCES

[1]   Chisholm, M. H. *Early transitions metal clusters with π-donor ligands*, 1995, VCH Publishers, New York.

[2]   Shibahara, T., *Adv. Inorg. Chem.* 1991, 37, 143-173.

[3]   Shibahara, T., *Coord. Chem. Rev.* 1993, 123, 73-147.

[4]   Saito, T., *Adv. Inorg. Chem.* 1996, 44, 45-91.

[5]   Stiefel, E. I., Matsumoto, K., *Ed.*, *Transition metal sulfur chemistry. ACS. Symp. Ser.* 653, 1996.

[6]   Hernandez-Molina,R.; A. G. Sykes., *J. Chem. Soc. Dalton Trans.* 1999, 3137-3148.

[7]   Hernández-Molina, R., Sokolov, M.N., Sykes, A. G., *Acc. Chem. Res.* 2001, 34, 223-230.

[8]   Llusar, R.; Uriel, S., *Eur. J. Inorg. Chem.* 2003, 1271-1290.

[9]   Sykes, A. G., Fedin, V. P., Sokolov, M. N., *Comprehensive Coordination Chemistry II*, V. 4, 2003, Elsevier, Ed. A.G. Wedd, 761-823.

[10]   Simon, G. L., Dahl, L. F., *J. Am. Chem. Soc.* 1973, 95, 2164-2174.

[11]   Lin, X.; Chen, H.-Y.; Chi, L.-S.; Lu, C.-Z.; Zhuang, H.-H., *Polyhedron*, 2000, 19, 925-929.

[12]   Feliz, M.; Llusar, R.; Andres, J.; Berski, S.; Silvi, B., *New J. Chem.* 2002, 26, 844–850.

[13]   Andrés, J.; Berski, S.; Feliz, M.; Llusar, R.; Sensato, F.; Silvi, B., *C. R. Chimie*, 2005, 8 1400–1412.

[14]   Wendan, C.; Qianer, Z.; Jinshun, H.; Jiaxi, L., *Polyhedron*, 1989, 8, 2785.

[15]   Wendan, C.; Qianer, Z.; Jinshun H.; Jiaxi, L., *Polyhedron*, 1990, 9, 1625.

[16]   Chen, Z.; Lu, J.; Liu, C.; Zhang, Q., *Polyhedron*, 1991, 10, 2799.

[17]   Wendan, C.; Guocong, G.; Jinshun, J.; Jiaxi, L., *Polyhedron*, 1995, 14, 3649.

[18] Li, J.; Liu, C.; J. Lu., *Polyhedron*, 1994, 13, 1841.

[19] Li, J.; Liu, C.; Lu, J.; *J. Clust. Sci.* 1994, 5, 505-521.

[20] Cotton, F. A.; Haas, T. E.; Inorg. Chem. 1964, 3, 10.

[21]   Cotton, F. A.; Haas, T.E.; *Inorg. Chem.* 1964, 3, 1217.

[22] Vergamini, P. J.; Vahrenkamp, H.; Dahl, L. F.; *J. Am. Chem. Soc.* 1971, 6327.

[23] Cotton, F. A.; Feng, X.; *Inorg. Chem.*, 1991, 30, 3666.

[24] Cramer, R. E.; Yamada, K.; Kawaguchi, H.; Tatsumi, K., *Inorg. Chem.* 1996, 35, 1743.

[25] Mizutani, J.; Imoto, H.; Saito, T.; *J. Cluster Sci.* 1995, 6, 523.

[26] Cotton, F. A.; Wilkinson, G.; Murillo, C. A..; Bochmann, M. Advanced Inorganic Chemistry. 6. Edition , Wiley-VCH, 1999.

[27] Fedin, V. P.; Sykes, A. G. *Inorg. Synth.* 2002, 35, 162.

[28] Fedin, V. P.; Sokolov, M. N.; Geras'ko, O. A.; Virovets, A. V.; Podberezskaya, N. V.; Fedorov, V. Ye. *Inorg. Chim. Acta* 1991, 187, 81.

[29] Müller, A.; Pohl, S.; Dartmann, M.; Cohen, J. P.; Bennet, J. M.; Kirchner, R. M., *Z. Naturforsch.* 34, 434-436.

[30] Fedin, V. P.; Sokolov, M. N.; Mironov, Y. V.; Kolesov, B. A.; S.V.; Tkachev, S. V.; Fedorov, V. Y.; *Inorg. Chim. Acta*, 1990, 167, 39-45.

[31] Akashi, H.; Shibahara, T.; Kuroya, H., *Polyhedron*, 1990, 9, 1671-1676.

[32] Hernandez-Molina, R. Elsegood, M. R. J.; Clegg, W.; Sykes, A. G.; *J. Chem. Soc., Dalton Trans.*, 2001, 2173–2178.

[33] Gushchin, A. L.; Ooi, B.-L.; Harris, P.; Vicent, C.; Sokolov, M. N., *Inorg. Chem.* 2009, 48, 3832-3839.

[34] Abramov, P. A.; Sokolov, M. N.; Hernandez-Molina, R.; Vicent, C.; Virovets, A. V.; Naumov, D. Y.; Gili, P.; Gonzalez-Platas, J.; Fedin, V. P., *Inorg. Chim. Acta*, 2010, 363, 3330-3337.

[35] Martinez, M.; Ooi, B.-L.; Sykes, A. G., *J. Am. Chem. Soc.* 1987, 109, 4615-4619.

[36] Lamprecht G.J.; Martinez M.; Nasreldin M.; Routledge C.A.; Al-Shatti N.; Sykes A.G., *J. Chem. Soc. Dalton Trans.* 1993, 747-754.

[37] Abramov, P.A.; Laricheva, Yu. A.; Peresypkina, E.V.; Mirzaeva, I.V.; Moroz, N.K.; Sokolov, M.N. *Inorg. Chim. Acta.* 2012, 383, 7-12.

[38] Liu Q.-T.; Lu, J.; Sykes, A.G. *Inorg. Chim. Acta*, 1992, 200, 623-626.

[39] Shibahara T.; Sakane G.; Mochida S., *J. Am. Chem. Soc.* 1993, 115, 10408 - 10421.

[40] Abramov P.A.; Sokolov M.N.; Virovets A.V.; Peresypkina E.V.; Fedin V.P., *J. Cluster Sci.* 2007. V. 18. N. 3. P. 597 – 605.

[41] Richens, D. T., *The chemistry of Aqua Ions, J. Wiley and Sons*, 1997, Chichester, pp. 301-304.

[42] Mironov, Yu.V.; Yarovoi, S.S.; Solodovnikov, S.F.; Fedorov, V.E., *J. Mol. Struct.* 2003, 656, 195-199.

[43] Richens, D. T.; Pittet, P.-A.; Merbach, A. E.; Humanes, M.; Lamprecht, G. J.; Ooi, B.-L.; Sykes, A. G., *J. Chem. Soc. Dalton Trans.* 1993, 2305.

[44] Gerasko O.A.; Sokolov M.N.; Fedin V.P., *Pure Appl. Chem.* 2004, 76, 1633–1646.

[45] Chubarova, E.V.; Sokolov, M.N.; Samsonenko, D.G.; Vicent, C.; Fedin, V.P.; *J. Struct. Chem.* 2006, 47, 939-945.

[46] Chubarova, E.V.; Samsonenko, D.G.; Platas, J.G.; Sokolov, M.N.; Fedin, V. P.; *J. Struct. Chem.* 2004, 45, 906-911.

[47] Sokolov M.N.; Hernandez-Molina R.; Dybtsev D.N.; Chubarova E.V.; Solodovnikov S.F.; Pervukhina N.V.; Vicent, C.; Llusar R.; Fedin V.P., *Z. Anorg. Allg. Chem.*, 2002, 628, 2335.

[48] Fedin V.P.; Virovets A.V.; Sokolov M.N.; Dybtsev D.N.; Gerasko O.A.; Clegg W., *Inorg. Chem.*, 2000, 39, 2227.

[49] Chubarova E.V.; Samsonenko D.G.; Sokolov M.N.; Gerasko O.A.; Fedin V.P.; Platas J.G., *J. Inclusion Phenomena and Macrocyclic Chem.*, 2004, 48, 31.

[50] Chubarova, E. V.; Samsonenko, D. G.; Platas, J. G.; Dolgushin, F. M.; Gerasimenko, A. V.; Sokolov, M. N.; Starikova, Z. A.; Fedin, V. P., *J. Struct. Chem.* 2004, 45, 1004-1013.

[51] Fedin V.P.; Sokolov, M.N.; Dybtsev D.N.; Gerasko O.A.; Virovets A.V.; Fenske D.; *Inorg. Chim. Acta,* 2002, 331, 31.

[52] Abramov, P.A.; Gushchin, A.L.; Sokolov, M.N.; Fedin, V.P.; *J. Struct. Chem.* 2010, 51, 378-381.

[53] Abramov, P.A.; Adonin, S.A.; Peresypkina, E.V.; Sokolov, M. N.; Fedin, V.P., *J. Struct. Chem.* 2010, 51, 731-736.

[54] Brorson M.; Hazell A.; Jacobsen J.H.; Schmidt I.; Villadsen J., *Inorg. Chem.* 2000, 39, 1346-1350.

[55] Müller, A.; Reinsch, U., *Angew. Chem. Int. Ed. Engl.* 1980, 19, 72-73.

[56] Müller, A.; Jostes, R.; Eltzner, W.; Nie, C.S.; Diemann, E.; Bögge, H.; Zimmermann, M.; Dartmann, M.; Reinsch-Vogell, U.; Che, S.; Cyvin, S.J.; Cyvin, B.N. *Inorg. Chem.* 1985, 24, 2872-2884.

[57] Howlander, N.C.; Haight, G.P.; Jr.; Hambley, T.W.; Lawrance, G.A.; Rahmoeller, K.M.; Snow, M.R. *Aust. J. Chem.,* 1983, 36, 377-383.

[58] Fedin, V.P.; Lamprecht, G.J.; Kohzuma, T.; Clegg, W.; Elsegood, M.R.J.; Sykes, A.G. *J. Chem. Soc., Dalton Trans.* 1997, 1747-1751.

[59] Kathirgamanathan P.; Martinez M.; Sykes A.G., *J. Chem. Soc., Chem. Commun.* 1985, 953-954.

[60] Nasreldin, M.; Henkel, G.; Kampmann, G.; Krebs, B.; Lamprecht, G.J.; Routledge, C.A.; Sykes, A.G., *J. Chem. Soc., Dalton Trans.,* 1993, 737-746.

[61] Shibahara T.; Yamada T.; Kuroya H.; Hills E.F.; Kathirgamanathan, P.; Sykes, A.G., Inorg. Chim. Acta, 1986, 113, L19-L22.

[62] Sokolov, M.N.; Gushchin, A.L.; Naumov, D.Y.; Gerasko, O.A.; Fedin, V.P., *Inorg. Chem.,* 2005, 44, 2431-2436.

[63] Shibahara, T.; Yoshida, Sh.; Maeyama, M.; Kojima, M., *Bull. Chem. Soc. Jpn.* 1999, 72, 2271-2275.

[64] Shibahara, T.; Akashi H.; Nagahata, Sh.; Hattori, H.; Kuroya, H., *Inorg. Chem.* 1989, 28, 362-370.

[65] Shibahara, T.; Miyake, H.; Kobayashi, K.; Kuroya, H., *Chem. Lett.*1986, 139-142.

[66] Shibahara, T.; Yamasaki, M.; Sakane, G.; Minami, K.; Yabuki, T.; Ichimura, A., *Inorg. Chem.* 1992, 31, 640-647.

[67] Hegetschweiler, K.; Wörle, M.; Meienberger, M.D.; Nesper, R.; Schmalle, H.W.; Hancock, R.D.; *Inorg. Chim. Acta*, 1996, 250, 35-47.

[68] Shibahara, T.; Kurimoto, N.; Kiyoda, S.; Kobayashi, Y.; Sakane, G., *J. Cluster Sci.,* 2000, 11, 333-341.

[69] Cotton, F.A.; Dori, Z.; Llusar, R.; Schwotzer, W., *Inorg. Chem.* 1986, 25, 3654-3658.

[70]   Yamaguchi, T.; Takagi, H.; Shibahara, T.; Akashi, H., *Inorg. Chem.* 2006, 45, 5429.

[71]   Cotton F.A.; Llusar R.; Schwotzer, W., *Inorg. Chim. Acta*, 1989, 155, 231-236.

[72]   Ama, T.; Rashid, M.M.; Saker, A.K.; Miyakawa, H.; Yonemura, T.; Kawaguchi, H.; Yasui, T., *Bull. Chem. Soc. Jpn.*, 2001, 74, 2327.

[73]   Hernández-Molina, R.; Sokolov, M.; Clegg, W.; Esparza, P.; Mederos, A., *Inorg. Chim. Acta*, 2002, 331, 52-58.

[74]   Saito, T.; Yamamoto, N.; Yamagata, T.; Imoto, H., *Chem. Lett.* 1987, 2025-2028.

[75]   Cotton, F.A.; Kibala, P.A.; Matusz, M.; McCaleb, Ch.S.; Sandor, R.B.W., *Inorg. Chem.* 1989, 28, 2623-2630.

[76]   Fedin, V.P.; Sokolov, M.N.; Gerasko, O.A.; Virovets, A.V.; Podberezskaya, N.V.; Fedorov, V.Y., *Inorg. Chim. Acta,* 1991, 187, 81-90.

[77]   Estevan, F.; Felix, M.; Llusar, R.; Mata, J.A.; Uriel, S., *Polyhedron,* 2001, 20, 527-535.

[78]   Feliz M.; Llusar R.; Uriel S.; Vicent C.; Humphrey M.G.; Lucas N.T.; Samoc M.; Luther-Davies B.; *Inorg. Chim. Acta*, 2003, 349, 69-77.

[79]   Frantz R.; Guillamon E.; Lacour J.; Llusar R.; Polo V.; Vicent C., *Inorg. Chem.* 2007, 46, 10717-10723.

[80]   Feliz M.; Guillamon E.; Llusar R.; Vicent C.; Stiriba S.-E.; Perez-Prieto J.; Barberis M., *Chem. Eur. J.* 2006, 12, 1486-1492.

[81]   Kawasaki H.; Sakane G.; Shibahara T.; *Inorg. Chem. Comm.* 2005, 8, 777-781.

[82]   Algarra, A. G.; Basallote, M. G.; Fernandez-Trujillo, M. J.; Guillamon,E.; Llusar, R.; Segarra, M. D.; Vicent, C., *Inorg. Chem.* 2007, 46, 7668-7677.

[83]   Acarvari N.; Kirakci K.; Llusar R.; Polo V.; Sorribes I.; Vicent C.; *Inorg. Chem.* 2010, 49, 1894-1904.

[84]   Algarra A.G.; Basallote M.G.; Fernandez-Trujillo M.J.; Feliz M.; Guillamon E.; Llusar R.; Sorribes I.; Vicent C., *Inorg. Chem.* 2010, 49, 5935-5942.

[85]   Llusar R.; Sorribes I.; Vicent C., *Inorg. Chem.* 2009, 48, 4837-4846.

[86]   Yao Y.; Akashi H.; Sakane G;, Shibahara T.; Ohtaki H., *Inorg. Chem.* 1995, 34, 42-48.

[87]   Huang, J.-Q.; Huang, J.-L.; Shang, M.-Y.; Lu, S.-F.; Lin, X.-T.; Lin, Y.-H.; Huang, M.-D.; Zhuang, H.-H.; Lu, J.-X. *Pure and Appl. Chem.* 1988, 60, 1185-1192.

[88]   Lu, S.; Huang, J.; Huang, M.; Huang, J., *Acta Chim. Sin.* 1989, 24-36.

[89]   Hu, J.; Zhuang, H.; Huang, J.; Huang, J. *Chinese J. Struct. Chem. (Jiegou Huaxue)* 1989, 8, 6-9.

[90]   Wu, L.; Xia, J.; Chen, C.; Huang, X.; Yao, Y.; Lu, J. *Polyhedron* 1998, 17, 4203-4212.

[91]   Xia, J.-B.; Yao, Y.-G.; Wu, L.; Huang, X.-Y.; Lu, J.-X. *Acta Crystallogr.* 1998, 1612-1615.

[92]   Chen Y., Wen Y., Qin Y., Kang Y., Li Z., Cheng J., Yao Y., *Inorg. Chem. Comm.* 2004, 7, 718-719.

[93]   Tang Y.; Qin Y.; Li Z., Zhang J.; Kang Y.; Hu R.; Wen Y.; Cheng J.; Yao Y., *Bull. Chem. Soc. Japan*, 2005, 78, 626.

[94]   Tang Y.; Yao Y.; Wu L.; Qin Y.; Kang Y.; Li Z., *Chem. Lett.* 2001, 542.

[95]   Hernandez-Molina, R.; Gonzalez-Platas, J.; Kovalenko, K. A.; Sokolov, M. N.; Virovets, A. V.; Llusar, R.; Vicent, C., *Eur. J. Inorg. Chem.* 2011, 683-693.

[96]   Hernandez-Molina, R.; Sokolov, M.; Nuñez, P.; Mederos, A.; *J. Chem. Soc. Dalton Trans.* 2002, 1072-1077.

[97]   Müller A.; Fedin V.P.; Kuhlmann C.; Fenske H.-D.; Baum G.; Bögge H.; Hauptfleisch B., *Chem. Commun.* 1999, 1189-1190.

[98] Duval, S.; Pilette, M. A.; Marrot, J.; Simonnet-Jegat, C.; Sokolov, M.; Cadot, E.; Chem.Eur. J. 2008, 14, 3457 – 3466.

[99] Izarova, N.V.; Sokolov, M.N.; Cadot, E.; Marrot, J.; Secheresse, F.; Fedin, V.P. Russ. Chem. Bull. 2004, 1503–1506.

[100] Sokolov, M.N.; Kalinina, I. V.; Peresypkina, E.V.; Cadot, E.; Tkachev, S.V.; Fedin, V.P., Angew. Chem. Int. Ed. 2008, 47, 1465 – 1468.

[101] Sokolov M.N.; Peresypkina, E.V.; Kalinina, I.V.; Virovets, A. V.; Korenev, V.S.; Fedin, V. P., Eur. J. Inorg. Chem. 2010, 5446-5454.

[102] Rink, B.; Brorson, M.; Scowen, I.J. Organometallics, 1999, 18, 2309-2313.

[103] Herbst, K.; Monari, M.; Brorson, M., Inorg. Chem. 2001, 40, 2979-2985.

[104] Beck, W.; Danzer, W.; Thiel, G. Angew. Chem., Ent. Ed. Engl. 1973, 85, 625-626.

[105] Cramer, R.E.; Yamada, K.I.; Kawaguchi, H.; Tatsumi, K. Inorg. Chem. 1996, 35, 1743.

[106] Abramov, P.A.; Sokolov, M.N.; et al. Inorg. Chem. submitted.

[107] Duval, S.; Marrot, J.; Simonnet-Jégat, C.; Cadot, E., Solid State Sciences, 2009, 11, 56-60.

[108] Duval, S.; Dumur, F.; Marrot, J.; Simonnet-Jégat, C.; Cadot, E., Inorg. Chem. Comm. 2012, 18, 11-14.

[109] Duval, S.; Floquet, S.; Simonnet-Jégat, C.; Marrot, J.; Biboum, R. N.; Keita, K. L.; Haouas, M.; Taulelle, F.; Cadot, E., J. Am. Chem. Soc., 2010, 132, 2069–2077.

[110] Shibahara, T.; Yamasaki, M.; Watase, T.; Ichimura, A., Inorg. Chem. 1994, 33, 292-301.

[111] Shibahara T.; Kuroya H., Polyhedron, 1986, 5, 357-361.

[112] Akashi H.; Shibahara T.; Kuroya H., Polyhedron, 1990, 9, 1671-1676.

[113] Shibahara T.; Yamamoto T.; Kanadani H.; Kuroya H., J. Am. Chem. Soc. 1987, 109, 3496.

[114] Sokolov, M.; Coichev, N.; Moya, H.; Hernandez-Molina, R.; Borman, C.; Sykes, A. G., J. Chem. Soc. Dalton Trans. 1997, 11, 1863-1869.

[115] Saito T.; Yamamoto N.; Nagase T.; Tsuboi T.; Kobayashi K.; Yamagata T.; Imoto H.; Unoura K., Inorg. Chem. 1990, 29, 764-770.

[116] (a) Petrov, P.A.; Virovets, A.V.; Alberola, A.; Llusar, R.; Konchenko, S.A. J. Chem. Soc. Dalton Trans., 2010, 39, 8875–8877 (b) Petrov, P.A.; Ph.D. Thesis, Novosibirsk, Nikolaev Institute of Inorganic Chemistry, 2010.

[117] Mizutani J.; Yamada S.; Imoto H.; Saito T. Inorg. Chem. 1996, 35, 244-247.

[118] Tsuge K., Mita S., Fujita H., Imoto H., Saito T. J. Clust. Sci. 1996, 7, 407-421.

[119] Tsuge K., Imoto H., Saito T., Inorg. Chem. 1992, 31, 4715-4716.

[120] Shibahara T.; Akashi H.; Kuroya H., J. Am. Chem. Soc. 1986, 108, 1342-1343.

[121] Hernandez-Molina, R.; Kalinina, I.V.; Sokolov, M.N.; Peris, G.; Llusar, R.; Synthesis and Reactivity in Inorganic, Metal-Organic and Nanometal Chemistry, 2007, 37, 765 – 770.

[122] Shibahara, T.; Sakane, G.; Mochida, S. J. Am. Chem. Soc. 1993, 115, 10408-10409.

[123] Takagi, H.; Ide, Y.; Shibahara, T., C. R. Chimie 8, 2005, 985-992.

[124] Takano, K.; Kawasaki, H.; Sakane, G.; T. Shibahara., J. Cluster Science, 2007, 18, 684-696.

[125] Ide, Y.; Shibahara T., Inorg. Chem. 2007, 46, 357-359.

[126] Ide Y., Shibahara T., Inorg. Chem. Comm. 2004, 7, 1132-1134.

[127] Bahn, C.S.; Tan, A.; and Harris, S.; Inorg. Chem. 1998, 37, 2770.

[128] Perrin, C.; Chevrel, R.; Sergent, M., *Compt. Rend*. 1975, 280, 94.

[129] Perrin, C.; Chevrel, R.; Sergent, M., *Compt. Rend*. 1975, 281, 23.

[130] Vandenberg, J. M.; Brasen, D., *J. Solid State Chem*. 1975, 14, 203-208.

[131] LeBeuze, A.; Zerrouki, M.C.; Loirat, H.; Lissillour, R., *J. Alloys Compd*. 1992, 190, 1-11.

[132] Shibahara, T.; Kuroya, H.; Matsumoto, K.; Ooi, S., *J. Am. Chem. Soc*. 1984, 106, 789-791.

[133] Henkel, G.; Kampmann, G.; Krebs, B.; Lamprecht, G. J.; Nasreldin, M.; Sykes, A. G., *J. Chem. Soc. Chem. Comm*. 1990, 1014-1016.

[134] Cotton, F.A.; Diebold, M.P.; Dori, Z.; Llusar, R.; Schwotzer, W. *J. Am. Chem. Soc*. 1985, 107, 6735 - 6736.

[135] Shibahara, T.; Kuroya, H.; Akashi, H.; Matsumoto, K.; Ooi, S. *Inorg. Chim. Acta*, 1993, 212, 251-263.

[136] McFarlane, N.; Nasreldin, M.; Saysell, D.M.; Jia, Z.-S.; Clegg, W.; Elsegood, M.R.J.; Murray, K.S.; Moubaraki, B.; Sykes, A.G. *J. Chem. Soc., Dalton Trans*. 1996, 363 - 369.

[137] Ooi, B.-L.; Sharp, C.; Sykes, A.G. *J. Am. Chem. Soc*. 1989, 111, 125 - 130.

[138] Hong, M.-C.; Li, Y.-J.; Lu, J.; Nasreldin, M.; Sykes, A.G. *J. Chem. Soc., Dalton Trans*., 1993, 2613 - 2619.

[139] Akashi, H.; Shibahara, T.; Narahara, T.; Tsuru, H.; Kuroya, H., *Chem. Lett*. 1989, 129-132.

[140] Li, Y.-L.; Nasreldin, M.; Humanes, M.; Sykes, A.G. *Inorg. Chem*. 1992, *31*, 3011-3017.

[141] Sokolov, M.; Esparza, P.; Hernandez-Molina, R.; Platas, J.G.; Mederos, A.; Gavin, J.A.; Llusar, R.; Vicent, C., *Inorg. Chem*. 2005, 44, 1132-1141.

[142] McLean, I.; Hernandez-Molina, R.; Sokolov, M.N.; Seo, M.-S.; Virovets, A.; Elsegood, M.; Clegg, W.; Sykes, A.G., *J. Chem. Soc. Dalton Trans*. 1998, 2557-2562.

[143] Baird, P.; Bandy, J.A.; Green, M.L.H.; Hamnett, A.; Marseglia, E.; Obertelli D.S.; Prout, K.; Qin J., *J. Chem. Soc. Dalton Trans*., 1991, 2377 – 2393.

[144] Bandy, J.A.; Davies, C.E.; Green, J.C.; Green, M.L.H.; Prout, K.; Rodgers, D.P.S., *J. Chem. Soc., Chem. Commun*, 1983, 1395-1397.

[145] Williams, P.D.; Curtis, M.D., *Inorg. Chem*. 1986, *25*, 4562-4570.

[146] Fedin, V.P.; Kalinina, I.V.; Samsonenko, D. G.; Mironov, Y.V.; Tkachev, S.V.; Virovets, A. V.; Podberezskaya, N. V.; Elsegood, M. R. J.; Clegg, W.; A.G. Sykes, A. G., Inorg. Chem. 1999, 38, 1956-1965.

[147] Fedin, V.P.; Virovets, A.V.; Kalinina, I.V.; Ikorskii, V.N.; Elsegood, M.R.J., Clegg, W., *Eur. J. Inorg. Chem*. 2000, 2341-2343.

[148] Fedin, V. P.; Kalinina, I. V.; Gerasimenko, A.; Virovets, A.V., *Inorg. Chim. Acta*, 2002, *331*, 28, 48-51.

[149] Kalinina, I.V.; Virovets, A.V.; Dolgushin, F.M.; M.Yu. Antipin, M.; Llusar, R.; Fedin, V.P.; *Inorg. Chim. Acta*, 2004, 357, 3390-3396.

[150] Shibahara, T.; Kuroya, H.; Akashi, H.; Matsumoto, K.; Ooi, S. *Inorg. Chim. Acta*, 1993, *212*, 251-263.

[151] Lu, S.-F.; Huang, J.-Q.; Zhuang, H.-H.; Li, J.-Q.; Wu, D.-M.; Huang, Z.-X.; Lu, C.-Z.; Huang, J.-L.; Lu, J.-X., *Polyhedron*, 1991, 10, 2203-2215.

[152] Coyle, C.L.; Eriksen, K.A.; Farina, S.; Francis, J.; Gea, Y.; Greaney, M.A.; Guzi, P.J.; Halbert, T.R.; Murray, H.H.; Stiefel, E.I., *Inorg. Chim. Acta*, 1992, *198*, 565-575.

[153] Cotton, F.A.; Dori, Z.; Llusar, R.; Schwotzer, W., *Inorg. Chem,* 1986, *25,* 3529-3533.

[154] Shibahara, T.; Kuroya, H.; Akashi, H.; Matsumoto, K.; Ooi, S., *Inorg. Chim. Acta,* 1993, *212,* 251-263.

[155] McFarlane, N.; Nasreldin, M.; Saysell, D.M.; Jia, Z.-S.; Clegg, W.; Elsegood, M.R.J.; Murray, K.S.; Moubaraki, B.; Sykes, A.G., *J. Chem. Soc., Dalton Trans.* 1996, 363 - 369.

[156] Hernandez-Molina, R.; Sokolov, M.N., *Russ. J. Coord. Chem.* 2012, 38, 163–170.

[157] Saysell, D.; Lamprecht, G.; Darkwa, J.; Sykes, A.G., *Inorg. Chem.,* 1996, 35, 5531.

[158] Dybtsev, D.N.; Geras'ko, O.A.; Virovets, A.V.; Weber T.A.; Fedin V.P., *Russ. J. Inorg. Chem.,* 2001, 46, 806-812.

[159] Murata, T.; Mizobe, Y.; Gao, H.; Ishii, Y.; Wakabayashi, T.; Nakano, F.; Tanase, T.; Yano S.; Hidai M., *J. Am. Chem. Soc.,* 1994, 116, 3389-3398.

[160] Fedin V.P.; Seo M.S.; Saysell D., et al., *Dalton Trans.,* 2002, 138.

[161] Dybtsev, D.N.; Sokolov, M.N.; Virovets, A.V.; Hegetschweiler, K.; Fedin, V.P., *Izv. Ross. Akad. Nauk, Ser. Khim.,* 2000, 1906 -1910.

[162] Akashi, H.; Uryu, N.; Shibahara, T. *Inorg. Chim. Acta,* 1997, 261, 53-57.

[163] Saysell, D.M.; Borman, C.D.; Kwak, C.H.; Sykes, A.G., *Inorg. Chem.,* 1996, 35, 173.

[164] Sokolov, M.N.; Virovets, A.V.; Dybtsev, D.N. ; et al., *Inorg. Chem.,* 2001, 40, 4816.

[165] Sokolov, M.N.; Chubarova, E.V.; Kovalenko, K.A.; Mironov, I.V.; Virovets, A.V.; Peresypkina, E.V.; Fedin, V.P. *Russ. Chem. Bull.* 2005, 615-622.

[166] Algarra, A.C.; Basallote, M.; Fernandez-Trujillo, M.J.; et al., *Chem. Commun.,* 2007, 3071.

[167] Andres, J.; Feliz, M.; Fraxedas, J.; Hernandez, V.; Lopez-Navarrete, J.T.; Llusar, R.; Sauthier, G.; Sensato, F.R.; Silvi, B.; Bo,.C.; Campanera, J.M.; *Inorg. Chem.* 2007, 46, 2159-2166.

[168] Feliz, M.; Garriga, J.M.; Llusar, R.; Uriel, S.; Humphrey, M.G.; Lucas, N.T.; Samoc, M.; Luther-Davies, B.; *Inorg. Chem.* 2001, 6132-6138.

[169] Llusar, R. ; Uriel, S. ; Vicent, C., *J. Chem. Soc. Dalton Trans.* 2001, 2813-2818.

[170] Hernandez_Molina, R.; Sykes, A.G., *Coord. Chem. Rev.,* 1999, 187, 291.

[171] Feliz, M.; Llusar, R.; Uriel, S.; Vicent, C.; Brorson, M.; Herbst, K., *Polyhedron,* 2005, 24, 1212-1220.

[172] Masui, D.; Yshii, Y.; Hidai, M., *Bull. Soc. Chem. Japan,* 2000, 73, 931-938.

[173] Feliz M.; Llusar R.; Uriel S.; Vicent C.; Coronado E.; Gomez-García C.J., *Chem. Eur. J.* 2004, 10, 4308-4314.

[174] Alberola A.; Llusar R.; Vicent C.: Andres J.; Polo V.; Gomez-García, C.J., *Inorg. Chem.* 2008, 47, 3661-3668.

[175] Algarra A.G.; Basallote, M.G.; Fernandez-Trujillo, M.J.; Llusar R.; Pino-Chamorro J.A.; Sorribes I.; Vicent C., Dalton Trans., 2010, 39, 3725-3735.

[176] Takei, I.; Suzuki, K.; Enta, Y.; Dohki, K.; Suzuki, T.; Mizobe Y., Hidai, M. *Organometallics,* 2003, 22, 1790-1792.

[177] Takei, I.; Enta, Y.; Wakebe, Y.; Suzuki, T.; Hidai, M., *Chem. Lett.* 2006, 35, 590-591.

[178] Takei I., Wakebe Y., Suzuki K., Enta Y., Suzuki T., Mizobe Y., Hidai M. Organometallics, 2003, 22, 4639-4641.

[179] Takei, I.; Dohki, K.; Kobayashi, K.; Suzuki, T.; Hidai, M., Inorg. Chem. 2005, 44, 3768-3770.

[180] Takei I.; Kobayashi K.; Dohki K.; Hidai M., *Inorg. Chem.,* 2007, 46, 1045-1047.

[181] Rink, B.; Brorson, M., Scowen, I., *J. Organometallics*, 1999, 18, 2309-2313.

[182] Herbst K.; Soderhjelm, E.; Nordlander, E.; Dahlenburg, L.; Brorson, M., *Inorg. Chim. Acta*. 2007, 360, 2697-2703.

[183] Herbst, K.; Monari, M.; Brorson, M.; *Inorg. Chem.* 2001, 40, 2979-2985.

[184] Herbst, K.; Rink, B., Dahlenburg, L.; Brorson, M., *Organometallics*, 2001, 20, 3655-3660.

[185] Herbst, K.; Zanello, P.; Corsini, M.; D'Amelio, N.; Dahlenburg, M.; Brorson. M.; *Inorg. Chem.* 2003, 42, 974-981.

[186] Chen, P.; Chen, Y.; Zhou, Y.; Peng, Y.; Qu, J.; Hidai, M., *Dalton Transactions,* 2010, 39, 5658-5663.

[187] Sakane, G.; Kawasaki, H.; Yamasaki, H.; Adachi, H.; Shibahara, T. *Chem. Lett.* 1999, 631-632.

[188] Sakane G., Kawasaki H., Oomori T., Yamasaki M., Adachi H., Shibahara T., *J. Clust. Sci.,* 2002, 13, 75.

[189] McLean, I.J.; Hernandez-Molina, R.; Sokolov, M.N.; Sykes, A.G.; *J. Chem. Soc., Dalton Trans.* 2002, 1941-1945.

[190] Gushchin, A.L.; Sokolov, M.N.; Naumov, D.Yu.; Fedin, V.P., *J. Struct. Chem.* 2008, 49, 748-752.

[191] Gushchin, A.L.; Kovalenko, K.A.; Sokolov, M.N.; Naumov, D.Yu.; Peresypkina, E.V. *Russ. Chem. Bull.*, 2007, 1707-1711.

[192] Duval S.; Marrot J.; Simonnet-Jegat C.; Mbomekalle I.M.; Sokolov, M.; Cadot, E.; Dalton Trans., 2012, 41, 3174-3184.

[193] Gushchin, A.L.; Sokolov, M. N.; Kovalenko, K.A.; Peresypkina, E.V.; Virovets, A.V.; Alferova, N.I.; Fedin, V.P.; *Russ. J. Coord. Chem.,* 2009, 35, 395–400.

[194] Hernandez-Molina, R.; Kalinina, I. V.; Abramov, P. A.; Sokolov, M. N.; Virovets, A. V.; Platas, J. G.; Llusar, R.; Polo, V.; Vicent, C.; Fedin, V. P., *Inorg. Chem.* 2008, 47, 306-314.

[195] Herbst, K.; Monari, M.; Brorson, M., *Inorg. Chem.* 2002, 41, 1336-1338.

[196] Taniguchi, M.; Imamura, D.; Ishige, H.; Ishii, Y.; Murata, T.; Hidai, M.; Tatsumi. T., *J. Catal.,* 1999, 187, 139.

[197] Tatsumi, T.; Taniguchi, M.; Ishige, H.; Ishii, Y.; Murata, T.; Hidai. M., *Appl. Surf. Sci.,* 1997, 121, 500.

[198] Taniguchi, M.; Ishii, Y.; Murata, T.; Tatsumi, T.; Hidai. M., *J. Chem. Soc., Chem. Commun.,* 1995, 2533.

[199] Hidai, M.; Kuwata, S.; Mizobe. Y., *Acc. Chem. Res.*, 2000, 33, 46.

[200] Guillamon E.; Llusar R.; Perez-Prieto J.; Stiriba S.-E., *J. Organom. Chem.* 2008, 693, 1723-1727.

[201] Hou, Y.; Abrams, B.L.; Vesborg, P.C.K.; Björketun, M.E., Herbst, K.; Bech, L.; Setti, A.M.; Damsgaard, C.D.; Pedersen, T.; Hansen, O.; Rossmeisl, J.; Dahl, S.; Nørskov, J.; Chrkendorff, I. *Nature Materials*, 2011, 10, 434-438.

In: Molybdenum
Editor: Alvin A. Holder

ISBN: 978-1-62417-272-4
© 2013 Nova Science Publishers, Inc.

Chapter 6

MODEL STUDIES OF MOLYBDENUM ELECTRON TRANSFER REACTIONS

Franklin A. Schultz[1], Richard L. Lord[2] and Mu-Hyun Baik[3]

[1]Department of Chemistry and Chemical Biology,
Indiana University Purdue University, Indianapolis, IN, US
Department of Chemistry, Indiana University, Bloomington, IN, US
[2]Department of Chemistry, Wayne State University, Detroit, MI, US
Department of Chemistry, Grand Valley State University, Allendale, MI, US
[3]Department of Chemistry, Indiana University, Bloomington, IN, US
Department of Chemistry, Korea University, Chochiwon, Chung-nam, South Korea

ABSTRACT

This Chapter describes the multidisciplinary efforts of our laboratories to understand relationships between the structure and reactivity of compounds that model the active sites of molybdenum-containing enzymes. Phenomena considered include (1) the role of coupled electron and proton transfer in modulating single versus multiple electron transfer in aqueous media, (2) the role of coordination geometry in modulating the electrochemical behavior of mononuclear oxomolybdenum complexes, and (3) the dramatic influence of sulfur versus oxygen ligation on potentials and rates of electron transfer reactions at molybdenum centers. The results of electrochemical and computational experiments are presented and interpreted with the goal of better understanding how changes in the coordination sphere of monometallic molybdenum species affect electron transfer properties.

LIST OF ABBREVIATIONS

Bu_4NPF_6 = tetra-*n*-butylammonium hexfluorophospate
Cat^{2-} = 1,2-benzenediolate (catecholate)
Cl_4cat^{2-} = tetrachlorocatecholate

DTBcat^{2-} = 3,5-di-*tert*-butylcatecholate
Et$_4$BF$_4$ = tetraethylammonium tetrafluoroborate
Et$_2$NCS$_2^-$ = N,N-diethyldithiocarbamate
HSAB = hard-soft acid-base
NHE = normal hydrogen electrode
NO$_2$cat^{2-} = 4-nitrocatecholate
RAMO = redox active molecular orbital
Sap^{2-} = N-salicylidene-2-aminophenolate
SCE = saturated calomel electrode
SMD = solvation model density
SOMO = singly occupied molecular orbital
SQ·$^-$ = semiquinone radial anion
Tp*$^-$ = hydrotris(3,5-dimethyl-1-pyrazolyl)borate

INTRODUCTION

Molybdenum is the only biologically essential second-row transition metal. It is found in two types of redox active metalloenzymes: the oxo transferases, [1-3] which catalyze a multitude of two-electron oxygen atom transfer reactions, and nitrogenase, [4-5] which catalyzes the reduction of atmospheric dinitrogen to ammonia. The active site structures of these enzymes are quite distinct. The cofactor of the oxo transferases contains a mononuclear molybdenum atom, one or more multiply bonded oxo groups, and a pterin-based enedithiolate ligand with the metal cycling through the +IV, +V, and +VI oxidation states. The nitrogenase cofactor consists of a polynuclear MoFe$_7$S$_9$X(homocitrate) (X = C, N or O) cluster with molybdenum in an intermediate oxidation state (most likely +IV) [6] and extensive sulfide bridging between metals.

Although the two families of molybdenum-containing enzymes differ considerably in structure and composition, they share important properties. These include multielectron transfer, the central role of sulfur in modulating redox potentials, and the possible involvement of metal-bound ligands in redox processes. Our laboratories have sought to understand relationships between structure and electron transfer reactivity with the objective of gaining fundamental understanding and practical implementation of these and other important natural processes. [7-10] Inorganic complexes that model the behavior of the mononuclear molybdenum enzymes are an excellent platform for such investigations. Herein we describe the results of electrochemical and computational studies of several oxomolybdenum systems that reveal the important influence of composition and structure on electron transfer reactivity.

COUPLED ELECTRON AND PROTON TRANSFER REACTIONS

Dioxomolybdenum(VI) centers occur commonly in the oxidized forms of molybdenum oxotransferase enzymes, which cycle through Mo^{VI}, Mo^{V} and Mo^{IV} oxidation states in the course of their catalytic reactions. [2] The *cis*-dioxo catecholato complex, $Mo^{VI}O_2(cat)_2^{2-}$ (1), is an accessible model of such systems.

Electrochemical reduction of $MoO_2(cat)_2^{2-}$ in aqueous solution [11] proceeds by sequential one- and two-electron transfers producing monomeric Mo^V and Mo^{III} species (Figure 1a). Each electron transfer is accompanied by the addition of two protons, which converts the multiply bonded oxo groups to coordinated water molecules:

$$Mo^{VI}O_2(cat)_2^{2-} + 2H^+ + e^- \rightleftharpoons Mo^VO(H_2O)(cat)_2^- \tag{1}$$

$$Mo^VO(H_2O)(cat)_2^- + 2H^+ + 2e^- \rightleftharpoons Mo^{III}(H_2O)_2(cat)_2^- \tag{2}$$

The Mo−bound aquo groups are coordinatively labile and can be replaced by ligands such as L = pyridine, NH_3 and other amines via the following reactions.

$$Mo^VO(H_2O)(cat)_2^- + L \rightleftharpoons Mo^VO(L)(cat)_2^- + H_2O \tag{3}$$

$$Mo^{III}(H_2O)_2(cat)_2^- + 2L \rightleftharpoons Mo^{III}(L)_2(cat)_2^- + 2H_2O \tag{4}$$

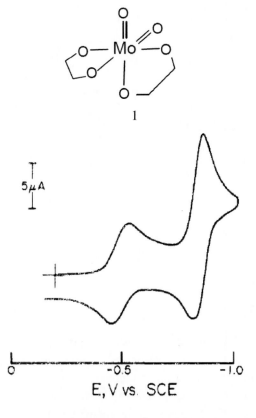

Figure 1a. Cyclic voltammetric reduction of $MoO_2(cat)_2^{2-}$ by sequential one- and two-electron transfers at a Hg drop electrode in pH 6.6 pyridine buffer; scan rate = 0.2 V s^{-1} (reprinted with permission from reference 11, Copyright 1980, American Chemical Society).

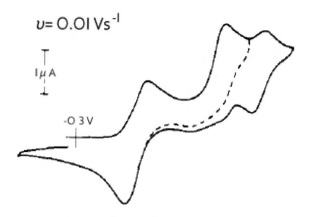

$v = 0.01\ Vs^{-1}$

$I\ \mu A$

$-0.3\ V$

Figure 1b. Cyclic voltammetric reduction of $MoO_2(cat)_2^{2-}$ by three sequential one-electron transfers at a Hg drop electrode in pH 7.7 ethylenediamine buffer containing 0.15 M H_2cat; scan rate = 0.01 V s^{-1}. Cathodic peak potentials (V vs. SCE) from left to right: -0.63, -1.08, -1.14 V (reprinted with permission from reference 12, Copyright 1982, American Chemical Society).

The above pattern of behavior changes dramatically in weakly alkaline solution containing excess catechol (Figure 1b). [12] Under these conditions catechol binds as a monodentate, monoprotonated ligand to the one-electron reduced Mo^VO^{3+} center. Following reduction of $Mo^VO(Hcat)(cat)_2^-$ to $Mo^{III}(H_2O)(Hcat)(cat)_2^-$, the third catechol ligand achieves bidentate coordination by displacing the coordinated aquo group. The $Mo(cat)_3^{3-}$ complex formed in this manner is then *oxidized* by one electron at the potential of $Mo^V \rightarrow Mo^{III}$ reduction to produce $Mo(cat)_3^{2-}$ resulting in a net one-electron transfer. $Mo(cat)_3^{2-}$ is subsequently reduced at a slightly more negative potential. These observations are described by the following sequence of reactions, wherein four oxidation states of molybdenum are produced within a range of ca. 500 mV.

$$Mo^{VI}O_2(cat)_2^{2-} + H_2cat + H^+ + e^- \rightleftharpoons Mo^VO(Hcat)(cat)_2^{2-} + H_2O \tag{5}$$

$$Mo^VO(Hcat)(cat)_2^{2-} + 2H^+ + 2e^- \rightleftharpoons Mo^{III}(H_2O)(Hcat)(cat)_2^{2-} \tag{6}$$

$$Mo^{III}(H_2O)(Hcat)(cat)_2^{2-} \rightleftharpoons Mo^{III}(cat)_3^{3-} + H_3O^+ \tag{7}$$

$$Mo^{III}(cat)_3^{3-} \rightleftharpoons Mo^{IV}(cat)_3^{2-} + e^- \tag{8}$$

$$Mo^{IV}(cat)_3^{2-} + e^- \rightleftharpoons Mo^{III}(cat)_3^{3-} \tag{9}$$

The dianionic product of reaction 8 may be formulated as either $Mo^{IV}(cat)_3^{2-}$ or $Mo^{III}(SQ)(cat)_2^{2-}$, where SQ· is a coordinated semiquinone radical anion. Definitive characterization of this entity has not been completed.

The $Mo^VO(Hcat)(cat)_2^{2-}$, $Mo^{IV}(cat)_3^{2-}$ and $Mo^{III}(cat)_3^{3-}$ species produced in reactions 6-8 have been investigated as electrocatalysts for the reduction of oxo anions. [13] The Mo^V and Mo^{IV} species are active catalysts for the reduction of NO_2^-, ClO_3^- and BrO_3^-, but not NO_3^- or ClO_4^-. This differentiation in reactivity suggests that substrate binding via the lone pair on its central atom is an important step in catalysis. Also, it is interesting to note that $Mo^{IV}(cat)_3^{2-}$ is a more effective catalytic reductant than either $Mo^VO(Hcat)(cat)_2^{2-}$ or $Mo^{III}(cat)_3^{3-}$.

Although $MoO_2(cat)_2^{2-}$ is not a precise model of the oxotransferase enzymes, its behavior illustrates several important aspects of molybdenum redox chemistry. (1) Coupled electron and proton transfer activates strongly bound oxo groups. (2) Coupled electron and proton transfer can produce multielectron behavior. (3) Changes in composition and structure enhance the accessibility of multiple oxidation states. (4) Coordinated ligands may be redox non-innocent and may promote catalytic activity.

INFLUENCE OF COORDINATION GEOMETRY

Proton transfer enhances the reversibility of oxomolybdenum redox processes in aqueous solution and in many instances leads to multielectron behavior. The characteristics of oxometal redox reactions differ in media of low proton availability. However, multiple electron transfer and chemical reversibility can be achieved by other means, such as modification of the metal's coordination environment.

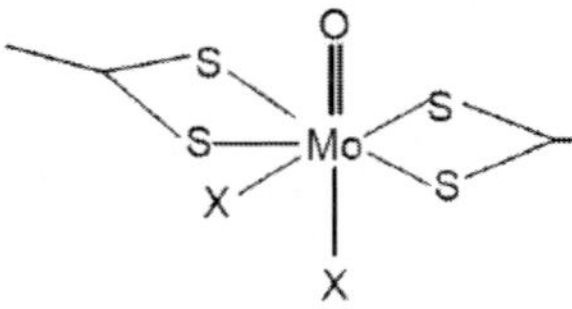

MoOX₂(S₂CNEt₂)₂

X = Cl⁻ (2a), Br⁻ (2b)

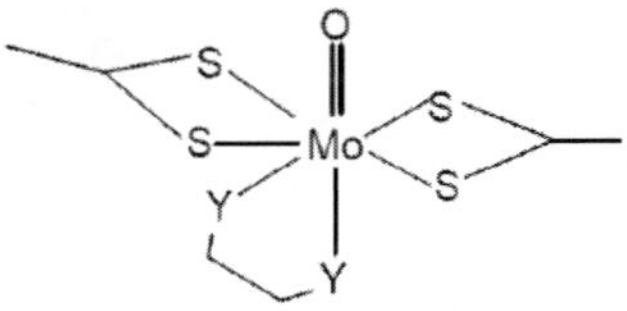

MoO(cat)(S₂CNEt₂)₂

Y—Y = Cl₄cat²⁻ (4a), NO₂cat²⁻ (4b),
Cat²⁻ (4c), DTBcat²⁻ (4d)

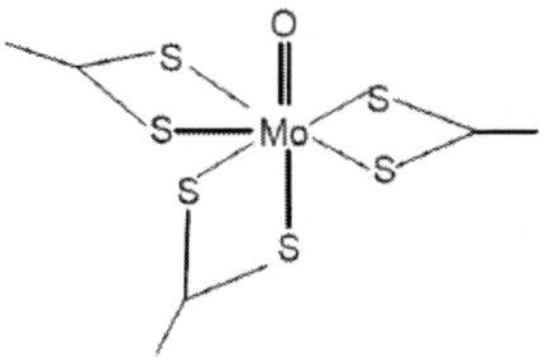

MoO(S₂CNEt₂)₃⁺ (3)

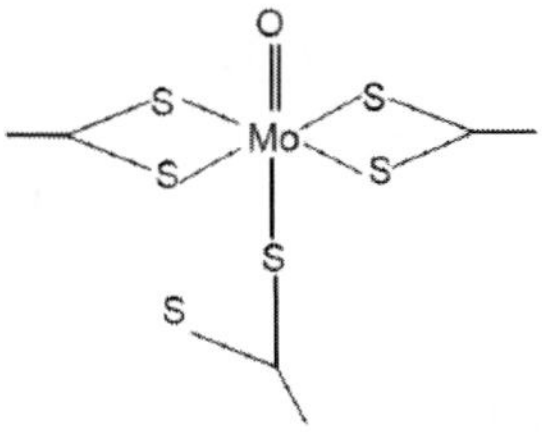

MoO(S₂CNEt₂)₃ (5)

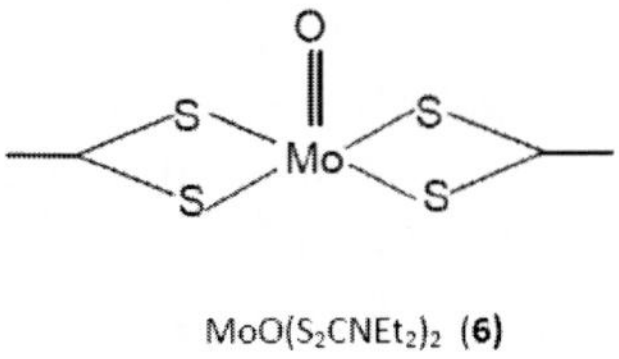

MoO(S₂CNEt₂)₂ (6)

Chart 1. Structural representations of mononuclear monooxo molybdenum complexes.

Compounds containing a mononuclear MoO^{4+} center frequently exist in seven-coordinate, pentagonal bipyramidal geometry. [14,15] Examples 2-4 in Chart 1 possess a multiply bonded oxo group in one axial position and two bidentate $Et_2NCS_2^-$ ligands in the equatorial plane. The remaining axial and equatorial coordination sites are occupied by either two monodentate halide ligands (2), a third bidentate dithiocarbamate ligand (3) or a bidentate catecholate ligand (4).

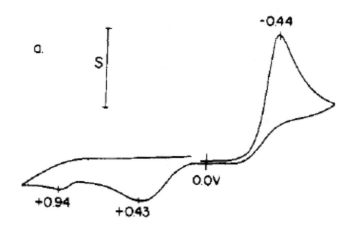

Figure 2. Cyclic voltammetric reduction of $MoOCl_2(S_2CNEt_2)_2$ (2a) at a Pt electrode in acetonitrile containing 0.1 M Et_4NBF_4; scan rate = 0.2 V s^{-1}; potentials in V vs. SCE (reprinted with permission from reference 16, Copyright 1986, American Chemical Society).

Electrochemical reduction of $MoOX_2(Et_2NCS_2)_2$ ($X^- = Cl^-$) in acetonitrile is illustrated by the results for 2a in Figure 2. [16] The magnitude of the cathodic peak at −0.44 V is consistent with an overall two-electron reduction. The electrode process is irreversible; i.e., no oxidative response is observed in the vicinity of −0.44 V following scan reversal. However, anodic peaks are detected at +0.43 and +0.94 V on further extension of the positive scan; these potentials coincide with those for oxidation of $Mo^{IV}O(Et_2NCS_2)_2$ (6) and Cl^-, respectively. Reduction of 2a or 2b in aprotic solvents therefore occurs by an irreversible two-electron transfer accompanied by a change in molybdenum coordination number from seven to five.

$$Mo^{VI}OX_2(Et_2NCS_2)_2 + 2e^- \rightarrow Mo^{IV}O(Et_2NCS_2)_2 + 2X^- \tag{10}$$

The individual steps in reaction 10 cannot be resolved on the time scale of cyclic voltammetry. However, it is likely that cleavage of a molybdenum-halide bond accompanies each electron transfer and that loss of chloride or bromide ion facilitates transfer of a second electron at the potential of the first by compensating for the electrostatic charge transferred to the metal. This hypothesis is supported by examination of complexes 3 and 4, which contain a third bidentate ligand spanning axial and equatorial positions. Cyclic voltammetric reduction of $[MoO(S_2CNEt_2)_3]^+$ at a slow scan rate (data not shown) reveals a single two-electron reduction peak at −0.32 V and anodic peaks at 0.0 and +0.47 V on scan reversal, which correspond to the oxidation of free $Et_2NCS_2^-$ and $MoO(S_2CNEt_2)_2$. If the experiment is carried out at a fast scan rate, the two-electron reduction is resolved into one-electron steps at −0.36

and −0.48 V as shown by the dashed line in the left-hand trace in Figure 3 with the third dithiocarbamate ligand being expelled from the complex following two-equivalent reduction. However, if the scan is reversed immediately following the first electron transfer at a fast scan rate (solid line, Figure 3, left), an anodic peak corresponding to reversible reoxidation of a Mo^V product is observed at −0.25 V, and the peaks corresponding to $Et_2NCS_2^-$ and $MoO(S_2CNEt_2)_2$ oxidation are absent. Thus, reduction of 3 proceeds by the following closely spaced one-electron reactions,

$$[Mo^{VI}O(S_2CNEt_2)_3]^+ + e^- \rightleftharpoons Mo^VO(S_2CNEt_2)_3 \tag{11}$$

$$Mo^VO(S_2CNEt_2)_3 + e^- \rightarrow Mo^{IV}O(S_2CNEt_2)_2 + Et_2NCS_2^- \tag{12}$$

wherein the molybdenum coordination number changes from seven to six and from six to five upon each electron transfer. The Mo^V intermediate, $MoO(S_2CNEt_2)_3$, is postulated to be a pseudo-octahedral complex with a pendant dithiocarbamate ligand (5). This sequence of structural changes is consistent with the characteristic seven-coordinate $Mo^{VI}O^{4+}$, six-coordinate Mo^VO^{3+} and five-coordinate $Mo^{IV}O^{2+}$ geometries displayed by monooxo molybdenum complexes [14,15].

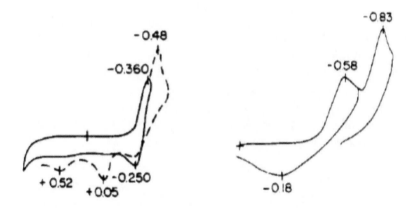

Figure 3. Cyclic voltammetric reduction at a Pt electrode of: (left) $[MoO(S_2CNEt_2)_3]^+$ (3) in acetonitrile containing 0.1 M Et_4NBF_4; *broken line*: scan reversed following second one-electron reduction; *solid line*: scan reversed following first one-electron reduction; scan rate = 25 V s^{-1}; (right) $MoO(Cl_4cat)(S_2CNEt_2)_2$ (4a) in N,N-dimethylformamide containing 0.1 M Et_4NBF_4; scan rate = 2 V s^{-1}; potentials in V vs. SCE (reprinted with permission from reference 16, Copyright 1986, American Chemical Society).

Complexes containing catecholate as the third bidentate ligand (4a-d) exhibit a similar pattern of behavior. [16] As shown on the right-hand side of Figure 3 these compounds display a larger separation between the potentials of $Mo^{VI/V}$ and $Mo^{V/IV}$ reduction and less reversible $Mo^{VI/V}$ electron transfer than 3. The scan rate dependence of the separation between cathodic and anodic peak potentials has been used to estimate the electron-transfer rate constant, $k_{s,h}$, of the $Mo^{VI/V}$ electrode reactions for 3 and 4a-d. [17] Table 1 summarizes these results.

The data indicate that the spacing between the $Mo^{VI/V}$ and $Mo^{V/IV}$ potentials increases and the rate of $Mo^{VI/V}$ electron transfer decreases as the donor strength of the third bidentate ligand increases. Thus, the composition of the inner coordination sphere exerts a dramatic influence on the thermodynamics and kinetics of electron transfer reactions at oxomolybdenum centers.

Table 1. Reduction potentials and heterogeneous electron-transfer rate constants of tris(bidentate) MoO^{4+} complexes [a,b]

Complex	$E^{o\prime}$ (V) [c]	ΔE (mV) [d]	$k_{s,h}$ (cm s^{-1})
MoO(S$_2$CNEt$_2$)$_3{}^+$ (3)	−0.30	+120	1.0 x 10^{-1}
MoO(Cl$_4$cat)(S$_2$CNEt$_2$)$_2$ (4a)	−0.44	+180	2.0 x 10^{-3}
MoO(NO$_2$cat)(S$_2$CNEt$_2$)$_2$ (4b)	−0.44	+160	5.4 x 10^{-4}
MoO(Cat)(S$_2$CNEt$_2$)$_2$ (4c)	−0.61	+320	1.5 x 10^{-4}
MoO(DTBcat)(S$_2$CNEt$_2$)$_2$ (4d)	−0.70	+400 [e]	1.2 x 10^{-4}

[a] In acetonitrile containing 0.1 M Et$_4$NBF$_4$ from reference 17.
[b] See Chart 1 for identification of catecholate ligands.
[c] Formal potential of Mo$^{VI/V}$ reduction in V vs. SCE.
[d] Separation between Mo$^{VI/V}$ and Mo$^{V/IV}$ potentials.
[e] Estimated value.

The metal-ligand bond cleavage that accompanies reduction of these seven-coordinate MoO^{4+} complexes is thought to arise from the change in occupancy of the redox-active Mo d_{xy} orbital upon electron transfer. As shown on the left-hand side of Figure 4 this orbital cannot orient its lobes among the five bonds in the equatorial plane of a pentagonal bipyramid without incurring unfavorable electrostatic interactions. Single occupancy of the orbital upon metal-centered reduction triggers metal-ligand bond cleavage and formation of a six-coordinate MoO^{3+} product. Subsequent reduction to Mo^{IV} proceeds with double occupancy of the Mo d_{xy} orbital and formation of a five-coordinate MoO^{2+} product.

Figure 4. Juxtaposition of the in-plane Mo d_{xy} redox-active orbital with five coordinate bonds in pentagonal bipyramidal geometry (left) and four coordinate bonds in octahedral geometry (right).

As a test of the above hypothesis we synthesized and characterized several complexes possessing an MoO^{4+} center in six-coordinate geometry. [18,19] The MoO(Sap)(cat) complex (7), which contains the tridentate Schiff base ligand, *N*-salicylidene-2-aminophenolate (Sap^{2-}) and a bidentate catecholate (cat^{2-}) ligand in addition to the lone Mo−oxo group, is an example of this structural type. As shown on the right-hand side of Figure 4 the singly occupied Mo d_{xy} orbital can now orient its lobes between four bonds in the equatorial plane of the pseudo-octahedral structure without incurring unfavorable electrostatic interactions. The Mo^{VI} to Mo^{V} reduction of complex 7 is fully reversible as shown by the cyclic voltammogram in Figure 5.

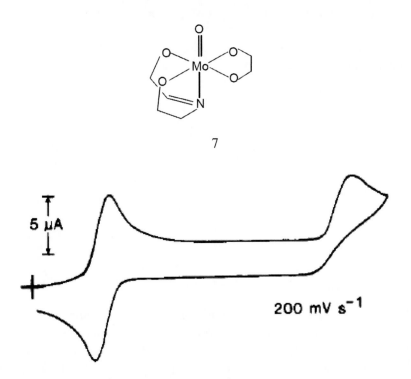

7

Figure 5. Cyclic voltammetric reduction of MoO(Sap)(cat) (7) in acetonitrile containing 0.1 M
Bu$_4$NPF$_6$; scan rate = 0.2 V s^{-1} (reprinted with permission from reference 18, Copyright 1988, American
Chemical Society).

Subsequent reduction to Mo^{IV} occurs at a much more negative potential and is not
reversible suggesting that one of the Schiff base donors has become detached in this step. The
electrode reactions of these six-coordinate MoO(Sap)(cat) complexes are summarized as:

$$Mo^{VI}O(Sap)(cat) + e^- \rightleftharpoons [Mo^{V}O(Sap)(cat)]^- \qquad (13)$$

$$[Mo^{V}O(Sap)(cat)]^- + e^- \rightarrow [Mo^{IV}O(Sap)(cat)]^{2-} \qquad (14)$$

INFLUENCE OF SULFUR VERSUS OXYGEN LIGATION

Sulfur long has been regarded as a crucial element in the coordination sphere of
molybdenum-containing enzymes. This is particularly so for the mononuclear
oxotransferases, whose active sites contain one or two 1,2-enedithiolate ligands and in many
cases a terminal sulfide and/or cysteine thiolate. [1-3]. It is thought that certain features
inherent in sulfur ligation, such as enhanced Mo−S covalency, facilitate electron transfer to
and from the active site by modulating metal-centered redox potentials and kinetic barriers.
[20-22] Among the mechanisms proposed for enhanced metal-sulfur interactions are those
based on the folding of a coordinated 1,2-dithiolene ligand along its S—S axis to increase
overlap of the out-of-plane S p-π orbitals with the metal in-plane redox orbital [23-26].

Experimental Studies. To address the question from an electron transfer perspective our laboratories have undertaken an exploration of sulfur's role in molybdenum redox chemistry by examining the electrochemical behavior of model complexes in which oxygen donors are systematically replaced by sulfur. [27,28].

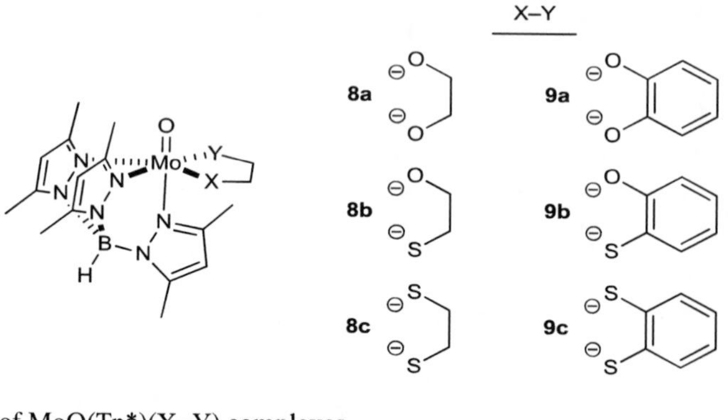

Chart 2. Structures of MoO(Tp*)(X−Y) complexes.

An informative example is provided by the monooxomolybdenum(V) complexes (8a-c, 9a-c; Chart 2), which contain a tridentate hydrotris(3,5-dimethyl-1-pyrazolyl)borate ligand (Tp*⁻) in addition to a bidentate 1,2-disubstituted aliphatic or aromatic ligand (X-Y) with systematically varied O or S donors. These compounds undergo reduction via the following one-electron transfer in non-aqueous solvents.

$$[Mo^VO(Tp^*)(X-Y)] + e^- \rightleftharpoons [Mo^{IV}O(Tp^*)(X-Y)]^- \qquad E^{\circ\prime}, k_{s,h} \qquad (15)$$

Figure 6 and Table 2 demonstrate the dramatic influence of donor atom identity on the thermodynamics of reaction 15. Substitution of two S for two O donors shifts the reversible potential of Mo^V reduction in the positive direction by over 700 mV for the aliphatic examples and over 600 mV for the aromatic ones. Moreover, complexes with aromatic bidentate ligands are more easily reduced than their aliphatic counterparts by some 300−400 mV. These results are consistent with previous observations of positively shifted redox potentials upon S for O substitution in molybdenum and other transition metal complexes [29,30].

Table 2. Electrochemical data for reduction of MoO(Tp*)(X−Y) complexes [a]

Complex	X−Y	$E^{\circ\prime}_{297}$ (V vs. Ag/AgCl)	$k_{s,h}^{297}$ (cm s⁻¹)	$\Delta H^{\ddagger}$ [b] (kcal mol⁻¹)	$\Delta H^{\ddagger}_{is}$ [c] (kcal mol⁻¹)	A [b] (cm s⁻¹)
8a	O,O	−1.145	7.7 x 10⁻³	8.6	5	1.3 x 10⁴
8b	O,S	−0.813	2.8 x 10⁻²	8.4	4	4.4 x 10⁴
8c	S,S	−0.402	2.4 x 10⁻¹	6.4	2	1.2 x 10⁴
9a	O,O	−0.721	2.6 x 10⁻²	5.5	2	2.5 x 10²
9b	O,S	−0.445	1.6 x 10⁻¹	3.3	0	0.5 x 10²
9c	S,S	−0.112	3.1 x 10⁻¹	3.1	0	0.5 x 10²

[a] In acetonitrile containing 0.3 M Bu₄NPF₆ at 297 K from reference 28.

[b] Determined from the temperature dependence of $k_{s,h}$; the uncertainty in $\Delta H^{\ddagger}$ is 1−2 kcal mol⁻¹.

[c] Estimated to one significant figure as $\Delta H^{\ddagger}_{is} = \Delta H^{\ddagger} - \Delta H^{\ddagger}_{os}$.

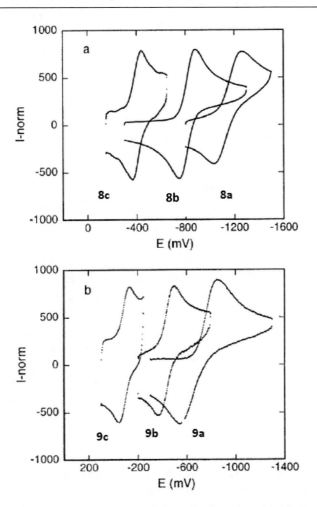

Figure 6. Current normalized cyclic voltammograms for reduction of MoO(Tp*)(X−Y) in acetonitrile containing 0.3 M Bu₄NPF₆. (a) Complexes bearing an aliphatic bidentate ligand (8a-c) at 297 K, scan rate = 5 V s⁻¹; (b) complexes bearing an aromatic bidentate ligand (9a-c) at 253 K, scan rate = 34 V s⁻¹ (reprinted with permission from reference 28, Copyright 2004, American Chemical Society).

Replacement of sulfur for oxygen donors also has a pronounced influence on the kinetics of reaction 15. Determination of the heterogeneous electron transfer rate constant, $k_{s,h}$, by variable scan rate cyclic voltammetry reveals that this change results in a 30-fold enhancement in $k_{s,h}$ for compounds 8a-c and a 10-fold enhancement for compounds 9a-c. Electron transfer rate constants for aromatic bidentate ligands also are uniformly greater than those for aliphatic ones. To obtain greater insight into the molecular features governing these kinetic trends the enthalpies of activation, $\Delta H^{\ddagger}$, and pre-exponential factors, A, for reaction 15 were determined from temperature dependent of measurements of $k_{s,h}$ [31] employing classical Marcus theory (eq 16) [32].

$$k_{s,h} = A \cdot \exp\left[-\Delta H^{\ddagger}/RT\right] \qquad (16)$$

The $\Delta H^{\ddagger}$ values so obtained parallel the trends in electron transfer rate constant. Larger activation barriers correlate with smaller rate constants for both O versus S donors and for aliphatic versus aromatic ligand frameworks. The enthalpy of activation in equation 16 equals the sum of contributions from the inner-shell (reactant) and outer-shell (solvent) reorganizations; i.e., $\Delta H^{\ddagger} = \Delta H^{\ddagger}_{is} + \Delta H^{\ddagger}_{os}$. For reactants of similar size and charge $\Delta H^{\ddagger}_{os}$ is nearly identical and for compounds 8a-c and 9a-c is estimated to be 4 ± 1 kcal mol^{-1}. [28] Therefore, the larger barrier heights that lead to smaller $k_{s,h}$ values for aliphatic frameworks and for oxygen donor ligands contain a significant contribution from the intramolecular reorganizations, $\Delta H^{\ddagger}_{is}$, that accompany electron transfer. These observations are consistent with the expectations of hard and soft acid-base theory, [33] wherein ligands with O versus S donors and aliphatic versus aromatic frameworks are more effective negative charge donors that produce a larger negative shift in redox potential. Stronger donors also establish stiffer bonds with electropositive metal centers resulting in larger internal reorganization energies and diminished electron transfer rates.

The experimentally determined pre-exponential factors of equation 16 show no dependence on the nature of the donor atom, but do exhibit larger values for aliphatic versus aromatic ligand frameworks. However, all results are close to the typical value of A = 3 x 10^3 cm s^{-1} observed for adiabatic electrode reactions in non-aqueous solvent. [34] The small differences in A do not obscure the influence of donor atom on electron transfer kinetics.

Computational Studies. Although the above explanations are self-consistent and intuitively satisfying, we pursued a more fundamental understanding of the experimental results. Thus, a theoretical study was undertaken to probe the influence of the molybdenum coordination sphere on the electron transfer energetics of complexes 8a-c and 9a-c using density functional theory. [35] Our study seeks to identify the underlying cause of the dramatic influence of molecular composition on the observed electron transfer rates and redox potentials. Of particular interest is whether or not the bidentate ligand displays redox non-innocent behavior. [36-38] Our density functional calculations include the effects of bulk solvation by acetonitrile as described in the final section of this chapter. Structural parameters obtained from geometry optimizations and their changes upon reduction are summarized in Table 3.

The calculated structural data in Table 3 show that very small changes of ≤0.01Å in the Mo=O, C−O and C−S bond lengths accompany reduction. The small change in bidentate ligand distances is noteworthy, because catecholate and arene dithiolate ligands have been implicated to be redox-active in other electron-transfer processes. More significant redox-induced structural changes occur in the bonds between molybdenum and the bi- and tridentate ligands. The largest elongations of 0.08−0.10Å are seen in the Mo−O bonds, which are several times greater than those observed for Mo−S bonds. The change in Mo−bidentate bond distances follows the trend O−O > O−S > S−S, which agrees qualitatively with the inner-shell reorganization energies derived from electron-transfer kinetic measurements (Table 2).

Mo−N$_{Tp}$ bond lengths also elongate upon reduction. The extent is several times greater for axial (0.06−0.08Å) than for equatorial bonds (0.01−0.03Å). This difference is consistent with weaker axial versus equatorial bonding as evidenced by Mo−N distances of ~2.4 and 2.2 Å, respectively, and likely is due to the stronger trans influence of the oxo group compared to that of the other donors. The disparity between the Mo−N$_{ax}$ and Mo−N$_{eq}$ distances increases upon reduction, but it appears that the axial nitrogen of the Tp*$^{-}$ ligand remains bound to Mo(IV) in all cases. Even so, the redox-induced Mo−N bond distance changes are significant and assuredly contribute to the inner-shell reorganization energy of reaction 15.

**Table 3. Calculated bond distances (Å) and fold angles (deg)
for MoO(Tp*)(X−Y) complexes and their changes upon reduction**

Species	Mo=O	Mo–O	Mo–S	Mo–N$_{eq}$	Mo–N$_{ax}$	C–O	C–S	Fold angle (θ)
8a^0	1.740	1.955	-	2.211	2.347	1.471	-	9.2
8a$^-$	1.754	2.032	-	2.221	2.423	1.467	-	14.4
8b^0	1.734	1.937	2.461	2.207	2.346	1.467	1.912	8.0
8b$^-$	1.744	2.032	2.481	2.222	2.418	1.463	1.920	12.3
8c^0	1.730	-	2.443	2.198	2.350	-	1.909	13.3
8c$^-$	1.737	-	2.469	2.225	2.414	-	1.920	12.6
9a^0	1.734	2.000	-	2.177	2.327	1.391	-	3.6
9a$^-$	1.742	2.082	-	2.193	2.399	1.381	-	10.4
9b^0	1.732	1.971	2.482	2.181	2.330	1.384	1.835	1.5
9b$^-$	1.738	2.068	2.495	2.203	2.396	1.376	1.840	10.6
9c^0	1.729	-	2.453	2.184	2.339	-	1.829	7.4
9c$^-$	1.733	-	2.472	2.215	2.400	-	1.842	11.4
8a^0 + e$^-$ → 8a$^-$	0.01	0.08	-	0.01	0.08	0.00	-	+5.2
8b^0 + e$^-$ → 8b$^-$	0.01	0.10	0.02	0.02	0.07	0.00	0.01	+4.3
8c^0 + e$^-$ → 8c$^-$	0.01	-	0.03	0.03	0.06	-	0.01	−0.7
9a^0 + e$^-$ → 9a$^-$	0.01	0.08	-	0.02	0.07	-0.01	-	+6.8
9b^0 + e$^-$ → 9b$^-$	0.01	0.10	0.01	0.02	0.07	-0.01	0.01	+9.1
9c^0 + e$^-$ → 9c$^-$	0.00	-	0.02	0.03	0.06	-	0.01	+4.0

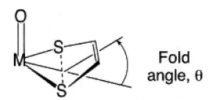

Figure 7. Definition of the bidentate ligand fold angle, θ, along its donor atom axis as illustrated for a 1,2-dithiolene ligand (reprinted with permission from reference 24, Copyright 2004, American Chemical Society).

An additional structural parameter of importance is the metal-bidentate ligand fold angle, θ, defined in Figure 7 as the extent to which the bidentate ligand has folded along its donor atom axis. An increase in θ is thought to increase the overlap between the out-of-plane bidentate donor π orbitals and the in-plane metal d_{xy} orbital, [23-26] thereby increasing the ligand character of the redox-active molecular orbital and modulating the redox potential and other properties of the molybdenum center. The results in Table 3 indicate that the Mo-bidentate fold angle is relatively small at ca. 1−15° and does not show a discernible dependence on donor atom or ligand structure. This proved to be the case even for optimizations started from multiple initial geometries including ones with ligands folded by 30–40°. Moreover, θ is seen to increase by 0–9° upon reduction in contrast to the expectation that this angle should decrease as the metal d-orbital occupancy increases. The potential energy profile along the Mo–bidentate ligand fold angle is evidently quite shallow. [24,26] For example, Drew and Hanson [26] found multiple minima for 9c with a thermodynamic difference of ~1 kcal mol^{-1} and a folding barrier of only ~2 kcal mol^{-1} for interconversion from the low energy state. Based on these results we expect multiple fold angle conformations to be sampled under the conditions of the electrochemical measurements, making it unlikely that the specific fold angle will have a large impact on electron transfer thermodynamics (i.e, 2 kcal mol^{-1} ≈ 87 mV). Inclusion of solvation effects during geometry optimization is a possible source of the differences between our results and the fold angles and energetic consequences reported by Enemark et al., [21-23] although such an analysis goes beyond the scope of this chapter. Whereas the implicit solvation models used herein can now be considered robust and established for redox potential calculations, it is unclear whether or not geometry optimizations that include implicit solvation models afford physically meaningful results. The concern is that the implicit solvation model, which simplifies the intrinsically complicated solvation phenomena into a continuous dielectric field, is not equipped to accurately reproduce structural changes that are likely the results of explicit solvent-solute interactions. Even with these fundamental uncertainties, our findings make clear that bidentate ligand fold angles exert only a minor influence on the electron-transfer energetics.

Table 4 summarizes the electron-transfer thermodynamics and redox orbital composition for species containing the ethylene glycolate-like (8a-c) and catecholate-like (9a-c) ligands. The experimental reduction potentials (E$^{o\prime}_{exp}$) span a thermodynamic window of ~1 V ranging from −1.15 to −0.11 V. A positive shift in this potential of 0.3−0.4 V is seen when: (i) each O is replaced by S and (ii) the alkane backbone is replaced by an aromatic one. These relative trends in reduction potential are well reproduced by our calculated values (E$^{o}_{calc}$), although a systematic underestimation of ~0.25 V is observed. This error is larger than those observed by our laboratories in computing redox potentials of low-valent Mo^{0}/Mo^{I}/Mo^{II} species, [8] and may be due to spin-orbit coupling effects that are neglected in our theoretical treatment of the high-valent Mo^{IV}/Mo^{V} states encountered here. Srnec et al. previously demonstrated for M(bpy)$_3^{3+/2+}$ redox couples that the error in neglecting spin-orbit coupling is small for Fe but leads to large deviations for Ru (~0.1 V) and Os (~0.3 V) [39].

Table 4. Comparison of experimental and calculated potentials and redox-active molecular orbital composition of MoO(Tp*)(X−Y) complexes

				RAMO Composition (%) [a]		
Redox Couple	E$^{o\prime}_{exp}$ [b]	E$^{o}_{calc}$ [b]	E$^{o}_{error}$	Mo=O	Tp	X–Y
8a^{0} + e^{-} → 8a^{-}	-1.145	-1.430	-0.285	84	4	11
8b^{0} + e^{-} → 8b^{-}	-0.813	-1.108	-0.295	84	5	12
8c^{0} + e^{-} → 8c^{-}	-0.402	-0.632	-0.230	87	5	8
9a^{0} + e^{-} → 9a^{-}	-0.721	-0.967	-0.246	83	5	11
9b^{0} + e^{-} → 9b^{-}	-0.445	-0.708	-0.263	83	5	12
9c^{0} + e^{-} → 9c^{-}	-0.112	-0.363	-0.251	79	5	16

[a] RAMO composition is computed for the SOMO of the oxidized species.
[b] Potentials in V vs. Ag/AgCl.

Given the prominence of catecholates and arene dithiolates in redox-active ligand studies [36-38] and our own experience with redox non-innocent behavior in phosphido- and sulfido-bridged Mo and W dimetallic species, [7,8] we suspected that the large variation in electron-transfer thermodynamics could be related to the degree of ligand character in the redox-active molecular orbital (RAMO). Thus, the RAMO was decomposed via Mulliken population analysis for each redox couple (Table 4). In every case the RAMO is revealed to be predominantly metal-centered ($83 \pm 4\%$) with a minor X–Y composition ($12 \pm 4\%$) that does not correlate with the electron-transfer thermodynamics or an increase in metal-ligand covalency upon substitution of S for O. Based on these results and the small C–O/C–S bond length changes attending electron transfer (Table 3), we conclude that the Mo^V/Mo^{IV} redox couple is a primarily metal-centered event with little direct ligand contribution to the RAMO.

Because the composition of the bidentate ligand does not reveal itself directly in the RAMO, it stands to reason that changes in Mo–(X–Y) bonding may instead be responsible for the large variation in electron-transfer thermodynamics.

To test this hypothesis, we computed the metal-ligand binding energy for each of the species. As depicted in Scheme 1 the binding strength is the sum of two components: (i) the interaction energy (E_{int}) of the bidentate ligand and the $[Mo(O)(Tp)]^{n+}$ fragment at the equilibrium geometry of the complex, and (ii) the distortion energy (E_{dist}) that captures the energy required to reorganize the geometries of the free fragments into those existing in the complex. E_{dist} is further decomposed into distortion energies for the bidentate ligand ($E_{X–Y}$) and $[Mo(O)(Tp)]^{n+}$ (E_{Mo}) fragments. The results of these calculations are presented in Table 5.

Before discussing changes in energy, it is useful to analyze E_{int}, E_{dist}, and E_{bind} values for the individual species (Table 5, top). All interaction energies E_{int} are highly favored with values of -87.2 to -215.3 kcal mol^{-1}, as expected for interaction of dianionic and positively charged fragments with larger energies resulting from the interaction with the 2+ fragment. The magnitude of E_{int} follows two important trends: (i) a > b > c, which indicates that the interaction energy is greater for O than S and (ii) 8 > 9, which indicates that the localized ethylene glycolate-like ligands interact more strongly with $[Mo(O)(Tp)]^{n+}$ than the delocalized catecholate-like ligands.

Both observations are consistent with hard and soft acid-base (HSAB) concepts and provide quantitative insight into the nature of the bidentate ligand bonding to Mo. Individual distortion energies, E_{dist}, are positive (as required by definition) and range from 6 to 36 kcal mol^{-1}. Three trends are observed for E_{dist} values: (i) oxidized species require more distortion than reduced species, (ii) the $[Mo(O)(Tp)]^{n+}$ fragment distorts more than the bidentate ligand, and (iii) the total distortion energies follow the same trends observed for E_{int}. Because distortion energies are much smaller (~one order of magnitude) than interaction energies, very exothermic binding energies, E_{bind}, ranging from -80.8 to -179.7 kcal mol^{-1} result. The differential interaction, distortion, and binding energies for the redox couples are listed in the bottom half of Table 5. ΔE_{bind} is positive, because the bonding to Mo^V is stronger than to Mo^{IV}. Recalling that 1 eV ~ 23 kcal mol^{-1} the 22.3 to 48.6 kcal mol^{-1} range in ΔE_{bind} is consistent with the experimentally observed thermodynamic window of ~1 V spanned by these redox couples.

Table 5. Energy decomposition of metal-ligand binding into the bidentate ligand distortion energy (E_{X-Y}), $[Mo(O)(Tp)]^{n+}$ fragment distortion energy (E_{Mo}), combined distortion energy (E_{dist}), interaction energy (E_{int}), and total binding energy ($E_{bind} = E_{int} + E_{dist}$). All energies are in kcal mol^{-1}

Individual Energies	E_{int}	E_{dist}	E_{X-Y}	E_{Mo}	E_{bind}
$8a^0$	-215.34	35.66	8.89	26.77	-179.68
$8a^-$	-156.43	25.37	4.82	20.54	-131.06
$8b^0$	-176.37	25.29	8.47	16.82	-151.09
$8b^-$	-127.51	16.82	3.76	13.06	-110.70
$8c^0$	-139.10	17.81	8.03	9.78	-121.30
$8c^-$	-105.46	13.06	3.64	9.42	-92.41
$9a^0$	-154.92	21.72	7.21	14.51	-133.19
$9a^-$	-107.75	11.80	2.67	9.13	-95.95
$9b^0$	-132.77	14.37	5.96	8.41	-118.40
$9b^-$	-94.73	7.77	2.19	5.58	-86.96
$9c^0$	-113.16	10.05	6.47	3.58	-103.11
$9c^-$	-87.24	6.41	3.12	3.30	-80.83
Differential Energies	ΔE_{int}	ΔE_{dist}	ΔE_{X-Y}	ΔE_{Mo}	ΔE_{bind}
$8a^0 + e^- \rightarrow 8a^-$	58.91	-10.29	-4.06	-6.23	48.62
$8b^0 + e^- \rightarrow 8b^-$	48.86	-8.47	-4.71	-3.76	40.39
$8c^0 + e^- \rightarrow 8c^-$	33.64	-4.75	-4.39	-0.36	28.89
$9a^0 + e^- \rightarrow 9a^-$	47.16	-9.92	-4.54	-5.38	37.24
$9b^0 + e^- \rightarrow 9b^-$	38.03	-6.59	-3.77	-2.83	31.44
$9c^0 + e^- \rightarrow 9c^-$	25.92	-3.64	-3.35	-0.29	22.28

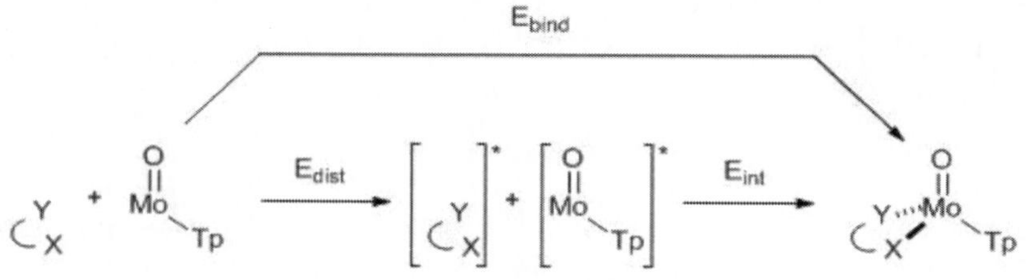

Scheme 1.

Moreover, the ΔE_{bind} ordering of $9c < 8c < 9b < 8a < 9b < 8a$ is identical to that of the electrochemical potentials, with the smallest (9c) and largest (8a) differential bonding energies corresponding to the most positive and negative reduction potentials, respectively. In addition to this qualitative ordering, the quantitative changes upon replacing O $\rightarrow$ S (10-15 kcal mol^{-1}) or between species 8 and 9 for a given set of contact atoms (8-12 kcal mol^{-1}) compares well with the 0.3-0.4 V shift in the experimental electrochemical potentials for both changes.

Decomposition of ΔE_{bind} into ΔE_{int} and ΔE_{dist} reveals that ΔE_{int} is large and positive with values ranging from 25.9 to 58.9 kcal mol^{-1}, while ΔE_{dist} is small and negative with values ranging from -3.6 to -10.3 kcal mol^{-1}. Therefore, ΔE_{int} dominates ΔE_{bind} as observed in the absolute interactions of the individual species. As noted for the individual interaction energies, the differential trends also follow the HSAB principle with oxygen showing stronger interactions than sulfur (a > b > c) and localized ligand charge showing stronger interactions than delocalized ligand charge (8 > 9). Given the high valence of Mo in these complexes it is reasonable that the harder localized oxygen-containing species 8a shows the strongest metal-ligand binding while the softer delocalized sulfur-containing species 9c shows the weakest metal-ligand interactions. However, not only are the absolute binding strengths dominated by HSAB, but the strongest interactions are *most sensitive to changes in the hardness of the metal center* as evidenced by the differential interaction (ΔE_{int}) and binding (ΔE_{bind}) energies shown in Table 5.

The results of these calculations are therefore consistent with the interpretation that differences in Mo–(X–Y) bonding are the predominant factor determining electron-transfer thermodynamics. Moreover, differences in ΔE_{bind} are dominated by ΔE_{int} rather than ΔE_{dist}, which suggests that straightforward electrostatic interactions are a reliable qualitative indicator of electron-transfer energetics in these circumstances.

It also is instructive to examine the distortion energies that accompanying electron transfer (ΔE_{dist}). The absolute magnitudes of these terms follow the order: 8a > 9a > 8b > 9b > 8c > 9c, which is in qualitative agreement with the heterogeneous electron transfer kinetic parameters reported in Table 2. Decomposition of ΔE_{dist} into ΔE_{X-Y} and ΔE_{Mo} reveals that the magnitude of ΔE_{X-Y} is approximately 4 kcal mol^{-1} for all six species and therefore that differential inner-shell reorganization occurs mostly within the $[Mo(O)(Tp)]^{2+/1+}$ fragment.

Computational Details. All calculations were completed using Gaussian [40] at the B3LYP/SDD level of theory. [41-46] Geometry optimizations [47] and wave function stability tests [48,49] were performed on the six species described in Chart 2 in both their neutral Mo^{V} doublet and anionic Mo^{IV} singlet states. All optimized structures were confirmed to be minima by analyzing the harmonic frequencies of each normal mode. The 3,5-dimethyl substituents on the pyrazolyl rings of Tp*$^-$ were replaced by H to speed up calculations and to avoid entropic artifacts associated with low-frequency rotational modes. [50].

The SMD continuum solvation model [51] (solvent = acetonitrile) was used to approximate solution conditions and was included in the geometry optimizations. Absolute redox potentials were obtained by relating the solution-phase free energy difference between the reduced and oxidized species (ΔG_{red}) to the absolute potential (E^{o}_{abs}) through equation 17. Computed potentials were corrected to values versus the NHE by application of the Truhlar-Cramer correction of 4.28 V [52,53] and thence to values versus Ag/AgCl by addition of 0.197 V (eq 18) [54].

$$E^{o}_{abs} = -\Delta G_{red}/nF \tag{17}$$

$$E^{o}_{Ag/AgCl} = E^{o}_{abs} - 4.28 - 0.197 \tag{18}$$

ACKNOWLEDGMENTS

This work was supported in part by the National Science Foundation (CHE-1001589 and CHE-0645381). One of the authors (F.A.S.) is greatly indebted to Ed Stiefel and Geoff Sykes for their memorable inspiration and collegiality.

REFERENCES

[1] Enemark, J.H.; Cooney, J.J.A.; Wang, J.-J.; Holm, R. H. *Chem. Rev.* 2004, *104*, 1175-1200.

[2] Majumdar, A.; Sarkar, S. *Coord. Chem. Rev.* 2011, *255*, 1039-1054.

[3] Hille, R.; Nishino, T.; Bittner, F. *Coord. Chem. Rev.* 2011, *255*, 1179-1205.

[4] Burgess, B.K.; Lowe, D.J. *Chem. Rev.* 1996, *96*, 2983-3011.

[5] Hoffman, B.M.; Dean, D.R.; Seefeldt, L.C. *Acc. Chem. Res.* 2009, *42*, 609-619.

[6] Pelmenschikov, V.; Case, D.A.; Noodleman, L. *Inorg. Chem.* 2008, *47*, 6162-6172.

[7] Schultz, F.A.; Lord, R.L.; Yang, X.; Baik, M.-H. *ACS Symp. Ser.* 2009, *1012*, 151-166.

[8] Lord, R.L.; Schultz, F.A.; Baik, M.-H. *Inorg. Chem.* 2010, *49*, 4611-4619.

[9] Ghosh, S.; Baik, M.-H. *Inorg. Chem.* 2011, *50*, 5946-5957.

[10] Schultz, F.A. *J. Solid State Electrochem.* 2011, *15*, 1833-1843.

[11] Charney, L.M.; Schultz, F.A. *Inorg. Chem.* 1980, *19*, 1527-1532.

[12] Charney, L.M.; Finklea, H.O.; Schultz, F.A. *Inorg. Chem.* 1982, *21*, 549-556.

[13] Lahr, S.K.; Finklea, H.O.; Schultz, F.A. *J. Electroanal. Chem.* 1984, *163*, 237-255.

[14] Stiefel, E.I. *Prog. Inorg. Chem.* 1977, *22*, 1-223.

[15] Garner, C.D.; Bristow, S. In *Molybdenum Enzymes.* Spiro, T.G., Ed.; Wiley: New York, 1987; Chapter 7.

[16] Bradbury, J.R.; Schultz, F.A. *Inorg. Chem.* 1986, *25*, 4408-4416.

[17] Schultz, F.A. *J. Electroanal. Chem.* 1986, *273*, 169-174.

[18] Mondal, J.U.; Schultz, F.A.; Brennan, T.D.; Scheidt, W.R. *Inorg. Chem.* 1988, *27*, 3950-3956.

[19] Mondal, J.U.; Schultz, F.A. *Inorg. Chim. Acta* 1989, *157*, 5-7.

[20] Carducci, M.D.; Brown, C.; Solomon, E.I.; Enemark, J.H. *J. Am. Chem. Soc.* 1994, *116*, 11856-11868.

[21] Inscore, F.E.; McNaughton, R.; Westcott, B.L.; Helton, M.E.; Jones, R.; Dhawan, I.K.; Enemark, J.H.; Kirk, M.L. *Inorg. Chem.* 1999, *38*, 1401-1410.

[22] McNaughton, R.L.; Helton, M.E.; Cosper, M.M.; Enemark, J.H.; Kirk, M.L. *Inorg. Chem.* 2004, *43*, 1625-1637.

[23] Joshi, H.K.; Cooney, J.J.A.; Inscore, F.E.; Gruhn, N.E.; Lichtenberger, D.L.; Enemark, J.H.; *Proc. Natl. Acad. Sci. U.S.A.* 2003, *100*, 3719-3724.

[24] Waters, T.; Wang, H.-B.; Yang, X.; Zhang, L.; O'Hair, R.A.J.; Wang, L.-S.; Wedd, A.G. *J. Am. Chem. Soc.* 2004, *126*, 5119-5129.

[25] Joshi, H.K.; Enemark, J.H. *J. Am. Chem. Soc.* 2004, *126*, 11784-11785.

[26] Drew, S.C.; Hanson, G.R. *Inorg. Chem.* 2009, *48*, 2224-2232.

[27] Olson, G.M.; Schultz, F.A. *Inorg. Chim. Acta* 1994, *225*, 1-7.

[28] Uhrhammer, D.; Schultz, F.A. *Inorg. Chem.* 2004, *43*, 7389-7395.

[29] Bond, A.M.; Martin, R.L.; Masters, A.F. *J. Electroanal. Chem.* 1976, *72*, 187-196.

[30] Schultz, F.A.; Ott, V.R.; Rolison, D.S.; Bravard, D.C.; McDonald, J.W.; Newton, W.E. *Inorg, Chem.* 1978, *17*, 1758-1765.

[31] Weaver, M.J. *J. Phys. Chem.* 1976, *80*, 2645-2651.

[32] Marcus, R.A. *Electrochim. Acta* 1968, *13*, 995-1004.

[33] Pearson, R.G. *Coord. Chem. Rev.* 1990, *100*, 403-425.

[34] Antonello, S.; Formaggio, F.; Moretto, A.; Toniolo, C.; Maran, F. *J. Am. Chem. Soc.* 2001, *123*, 9577-9584.

[35] Parr, R.G.; Yang, W. *Density Functional Theory of Atoms and Molecules*. Oxford University Press: New York, 1989.

[36] Chatterjee, P.B.; Goncharov-Zapata, O.; Quinn, L.L.; Hou, G.; Hamaed, H.; Schurko, R.W.; Polenova, T.; Crans, D.C. *Inorg. Chem.* 2011, *50*, 9794-9803.

[37] Eisenberg, R.; Gray, H.B. *Inorg. Chem.* 2011, *50*, 9741-9751.

[38] Sproules, S.; Wieghardt, K. *Coord. Chem. Rev.* 2011, *255*, 837-860.

[39] Srnec, M.; Chalupský, J.; Fojta, M.; Zendlová, L.; Havran, L.; Hocak, M.; Kývala, M.; Rulíšek, L. *J. Am. Chem. Soc.* 2008, *130*, 10947-10954.

[40] Gaussian 09, Revision B.01, Frisch, M.J.; Trucks, G. W.; Schlegel, H. B.; Scuseri, G. E.; Robb, M. A.; Cheeseman, J. R.; Scalmani, G.; Barone, V.; Mennucci, B.; Petersson, G. A.; Nakatsuji, H.; Caricato, M.; Li, X.; Hratchian, H.P.; Izmaylov, A.F.; Bloino, J.; Zheng, G.; Sonnenberg, J.L.; Hada, M.; Ehara, M.; Toyota, K.; Fukuda, R.; Hasegawa, J.; Ishida, M.; Nakajima, T.; Honda, Y.; Kitao, O.; Nakai, H.; Vreven, T.; Montgomery Jr., J.A.; Peralta, J.E.; Ogliaro, F.; Bearpark, M.; Heyd, J.J.; Brothers, E.; Kudin, K.N.; Staroverov, V.N.; Keith, T.; Kobayashi, R.; Normand, J.; Raghavachari, K.; Rendell, A.; Burant, J.C.; Iyengar, S.S.; Tomasi, J.; Cossi, M.; Rega, N.; Millam, J.M.; Klene, M.; Knox, J.E.; Cross, J.B.; Bakken, V.; Adamo, C.; Jaramillo, J.; Gomperts, R.; Stratman, R.E.; Yazyev, O.; Austin, A.J.; Cammi, R.; Pomelli, C.; Ochterski, J.W.; Martin, R.L.; Morokuma, K.; Zakrzewski, V.G.; Voth, G.A.; Salvador, P.; Dannenberg, J.J.; Dapprich, S.; Daniels, A.D.; Farkas, O.; Foresman, J.B.; Ortiz, J.V.; Cioslowski, J.; Fox, D.J. Gaussian, Inc., Wallingford, CT, 2010.

[41] Vosko, S.H.; Wilk, L.; Nusair, M. *Can. J. Phys.* 1980, *58*, 1200-1211.

[42] Lee, C.; Yang, W.; Parr, R.G. *Phys. Rev. B* 1988, *37*, 785-789.

[43] Becke, A.D. *J. Chem. Phys.* 1993, *98*, 5648-5652.

[44] Stephens, P.J.; Devlin, F.J.; Chabalowski, C.F.; Frisch, M.J. *J. Phys. Chem.* 1994, *98*, 11623-11627.

[45] Andrae, D.; Haussermann, U.; Dolg, M.; Stoll, H.; Preuss, H. *Theor. Chim. Acta* 1990, *78*, 247-266.

[46] Dunning Jr., T.H.; Hay, P.J. In *Modern Theoretical Chemistry, Vol. 3*. Schaefer III, H.F., Ed.; Plenum: New York, 1976.

[47] Schlegel, H.B.; Geometry Optimization, *WIREs* Comput. *Mol. Sci.* 2011, *1*, 790-809.

[48] Schlegel, H.B.; McDouall, J.J. In *Computational Advances in Organic Chemistry*. Ögretir, C.; Csizmadia, I.G., Eds.; Kluwer Academic: Amsterdam, The Netherlands, 1991.

[49] Bauernschmitt, R.; Ahlrichs, R. *J. Chem. Phys.* 1996, *104*, 9047-9052.

[50] Lord, R.L.; Schauer, C.K.; Schultz, F.A.; Baik, M.-H. *J. Am. Chem. Soc.* 2011, *133*, 18234-18242.

[51] Marenich, A.V.; Cramer, C.J.; Truhlar, D.G. *J. Phys. Chem. B* 2009, *113*, 6378-6396.

[52] Kelly, C.P.; Cramer, C.J.; Truhlar, D.G. *J. Phys. Chem. B* 2007, *111*, 408-422.

[53] Isse, A.A.; Gennaro, A. *J. Phys. Chem. B* 2010, *114*, 7894-7899.

[54] Bard, A.J.; Faulkner, L.R. *Electrochemical Methods*. John Wiley and Sons, Inc.: New York, 1980.

In: Molybdenum   ISBN: 978-1-62417-272-4
Editor: Alvin A. Holder   © 2013 Nova Science Publishers, Inc.

Chapter 7

COORDINATION CHEMISTRY OF MOLYBDENUM WITH CATECHOLATE LIGANDS

Cortlandt G. Pierpont[*1] and Ebbe Nordlander[2]*

[1]University of Colorado,
Department of Chemistry and Biochemistry, Boulder, CO, US
[2]Lund University, Inorganic Chemistry Research Group,
Chemical Physics, Chemical Center, Lund University, Lund, Sweden

ABSTRACT

Complexes of molybdenum with catecholate ligands have been studied for nearly a century. The catecholates tend to be strong σ- and π-donors in their bonding with molybdenum. Consequently, the metal in these compounds is d^0 Mo(VI), and the few known examples containing Mo(V) tend to be strong reducing agents. This chapter will focus on recent chemistry of molybdenum with the 3,6-di-tertbutylcatecholate ligand in the first section. The second section will concern a study on the formation of complexes containing multiple Mo-Mo bonds with tetrachlorocatecholate ligands as an extension of related chemistry with rhenium.

I. INTRODUCTION

The coordination chemistry of molybdenum with catecholate ligands has had a long history. Nearly a century ago catecholate complexes of molybdenum were found to exhibit intense electronic transitions in the visible, and catechol became useful as a reagent for the analytical identification of molybdenum. [1] Complex products formed in these analytical procedures were subsequently found to be highly colored $[Mo^{VI}O_2(Cat)_2]^{2-}$ (1) and $[Mo_2O_5(Cat)_2]^{2-}$ (2) dianions as species that could be detected visually [2].

---

* Telephone: 303-492-8420, E-mail: Pierpont@colorado.edu.

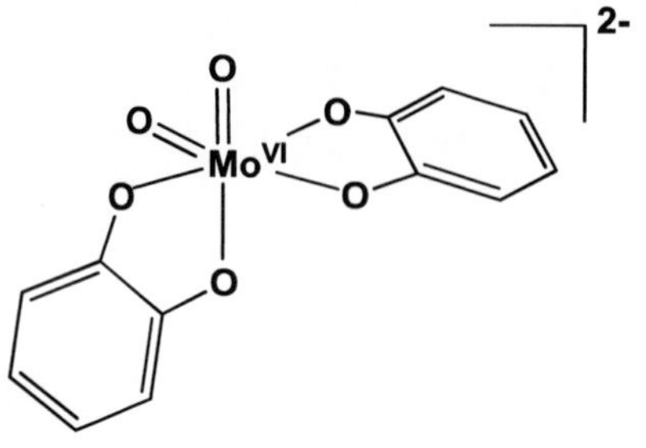

(1)

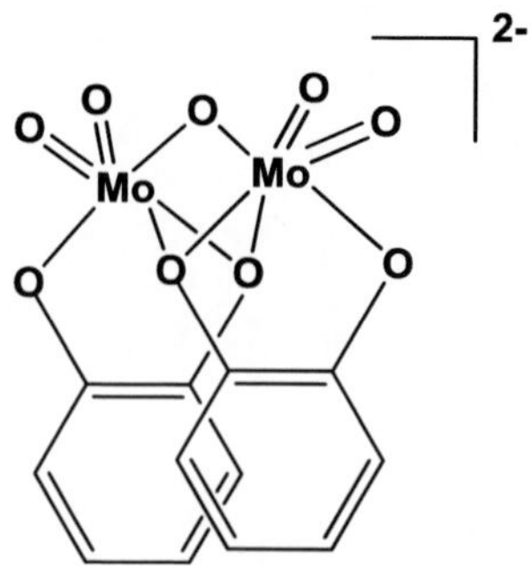

(2)

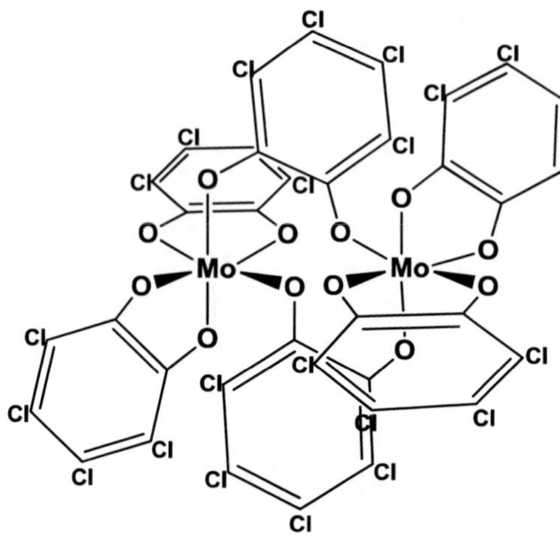

(3)

Within the past few decades, the coordination chemistry of molybdenum with catecholate ligands has been shown to have remarkable diversity. As a general result, strong π-donation by catecholate ligands stabilizes d^0 Mo(VI) in much the same way as the oxo ligand. [3] In this relationship neutral $Mo^{VI}(Cat)_3$ molecules would be related to $Mo^{VI}O_3$. By far the most common structural motif is the cis-$[Mo^{VI}O_2(RCat)_2]^{2-}$ dianion where the R catechol substituent is neither strongly electron releasing or withdrawing with ligand π-donation to the Mo(VI) ion similar to unsubstituted catechol. [4] Catecholates substituted with electron withdrawing chloro substituents form air-stable $Mo^{VI}(Cat)_3$ complexes as, for example, dimeric $[Mo(Cl_4Cat)_3]_2$ (3) [5].

With electron-releasing substituents catechols also form $Mo^{VI}(Cat)_3$ species, for example, Mo(3,5-DBCat)$_3$, however these molecules are extremely oxygen sensitive, reacting with trace quantities of O_2 to form oxomolybdenum(VI) products. [6, 7] At the time that this chemistry was initially reported tris(catecholato)molybdenum(VI) and monooxomolyb-denum(VI) complexes were unusual and considered to be oxo-deficient. The difference between the more common $[Mo^{VI}O_2(RCat)_2]^{2-}$ dianion and molecular $[MoO(3,5-DBCat)_2]_2$ (4) was attributed to stronger catecholate-to-molybdenum π-donation. Catechol substituent effects have been shown to be responsible for the diverse properties of their complexes with the ligands shown in Table 1.

$$2 \text{ Mo}^{VI}(3,5\text{-DBCat})_3 \; + \; O_2 \; \longrightarrow \; [\text{Mo}^{VI}O(3,5\text{-DBCat})_2]_2 \; + \; 2 \; 3,5\text{-DBBQ} \qquad (1)$$

(4)

Table 1. Catecholate Ligands and Abbreviations

Tetrachlorocatecholate	3,5-Di-*tert*butylcatecholate	3,6-Di-*tert*butylcatecholate
Cl$_4$Cat	3,5-DBCat	3,6-DBCat

Much of this chemistry has been described in reviews published earlier. [8] The focus in the first section of this review will be on more recent studies with the 3,6-di-*tert*butylcatecholate ligand.

II. MOLYBDENUM COMPLEXES CONTAINING 3,6-DI-*TERT*BUTYLCATECHOL AS A LIGAND

Synthetic routes to the molybdenum complexes of 3,6-di-*tert*butylcatechol were similar to procedures followed in the preparation of complexes with 3,5-di-*tert*butylcatechol. Whether the reaction is carried out by the addition of 3,5- or 3,6-di-*tert*butyl-1,2-benzoquinone to Mo(CO)$_6$ or by treating cis-Mo^{VI}O$_2$(acac)$_2$ with 3,5- or 3,6-di-*tert*butylcatechol the reaction product is the same. [7,9,10] Reactions between Mo(CO)$_6$ and 3,5-di-*tert*butyl-1,2-benzoquinone may be carried out in hydrocarbon solvents under scrupulously oxygen-free conditions to give a product characterized by ^{1}H-NMR and mass spectrometry as Mo^{VI}(3,5-DBCat)$_3$ [7].

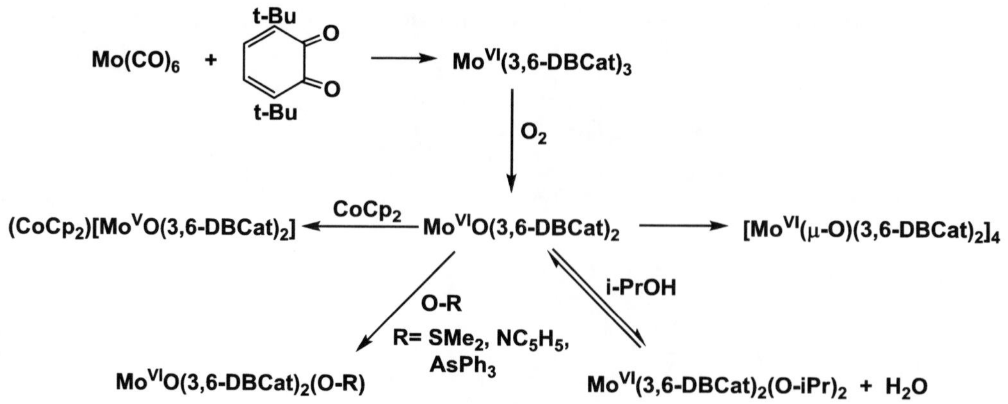

Scheme 1. Reactions beginning with $Mo^{VI}(3,6\text{-}DBCat)_3$.

Two resonances were observed for the unique catecholate *tert*-butyl groups as the result of a dynamic process in solution that rapidly equilibrates C_1 and C_3 isomers in solution at room temperature. [11] Subsequent examination of the temperature dependence of this spectrum in d^6-toluene has revealed a pattern at low temperature that is consistent with the formation of dimeric or oligomeric forms for the complex in solution. The most striking aspect of the chemistry of this compound is its sensitivity to trace quantities of dioxygen. This reaction gave as a product the dimeric monooxomolybdenum(VI) complex $[Mo^{VI}O(3,5\text{-}DBCat)_2]_2$ (4) with Mo centers bridged by the oxygen atoms of a catecholate ligand chelated to the adjacent Mo. [6,7].

A coproduct of the reaction with dioxygen was 3,5-di-tertbutyl-1,2-benzoquinone formed by reduction of O_2 at the complex with oxidation of one ligand. Further, it was found that $[Mo^{VI}O(3,5\text{-}DBCat)_2]_2$ could be used to reform $Mo^{VI}(3,5\text{-}DBCat)_3$ by treating the complex with a slight excess of 3,5-di-tertbutylcatechol under inert conditions. With this observation, and from earlier experience with related complexes of vanadium, [12] a cycle was proposed in which 3,5-di-tertbutylcatechol and dioxygen react to give 3,5-di-tertbutyl-1,2-benzoquinone and water (Scheme 1). This chemistry takes advantage of the electron-releasing substituents of the catecholate ligand, shifting the redox potential of the ligand negatively, relative to catechol, and its coordination with Mo(VI) as a strong π-donor. With this experience, the reaction between 3,6-di-*tert*butyl-1,2-benzoquinone and $Mo(CO)_6$ was investigated. [10] The bridged structure of $[Mo^{VI}O(3,5\text{-}DBCat)_2]_2$ (4) illustrates the tendency for the 3,5-DBCat ligand to form bonds with adjacent metals through the oxygen atom at the 1-position of the ring.

The 3,6-DBCat ligand appears unable to bridge metal ions due to the blocking effect of bulky substituents adjacent to both oxygen atoms. [13] It was thus anticipated that the products of the $Mo(CO)_6$/3,6-DBBQ reaction would have different structural features and, potentially, different chemical properties, from the products obtained with 3,5-DBCat. The reaction between $Mo(CO)_6$ and 3,6-DBBQ carried out under scrupulously oxygen-free conditions was observed to initially form air-sensitive $Mo^{IV}(3,6\text{-}DBCat)_3$ similar to the reaction with 3,5-DBBQ. [10] Similarly, subsequent reaction with O_2 was found to give a monomeric oxomolybdenum(VI) product, $Mo^{VI}O(3,6\text{-}DBCat)_2$, obtained from the reaction as a collection of oligomers identified by mass spectrometry.

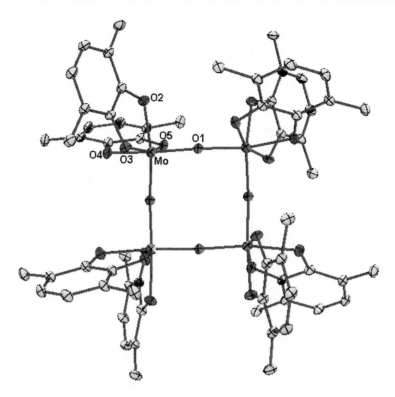

Figure 1. View of the $\Lambda\Lambda\Lambda\Lambda$ optical isomer of the [Mo^{VI}O(3,6-DBCat)$_2$]$_4$ square tetramer. Methyl carbon atoms of the *tert*butyl groups have been omitted.

Crystallographic characterization on the product obtained in highest yield revealed that it had a tetrameric structure of 4-fold symmetry with adjacent Mo centers linked by bridging oxo ligands (Figure 1) as a symmetrical product resulting from condensation of Mo^{VI}O(3,6-DBCat)$_2$ monomers. Each of the Mo centers has C$_2$ symmetry and is optically active. Steric interactions direct condensation resulting in homochiral tetramers of $\Delta\Delta\Delta\Delta$ and $\Lambda\Lambda\Lambda\Lambda$ stereochemistry in the solid-state crystal structure (Scheme I). Two proton NMR resonances are observed for ligand t-butyl groups of the tetramer indicating that it is structurally rigid in solution. The Mo-O bond length of 1.8761(4) along edges of the square is roughly 0.2 Å longer than terminal Mo^{VI}=O lengths showing that with strong π-donation from the 3,6-di-*tert*butylcatecholate ligands oxo π-donation is a weaker than for the more common cis-[Mo^{VI}O$_2$(Cat)$_2$]$^{2-}$ dianions.

It was of interest to observe the potential transfer of an oxido oxygen to the Mo^{VI}O(3,6-DBCat)$_2$ monomer for reasons associated with the chemistry of oxotransferase molybdenum centers. [14] Reactions between Mo(CO)$_6$ and 3,6-DBBQ were carried out in the presence of oxygen-atom donors including DMSO, pyridine-N-oxide, and OAsPh$_3$. Structural characterization on products MoO(3,6-DBCat)$_2$(OR), R= SMe$_2$, py, AsPh$_3$ showed that addition occurred selectively at a site cis to the terminal oxo ligand and that the Mo-O bond to the oxygen of the addition product was the longest of the molecule, longer than the catecholate Mo-O bond *trans* to the oxo ligand.

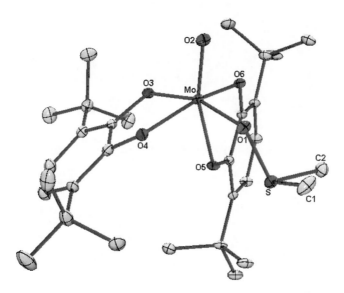

Figure 2. View of the $Mo^{VI}O(3,6\text{-}DBCat)_2(OSMe_2)$ molecule. The bond length from the Mo atom to the oxo oxygen, O2, is 1.690(2) Å, lengths to the catecholate oxygens range from 1.951(2) Å to 2.077(2) Å to O5 *trans* to the oxo ligand, and the Mo-O1 length to the dmso oxygen is 2.084(2) Å.

A view of cis-$MoO(3,6\text{-}DBCat)_2(dmso)$ is shown in Figure 2. At room temperature in solution a single resonance is observed for the t-butyl groups of the catecholate ligands as the effect of a non-dissociative stereodynamic process.

Site exchange by the ring and t-butyl proton resonances of the catechol ligands is consistent with rotation about a pseudotrigonal axis of the complex as a Bailar twist, as this isomerization mechanism yields an intermediate with C_s symmetry (5) that was identified by NMR spectroscopy. Resonances for the methyl groups of a free dmso molecule obtained with the complex as a molecule of crystallization remain unchanged through the dynanic process indicating that dmso dissociation is not a factor despite the long Mo-O bond length to the dmso ligand.

(5)

With the O-R substituent bound cis to the oxo ligand the addition products are poised to form the cis-$[Mo^{VI}O_2(3,6\text{-}DBCat)_2]^{2-}$ dianion upon reduction with release of R. Electrochemical characterization on $MoO(3,6\text{-}DBCat)_2(dmso)$ gave an irreversible two-electron reduction consistent with the formation of a $[Mo^{VI}O_2(3,6\text{-}DBCat)_2]^{2-}$ dianion.

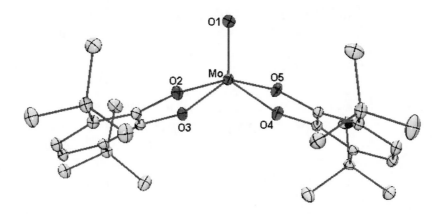

Figure 3. View of the $[Mo^{V}O(3,6\text{-DBCat})_2]^-$ monoanion obtained as the cobaltocenium salt. The Mo-O1 bond length to the oxo ligand is 1.690(2) Å. Lengths to the catecholate oxygens average to 1.977 Å and bond angles to the apical oxo ligand average to 110.0°.

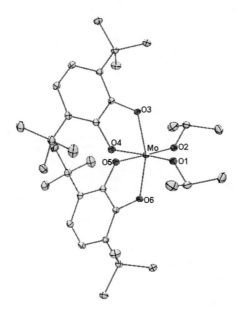

Figure 4. View of the $Mo^{VI}(3,6\text{-DBCat})_2(O\text{-iPr})_2$ molecule. Mo-O lengths to the isopropoxide ligands are 1.848(1) Å, lengths to the catecholate oxygens average to 1.961 Å.

Chemical reduction of $MoO(3,6\text{-DBCat})_2(dmso)$ with cobaltocene gave instead the air sensitive Mo(V) anion $[Mo^{V}O(3,6\text{-DBCat})_2]^-$ formed by one-electron reduction at the metal (Figure 3). To date, there have been no observations on a $[Mo^{VI}O_2(DBCat)_2]^{2-}$ dianion for either 3,5-DBCat or 3,6-DBCat.

Recrystallization of the $[Mo^{VI}O(3,6\text{-DBCat})_2]_4$ tetramer from a hexane/i-propanol solution gave an unexpected result. The product obtained was cis-$Mo(3,6\text{-DBCat})_2(O\text{-iPr})_2$ (Figure 4) formed as the apparent product of a dehydration reaction. ^{1}H-NMR spectra recorded on the isopropoxide product indicate that it is stereochemically rigid. This reaction further illustrates the strength of π-donation to the Mo(VI) center by the 3,6-DBCat ligands.

The stereodynamic properties of the O-R addition products, $MoO(3,6\text{-}DBCat)_2(OR)$, result from weak donation by the O-R oxygen to the d^0 Mo(VI) center stabilized by the oxo and catecholate ligands.

III. CATECHOLATE COMPLEXES OF MOLYBDENUM CONTAINING MULTIPLE Mo-Mo BONDS

Complexes containing multiple metal-metal bonds contain a reservoir of charge that may be used in substrate activation reactions. Strong σ- and π-donation from catecholate electron pairs into metal orbitals associated with the M-M bond may further activate the complex, and the electrochemical activity of catecholate ligands could further increase the number of electrons available for substrate reduction. Kitagawa and coworkers have described complexes of ruthenium containing multiple Ru-Ru bonds with chelating catecholate ligands. [15].

Treatment of $Ru_2(OAc)_4Cl$ with catechols may be used to form dimeric $[Ru_2(Cat)_4]^{3-}$ trianions with a Ru-Ru bond order of 2.5. One-electron oxidation to $[Ru_2(Cat)_4]^{2-}$ increased the Ru-Ru bond order to a triple bond. In an attempt to extend these reactions to quadruply bonded dimers we treated the $[Re_2Cl_8]^{2-}$ dianion with tetrachlorocatechol. [16].

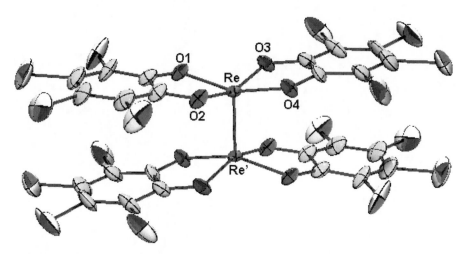

Figure 5. View of the $[Re_2(Cl_4Cat)_4]^{2-}$ dianion containing a quadruple Re-Re bond. The Re-Re' bond length is 2.2067(7) Å.

The product of this reaction shown in Figure 5 is the $[Re_2(Cl_4Cat)_4]^{2-}$ dianion containing a Re-Re bond length of 2.2067(7) Å. This length is well within the range of Re-Re lengths reported for quadruply bonded dimers of rhenium. The short bond length and the eclipsed orientation of the catecholate ligands show that the strong quadruple bond of $[Re_2Cl_8]^{2-}$ remains intact in this ligand replacement reaction.

It was of interest to extend this reaction to form a quadruply-bonded dimer of molybdenum similar to $[Re_2(Cl_4Cat)_4]^{2-}$. However, with molybdenum the dimer would have a charge of 4– as $[Mo_2(Cl_4Cat)_4]^{4-}$, and from earlier experience with the chemistry of molybdenum-catecholate complexes it was anticipated to be extremely oxygen sensitive, contrasting with the air-stability of the rhenium dimer. The synthetic route chosen to form $[Mo_2(Cl_4Cat)_4]^{4-}$ involved treating $Mo_2(OAc)_4$ with tetrachlorocatechol in THF solution. [16] A methanol solution of $(NEt_4)I$ was added once the reaction had taken place, and the tetraethylammonium cation successfully gave crystalline reaction products.

We speculate that the initial product formed in the reaction between $Mo_2(OAc)_4$ and tetrachlorocatechol is the quadruply-bonded dimer $[Mo_2(Cl_4Cat)_4]^{4-}$ and that reaction with trace quantities of O_2 in the reaction medium gives the dimer $[(Cl_4Cat)_2Mo^{IV}(\mu\text{-}O)_2Mo^{IV}(Cl_4Cat)_2]^{4-}$ (6). This dimer has been obtained by Chang and coworkers in reactions between $Mo_2(OAc)_4$ and tetrabromocatechol and characterized structurally. [17] The Mo(IV) centers in the dimer are bridged by oxo ligands presumably derived from O_2 and the metals are linked by a strong Mo-Mo double bond. Other products obtained from this reaction appear to be either derived from $[(Cl_4Cat)_2Mo^{IV}(\mu\text{-}O)_2Mo^{IV}(Cl_4Cat)_2]^{4-}$ or are products of further steps in oxidation (Scheme 2).

The Mo-Mo double bond of (6) remains quite reactive. It reacts with O_2 upon recrystallization in air to give the monomeric $[Mo^{VI}O_2(Cl_4Cat)_2]^{2-}$ dianion shown in Figure 6 as the final product in the series of oxidation reactions of $[Mo_2(Cl_4Cat)_4]^{4-}$. This dianion is an example of the catecholate complexes shown above in drawing (1).

Simple one-electron oxidation of (6) at each Mo(IV) center in THF solution results in dissociation to give the oxomolybdenum(V) product shown in Figure 7. In solution monomeric $[Mo^{V}O(Cl_4Cat)_2(thf)]^{-}$ is oxygen sensitive forming $[Mo^{VI}O_2(Cl_4Cat)_2]^{2-}$, but if the reaction is carried out slowly with an O_2/Ar gas mixture the product obtained is a mixed-valence $Mo^{V}Mo^{VI}$ product $[(Cl_4Cat)_2Mo^{V}O(\mu\text{-}O)Mo^{VI}O(Cl_4Cat)_2]^{3-}$ formed as a dimeric condensation product of $[Mo^{VI}O_2(Cl_4Cat)_2]^{2-}$ and $[Mo^{V}O(Cl_4Cat)_2(thf)]^{-}$.

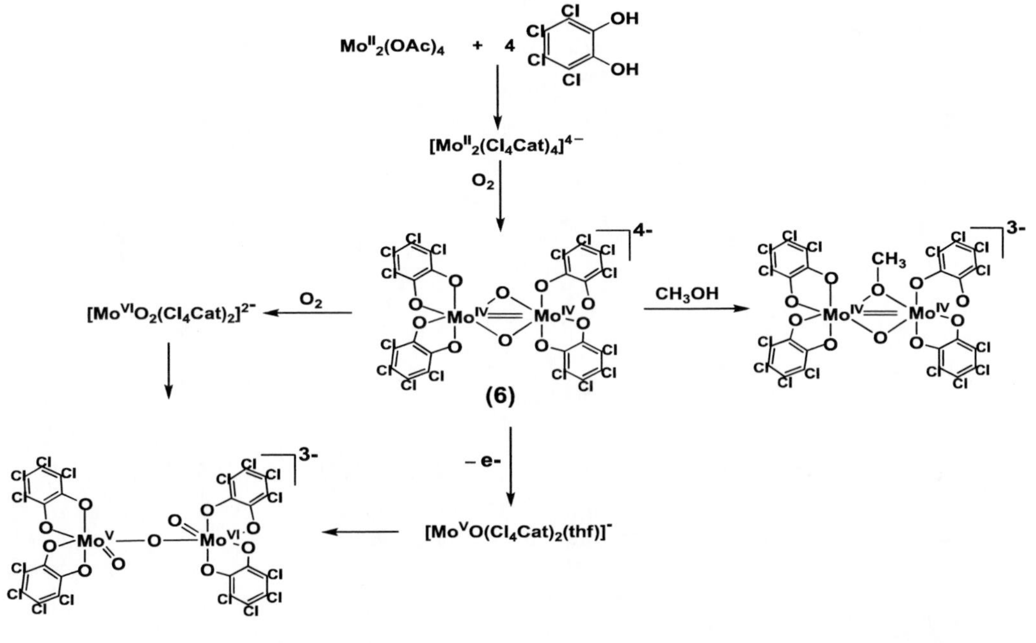

Scheme 2. Tetrachlorocatecholate complexes of molybdenum containing multiple Mo-Mo bonds and their reactions.

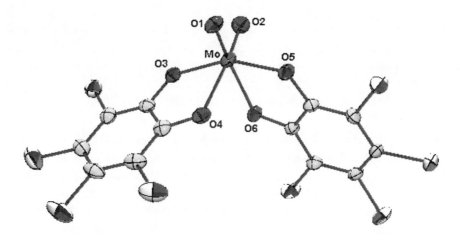

Figure 6. View of the $[Mo^{VI}O_2(Cl_4Cat)_2]^{2-}$ dianion.

In solution the isotropic EPR spectrum of this product shows an 11-line hyperfine coupling pattern to the $^{95,97}Mo$ nuclei indicating spin delocalization through the bridging oxo ligand. The X-ray structure of the trianion places the complex about a center of inversion symmetry (Figure 8). Large thermal parameters for the ligands have limited the precision of the structure determination and may indicate a charge-localized electronic structure in the solid state. Superposition of Mo(V) and Mo(VI) halves of the anion, with slightly different metrical parameters, may be the source of disorder in the structure determination.

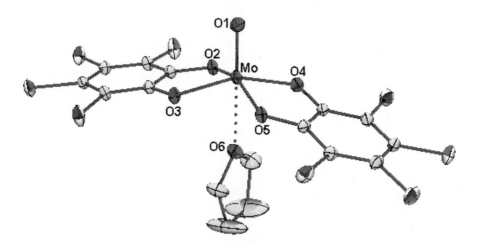

Figure 7. View of the $[Mo^VO(Cl_4Cat)_2(thf)]^-$ monoanion. The Mo-O1 bond length to the oxo ligand is 1.678(5) Å. Lengths to the catecholate oxygens average to 2.001 Å and bond angles to the apical oxo ligand average to 102.3°. The Mo-O length to the thf ligand is 2.439(6).

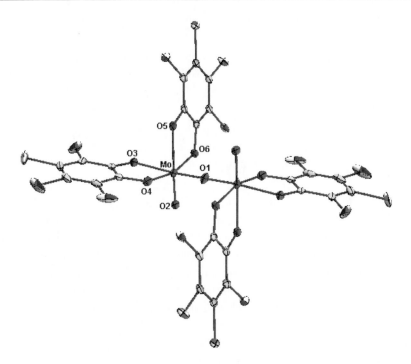

Figure 8. View of the $[(Cl_4Cat)_2Mo^VO(\mu-O)Mo^{VI}O(Cl_4Cat)_2]^{3-}$ anion. Oxygen O1 is located about a center of inversion with a Mo-O1 bond length of 1.859(4) Å. The Mo-O2 length is 1.690(4) Å and lengths to the catecholate oxygens range from 1.991(5) to 2.150(5) Å.

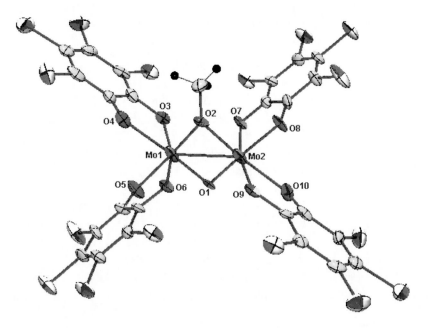

Figure 9. View of the $[(Cl_4Cat)_2Mo^{IV}(\mu-O)(\mu-OMe)Mo^{IV}(Cl_4Cat)_2]^{3-}$ anion. The Mo1-Mo2 bond length is 2.436(1) Å, consistent with a Mo=Mo double bond.

The addition of $(NEt_4)I$ in methanol solution to a THF solution of (6) to provide a cation suitable for crystallization gave $[(Cl_4Cat)_2Mo^{IV}(\mu-O)(\mu-OMe)Mo^{IV}(Cl_4Cat)_2]^{3-}$ shown in Figure 9. The substitution of a bridging methoxide ion for one bridging oxo ligand of (6) appears to occur without cleavage of the Mo-Mo double bond. Alternatively, this product may form during the oxidation of $[Mo_2(Cl_4Cat)_4]^{4-}$ since the addition of the methanol solution occurred in conjunction with the reaction between $Mo_2(OAc)_4$ and tetrachlorocatechol.

CONCLUSION

Molybdenum in its higher oxidation states has a great affinity for oxo and oxygen-donor ligands. Complexes formed with catecholate ligands illustrate this affinity and show an interesting dependence on ligand substituents. With electron-releasing t-butyl substituents the 3,6-DBCat ligand forms stable oxo-deficient complexes of Mo(VI). Donation effects are less significant for the Cl_4Cat ligand with its ability to form stable, but reactive, complexes of molybdenum in lower oxidation states containing multiple Mo-Mo bonds. The chemistry of these compounds has yet to be developed in organometallic applications.

ACKNOWLEDGMENTS

Research at Lund University was supported by the Swedish Research Council (VR). Research at the University of Colorado was supported by the National Science Foundation. CGP would like to thank The Swedish Foundation for International Cooperation in Research (STINT) for a research fellowship.

REFERENCES

[1]   (a) Weinland, R. F.; Gaisser, F. Z. Anorg. Allg. Chem. 1919, 108, 231. (b) Weinland, R. F.; Huthmann, P. Arch. Pharm. 1924, 262, 329. (c) Weinland, R. F.; Babel, A.; Gross, K.; Mai, H. Z. Anorg. Allg. Chem. 1926, 150, 177.

[2]   (a) Atovmyan, L. O.; Sokolova, Yu. A.; Tkachev, V. V. Dokl. Akad. Nauk SSSR 1970, 195, 1355. (b) Atovmyan, L. O.; Tkachev, V. V.; Shishova, T. G. Dokl. Akad. Nauk SSSR 1972, 205, 609.

[3]   Kopec, J. A.; Shekar, S.; Brown, S. N. Inorg. Chem. 2012, 51, 1239.

[4]   (a) Kustin, K.; Liu, S.-T. J. Am. Chem. Soc. 1973, 95, 2487. (b) Charney, L. M.; Finklea, H. O.; Schultz, F. A. Inorg. Chem. 1982, 21, 549. (c) Griffith, W. P.; Nogueira, H. I. S.; Parkin, B. C.; Sheppard, R. N.; White, A. J. P.; Williams, D. J. J. Chem. Soc., Dalton Trans. 1995, 1775. (d) Duhme, A.-K.; Dauter, Z.; Hider, R. C.; Pohl, S. Inorg. Chem. 1996, 35, 3059. (e) Duhme, A.-K.; Davies, S. C.; Hughes, D. L. Inorg. Chem. 1998, 37, 5380.

[5]   (a) Pierpont, C. G.; Downs, H. H. J. Am. Chem. Soc. 1975, 97, 2123. (b) deLearie, L. A.; Haltiwanger, R. C.; Pierpont, C. G. Inorg. Chem. 1988, 27, 3842.

[6]   Buchanan, R. M.; Pierpont, C. G. Inorg. Chem. 1979, 18, 1616.

[7]   Cass, M. E.; Pierpont, C. G. *Inorg, Chem.* 1986, *25*, 122.

[8]   (a) Pierpont, C. G.; Buchanan, R. M. *Coord. Chem. Rev.* 1981, *38*, 45. (b) Pierpont, C. G.; Lange, C. W. *Prog. Inorg. Chem.* 1994, *41*, 331. (c) Pierpont, C. G. *Coord. Chem. Rev.* 2001, *219-221*, 415.

[9]   (a) Wilshire, J. P.; Leon, L.; Bosserman, P.; Sawyer, D. T. *J. Am. Chem. Soc.* 1979, *101*, 3379. (b) Wilshire, J. P.; Leon, L.; Bosserman, P.; Sawyer, D. T.; Buchanan, R. M.; Pierpont, C. G. In *Third International Conference on the Chemistry and Uses of Molybdenum*; Barry, H. F., Mitchell, P. C. H., Eds.; Climax Molybdenum Co.: Ann Arbor 1979, p. 264. (c) Wilshire, J. P.; Leon, L.; Bosserman, P.; Sawyer, D. T. In *Molybdenum Chemistry of Biological Significance*; Newton, W. E., Otsuka, S., Eds.; Plenum Press, New York 1980, p. 327. (d) Lim, M.-C.; Sawyer, D. T. *Inorg. Chem.* 1982, *21*, 2839. (e) Sawyer, D. T.; Tsuchiya, T.; Po, H. N.; Pham, K. Q. In *Fourth International Conference on the Chemistry and Uses of Molybdenum*; Barry, H. F., Mitchell, P. C. H., Eds.; Climax Molybdenum Co., Golden, Colorado 1982, p. 107.

[10]   Liu, C.-M.; Nordlander, E.; Schmeh, D.; Shoemaker, R.; Pierpont, C. G. *Inorg. Chem.* 2004, *43*, 2114.

[11]   See for example: Bhattacharya, S.; Boone, S. R.; Fox, G. A.; Pierpont, C. G. *J. Am. Chem. Soc.* 1990, *112*, 1088.

[12]   Cass, M. E.; Greene, D. L.; Buchanan, R. M.; Pierpont, C. G. *J. Am. Chem. Soc.* 1983, *105*, 2680.

[13]   Lange, C. W.; Conklin, B. J.; Pierpont, C. G. *Inorg. Chem.* 1994, *33*, 1276.

[14]   (a) Holm, R. H. *Chem. Rev.* 1987, *87*, 1401. (b) Enemark, J. H.; Cooney, J. J. A.; Wang, J.-J.; Holm, R. H. *Chem. Rev.* 2004, *104*, 1175.

[15]   (a) Kondo, M.; Hamatani, M.; Kitagawa, S.; Pierpont, C. G.; Unoura, K. *J. Am. Chem. Soc.* 1998, *120*, 455. (b) Miyasaka, H.; Chang, H.-C.; Mochizuki, K.; Kitagawa, S. *Inorg. Chem.* 2001, *40*, 3544. (c) Chang, H.-C.; Mochizuki, K.; Kitagawa, S. *Inorg. Chem.* 2005, *44*, 3799. (d) Chang, H.-C.; Mochizuki, K.; Kitagawa, S. *Inorg. Chem.* 2005, *44*, 3810. (e) Mochizuki, K.; Chang, H.-C.; Kawamura, I.; Kitagawa, S. *Chem. Lett.* 2005, *34*, 1662. (f) Mochizuki, K.; Kawamura, I.; Chang, H.-C.; Kitagawa, S. *Inorg. Chem.* 2006, *45*, 3990.

[16]   Christ, J.; Epps, C.; Pritchard, V.; Schmeh, D.; Pierpont, C. G.; Nordlander, E. *Inorg. Chem.* 2010, *49*, 2029.

[17]   Matsumoto, T.; Yano, H.; Chang, H.-C.; Wakizaka, M.; Kobayashi, A.; Kato, M. Manuscript submitted for publication. .

In: Molybdenum
Editor: Alvin A. Holder

ISBN: 978-1-62417-272-4
© 2013 Nova Science Publishers, Inc.

Chapter 8

MOLYBDENUM-BASED COMPOUNDS IN CATALYSIS REACTIONS

Rajan Deepan Chakravarthy and Dillip Kumar Chand[*]
Department of Chemistry, Indian Institute of Technology
Madras, Chennai, Tamil Nadu, India

ABSTRACT

Molybdenum compounds exhibit unique catalytic applications in various organic reactions. Molybdenum possesses a large number of stable and variable oxidation states as well as coordination numbers. This special property is exploited by the researchers to fine tune the catalytic organic reactions such as metathesis reaction (Mo(VI) alkylidene compounds), allylic substitution (Mo(0), Mo(II), Mo(IV) and Mo(VI) compounds), oxidation and reduction reactions (Mo(VI)-dioxo compounds).

In addition to these applications, the catalytic activity of molybdenum compounds has also been studied in numerous organic reactions. Moreover, the molybdenum compounds find significant roles in various asymmetric organic reactions. This chapter covers the application of molybdenum compounds in some successful organic transformations.

1. INTRODUCTION

Molybdenum compounds exhibit unique catalytic applications in several organic reactions. They possess a large number of stable and variable oxidation states as well as coordination numbers. This special property is exploited by the researchers to fine tune the catalytic organic transformations. In particular, Mo(VI) alkylidene compounds have been found as remarkable catalysts for olefin metathesis reaction. [1, 2, 3, 4, 5] Allylic substitution reactions [6] are another important transformation where molybdenum compounds of different oxidation states (Mo(0), Mo(II), Mo(IV) and Mo(VI) compounds) have been found

[*] Phone: +91-44-2257-4224, Fax: +91-44-2257-4202, E-mail: dillip@iitm.ac.in.

as efficient catalysts. Dioxomolybdenum(VI) compounds have been reported as effective catalysts for various oxidation reactions. Along with hydrosilane, the oxomolybdenum compounds catalyze reduction reactions of various functional groups. [7] In addition to these applications, numerous organic reactions [8, 9, 10] are also successfully promoted by molybdenum compounds. Moreover, the molybdenum compounds find significant roles in catalytic asymmetric organic reactions. [11] The focus of this chapter is the application of molybdenum compounds in some successful organic transformations.

2. OLEFIN METATHESIS REACTIONS

Olefin metathesis is a unique organic reaction catalyzed by metal carbene complexes. It involves the exchange of alkylidene units between the molecules. The reaction generally proceeds through the formation of metallacyclobutane intermediate (Figure 1). The metallacyclobutane rearranges to give a new alkene and a carbene complex. This mechanism which is most widely accepted was proposed by Yves Chauvin and Hérisson in 1971.

Many research groups were involved for the development of catalytic olefin metathesis based on Chauvin's proposal, but major success was attained by Schrock and Grubbs groups (Figure 2). The catalysts developed by these two groups are, nowadays, the most commonly used for olefin metathesis reactions. These achievements were recognized by the Royal Swedish Academy of Sciences and the Nobel Prize in Chemistry was awarded to Yves Chauvin, Richard R. Schrock and Robert H. Grubbs "for the development of the metathesis method in organic synthesis" in the year 2005.

The fundamental olefin metathesis reactions are as follows (Figure 3) [12].

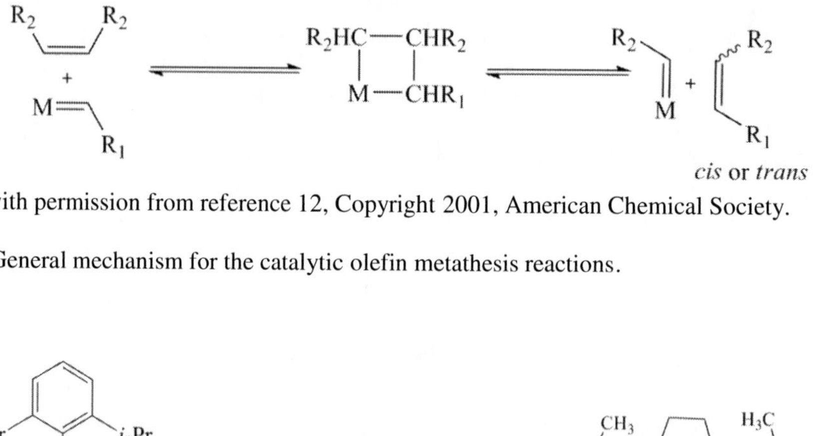

Adapted with permission from reference 12, Copyright 2001, American Chemical Society.

Figure 1. General mechanism for the catalytic olefin metathesis reactions.

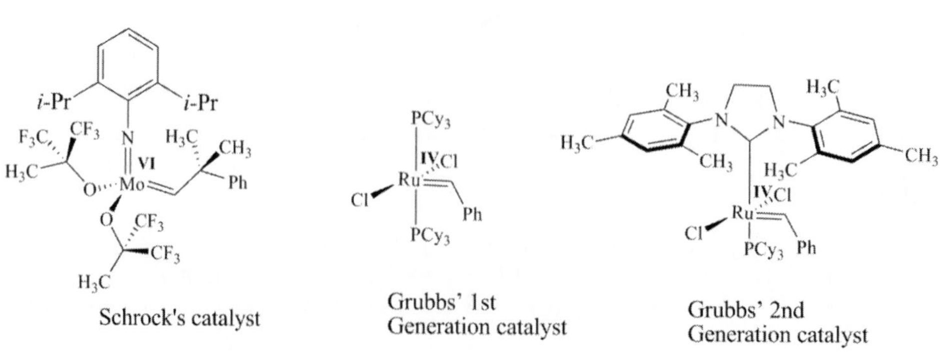

Figure 2. Representative catalysts for olefin metathesis reactions.

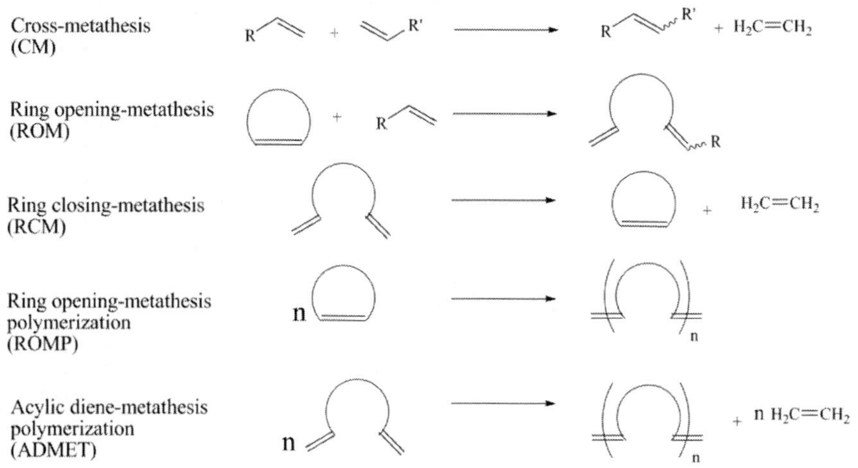

Adapted with permission from reference 12, Copyright 2001, American Chemical Society.

Figure 3. Types of olefin metathesis reactions.

In this chapter we will discuss some useful applications of molybdenum based alkylidene complexes. The first well-defined molybdenum compounds for olefin metathesis were developed by Schrock and co-workers in the year 1990. [13] These compounds are sensitive towards air and moisture when compared to the ruthenium catalysts and, therefore, the reaction should be performed in a nitrogen or argon atmosphere. However, several potential reactions are successfully catalyzed by molybdenum compounds because of their higher activity.

2.1. Ring- Closing Metathesis

In 1992, Grubbs and Fu developed the catalytic ring closing metathesis reaction of various diene-ether in the presence of the molybdenum alkylidene catalyst **1**. [14] Unsaturated five, six and seven membered oxygen heterocycles were obtained in high yields by this methodology with 5 mol% Mo-catalyst in benzene at 20 □C (Scheme 1). Substantial catalytic activity was also observed in case of tri-substituted olefin substrate. The mechanistic pathway involved in this reaction is shown in figure 4.

Further, they extended this methodology for the synthesis of nitrogen heterocycles. Ring closing metathesis reactions of various diallylamine were successfully catalyzed with molybdenum compound **1** in high yields. [15] This catalytic system is also effective for cyclization of amides (Scheme 2).

Application of the catalytic metathesis process to the various acyclic enol ethers afforded the corresponding cyclized products. Reaction of acyclic enol ethers with catalyst **1** led to the formation of five and six-member carbocycles. Substituted benzofurans have also been synthesized in this method in high yields (Scheme 3) whereas no significant metathesis reactions were observed with ruthenium catalysts. [16]

In 1999, Postema and co-workers successfully applied the ring closing metathesis strategy for the preparation of *C-1* glycals (Scheme 4). Cyclization of olefin-enol ethers were realized with 25 mol% molybdenum catalyst **1** in high yield. [17]

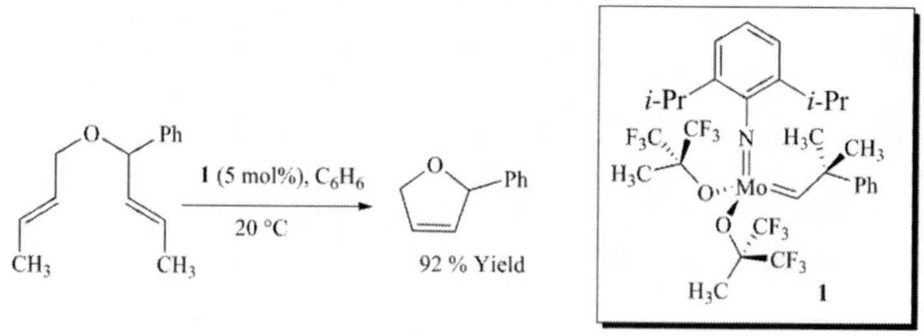

Scheme 1. A representative catalytic ring closing metathesis reaction of diene-ether.

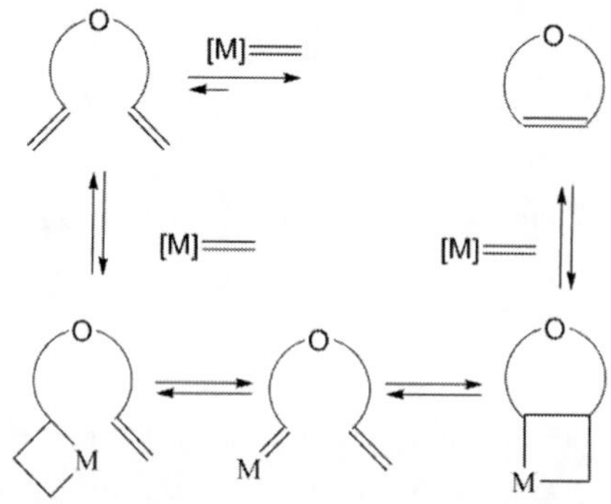

Adapted with permission from reference 14, Copyright 1992, American Chemical Society.

Figure 4. General mechanism for catalytic ring closing olefin metathesis reactions.

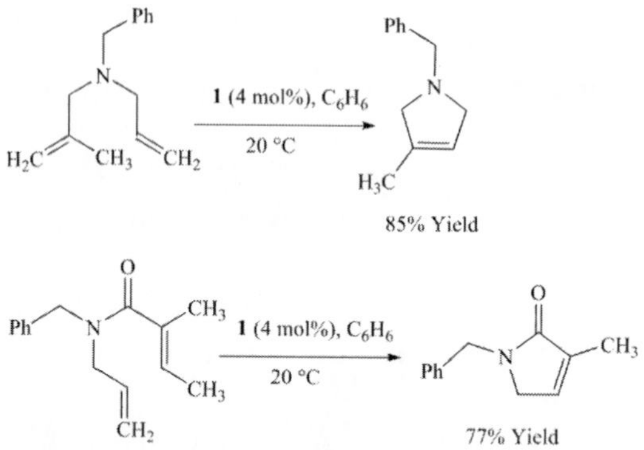

Scheme 2. A representative catalytic ring closing metathesis reaction of diallyl amine.

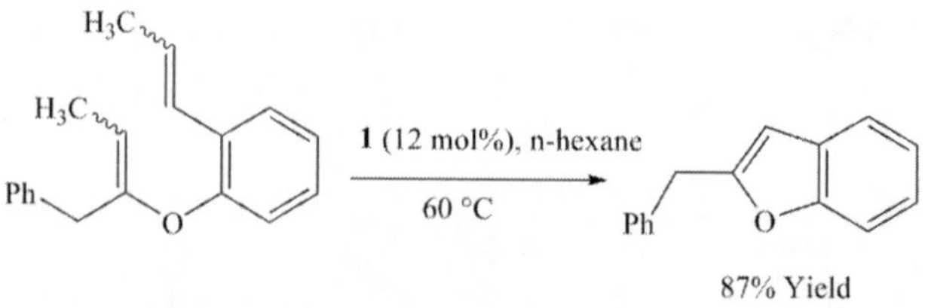

Scheme 3. A representative catalytic ring closing metathesis reaction of allylic enol ethers.

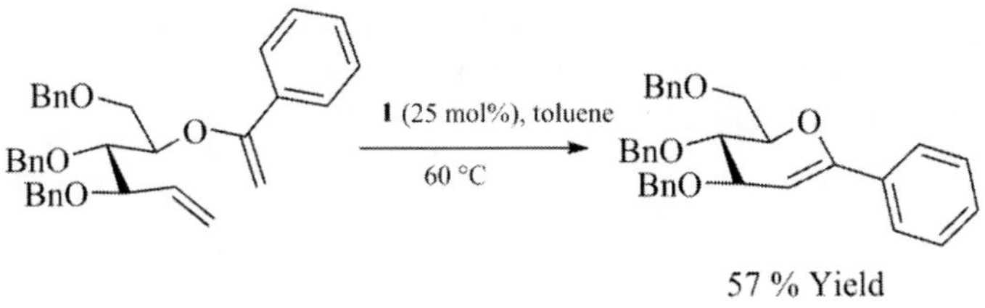

Scheme 4. A representative catalytic ring closing metathesis for the synthesis of *C-1* glycals.

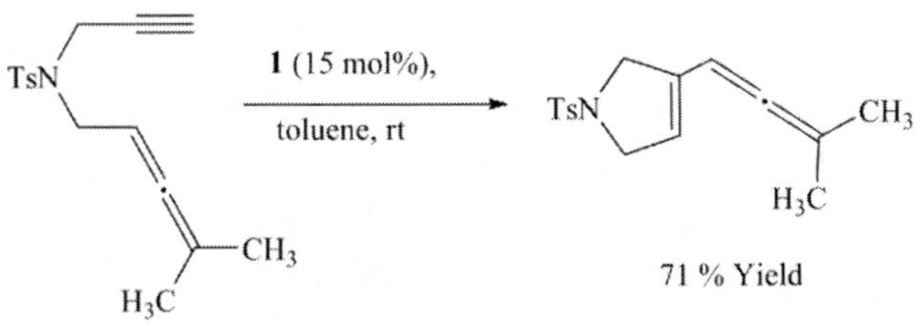

Scheme 5. A representative catalytic ring closing metathesis reaction of allenyne.

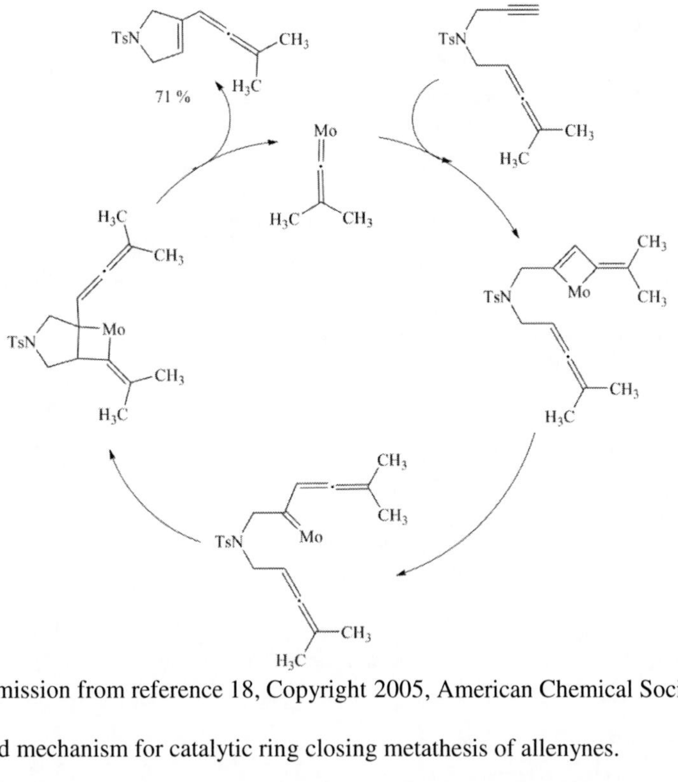

Adapted with permission from reference 18, Copyright 2005, American Chemical Society.

Figure 5. Proposed mechanism for catalytic ring closing metathesis of allenynes.

The first catalytic ring closing metathesis reaction of allenynes was reported by Murakami and co-workers in 2005. [18] The reaction of allenynes with molybdenum catalyst **1** at room temperature provided the cyclized product having an allene side chain (Scheme 5). The authors claimed that the reactions were successful only with Schrock's catalyst. Ruthenium based catalysts gave a mixture of products. The proposed mechanism involves the formation of molybdenum vinylidene species from allenyne and catalyst. This active vinylidene species underwent a sequence of cycloaddition and ring-opening reactions with the allenynes to afford products (Figure 5).

2.2. Cross Metathesis Reactions

In 1993, Crowe and Zhang demonstrated the application of Schrock's catalyst for cross metathesis reactions. The metathesis reaction of substituted styrenes with various functionalized terminal olefins have been successfully carried out with molybdenum catalysts. [19] Generally the metathesis reaction of two different olefins afforded both homodimeric and heterodimeric products (Scheme 6). The homodimerization or self-metathesis reaction of styrenes with molybdenum catalyst was found to be very slow. But along with alkyl substituted terminal olefins, the catalyst induces the cross metathesis reaction with high selectivity (Scheme 7). Electronic effects of the substituent play a crucial role in the selectivity of the products. Low yields were observed for the olefins having electron withdrawing substituent.

In 1995, Crowe and Goldberg investigated a similar reaction with acrylonitrile. [20] In the case of acrylonitrile, no significant homodimerization was observed because of its poor nucleophilicity. When treated with more nucleophilic alkyl olefins along with molybdenum catalyst **1**, the selective cross metathesis reactions were realized in high yield (Scheme 8). Mo-catalyzed cross metathesis reactions are also reported with allylsilane and allyl ester. [21, 22]

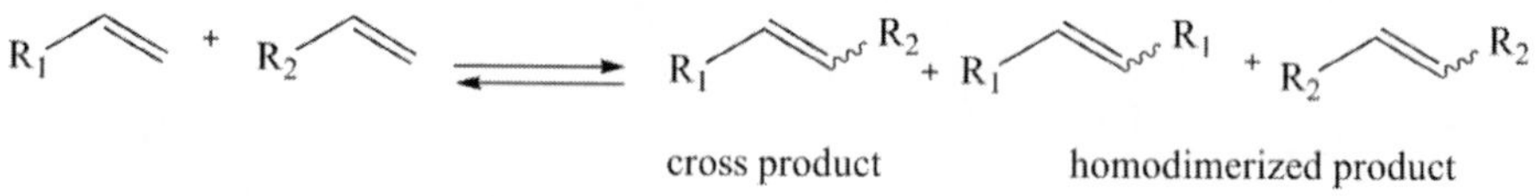

Scheme 6. The metathesis reaction of two different olefins.

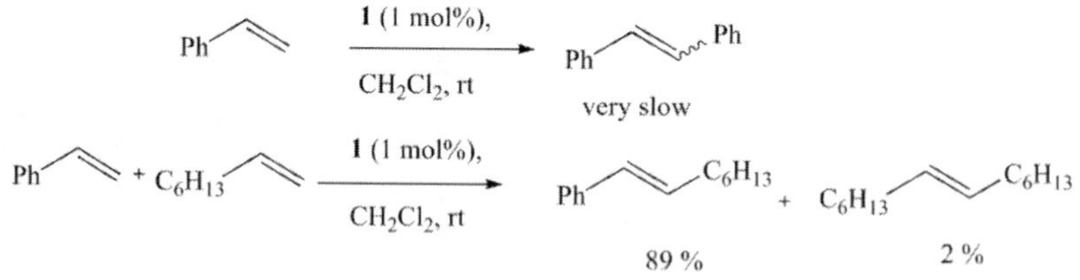

Scheme 7. Catalytic cross metathesis reaction of styrene with oct-1-ene.

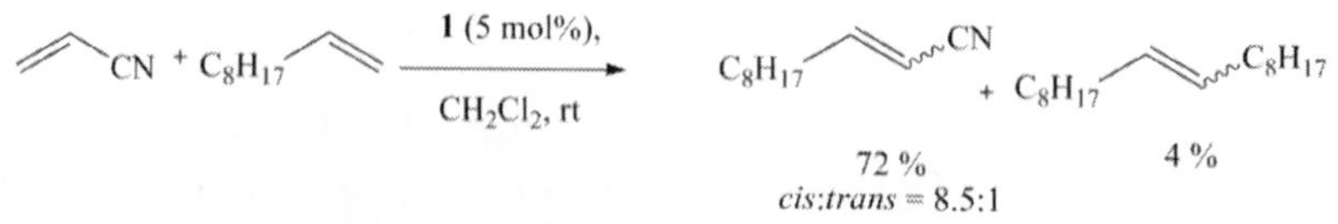

Scheme 8. Catalytic cross metathesis reaction of acrylonitrile with dec-1-ene.

2.3. Asymmetric Ring Closing Metathesis Reactions

Another important achievement in the field of metathesis is the development of chiral catalysts for enantioselective reactions. Initial studies on asymmetric ring closing metathesis of molybdenum alkylidene complexes were successfully carried out by Grubbs and Fujimura in the year 1996. The chiral molybdenum catalyst **2** was utilized for the kinetic resolution of various racemic dienes through ring closing protocol. [23, 24] They have explained that the *R*-isomers were consumed at a faster rate in case of the five membered cyclization reactions resulted in the *S*-enriched acyclic dienes. But in case of six membered ring formation reactions, *R*-isomers were recovered. In most cases, only low enantioselectivity were observed (Scheme 9).

Schrock and co-workers investigated similar kinetic resolution reactions with chiral Mo-Biphen catalysts. [25] This catalyst system exhibited excellent efficiency on resolution of various dienes. Both recovered starting material and cyclized products can be obtained in high enantioselectivity under this catalytic condition.

However, yields were decreased due to the formation of undesired dimeric products. The dimer formation was considerably suppressed in case of less substituted olefins (Scheme 10).

The same group extended the application of ring closing metathesis for enantioselective desymmetrization reactions. [26] This is the first successful cyclization reaction of various trienes to chiral furans with high enantioselectivity.

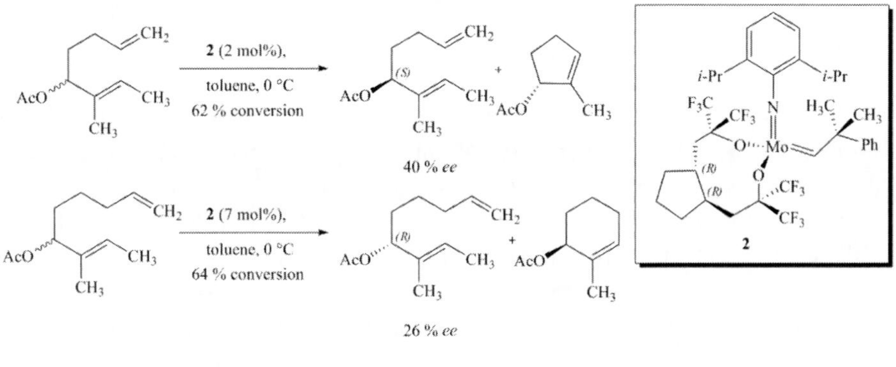

Scheme 9. Catalytic kinetic resolution of various racemic dienes through ring closing protocol.

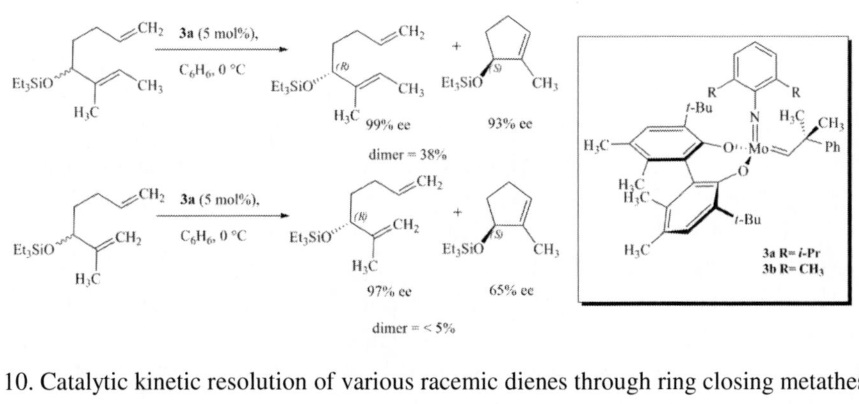

Scheme 10. Catalytic kinetic resolution of various racemic dienes through ring closing metathesis.

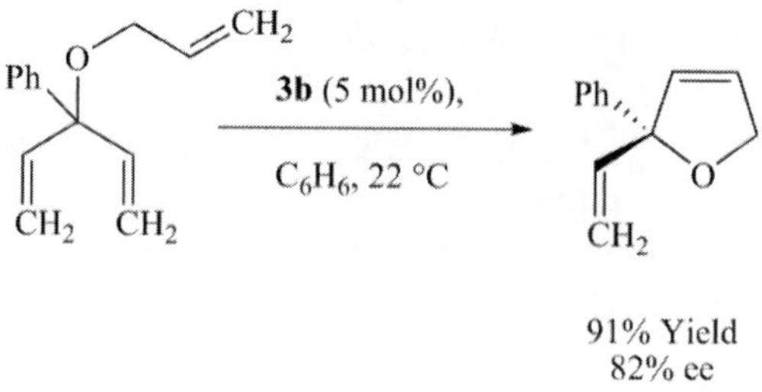

Scheme 11. Ring closing metathesis for the synthesis of chiral five membered heterocycles.

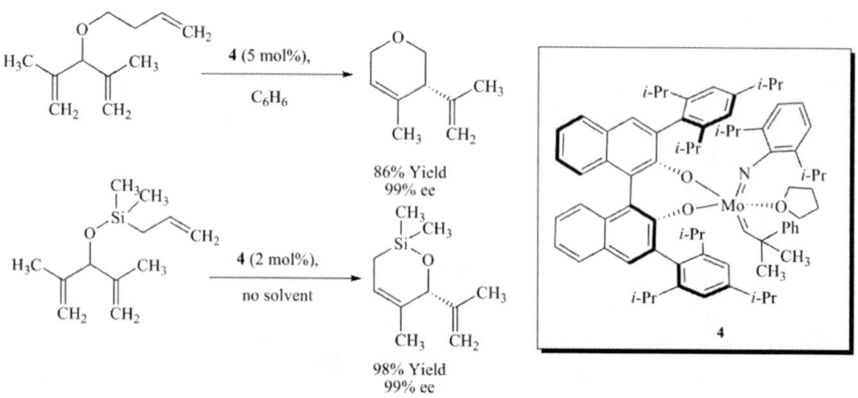

Scheme 12. Ring closing metathesis for the synthesis of chiral six membered heterocycles.

Tertiary ethers also effectively catalyzed by the Mo-Biphen compound resulted in products having the asymmetric quaternary carbon centers (Scheme 11). In contrast, decrease in activity was observed for the synthesis of chiral pyran and cyclohexenes.

Another important class of molybdenum compounds with chiral Binol based ligands has also been developed. The chiral Mo-Binol complexes were found to be effective catalyst for the enantioselective synthesis of six membered carbo and heterocycles. [27] Interestingly, the excellent efficiency was also observed in the absence of solvents (Scheme 12).

2.4. Tandem Asymmetric Ring Opening/ Cross Metathesis Reactions

The applications of molybdenum catalysts for tandem asymmetric ring opening/cross metathesis reactions were investigated by Hoveyda and co-workers. [28, 29] The reaction of various functionalized norbornenes with styrenes in presence of molybdenum catalysts afforded the corresponding cyclopentyl dienes in high yields and enantioselectivity. The reactions of norbornene with various styrenes resulted in significant amount of polymerized product only. However, the tandem catalytic asymmetric reactions were achieved with various 7-Norbornyl ethers in the presence of chiral Mo-Biphen catalyst (Scheme 13). The potential side reactions such as the formation of polymeric and meso diene products were suppressed under this catalytic condition. Vinyl silane is also an effective olefin partner for tandem reactions and enantiomeric excess up to 98% was achieved. When acrylonitrile was subjected to this tandem reaction, no significant products were observed.

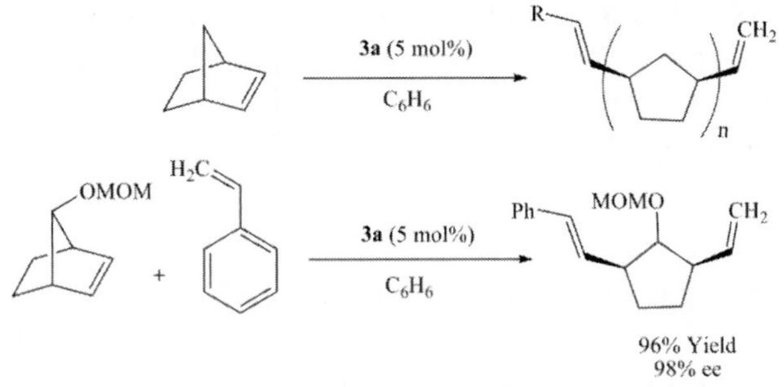

Scheme 13. Molybdenum catalyzed tandem asymmetric ring opening/ cross metathesis reactions.

2.5. Tandem Asymmetric Ring Opening/ Ring Closing Metathesis Reactions

Another excellent tandem reaction which involves the asymmetric ring opening/ring closing metathesis reactions was also performed with molybdenum catalysts. [30] The meso-trienes underwent a sequence of metathesis reaction in presence of Mo-catalysts and afforded the products with high yields and enantioselectivity (Scheme 14).

2.6. Ring Closing Metathesis - Molybdenum Catalyst Having Stereogenic Metal Centre

A study of the asymmetric metathesis reactions with chiral molybdenum complexes having stereogenic metal centre 5 was carried out by Schrock and Hoveyda. The catalysts of this new class were found to be very effective for ring closing metathesis reactions with high reactivity and enantioselectivity. [31]

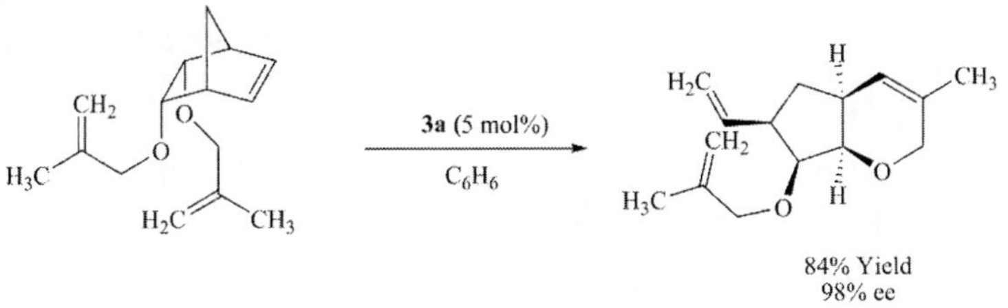

Scheme 14. Molybdenum catalyzed tandem asymmetric ring opening/ring closing metathesis reactions.

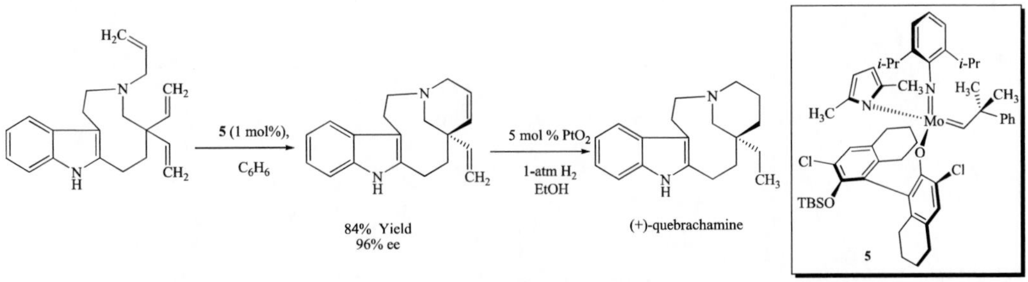

Scheme 15. Catalytic ring closing metathesis reaction for the synthesis of quebrachamine.

Further the importance of the catalyst was justified for the enantioselective synthesis of *Aspidosperma* alkaloid, quebrachamine. The Mo-catalyst facilitates the ring closing reaction with high yield and 96% enantioselectivity which cannot be induced by any of the available chiral catalysts (Scheme 15).

3. ALLYLIC SUBSTITUTION REACTIONS

3.1. Molybdenum(0) Complexes Catalyzed Reactions

Metal catalyzed allylic alkylation reaction is a nucleophilic substitution reaction of various allylic compounds by carbon nucleophiles. The reaction generally proceeds through the formation of electrophilic π-allylmetal complex intermediates shown in figure 6. It has been reported as a stoichiometric reaction by Jiro Tsuji and co-workers in the year 1965. [32] They found the reactivity of π-allylpalladium chloride complex with carbon nucleophiles such as malonate, acetoacetate and enamine. The first catalytic allylic substitution reaction with palladium complexes was reported during 1970. [33, 34] Nowadays this is potentially a very useful method for the formation of C-C, C-O, and C-N bonds with high regio- and stereoselectivity. Palladium compounds dominate the chemistry of allylic substitution reaction until Trost found the complementary regioselectivity of molybdenum catalysts. [35]

In the case of unsymmetrical substrates palladium catalyzed allylic substitution reaction preferentially forms linear product which leads to the formation of achiral regioisomers whereas molybdenum forms branched product (Scheme 16). In addition to molybdenum, metal complexes of iridium and tungsten also yields branched products. This regio-selective ability along with the easily available catalytic precursors of molybdenum made it interesting for further development of molybdenum catalyzed allylic substitution reactions. [6] Allylic substitution of various allyl acetates, carbonates and sulfonates were successfully catalyzed by the molybdenum compounds. Molybdenum catalysts showed unique regioselective allylic alkylation in contrast to palladium complexes which can be realized as in the case of allyl sulfone substrates. [36] Excellent selectivity was observed with $Mo(CO)_6$ catalyst where the alkylation takes place at more substituted allylic site thereby forming the products having quaternary carbon centre (Scheme 17).

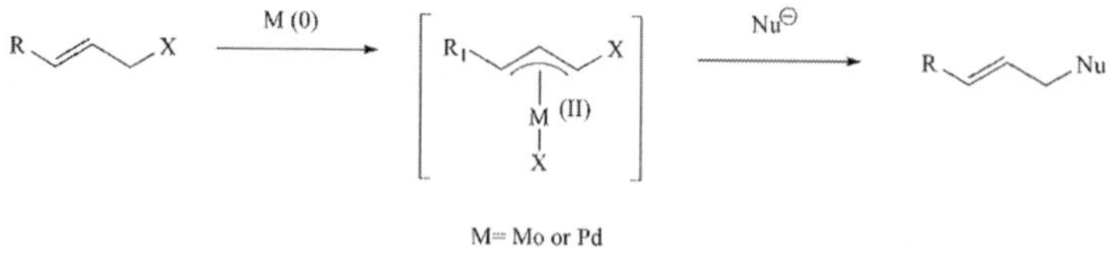

Figure 6. General mechanism for allylic substitution reactions.

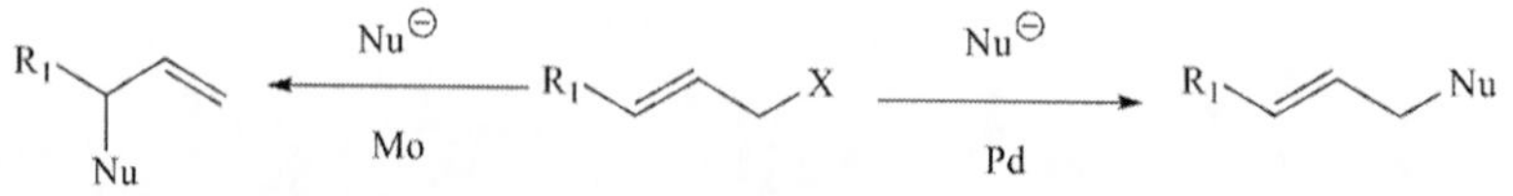

Adapted with permission from reference 6, Copyright 2004, American Chemical Society.

Scheme 16. Regioselectivity in Mo or Pd catalyzed allylic substitution reactions.

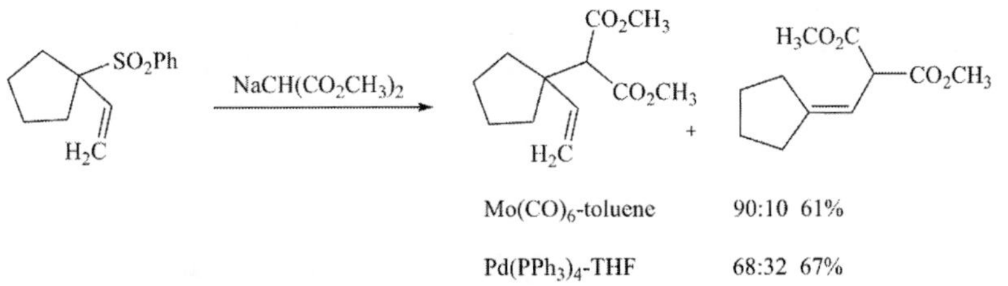

Scheme 17. A representative example shows the regioselectivity by Mo catalysts.

In the case of asymmetric allylic alkylation (AAA) reactions molybdenum was believed as *"not useful as a catalyst"*. A breakthrough happened in the year 1998 when Trost and Hachiya published the first molybdenum catalyzed asymmetric allylic alkylation reaction. [37] The highly regio and stereoselective methodology was reported with $(C_2H_5CN)_3Mo(CO)_3$ and chiral bis(pyridylamide) ligand (**L1**). Allyl carbonates are the most widely used model substrate for asymmetric allylic alkylation reactions because of their higher reactivity. Reaction of cinnamyl carbonate (linear carbonate) with sodium dimethyl malonate nucleophile provided the product with very good regioselectivity (49:1 ratio of branched to linear product) and enantiomeric excess (99% *ee*). Both enantioselectivity and regioselectivity decreases for branched carbonates under similar condition (Scheme 18).

The microwave assisted asymmetric reactions with more stable and commercially available molybdenum source, $Mo(CO)_6$ were developed by Larhed and Hallberg groups. [38] Cinnamyl carbonate undergoes substitution reaction with malonate nucleophile and Mo-bis(pyridylamide) catalyst in presence of bis-(trimethylsilyl)acetamide (BSA) base (Scheme 19). The advantage of this method is that the reaction was completed within a few minutes and gave comparable regio and enantioselectivity when compare to the conventional method. [39]

Various substituted chiral bis(pyridylamide) ligands were tested for this microwave protocol in order to study the steric and electronic effects of the chiral ligands on the catalytic system. The ligand **L2** exhibits very high branched-to-linear ratio (88:1) with 96% *ee*. [40]

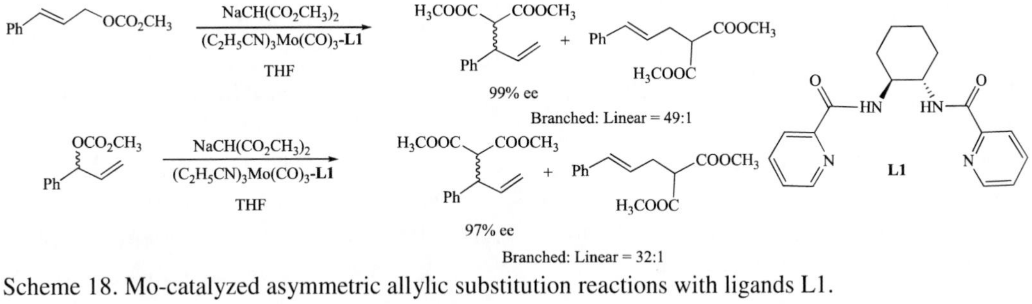

Scheme 18. Mo-catalyzed asymmetric allylic substitution reactions with ligands L1.

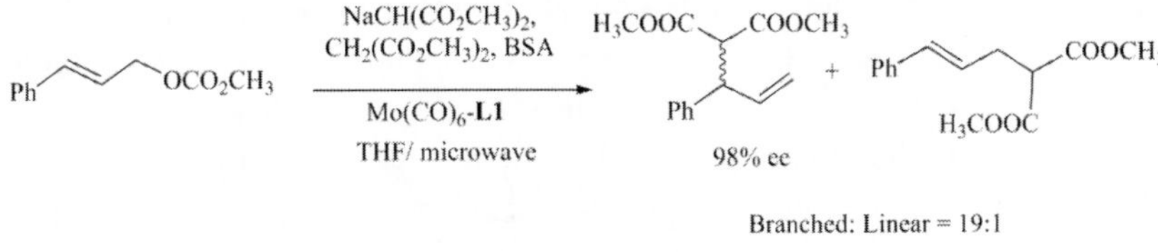

Scheme 19. Microwave assisted asymmetric allylic substitution with Mo-catalysts.

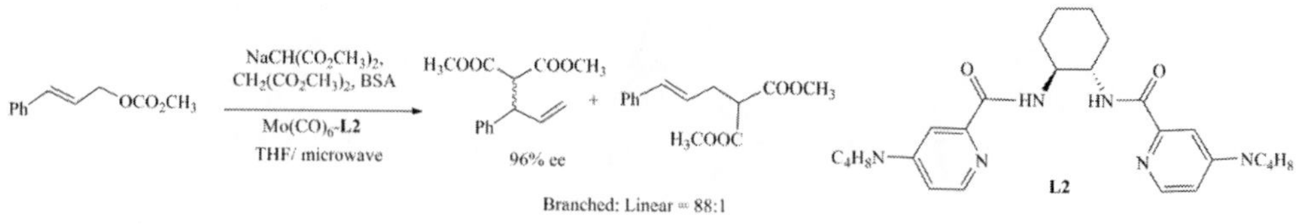

Scheme 20. Ligand effects on microwave assisted asymmetric allylic substitution.

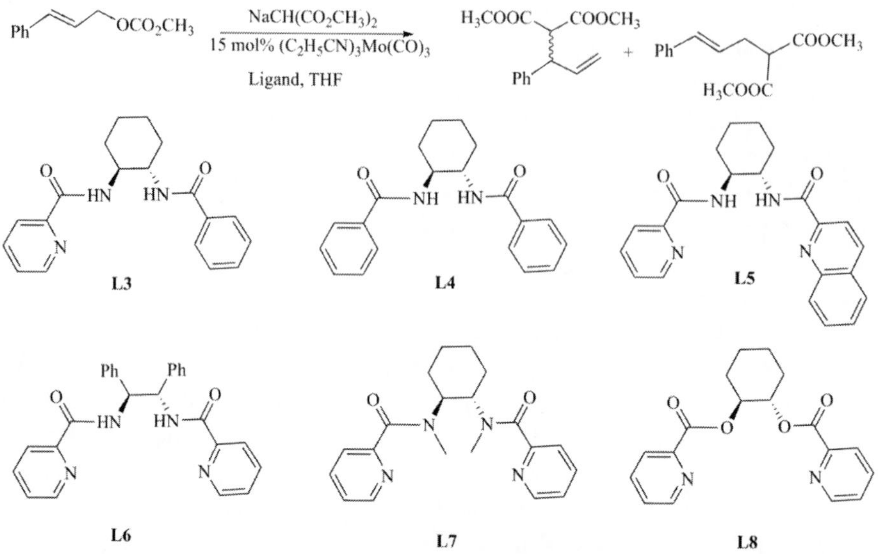

Scheme 21. Mo-catalyzed asymmetric allylic alkylation with chiral ligands of various backbones.

In order to find the effectiveness of the catalyst, Trost and co-workers developed several chiral ligands with different backbone for allylic alkylation reactions (Scheme 21). [41] Increase in regioselectivity (60:1) was observed when one of the two picolinamide groups of ligand **L1** is replaced with a benzoyl amide group **L3**. But poor selectivity was observed in the case of ligand **L4**. Molybdenum complexes bearing quinoline based ligands were found to be less efficient under this condition. Chiral complex of ligand **L6** derived from 1,2-diphenylethylenediamine showed high enantioselectivity with a decrease in branched to linear ratio.

Allylic alkylation reaction catalyzed by Mo-complex of chiral amide ligand **L7** was found to be 200 times less reactive than ligand **L2**. However no observable reaction took place in case of ester based ligand **L8** along with molybdenum complex. These examples show the significance of secondary amide ligands for the catalytic asymmetric allylic substitution reactions.

Koćovský and co-workers demonstrated the allylic substitution of molybdenum catalysts with a new class of C_1- symmetric chiral ligands (Scheme 22). [42] They found that the molybdenum catalyst with isopropyl-based ligand **L9** is highly efficient for allylic substitution reaction of cinnamyl carbonate. The catalytic substitution reaction with chiral ligand **L9** also gave excellent regio and enantioselectivity. The authors suggested that the chiral amide ligands with one stereogenic centre are also capable of inducing high enantioselectivity during catalysis.

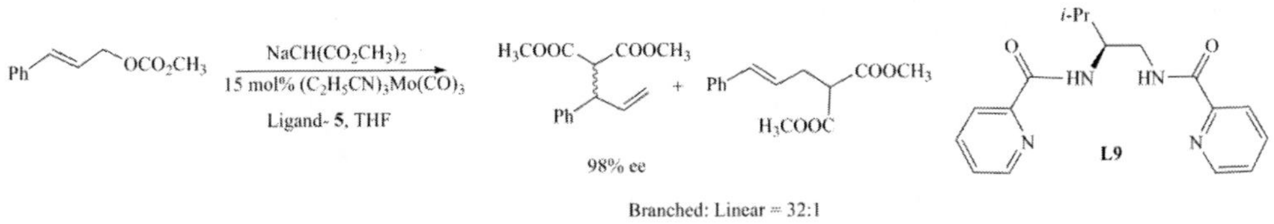

Scheme 22. Mo-catalyzed asymmetric allylic alkylation with C_1- symmetric chiral ligands.

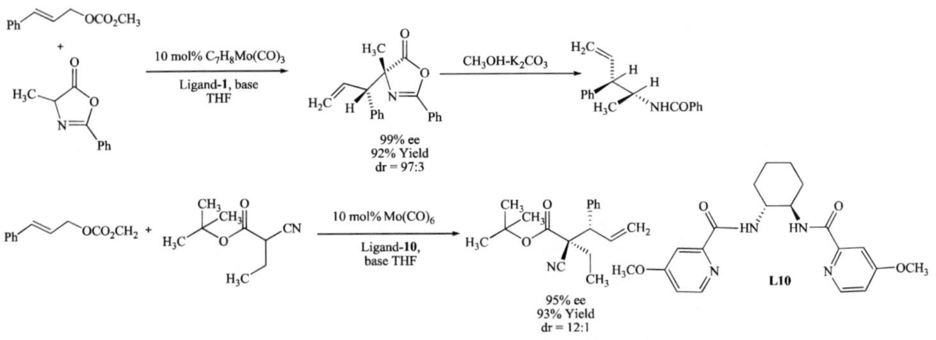

Scheme 23. Mo-catalyzed asymmetric allylic alkylation with azlactone and cyanoester nucleophiles.

The synthetic approach for the asymmetric formation of quaternary carbon with molybdenum catalysts was reported by Trost and co-workers. Allylic alkylation of cinnamyl carbonates with nucleophile of azlactone can be successfully catalyzed by $C_7H_8Mo(CO)_3$ precatalyst and chiral ligand **L1**. The alkylated products thus formed on solvolysis by basic methanol led to the formation of quaternary α-amino acids with high enantio and diastero selectivity. Under this condition several allyl substrates can be successfully converted into corresponding amino acids. [43] When cyanoesters [44] were used, Mo-AAA reactions provide access to the formation of β-amino acids (Scheme 23). In addition, this catalytic system worked well for the nucleophiles of oxazolones [45] and 3-aryloxindoles [46] with high regio, enantio and diasteroselectivity.

3.2.1. Molybdenum(II) Complexes Catalyzed Reactions

Kočovský and co-workers employed Mo(II)-catalysts for allylic substitution reactions. Although molybdenum carbonyl compounds catalyzed reactions have attained useful applications in organic synthesis, their restriction towards narrow range of nucleophiles and high reaction temperatures turned the attention towards the development of highly reactive catalysts. Complexes such as $Mo(CO)_5(OTf)_2$, $[Mo(CO)_4Br_2]_2$, and bimetallic complex $Mo(CO)_3(MeCN)_2(SnCl_3)Cl$ have been successfully applied as catalysts for allylic alkylation reactions of various allyl acetates with silyl enol ethers at ambient temperature. Silyl enol ether derived from β-carbonyls, ketones, aldehydes, and esters were applied as nucleophiles under this mild condition. In addition to the carbon nucleophiles, methanol was used as an oxygen nucleophile (Scheme 24) which reacts in the similar fashion for the C-O bond formation reaction. [47, 48, 49]

Further interesting application of these catalysts is the development of allylic alkylation methodology with electron rich aromatics and heteroaromatics as nucleophiles. [50, 51] In the reaction of allyl acetates with anisole, significant *para*-selective products were observed.

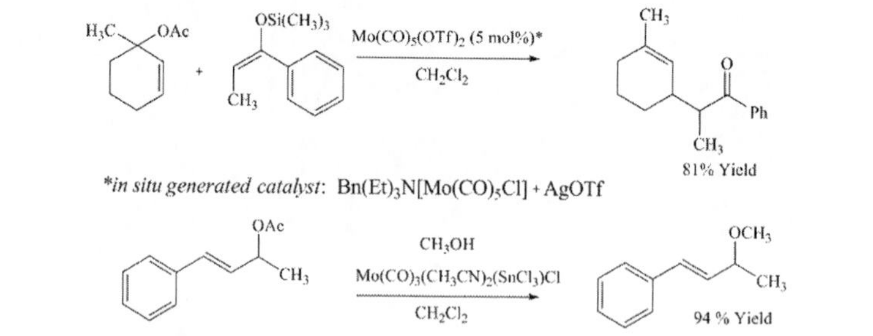

Scheme 24. Mo(II) -catalyzed allylic substitution reaction with carbon and oxygen nucleophiles.

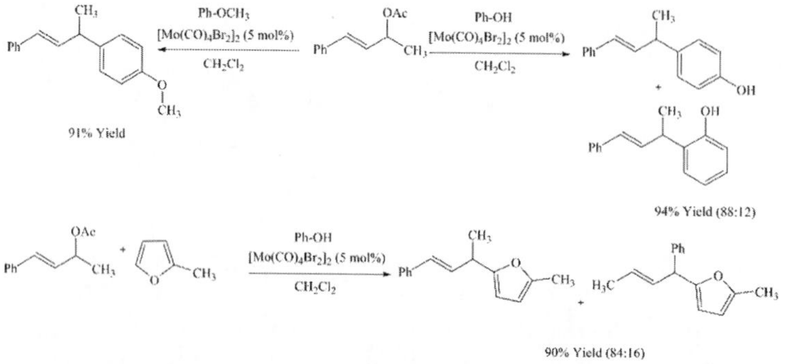

Scheme 25. Mo(II) -catalyzed allylic alkylation with electron rich and hetero-aromatic nucleophiles.

Aromatic compounds bearing electron withdrawing substituents like chlorobenzene, acetophenone, nitrobenzene and chlorophenols were found to be inert under these catalytic conditions. Heteroaromatic compounds such as 2-methyl furan and N-methyl indole have been applied for Friedel-Crafts type allylation reaction. Substitution preferentially takes place at 5-position of the furan derivatives (Scheme 25).

3.2.2. Mo (IV) Complexes Catalyzed Reaction

Encouraged by the successful application of Mo(II) catalysts, the same group Koćovský and co-workers developed Mo(IV) catalyst for allylic substitution of less reactive allylic alcohol substartes. [52]

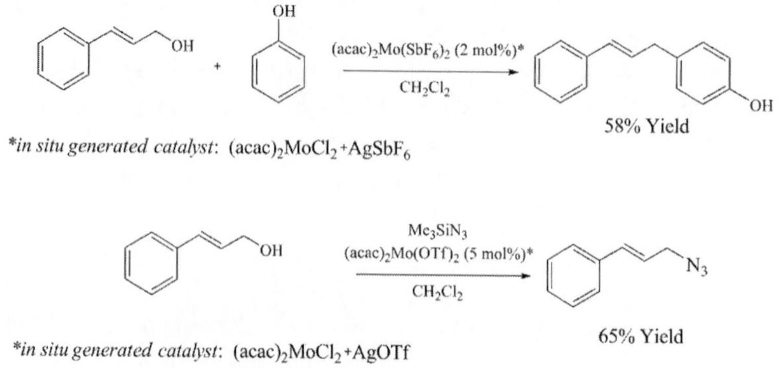

Scheme 26. Mo(IV) -catalyzed allylic substitution reaction with carbon and nitrogen nucleophiles.

Cinnamyl alcohol undergoes nucleophilic substitution reaction with phenol in presence of $(acac)_2Mo(SbF_6)_2$ catalyst gave *para*-cinnamyl phenol. Anisole also reacted in similar fashion. Further investigation for C-N bond formation reaction with trimethyl silyl azide in presence of $(acac)_2Mo(OTf)_2$ resulted in cinnamyl azide (Scheme 26).

3.2.3. Mo(VI) Complexes Catalyzed Reaction

Another interesting approach for allylic substitution reaction with Mo(VI) catalyst was investigated by Zhu and co-workers. [53] They found that $MoO_2(acac)_2/NH_4PF_6$ catalytic system was very effective for nucleophilic substitution reaction of allyl alcohol with various nitrogen, oxygen and carbon nucleophiles. The reactions were successfully carried out with various nitrogen nucleophiles such as benzamides, nitro anilines, sulfonamides and formamides. The allyl alcohols under this catalytic condition resulted in the formation of products with high yields. Similarly, allyl ethers were prepared from this protocol by utilizing alcohols as oxygen nucleophiles. Molybdenum catalyzed C-C bond formation reactions were also performed with wide range of carbon nucleophiles. The Friedel-Crafts type reactions were observed for phenol and heteroaromatic compounds such as pyrrole and indole. Acetyl acetone, acetone and cyclohexanone underwent alkylation in high yields (Scheme 27).

4. EPOXIDATION REACTIONS

Epoxidation is one the most fundamental reactions in the field of organic chemistry. Molybdenum based catalysts are well known for epoxidation reactions with alkyl hydroperoxide oxidant.

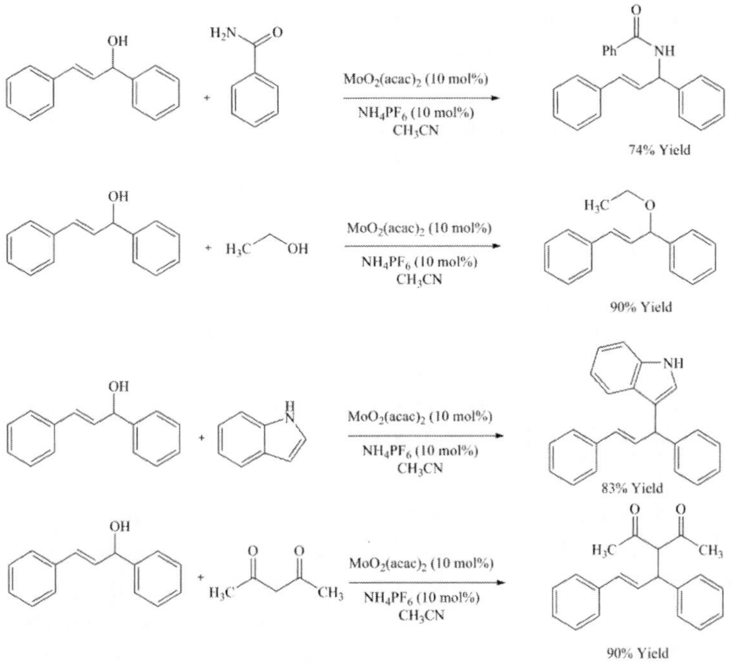

Scheme 27. Mo(VI) -catalyzed allylic substitution reaction with carbon and nitrogen nucleophiles.

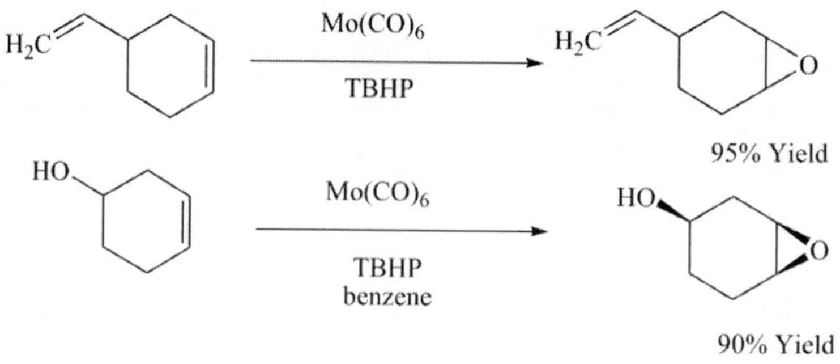

Scheme 28. Epoxidation reactions with TBHP in presence of Mo(CO)$_6$.

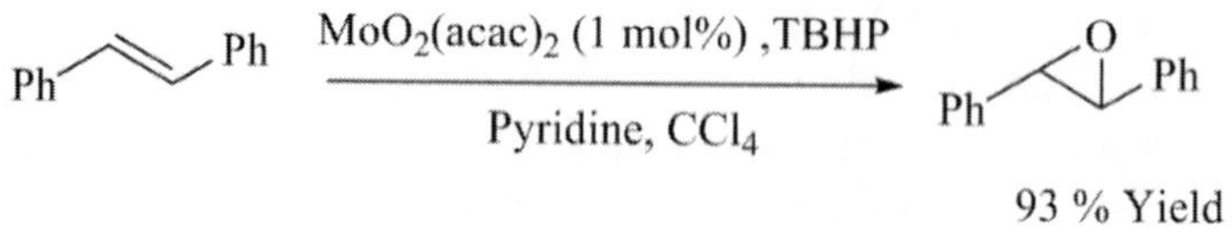

Scheme 29. Epoxidation reactions with TBHP in presence of MoO$_2$(acac)$_2$.

Two industrial processes Halcon [54] and ARCO [55] found the significant role of molybdenum catalyst for the epoxidation reaction in the late 1970. Thereafter several research groups involved in the development of efficient molybdenum catalysts for epoxidation reactions. A few representative examples are shown in this part. In earlier studies, molybdenum hexacarbonyl catalyzed epoxidation of alkenes were known. The reaction of molybdenum hexacarbonyl with hydroperoxide forms active Mo(VI) species which is believed as the actual catalyst. Several olefins and allylic compounds were successfully oxidized with the molybdenum catalysts. [56] Interestingly, the epoxidation of homoallylic alcohol with *tert*-butyl hydroperoxide leads to the preferential formation *syn*- epoxy alcohol (Scheme 28). [57]

Dioxo molybdenum(VI) compounds are another important type of catalysts successfully applied for epoxidation reactions. Kato and co-workers demonstrated the epoxidation reaction with the simple MoO$_2$(acac)$_2$ complex. [58] Various aliphatic and aromatic olefins were converted into the corresponding epoxides in presence of *tert*-butyl hydroperoxide oxidant (Scheme 29).

In addition to these several dioxomolybdenum complexes with ligands of different organic backbones were developed and applied for epoxidation reactions. [9]

Castillón and co-workers developed tandem epoxidation-alcoholysis method with molybdenum catalysts for oxidation of various glucal and galactal derivatives (Scheme 30). High stereoselectivity was achieved with both hydrogen peroxide as well as *tert*-butyl hydroperoxide oxidant. [59]

Asymmetric epoxidation reactions have been studied with chiral ligands of various backbones but low enantioselectivity was observed in most of the cases due to the weak coordination of the chiral ligands. Yamamoto and co-workers developed the successful catalytic system with chiral *bis*-hydroxamic acid and MoO$_2$(acac)$_2$for asymmetric epoxidation of various mono-, di-, and tri-substituted alkenes. [60] The active catalyst generated *in situ* induces the enantioselectivity up to 96% (Scheme 31).

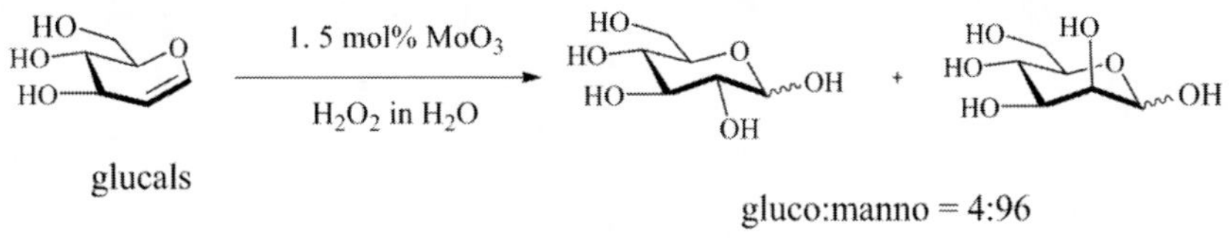

glucals

gluco:manno = 4:96

Scheme 30. Tandem epoxidation/hydrolysis with H_2O_2 in presence of $MoO_2(acac)_2$.

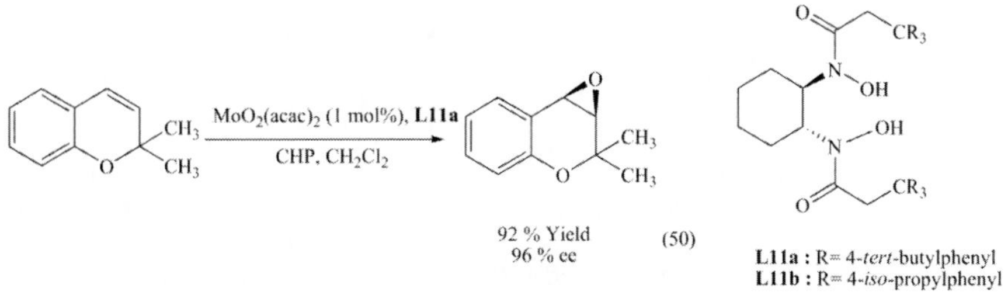

92 % Yield
96 % ee   (50)

L11a : R= 4-*tert*-butylphenyl
L11b : R= 4-*iso*-propylphenyl

Scheme 31. A representative catalytic asymmetric epoxidation reaction with Mo-**L11a**.

5. OXIDATION OF SULFIDES

The potential application of molybdenum catalyst for selective oxidation of sulfides to sulfoxides and sulfones with hydrogen peroxide oxidant were investigated by Chand and co-workers. Molybdenum dioxide dichloride catalyzed sulfoxidation reaction shows remarkable tolerance towards a wide range of functional groups. Organic sulfides possessing additional alkene, aldehyde, imine, alcohol and oxime (Scheme 32) functional groups which are susceptible to oxidation or deprotection are found to be intact under this condition. [61]

In another interesting approach, Gozin and co-workers demonstrated the molybdenum-copper bimetallic catalytic system for sulfoxidation reactions with nitrate salt as the oxygen source. Sulfoxides were obtained in high yields without the formation of the overoxidized product sulfone. It is important here to mention that Mo-Cu bimetallic catalytic system is the first efficient method for the sulfoxidation of organic sulfides bearing the boronic acid and boronic ester functional groups (Scheme 33). [62]

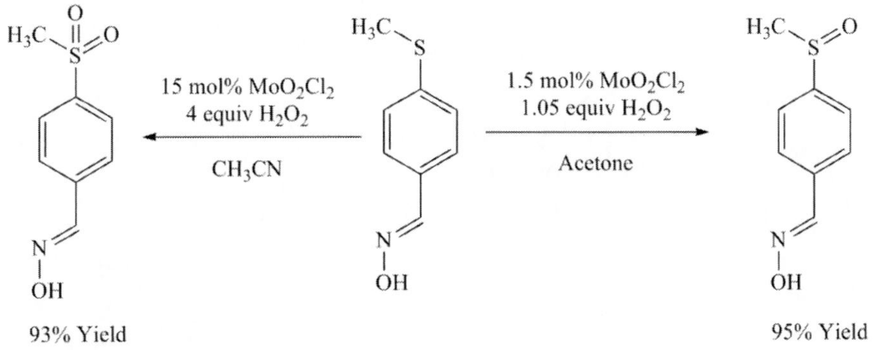

93% Yield

95% Yield

Scheme 32. Chemoselective sulfoxidation with H_2O_2 in presence of MoO_2Cl_2.

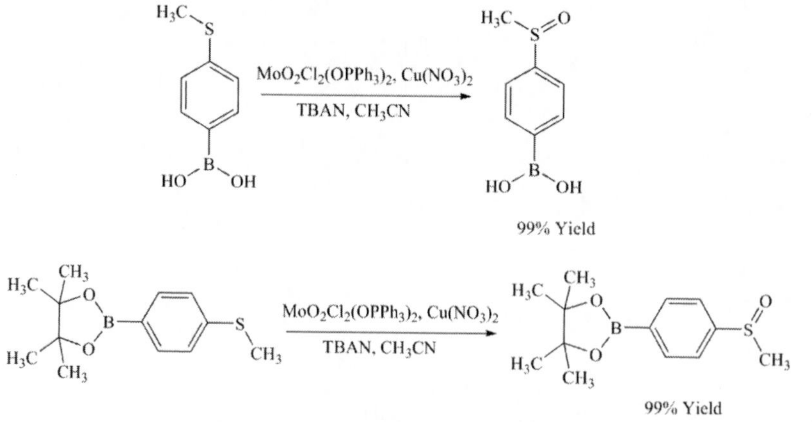

Scheme 33. Chemoselective sulfoxidation with H_2O_2 in presence of Mo-Cu heterobimetallic catalysts.

Yamamoto and co-workers developed the first successful asymmetric sulfoxidation reaction with dioxomolydenum complexes and chiral *bis*-hydroxamic acid ligands. [63] The reaction of various sulfides with trityl hydroperoxide oxidant in presence of catalyst generated *in situ* afforded the chiral sulfoxides with moderate to good enantioselectivity (Scheme 34).

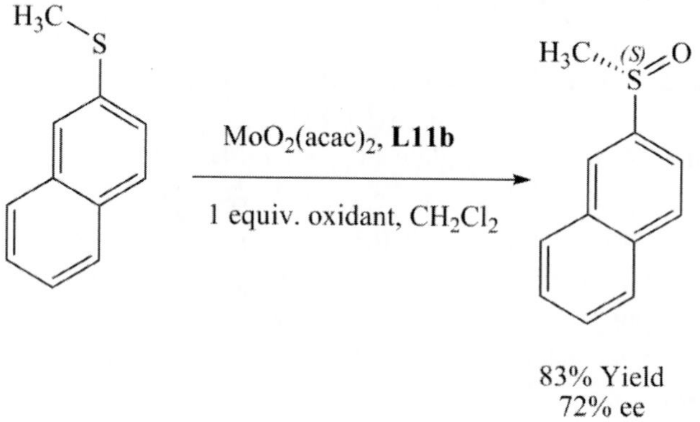

Scheme 34. A representative catalytic asymmetric sulfoxidation reaction with Mo-**L11b**.

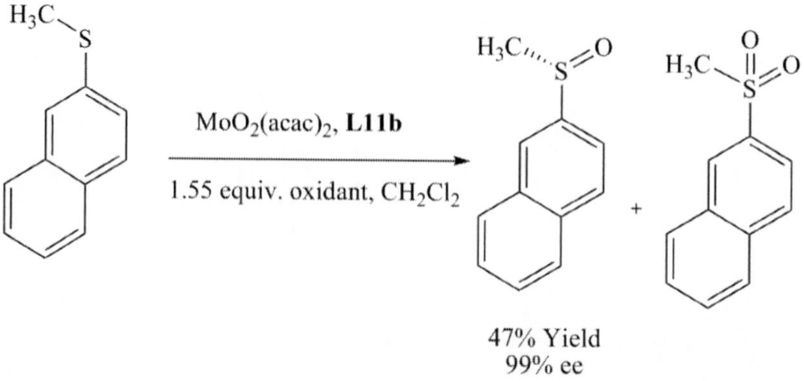

Scheme 35. Tandem asymmetric sulfoxidation/kinetic resolution with Mo-**L11b**.

Further they extended the scope for tandem reaction which involves sulfoxidation followed by kinetic resolution with little excess of oxidant. High enantioselectivity up to 99% ee was achieved with appreciable yield of sulfoxide products (Scheme 35). [63]

6. OXIDATION OF THIOLS TO DISULFIDES

A mild and efficient method for selective oxidation of thiols to the corresponding disulfides has been achieved by using molybdenum(VI) complexes in DMSO solvent. [64] Various aromatic and non-aromatic thiols were oxidized into disulfides in high yield. The general order of reactivity of thiols are $ArSH>ArCH_2SH> AlkSH$. Although other methods are available, this protocol is attractive because of its simplicity, general applicability and excellent yields (Scheme 36).

7. AEROBIC OXIDATION OF ALCOHOLS

Aerobic oxidation involves the conversion of various alcohols into corresponding carbonyl compounds with molecular oxygen. Few examples of aerobic oxidation with oxomolybdenum catalysts have been reported in the literature. Osborn and co-workers developed the heterometallic Mo-Cu system for oxidation of various primary and secondary alcohols. The role of carboxylic acid in this condition is to promote the reaction rate and yield of the reaction. A powdered molecular sieve was used to trap water molecules formed during the course of the reaction. The catalyst facilitates the oxidation of primary benzyl alcohols into aldehydes without the formation of overoxidized product (Scheme 37). [65]

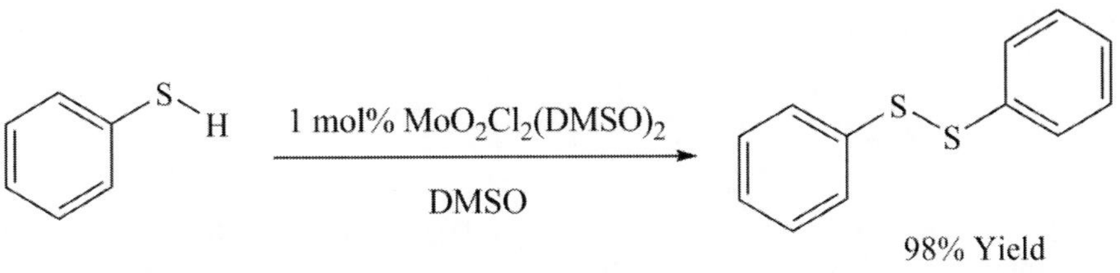

Scheme 36. Selective oxidation of thiols to the corresponding disulfides with Mo(VI) catalyst.

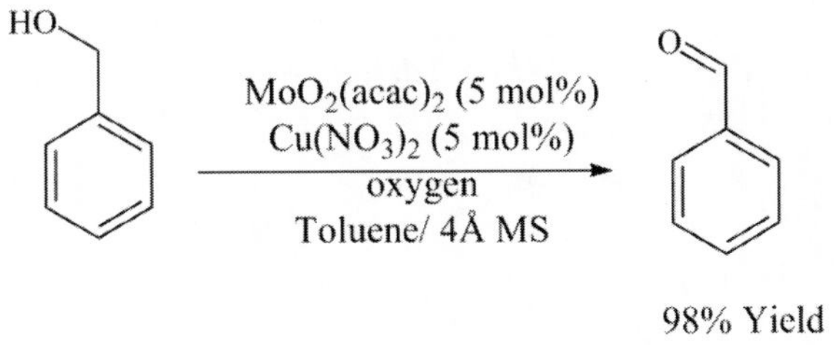

Scheme 37. Aerobic oxidation of benzyl alcohol with Mo-Cu bimetallic catalytic System.

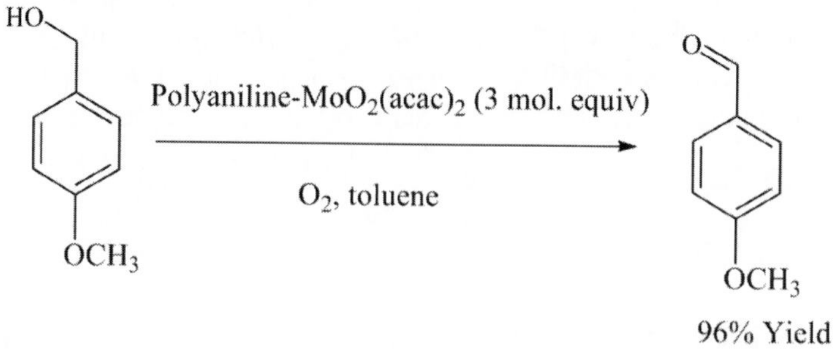

Scheme 38. Aerobic oxidation of benzyl alcohol with Polyaniline supported Mo-catalysts .

A simple heterogeneous protocol for aerobic oxidation of alcohols was developed by Punniyamurthy and co-workers. [66] The catalyst $MoO_2(acac)_2$ supported with commercially available polyaniline promotes the aerobic oxidation of various primary and secondary alcohol in high yield and selectivity. Primary alcohols were found to be more reactive than secondary alcohols. Moreover, the catalyst has been recycled up to three runs without loss of activity (Scheme 38).

8. AEROBIC OXIDATION OF BENZYLIC AZIDE

Prabhu and Maddani reported the aerobic oxidation of benzylic azides using molybdenum xanthate catalyst. [67] The oxidation of benzylic azides afforded the corresponding aldehydes in excellent yields without any over-oxidation. The reaction proceeds nearly quantitatively in both toluene and water solvent systems. Azides having additional functional groups like alcohol, alkene, ketone and esters were well tolerated under this condition (Scheme 39).

9. REDUCTION WITH HYDROSILANES

Oxo-molybdenum compounds involve unique catalytic reduction reactions with various hydrosilane compounds. Royo and co-workers first observed this protocol for hydrosilylation of carbonyl compounds with molybdenum catalyst.

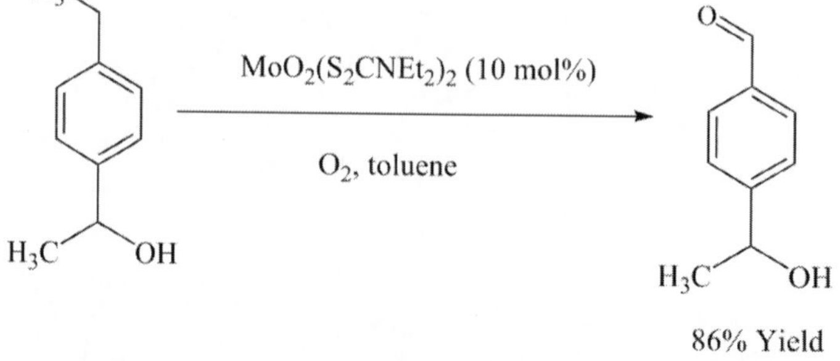

Scheme 39. Aerobic oxidation of azides into corresponding aldehydes with Mo(VI) catalyst.

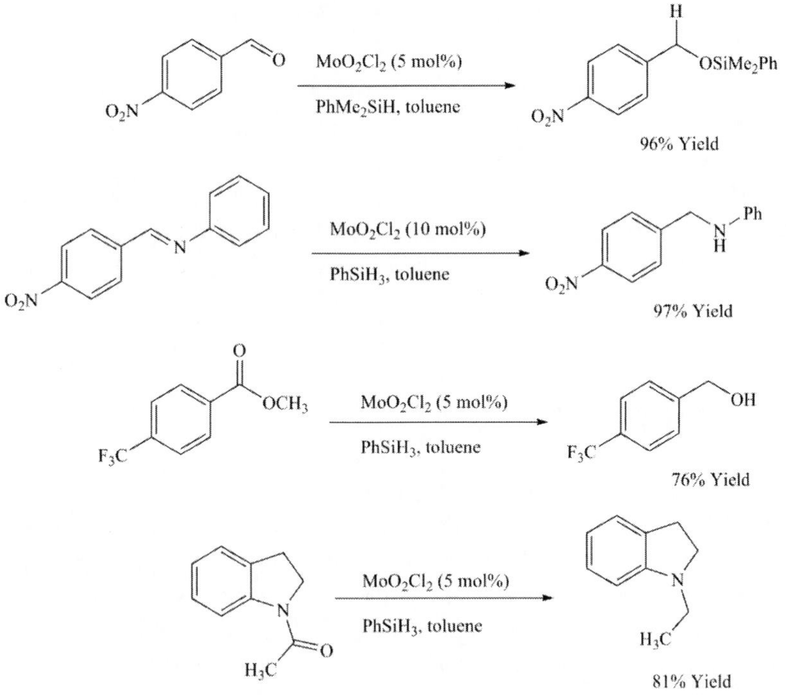

Scheme 40. Mo(VI)-Silane system for reduction of various functional groups.

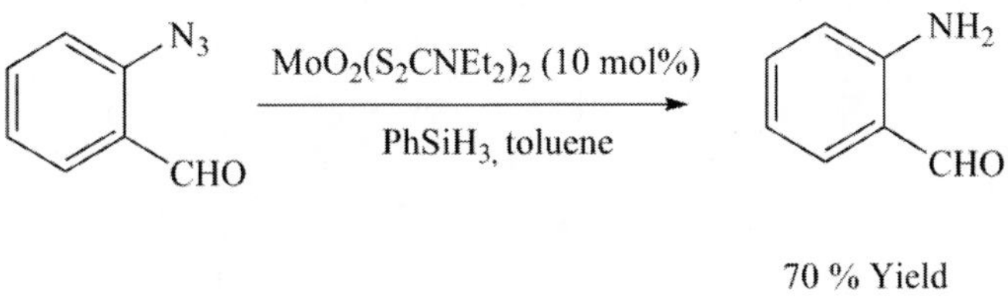

Scheme 41. Mo(VI)-Silane system for selective reduction of azides.

The reaction of aldehydes and ketones with dimethylphenyl silane were carried out with catalytic amount of MoO_2Cl_2 which afforded the corresponding silyl ether in high yield. [68] Based on this initial study, Fernandes and co-workers investigated the application of Mo-silane system for reduction of imines. Imines were chemoselectively reduced to the corresponding amines in excellent to moderate yield. [69] The same group extended the scope of the catalytic system for reduction of esters. The catalytic reaction proceeds smoothly for various aromatic and aliphatic esters with dimethylphenyl silane in nearly quantitatively. [70] It is shown that no reaction was observed with bulky triphenyl silane. A useful extension of this catalytic system involves the synthesis of amines form amides. The reduction of secondary and tertiary amides was carried out with MoO_2Cl_2-silane system (Scheme 40). [71]

Prabhu and co-workers developed molybdenum xanthate-silane system for reduction of azides. [72] Chemoselective reduction of various azides has been achieved in quantitative yield. Azides with additional functional groups like ester, ketone and amides are found to be remains unaffected under this condition (Scheme 41).

10. Reductive Cyclization

Another important application of dioxomolybdenum complexes involves the synthesis of various functionalized carbazoles and indoles through reductive cyclization. Sanz and co-workers demonstrated this transformation with $MoO_2Cl_2(dmf)_2$ in presence of triphenyl phosphine. [73] A wide range of carbazoles and indoles have been prepared from nitrobiphenyl and nitrostyrenes in quantitative yields. Furthermore, the one pot synthesis involves Wittig reaction followed by reductive cyclization has also been achieved with 2-nitrobenzaldehyde (Scheme 42).

11. Meyer-Schuster Rearrangement

Meyer-Schuster rearrangement is a chemical reaction that involves the conversion of propargyl alcohol into α,β-unsaturated carbonyl compounds. This rearrangement reaction can be achieved in strong acid condition, but in many cases poor selectivity was observed due to the formation of mixture of E and Z stereoisomers. Several transition metal catalysts have also been successfully applied for this rearrangement. Osborn and Lorber demonstrated the Meyer-Schuster rearrangement with dioxomolybdenum complexes. [74] This catalytic system is effective for isomerization of tertiary propargyl alcohols at high temperature with high selectivity (Scheme 43). The mechanism involves the transesterification reactions of the catalyst with propargyl alcohol to form an intermediate which then undergoes [3,3] sigmatropic rearrangement to give allenyloxo molybdenum complex. The allenyloxo compound undergoes alkoxide exchange with another propargyl alcohol thereby liberating the allenol and finally the tautomerization of allenols yield the products (Figure 7).

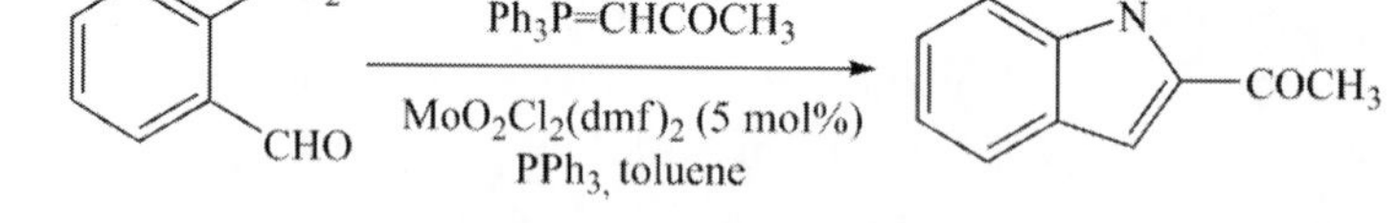

Scheme 42. Mo-catalyzed reductive cyclization of nitroaromatics.

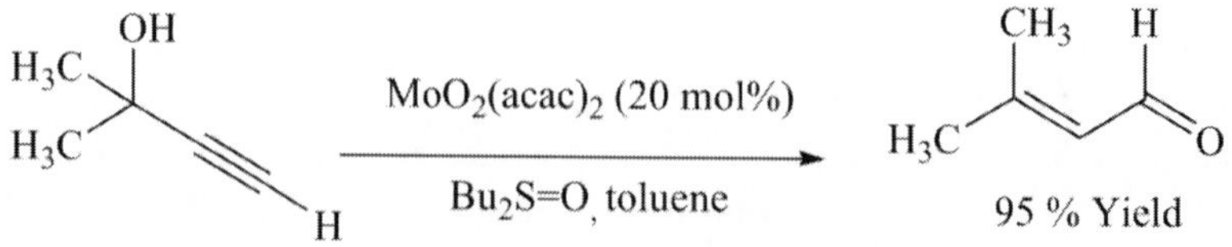

Scheme 43. Meyer-Schuster rearrangement with $MoO_2(acac)_2$.

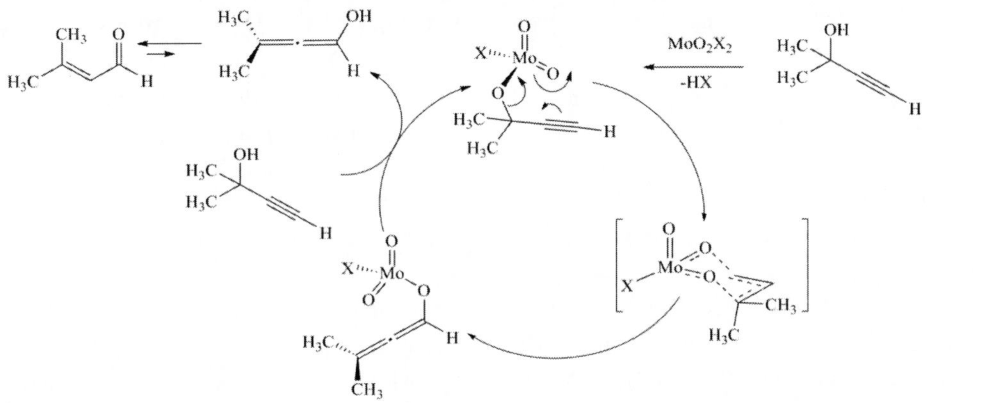

Adapted with permission from reference 74, Copyright 1996, Elsevier.

Figure 7. Proposed mechanism for Mo-catalyzed Meyer-Schuster rearrangement.

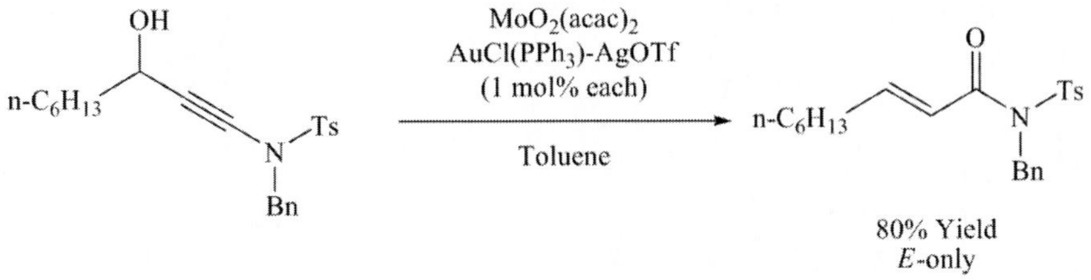

Scheme 44. Meyer-Schuster rearrangement with Mo-Au-Ag trimetallic catalytic system.

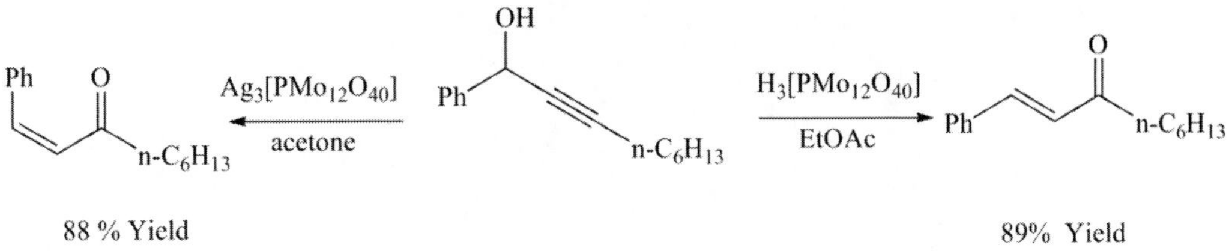

Scheme 45. Meyer-Schuster rearrangement with heteropolyacids.

Akai and co-workers developed trimetallic catalytic system of Mo, Au and Ag for Meyer-Schuster rearrangement. [75] They found that various primary, secondary and tertiary alcohols afforded the products with excellent yield and selectivity even at room temperature. It is important to note that this is the first successful catalytic system for the preparation of α,β-unsaturated amide with complete E-selectivity (Scheme 44).

The same authors extended the application of this reactions for the stereoselective preparation of both E and Z-α,β-unsaturated carbonyl compounds with heteropoly acid catalysts. [76] The reaction of secondary propargyl alcohol with the $H_3[PMo_{12}O_{40}]$ catalyst at 50 □C in ethyl acetate afforded the products with E-selectivity. The same reaction with $Ag_3[PMo_{12}O_{40}]$ catalyst in acetone resulted in the formation of thermodynamically unfavorable Z isomer. This is the first successful method for the preparation of Z-α,β-unsaturated carbonyl compounds through Meyer-Schuster rearrangement (Scheme 45).

12. ASYMMETRIC PINACOL COUPLING REACTIONS

An unusual application of oxo-molybdenum complexes for asymmetric pinacol coupling reactions was reported by Zhu and co-workers. [77] Pinacol coupling is the reaction that involves the conversion of aldehyde into the corresponding 1,2-diol.

Dioxomolybdenum complexes having salan based chiral ligand have been applied as a precatalyst for asymmetric pinacol coupling reactions in presence of zinc as co-reductant (Scheme 46).

Under this condition, chiral 1,2-diols were prepared from various aromatic aldehydes with excellent diastereo- and enantioselectivity. The mechanism involves the formation of intermediate mono-oxo Mo(IV) complexes. The Mo(IV) is the active catalyst which is generated by the reaction of dioxo molybdenum compound with trimethylsilyl chloride and zinc powder (Scheme 47). The active catalyst thus formed react with the benzaldehyde to form diketyl radical which undergo intra-molecular coupling followed by cleavage with the subsequent regeneration of Mo(IV) catalyst (Scheme 48). The inter-molecular coupling of the diketyl radical resulted in the formation of optically inactive *meso* compounds which is less favourable.

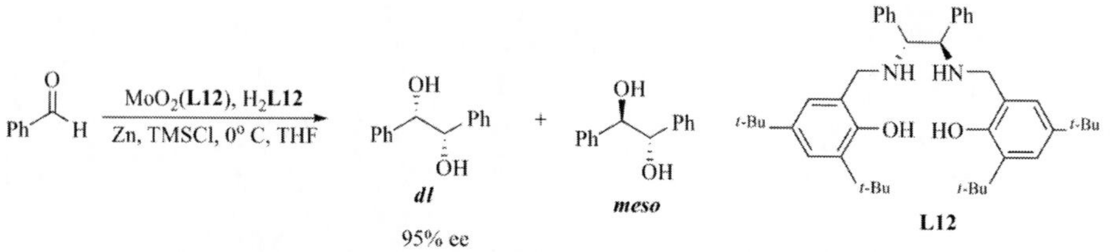

Scheme 46. Mo catalyzed asymmetric pinacol coupling of benzaldehyde.

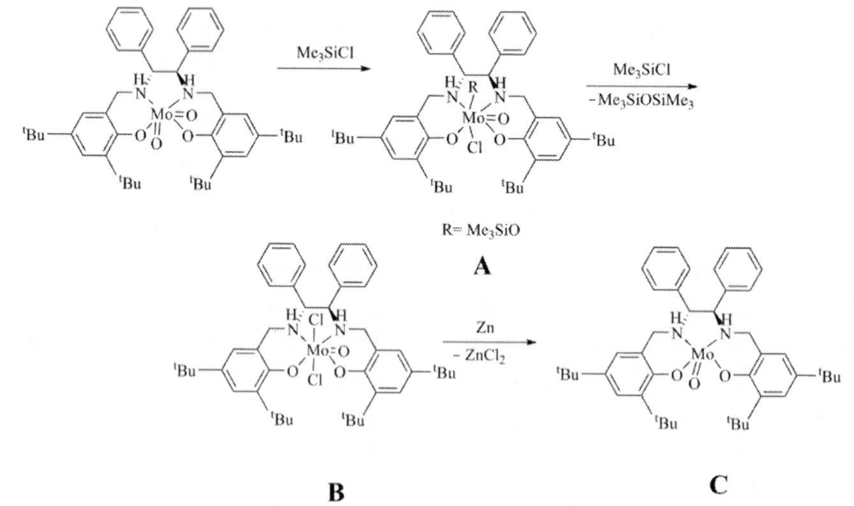

Adapted with permission from reference 77, Copyright 2007, American Chemical Society.

Scheme 47. The reaction of dioxo molybdenum compound with trimethylsilyl chloride and zinc.

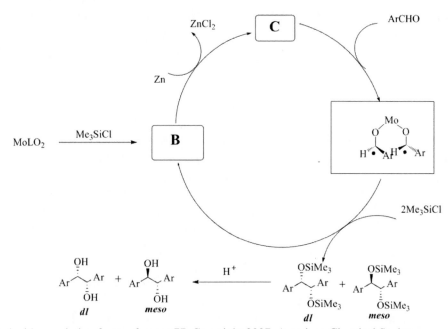

Adapted with permission from reference 77, Copyright 2007, American Chemical Society.

Scheme 48. Proposed mechanism for Mo-catalyzed asymmetric pinacol coupling.

In summary, this chapter clearly demonstrates the potential applications of molybdenum catalysts in few organic transformations. Molybdenum alkylidene complexes provided the access to the various olefin metathesis reactions with high reactivity and selectivity. Molybdenum catalyzed allylic substitution reactions have been achieved with unique regio- and enantioselectivity. Several oxidation and reduction reactions have been successfully catalyzed with dioxomolybdenum compounds. In addition to these reactions, alkyne metathesis, Pauson-Khand reactions, isomerization reactions and cycloaddition reactions are also well studied with molybdenum catalysts. Molybdenum compounds have also been used as stoichiometric reagents for some organic reactions. Several new organic reactions promoted by molybdenum compounds are expected in the near future.

REFERENCES

[1]   Grubbs, R. H.; Miller, S. J.; Fu, G. C. *Acc. Chem. Res.* 1995, *28*, 446.
[2]   Schrock, R. R. *Tetrahedron* 1999, *55*, 8141.
[3]   Schrock, R. R.; Hoveyda, A. H. *Angew. Chem. Int. Ed.* 2003, *42*, 4592.
[4]   Astruc, D. *New J. Chem.* 2005, *29*, 42.
[5]   Casey, C. P. *J. Chem. Educ.* 2006, *83*, 192.
[6]   Belda, O.; Moberg, C. *Acc. Chem. Res.* 2004, *37*, 159.
[7]   Maddani, M. R.; Prabhu, K. P. *J. Indian Inst. Sci.* 2010, *90*, 287.
[8]   Jeyakumar, K.; Chand, D. K. *J. Chem. Sci.* 2009, *121*, 111.
[9]   Sanz, R.; Pedrosa, M. *Curr. Org. Synth.* 2009, *6*, 239.
[10]   Khurana, J. M.; Chauhan, S.; Agrawal, A. *Org. Prep. Proced. Int.* 2004, *36*, 201.

[11] Brito, J. A.; Royo, B.; Gómez, M. *Catal. Sci. Technol.* 2011, *1*, 1109.

[12] Trnka, T. M.; Grubbs, R. H. *Acc. Chem. Res.* 2001, *34*, 18.

[13] Schrock, R. R.; Murdzek, J. S.; Bazan, G. C.; Robbins, J.; DiMare, M.; O'Regan, M. *J. Am. Chem. Soc.* 1990, *112*, 3875.

[14] Fu, G. C.; Grubbs, R. H. *J. Am. Chem. Soc.* 1992, *114*, 5426.

[15] Fu, G. C.; Grubbs, R. H. *J. Am. Chem. Soc.* 1992, *114*, 7324.

[16] Fujimura, O.; Fu, G. C.; Grubbs, R. H. *J. Org. Chem.* 1994, *59*, 4029.

[17] Calimente, D.; Postema, M. H. D. *J. Org. Chem.* 1999, *64*, 1770.

[18] Murakami, M.; Kadowaki, S.; Matsuda, T. *Org. Lett.* 2005, *7*, 3953.

[19] Crowe, W. E.; Zhang, Z. J. *J. Am. Chem. Soc.* 1993, *115*, 10998.

[20] Crowe, W. E.; Goldberg, D. R. *J. Am. Chem. Soc.* 1995, *117*, 5162.

[21] Crowe, W. E.; Goldberg, D. R.; Zhang, Z. J. *Tetrahedron Lett.* 1996, *37*, 2117.

[22] Brümmer, O.; Rückert, A.; Blechert, S. *Chem. Eur. J.* 1997, *3*, 441.

[23] Fujimura, O.; Grubbs, R. H. *J. Am. Chem. Soc.* 1996, *118*, 2499.

[24] Fujimura, O.; Grubbs, R. H. *J. Org. Chem.* 1998, *63*, 824.

[25] Alexander, J. B.; La, D. S.; Cefalo, D. R.; Hoveyda, A. H.; Schrock, R. R. *J. Am. Chem. Soc.* 1998, *120*, 4041.

[26] La, D. S.; Alexander, J. B.; Cefalo, D. R.; Graf, D. D.; Hoveyda, A. H.; Schrock, R. R. *J. Am. Chem. Soc.* 1998, *120*, 9720.

[27] Zhu, S. S.; Cefalo, D. R.; La, D. S.; Jamieson, J. Y.; Davis, W. M.; Hoveyda, A. H.; Schrock, R. R. *J. Am. Chem. Soc.* 1999, *121*, 8251.

[28] La, D. S.; Ford, J. G.; Sattely, E, S.; Bonitatebus, P. J.; Schrock, R. R.; Hoveyda, A. H. *J. Am. Chem. Soc.* 1999, *121*, 11603.

[29] La, D. S.; Sattely, E. S.; Ford, J. G.; Schrock, R. R.; Hoveyda, A. H. *J. Am. Chem. Soc.* 2001, *123*, 7767.

[30] Weatherhead, G. S.; Ford, J. G.; Alexanian, E. J.; Schrock, R. R.; Hoveyda, A. H. *J. Am. Chem. Soc.* 2000, *122*, 1828.

[31] Malcolmson, S. J.; Meek, S. J.; Sattely, E. S.; Schrock, R. R.; Hoveyda, A. H. *Nature* 2008, *456*, 933.

[32] Tsuji, J.; Takahashi, H.; Morikawa, M. *Tetrahedron Lett.* 1965, *6*, 4387.

[33] Hata, G.; Takahashi, H.; Miyake, A. *J. Chem. Soc., Chem. Commun.* 1970, 1392.

[34] Atkins, K. E.; Walker, W. E.; Manyik, R. M.; *Tetrahedron Lett.* 1970, *11*, 3821.

[35] Trost, B. M.; Lautens, M. *J. Am. Chem. Soc.* 1982, *104*, 5543.

[36] Trost, B. M.; Merlic, C. A. *J. Org. Chem.* 1990, 55, 1127.

[37] Trost, B. M.; Hachiya, I. *J. Am. Chem. Soc.* 1998, *120*, 1104.

[38] Kaiser, N.-F. K.; Bremberg, U.; Larhed, M.; Moberg, C.; Hallberg, A. *Angew. Chem. Int. Ed.* 2000, *39*, 3596.

[39] Palucki, M.; Um, J. M.; Conlon, D. A.; Yasuda, N.; Hughes, D. L.; Mao, B.; Wang, J.; Reider, P. J. *Adv. Synth. Catal.* 2001, *343*, 46.

[40] Belda, O.; Moberg, C. *Synthesis* 2002, 1601.

[41] Trost, B. M.; Dogra, K.; Hachiya, I.; Emura, T.; Hughes, D. L.; Krska, S.; Reamer, R. A.; Palucki, M.; Yasuda, N.; Reider, P. J. *Angew. Chem. Int. Ed.* 2002, *41*, 1929.

[42] Malkov, A. V.; Spoor, P.; Vinader, V.; Kočovský, P. *Tetrahedron Lett.* 2001, *42*, 509.

[43] Trost, B. M.; Dogra, K. *J. Am. Chem. Soc.* 2002, *124*, 7256.

[44] Trost, B. M.; Miller, J. R.; Hoffman Jr., C. M. *J. Am. Chem. Soc.* 2011, *133*, 8165.

[45] Trost, B. M.; Dogra, K.; Franzini, M. *J. Am. Chem. Soc.* 2004, *126*, 1944.

[46] Trost, B. M.; Zhang, Y. *J. Am. Chem. Soc.* 2007, *129*, 14548.

[47] Dvořáková, H.; Dvořák, D.; Šrogl, J.; Kočovský, P. *Tetrahedron Lett.* 1995, *36*, 6351.

[48] Malkov, A. V.; Baxendale, I.; Mansfield, D. J.; Kočovský, P. *Tetrahedron Lett.* 1997, *38*, 4895.

[49] Malkov, A. V.; Baxendale, I. R.; Dvořák, D.; Mansfield, D. J.; Kočovský, P. *J. Org. Chem.* 1999, *64*, 2737.

[50] Malkov, A. V.; Davis, S. L.; Mitchell, W. L.; Kočovský, P. *Tetrahedron Lett.* 1997, *38*, 4899.

[51] Malkov, A. V.; Davis, S. L.; Baxendale, I. R.; Mitchell, W. L.; Kočovský, P. *J. Org. Chem.* 1999, *64*, 2751.

[52] Malkov, A. V.; Spoor, P.; Vinader, V.; Kočovský, P. *J. Org. Chem.* 1999, 64, 5308.

[53] Yang, H.; Fang, L.; Zhang, M.; Zhu, C. *Eur. J. Org. Chem.* 2009, 666.

[54] Halcon, (J. Kollar), US 3.351.635, 1967.

[55] ARCO (M. N. Sheng, J. G. Zajacek), GB 1.136.923, 1968.

[56] Sheng, M. N.; Zajacek, J. G. *J. Org. Chem.* 1970, *35*, 1839.

[57] Sharpless, K. B.; Michaelson, R. C. *J. Am. Chem. Soc.* 1973, *95*, 6136.

[58] Kato, J. -I.; Ota, H.; Matsukawa, K.; Endo, T. *Tetrahedron Lett.* 1988, *29*, 2843.

[59] Marín, I.; Matheu, M. I.; Díaz, Y.; Castillón, S. *Adv. Synth. Catal.* 2010, *352*, 3407.

[60] Barlan, A. U.; Basak, A.; Yamamoto, H. *Angew. Chem. Int. Ed.* 2006, *45*, 5849.

[61] Jeyakumar, K.; Chand, D. K. *Tetrahedron Lett.* 2006, *47*, 4573.

[62] Marom, H.; Antonov, S.; Popowski, Y.; Gozin, M. *J. Org. Chem.* 2011, *76*, 5240.

[63] Basak, A.; Barlan, A. U.; Yamamoto, H. *Tetrahedron: Asymmetry* 2006, *17*, 508.

[64] Sanz, R.; Aguado, R.; Pedrosa, M. R.; Arnáiz, F. J. *Synthesis* 2002, 856.

[65] Lorber. C. Y.; Smidt, S. P.; Osborn, J. A. *Eur. J. Inorg. Chem.* 2000, 655.

[66] Velusamy, S.; Ahamed, M.; Punniyamurthy. T. *Org. Lett.* 2004, *6*, 4821.

[67] Maddani, M.; Prabhu, K. R. *Tetrahedron Lett.* 2008, *49*, 4526.

[68] Fernandes, A. C.; Fernandes, R.; Romão, C. C.; Royo, B. *Chem. Commun.* 2005, 213.

[69] Fernandes, A. C.; Romão, C. C. *Tetrahedron Lett.* 2005, *46*, 8881.

[70] Fernandes, A. C.; Romão, C. C. *J. Mol. Catal. A: Chem.* 2006, *253*, 96.

[71] Fernandes, A. C.; Romão, C. C. *J. Mol. Catal. A: Chem.* 2007, *272*, 60.

[72] Maddani, M. R.; Moorthy, S. K.; Prabhu, K. R. *Tetrahedron* 2010, *66*, 329.

[73] Sanz, R.; Escribano, R.; Aguado, R.; Pedrosa, M. R.; Arnáiz, F. J. *Adv. Synth. Catal.* 2007, *349*, 713.

[74] Lorber, C. Y.; Osborn, J. A. *Tetrahedron Lett.* 1996, *37*, 853.

[75] Egi, M.; Yamaguchi, Y.; Fujiwara, N.; Akai, S. *Org. Lett.* 2008, *10*, 1867.

[76] Egi, M.; Umemura, M.; Kawai, T.; Akai, S. *Angew. Chem. Int. Ed.* 2011, *50*, 12197.

[77] Yang, H.; Wang, H.; Zhu, C. *J. Org. Chem.* 2007, *72*, 10029.

In: Molybdenum
Editor: Alvin A. Holder

ISBN: 978-1-62417-272-4
© 2013 Nova Science Publishers, Inc.

Chapter 9

MOLYBDENUM AND PTERINS

Sharon J. Nieter Burgmayer[*]
Bryn Mawr College, Bryn Mawr, Pennsylvania, US

'Dedicated to the memory of Ed Stiefel who inspired all who met him'

ABSTRACT

The combination of a pterin and molybdenum in the mononuclear molybdenum enzymes is the motivation for exploring the chemistry of molybdenum with pterins. Pterin is one of a large family of bicyclic N-heterocycles called pteridines. Unlike other common biological ligands like porphyrins, pterins are unique in their ability to do multi-electron, proton coupled redox reactions, such as the proton coupled redox reactions performed by the molybdenum enzymes. This chapter surveys the literature of molybdenum-pterin complexes that has appeared since 1986 when the first molybdenum pterin complex was reported. The chapter begins with introductory material about the molybdenum enzymes and the molybdenum cofactor, provides a synopsis of pterin and pyranopterin redox chemistry, then discusses two areas of studies on molybdenum-pterin chemistry. The first area concerns molybdenum coordinated directly to pterins while the second area describes research directed at synthesis and study of molybdenum coordinated to a pterin-dithiolene.

1. INTRODUCTION

In 1984 I joined the labs of Ed Stiefel at the Exxon Research and Engineering Corporate Research Center in Annandale, New Jersey as a post-doctoral research fellow. My role in his group was to bring the expertise of an inorganiker to the molybdenum enzymes projects involving both nitrogenase and the mononuclear molybdenum enzymes. The discovery of the pterin in molybdenum enzymes by Rajagopalan was barely two years old. Not much was known about this pterin portion of the molybdenum cofactor. How exactly did it bind Mo?

---

[*] Department of Chemistry, Bryn Mawr College, Bryn Mawr, Pennsylvania 19010.

What was its function? The area was ripe with speculation. Soon after I began my post-doc, I immersed myself in the pterin literature to attempt mastery of this very foreign area. (Ed would eventually tell me to get out of the books and into the labs!) Within a year, we had the crystal structure of the first example of molybdenum coordinated by pterin.

Since 1986, my research program at Bryn Mawr College has continued to pursue the answer to the question "why a pterin?" in regards this unusual structure within the catalytic site of the molybdenum enzymes. After the presence of the dithiolene chelate was established and the pyran ring appended to the pterin was revealed by X-ray crystallography, our research program evolved to answer questions using model complexes that are not easily addressed in the holoenzymes. Ed's spirit has remained with me throughout my work and to this day. His enthusiasm, his love of molybdenum, his fascination for the intertwined nature of biogeochemistry, his warmth and his integrity still inform what I do and I'm forever grateful to have had his mentorship.

1.1. The Molybdenum Cofactor in Biology

Molybdenum made a partnership with pterin in bacteria many thousands of years ago, [1] but this partnership remained hidden from scientists until 1982. [2,3] Biomolecules containing molybdenum and pterin can be found in organisms throughout the entire kingdom of life from bacteria to humans. [4-5] Most are enzymes that catalyze primarily redox reactions essential to the survival of the organism. Approximately 100 enzymes have been identified which share a number of common traits. [6,7] All of the pterin-dithiolene-containing molybdenum enzymes have a single metal at the catalytic site. For this reason they are referred to as mononuclear molybdenum enzymes to distinguish them from nitrogenase which uses a polynuclear Mo/Fe/S cluster with no pterin-dithiolene ligands. [8] The mononuclear enzymes are sorted into three main families based on the number of oxo and pterin-dithiolene ligands (Figure 1). [7] The common attributes among the three families are the pterin-dithiolene ligand (with minor variations remote from Mo), the cycling of molybdenum oxidation states between +4, +5 and +6, and the presence of an oxo ligand (Mo=O) in at least one of the oxidation states of the enzyme in nearly every member. The three main families are differentiated according to oxo vs. sulfido ligation at molybdenum, the number of associated pterin-dithiolene ligands and the type of additional prosthetic groups involved in electron transfer.

It should be noted that tungsten, the heavier congener of molybdenum, is used rather than Mo by one family of enzymes where it is also bound to a pterin-dithiolene ligand. [9, 10] For both molybdenum and the tungsten enzymes, it is certainly the partnership of the metal *and* the unique pterin-dithiolene which is, along with the protein, responsible for the biological function in these enzymes.

Molybdenum and tungsten enzymes have great importance to the biosphere where they have major roles in the global cycling of the bulk elements: carbon, [11,12] nitrogen, [12] and sulfur [13,14]. A great diversity of organisms and substrates uses molybdenum and tungsten enzymes to catalyze very simple chemical reactions on carbon, nitrogen and sulfur-containing substrates.

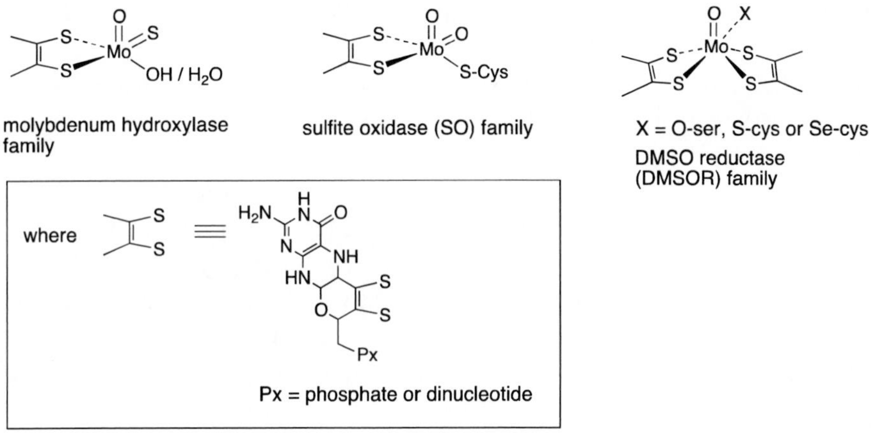

Figure 1. The three families of molybdenum enzymes.

A few examples will illustrate why molybdenum enzymes are essential for the health of selected organisms. All plants depend on nitrate reductase to accomplish the seemingly trivial reaction of nitrate reduction to nitrite that is the first step of nitrogen assimilation into compounds required for growth. [15,16] Many bacteria use molybdenum or tungsten enzymes in anaerobic respiration where the terminal electron acceptor is a reducible molecule other than oxygen, such as nitrate, [4,17,18] polysulfide, [4,18,19] trimethylamine oxide [4,18, 20] or dimethylsulfoxide [4,18,21,22]. Mammals have several molybdenum enzymes. In humans, genetic diseases involving these Mo enzymes lead to severe, albeit rare, and usually fatal neurological problems. [2,3,23]

While molybdenum enzymes impact our contemporary, largely aerobic, biogeochemistry, the biochemical transformations and host organisms of the tungsten enzymes point back to an ancient evolutionary era when biogeochemistry was anaerobic and life persisted through extracting energy from carbon and sulfur sources. Many of the known tungsten enzymes are isolated from hyperthermophilic archae and bacteria—organisms that may be our evolutionary ancestors—which thrive at elevated temperatures typical of the ancient environment. [10] The same ligand—a pterin-dithiolene—is found in both molybdenum and ancient tungsten enzymes. This ligand has changed little through evolution over millennia as it was incorporated into the catalytic site of molybdenum enzymes in higher organisms and the conservation of its basic structure is convincing evidence for the special role of the metal-pterin-dithiolene group that carries out a variety of chemical jobs in Nature.

1.2. The Pterin-Dithiolene Ligand

The necessity of molybdenum as an essential trace element was recognized for many decades even though its coordination environment was unknown. Experiments suggested that the molybdenum atom and its complement of ligands could be removed from a protein, would remain intact and could be inserted in a different apoprotein in a process called *reconstitution*. As a result, the dissociable molybdenum unit was called the *molybdenum cofactor*, abbreviated as *Moco*. [24-26] Only much later was the pterin-dithiolene structural unit that is common and required by all Mo (and W) enzymes identified definitively [2,3] from evidence from X-ray crystallography in 1995. [27]

Prior to the initial suggestion based on chemical evidence [28] that a pterin-dithiolene was a necessary component of the so-called molybdenum cofactor, the molybdenum coordination sphere was presumed to comprise several thiolate or thioether ligands and one or more oxido and sulfido ligands. This coordination environment had been deduced from matching spectroscopic characteristics obtained from the enzymes with those from synthetic compounds prepared by inorganic chemists. [29] Electron paramagnetic resonance (EPR) and extended X-ray absorption fine structure (EXAFS) were the most informative methods in this process of teasing out the metal coordination sphere, but they were not capable revealing the pterin-dithiolene. The pterin-dithiolene remained hidden from analytical view until methodology for producing and characterizing its many degradation products was developed. [2,3] The name *molybdopterin* was first assigned to this unique pterin-dithiolene ligand during the early discovery of its existence, a name chosen to designate *'the special ligand for molybdenum which contains a pterin'* (Figure 2). Subsequently it was discovered that there is not just one form of molybdopterin and that it also chelates tungsten in the tungsten enzymes. [18,10,11] These additional derivatives are differentiated at the phosphate portion of molybdopterin where the simple monophosphate terminus of molybdopterin in higher organisms is appended to a dinucleotide (Figure 2) forming modified versions of molybdopterin found solely in bacterial enzymes. The term 'molybdopterin' has largely been replaced by 'pyranopterin dithiolene' in the recent literature.

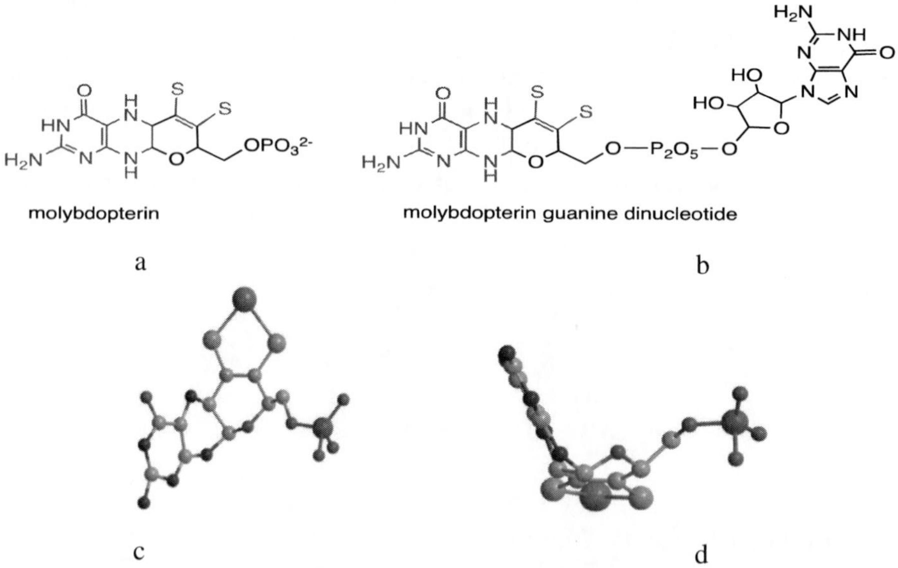

molybdopterin

a

molybdopterin guanine dinucleotide

b

c

d

Figure 2. (A) The pyranopterin-dithiolene structure of molybdopterin, the ligand required in molybdenum and tungsten enzymes. The pterin portion is in blue, the dithiolene is in red and the pyran ring extension of the pterin is in black. (B) An example of the dinucleotide form of the molybdenum cofactor often used by bacteria, here presented as a guanine dinucleotide. (C) Molybdopterin bound to Mo (green ball) with the conformation found in carbon monoxide dehydrogenase, protein data bank (PDB) #1QJ2. (D) The same structure as in (C) but rotated 90 ° to illustrate the angle between the pterin and pyran ring systems.

The particular pterin-dithiolene chosen by Nature for catalytic systems may appear very strange. Several views of molybdopterin (Figure 2C, D) illustrate the buckled conformation of the pyranopterin ring system to aid the reader to understand the pieces and shape of this odd ligand. A considerable body of Mo/S coordination chemistry from inorganic studies provides a wealth of examples for the special capability of the Mo and sulfur pair that was understood to make a crucial contribution to molybdenum-dependent biochemistry. The discovery of the pyranopterin-dithiolene required an expanded view that specialized features of the pyranopterin-dithiolene ligand are critical for the catalytic function of these Mo and W enzymes.

1.3. Pterin Redox Chemistry

Pterins appear in biological systems in one of two functions, either as a pigment or as a redox component. [30,31] Their participation in the second role results from their nitrogen heterocyclic structure that supports multiple reduction levels and tautomeric forms. The N-heterocyclic structure of the bicyclic pterin system exhibits a wealth of redox reactions in ways similar to the related N-heterocycle isoalloxazine in flavin adenine dinucleotide (FAD). Unlike FAD where redox reactions are limited to 2 e-, 2 H+ processes, pterins are able to transfer up to 4 e-, 4H+ units in sequential reactions. This section describes the different redox states of pterins, how they are produced chemically and detected electrochemically.

1.3.1. Pterin Redox States

The fully oxidized state, the semi-reduced or dihydro state and the fully reduced or tetrahydro state (Figure 3, a-c) are the three main redox states of pterins. These are interconverted by 2e-, 2H+ reactions as described in more detail below. The complexity of pterin redox chemistry is largely due to the many tautomers of the semi-reduced state (Figure 3, d-h). All dihydropterin tautomers, unless highly substituted, [32] will eventually rearrange to the most thermodynamically stable form, the 7,8-dihydropterin (Figure 3, b).

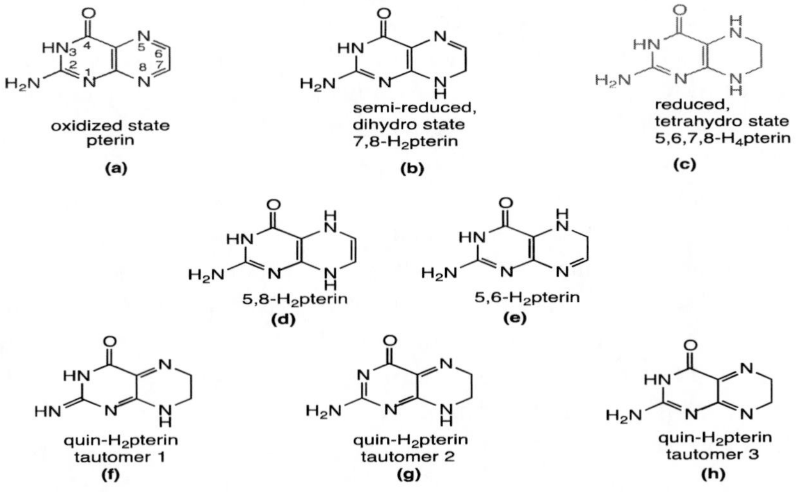

Figure 3. The three oxidation states of pterin (a-c, top row) and the multiple dihydropterin tautomers (d-h) that are less thermodynamically stable.

The most thorough investigation of the redox processes of pterins has been accomplished in a series of studies by Dryhurst using several voltammetric methods. [33-38] The processes determined for unsubstituted pterin (Figure 4) reveal the key features of pterin redox reactions, which were found to be generally applicable to 6- and 6,7-methylated pterins. The scheme is arranged with the most reduced species at the top, the most oxidized species at the bottom and semi-reduced species in the middle of the diagram.

Tetrahydropterins undergo reversible oxidation to an unstable quinonoid tautomer of dihydropterin in step (a) which can be observed under rapid scanning of potential. If not rapidly re-reduced, the quinonoid dihydropterin rearranges to the 7,8-dihydro tautomer in step (b). The 7,8-dihydropterin is oxidizable to pterin in step (c) but at potentials ~500 mV more positive than that for the reversible tetrahydro/quinonoid oxidation. Likewise 7,8-dihydropterin is reducible to tetrahydropterin but at potentials over 1 V more negative than reversible quinonoid / tetrahydro reduction. Fully oxidized pterin may be reduced by 2 e-, 2 H+ in step (d) to generate another unstable dihydropterin, the 5,8-dihydro tautomer. This unstable semi-reduced pterin rearranges to 7,8-dihydropterin in step (e) before further reduction to tetrahydropterin can occur. Use of methylated tetrahydropterins which "locked" the initially formed quinonoid tautomers allowed the determination that quinonoid tautomer 1 (Figure 3f) was the most likely product formed upon tetrahydropterin oxidation. [32]

1.3.2. Redox State of the Pyranopterin System

Soon after the discovery of the pyranopterin ligand in Moco by protein crystallography there was some confusion about its redox state. The saturated, quaternary carbons of the middle pyrazine ring in the pyranopterin seem similar to the structure of a tetrahydropterin but reversing the pyran ring cyclization reaction reveals a 5,6-dihydropterin (Figure 5). The ring-opened, 5,6-dihyropterin form of molybopterin might then be anticipated to tautomerize to other dihydro- structures and further reduced to a true tetrahydropterin or oxidized to an oxidized pterin.

Figure 5 shows the pyranopterin-dithiolene along with possible interconversions based on known pterin chemistry. The intent of Figure 5 is to suggest a variety of reactions but these certainly do not exhaust the possibilities. For example, the possibility of a radical role remains open for molybdopterin in Moco in molybdenum enzymes since a trihydropterin radical was detected by EPR in aldehyde dehydrogenases. [39] The interpretation of the pyranopterin structure as a protected form of a 5,6-dihydropterin is intriguing, especially in light of early attempts to define the reduction state of the pterin in Moco prior to its X-ray structure determination. Rajagopalan concluded from redox titration studies that Moco contained a dihydro-, not tetrahydro-, pterin based on the reaction stoichiometry with the redox dye dichlorophenolindophenol (DCIP) and ferricyanide. [40,41] He further speculated that the isomeric form of the dihydropterin was more likely a quinonoid or another unstable tautomer.

In order to establish the redox chemistry of pyranopterin, we investigated the redox behavior of pyranopterin system using a polyhydroxlated pyranopterin as a model for molybdopterin. [42-44] Our results confirmed that pyranopterin behaves as a dihydropterin under oxidative conditions, where it undergoes a 2 e-, 2H+ oxidation to yield the fully oxidized neopterin (Figure 6). [45] Kinetic analysis showed this pyranopterin oxidation to neopterin was slower than tetrahydropterin oxidation to 7,8-dihydropterin, thereby confirming that the fused pyran ring contributes a stabilizing effect. The oxidation reaction of pyranopterin exhibits a minimal pH and solvent dependence, in marked contrast to tetrahydropterin oxidation that is strongly pH and solvent dependent. The pyranopterin in this study resisted further reduction to a tetrahydropterin using a variety of reducing agents known to reduce oxidized and 7,8-dihydropterins to tetrahydropterins. This experimental work proves that pyranopterin possesses distinctive redox chemistry unlike that of the simple pterin system, a result that may be critical to its use as part of the molybdopterin ligand for molybdenum and tungsten in enzymes.

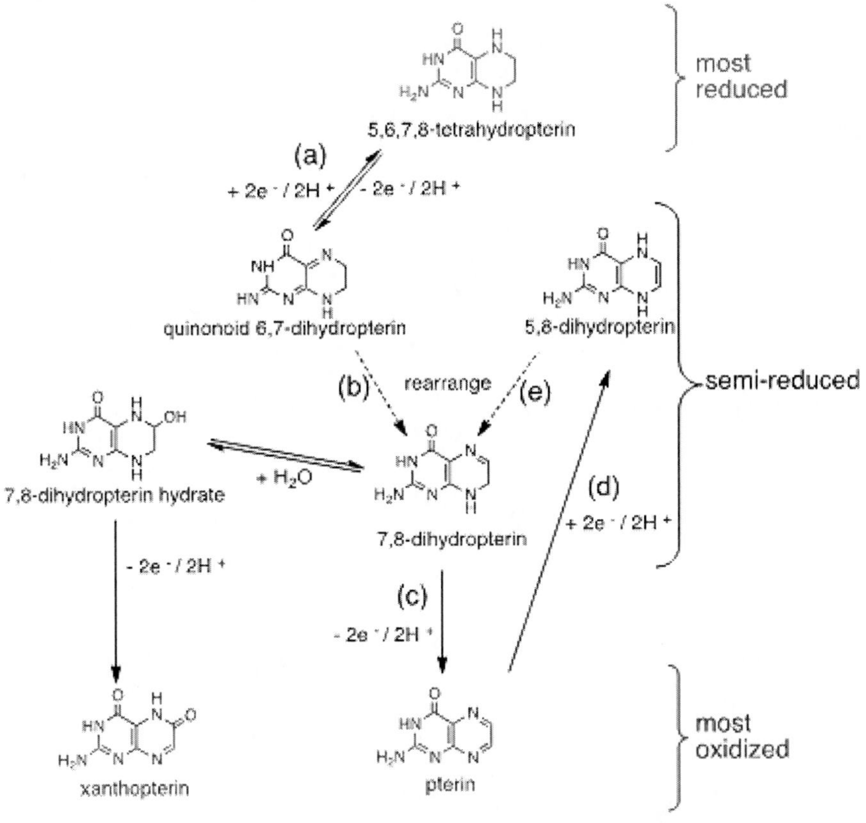

Figure 4. Reaction scheme relating the various redox species generated from unsubstituted pterin.

There is little data to suggest how these redox reactions of the pterin system in molybdopterin will change as a result of appending a dithiolene and a fused pyran ring to the pterin system. Degradation and derivative products have been isolated from some enzymes subjected to oxidizing or other denaturing conditions and suggest some reactivity characteristics of molybdopterin. [2,3]

Still, specific details of how the redox-rich pterin system of molybdopterin interacts with oxidation state changes at the molybdenum or tungsten atom, as well as by the redox active dithiolene unit, are entirely unknown. For molybdenum and tungsten enzymes, the unknown redox reactivity of metal-coordinated molybdopterin is one big mystery remaining to be solved.

7,8-dihydro- form
pyran ring scission
reduction
tetrahydro- form
Molybdopterin
5,6-dihydro- form
oxidation
5,8-dihydro- form

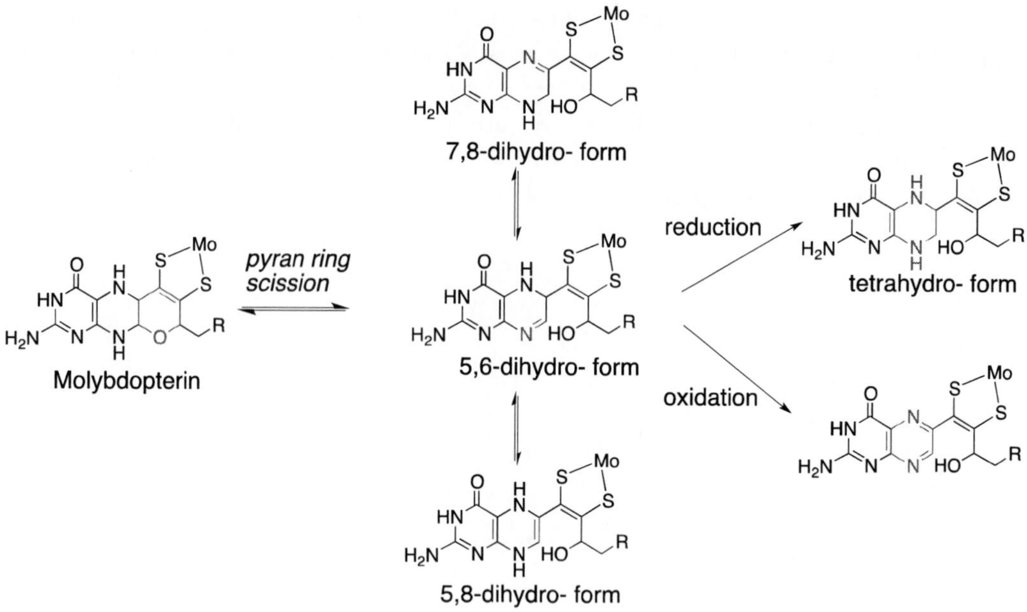

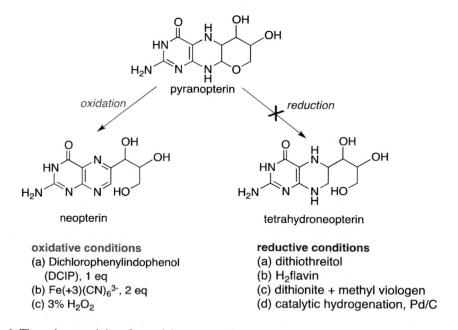

Figure 5. A few of many possible outcomes of redox reactions at molybdopterin after pyran ring scission.

pyranopterin
oxidation
reduction
neopterin
tetrahydroneopterin
oxidative conditions
(a) Dichlorophenylindophenol (DCIP), 1 eq
(b) Fe(+3)(CN)$_6^{3-}$, 2 eq
(c) 3% H_2O_2
reductive conditions
(a) dithiothreitol
(b) H_2flavin
(c) dithionite + methyl viologen
(d) catalytic hydrogenation, Pd/C

Figure 6. The redox reactivity of a model pyranopterin.

2. Studies on the Molybdenum-Pterin Duo

The discussion will now turn to two areas of research involving molybdenum and pterins. The first section will address synthetic work preparing molybdenum–pterin complexes and investigations of their reaction chemistry. Several themes in this section include the favorable coordination of molybdenum in several oxidation states to the O4,N5 chelate site in pterin, the variety of reactivities exhibited by molybdenum (+6)-tetrahydropterin systems and the highly delocalized electronic structures in molybdenum-pterin complexes which create difficulty in assigning formal oxidation states to Mo and pterin. In the second section, the focus is on the development of Moco model systems where molybdenum is coordinated by pterin-substituted dithiolenes.

2.1. Molybdenum Coordinated Directly to Pterins

The area of molybdenum-pterin coordination chemistry was prompted by the discovery of a pterin group in the molybdenum cofactor. The presence of a pterin requirement in Moco was intriguing—why would Nature select such a complicated heterocyclic substituent for the dithiolene tether to molybdenum? The original molybdopterin structure as proposed by Rajagopalan, [28] suggested several metal binding sites in addition to the pterin-dithiolene (Figure 7). Was the reason for the pterin to offer the molybdenum alternative coordination environments?

A second provocative aspect of Rajagopalan's proposed structure was the pairing of an oxidized Mo(+6) center with a reduced tetrahydropterin. Could such an incongruous pair exist simultaneously or would this pair exhibit redox reactions between the metal and the organic cofactor? Both hypotheses—alternative binding sites and likely redox reactions—were the motivation for initial studies of tetrahydropterin reactions with molybdenum(+6) complexes. Prior to these studies there was only one report of a reaction between reduced pterins and transition metals. [46]

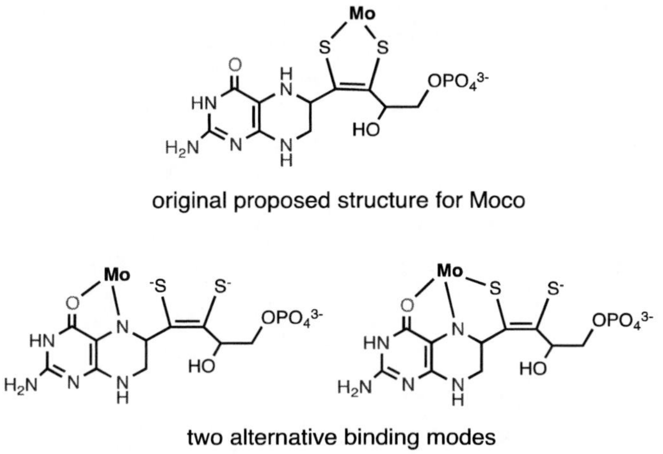

original proposed structure for Moco

two alternative binding modes

Figure 7. The proposed structure of molybdenum-bound pterin portion of Moco after Rajagopalan and an alternative molybdenum binding mode.

The first molybdenum pterin complex reported established the affinity of Mo(+6) for chelation at the O4,N5 site of a deprotonated pterin. [47] Reaction of the yellow butterfly pigment xanthopterin with molybdate as a mixture of ammonium and sodium salts produced a dimeric Mo_2O_5bis(xanthopterinate) complex with an amusing butterfly conformation of the two bridging pterin chelates (Figure 8).

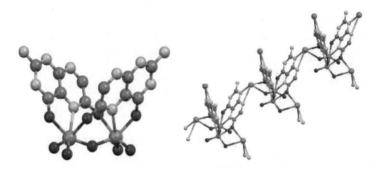

Figure 8 (left) The dimeric molybdenum complex of xanthopterin, $[Mo_2O_5(xanthopterinate)_2]^{2-}$. (right) A portion of the sodium bridged lattice of butterfly-shaped molecules. Color key: green = Mo, red = O, Blue = N, grey = C, purple = Na.

2.1.2. Molybdenum Reactions with Reduced Pterins

The rich redox activity of pterins suggests they have a natural compatibility with redox active transition metals such as molybdenum. Consequently the majority of Mo-pterin coordination chemistry has focused on understanding the redox reactions between these two.

The first redox investigation explored the reaction between $MoO_2(detc)_2$ (detc = diethyldithiocarbamate, $Et_2NCS_2^-$) and 6,7-dimethyltetrahydropterin [H_4DMP] (Eq. 1). [48] Simply mixing these two reagents at room temperature produced an immediate reaction that is visibly apparent by the solution color change from yellow to purple. Since the formation of an intensely purple solution with λ_{max} at 505 nm from yellow $MoO_2(detc)_2$ typically indicates a molybdenum reduction reaction in molybdenum-oxo chemistry, a redox reaction was presumed to have occurred. Monitoring the reaction by ^{1}H NMR revealed that the tetrahydropterin was transformed into a new pterin species with proton resonances characteristic of quinonoid-dihydropterin. [48] On the basis of these two pieces of spectroscopic data the outcome of Eq. 1 was initially interpreted as a two-electron redox reaction yielding a purple Mo(+4) complex bound to a quinonoid dihydropterin at atoms O4 and N5. The importance of this interpretation, which would be challenged later, was that it implied an unusual stability of coordinated quinonoid dihydropterin. This stability prevented the expected rearrangement of the unstable quinonoid dihydropterin to the 7,8-dihydro isomer (see Figure 4). Unfortunately the product of Eq. 1 resisted isolation and its exact structure would remain unknown for seven years until a different preparative method was devised (see below).

MoO$_2$detc$_2$ H$_4$DMP · 2HCl   Mo^{4+}O(quin-H$_2$DMP)(detc)$_x$

Eq. 1

Other dioxo-Mo(+6) reagents were investigated in reactions with tetrahydropterin to determine if quinonoid dihydropterin formation and coordination was a general consequence (Figure 9). [49-52] These studies showed that a variety of Mo(+6) complexes reacted with tetrahydropterins to produce intensely purple-red colored mono-oxo Mo complexes. $MoO_2(acac)_2$ reacted with H_4DMP to produce a purple solution exhibiting the characteristic downfield ^1H NMR resonances of quinonoid dihydropterin (Figure 9A). [51] Likewise, tetrahydrobiopterin (H_4B) and the molybdenum(6+) reagent MoO_2Cl_2 generate a red-purple material (λ_{max} at 487 nm) having $\nu_{Mo=O}$ at 985 cm^{-1} (Figure 9B). [52] Use of $MoOCl_2(detc)_2$ with H_4DMP reproduced the spectral data observed for $MoO2(detc)2$ with $H4DMP$ (Eq. 1) and finally yielded crystalline material for X-ray analysis (Figure 9C). [49] Products of each of the reaction types in Figure 9 were characterized by X-ray crystallography. The product of the $MoO_2(acac)_2$ (acac = acetylacetonate) reaction was unexpectedly a dimer [51] whereas the X-ray structures of **2a**, **2b** and **3a** showed these are monomeric complexes [49-52]. The product observed in the initial studies (Eq. 1) using MoO_2detc_2 was eventually proved to have the stoichiometry [MoOCl(H_4DMP)(detc)]Cl **3a**. [49]

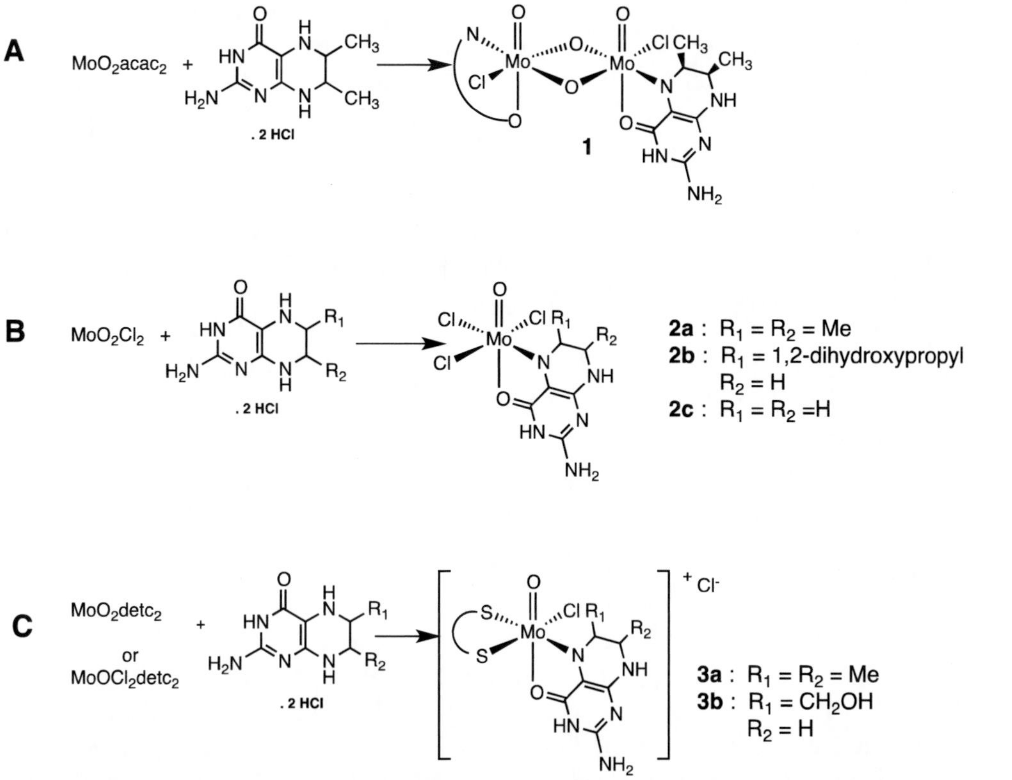

Figure 9. A summary of the variety of tetrahydropterin reactions with dioxomolybdenum(6+) reagents.

The X-ray structures of **1**, **2a**, **2b**, and **3a** confirmed pterin chelation at the O4,N5-site (Figure 10). The structures clearly showed saturation of the bond C6,C7 as expected for a quinonoid isomer of dihydropterin.

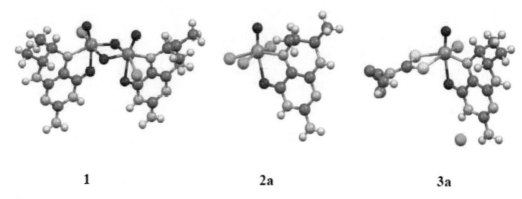

1   **2a**   **3a**

Figure 10. Mercury drawings of the crystal structure of $Mo_2O_4Cl_2(H_3DMP)_2$ **1**, $MoOCl_3(H_3DMP)$ **2a** and $[MoO(detc)Cl(H_3DMP)]Cl$ **3a**. Color key: teal = Mo, red = O, Blue = N, grey = C, green = Cl, white = H.

Despite the similarity of pterin coordination, the molybdenum and pterin oxidations states in complexes **1**, **2a**, **2b** and **3a** were assigned differently. In dimer **1**, the metrical parameters around the molybdenum atoms indicated that this structure was *not* compatible with formal oxidation state assignments of Mo(+4) and *quin*-H_2pterin. A Mo(+4) dimer would be expected to have a Mo-Mo bond but the long Mo-Mo distance of 3.01 Å in **1b** exceeds a normal Mo-Mo bond length. [51] Instead, the dimensions of the Mo_2O_4-core were entirely consistent with those reported for a related Mo(+6) dimer, $[([9]aneN_3)_2Mo_2O_4]^{2+}$ ([9]aneN$_3$ = 1,4,7-triaza**cyclononane**). [53]

Turning to the pterin redox level in dimer **1**, if the Mo(+6) in the reagent was not reduced by the tetrahydropterin reagent, then dimer **1** still contains tetrahydropterin ligands. Charge balance within the neutral dimer required that the coordinated tetrahydropterin exist in a deprotonated form (H_3pterinate⁻), therefore dimer **1** was formulated as $Mo(+6)_2O_4Cl_2$ $(H_3DMP^-)_2$. [51] Subsequently complex **2a** having very similar Mo-N, Mo-O, C-N and C-C bond distances within the Mo-pterin unit was likewise described as Mo(+6) $OCl_3(H_3pterinate^-)$. [50]

In contrast, the X-ray structure and properties of complex **2b** were interpreted as a Mo(+4) complex of a protonated quinonoid-H$_2$biopterin formulated as Mo(+4) OCl_3(quinonoid-H$_2$biopterinH⁺). [52] Facts consistent with this assignment were the high stretching frequency observed for the Mo=O bond, the intense electronic absorption near 500 nm, and the bond distances within the pterin suggestive of localized -C=C- and -C=N- bonds.

These two examples of Mo(+6) reactions with tetrahydropterins were explained using two contradictory interpretations: one described as a redox reaction and the other as simple ligand substitution (Figure 11). In order to resolve these contradictory interpretations, a series of investigations into the chemical reactivity of these different Mo-pterins complexes was done.

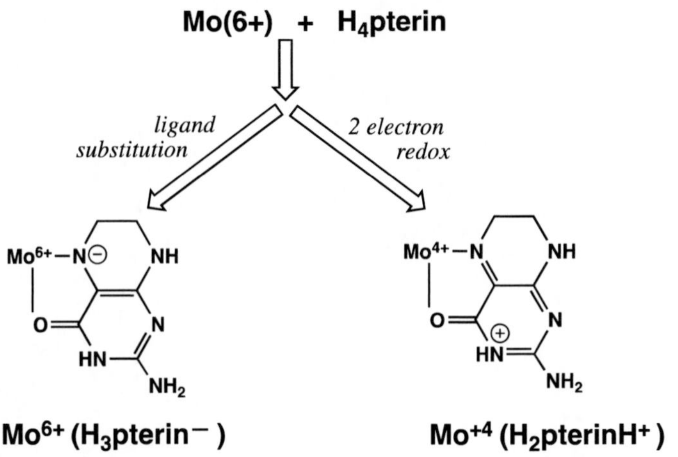

Figure 11. Two views of oxidation state assignments for molybdenum complexes of reduced pterins.

2.1.3.1. Molybdenum Complexes of Reduced Pterins: How do they React?

To resolve the contradictory Mo and pterin oxidation state assignments, a series of experiments were designed to reveal the correct formal oxidation state using the following reasoning. If the complexes consisted of a reduced Mo(+4) bound to a (quinonoid-H_2pterinH+) ligand, dissociation of the unstable quinonoid-H_2pterin tautomer would be expected to initiate rapid pterin isomerization to the stable 7,8-dihydropterin isomer (see Figure 4b). [54] On the other hand, if the complexes were best considered as Mo(+6) ions coordinated by tetrahydropterinate (i.e., deprotonated pterin) chelates, then H_4pterinate dissociation would simply result in formation of free tetrahydropterin after reprotonation in solution.

These two scenarios could easily be distinguished using ^{1}H NMR to monitor different resonances expected for tetrahydropterin vs. 7,8-dihydropterin. Pterin dissociation was accomplished by the addition of either 8-hydroxyquinoline or hydrochloric acid. The same result was observed for all Mo-H_4pterin complexes **1**, **2a**, **2c**, **3a** and **3b**: *only* tetrahydropterin and *no* 7,8-dihydropterin was detected in the ^{1}H NMR spectrum following pterin dissociation (illustrated in Figure 12 for **1**). These results supported a formal oxidation state assignment of Mo(+6)(H_3pterinate⁻) for these complexes indicating that *no* complete transfer of 2 electrons from pterin to molybdenum occurred.

Adopting the formal oxidation state assignment Mo(+6)-(H_3pterinate⁻) made sense of a peculiar observation reported for as-formulated $MoOCl_3$(H_2biopterinH+) **2b**. [52] It was reported that $MoOCl_3$(H_2biopterinH+) **2b** was unstable in methanol towards a decomposition where the dissociated quinonoid dihydropterin reformed a tetrahydropterin. This explanation invoking an odd reversal of a redox reaction is unnecessary, however, if that complex is instead formulated as Mo(+6)-(H_3pterinate⁻) where methanol dissolution promotes H_4pterin dissociation.

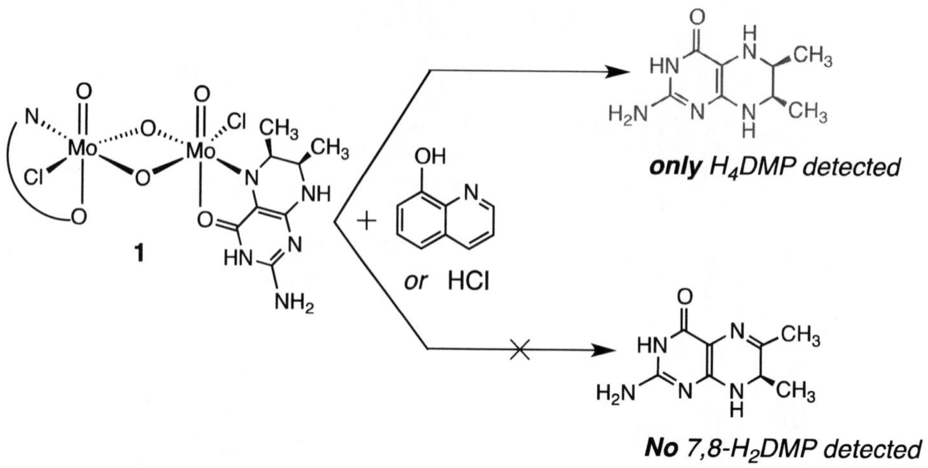

Figure 12. Results of pterin dissociation reactions of $Mo_2O_4Cl_2(H_4DMP)_2$ 1.

2.1.3.2. Dichlorophenolindophenol Oxidation

The pterin reduction state in Moco had been probed using the redox dye dichlorophenolindophenol (DCIP) before its structure was available by X-ray crystallography. [3,40-41] The intensely blue solution of oxidized DCIP is bleached to colorless when DCIP is reduced by two electrons, providing a convenient visual and spectroscopic monitor. Tetrahydropterins reduce DCIP instantaneously while quinonoid dihydropterins react slowly and 7,8-dihydropterin does not reduce DCIP at all. [54] Previously the results obtained from DCIP additions to Moco in several molybdoenzymes were consistent with a dihydropterin reduction state, speculated as one of the quinonoid forms, and eliminating the possibility of a 7,8-dihydropterin structure. It seemed appropriate to use this technique on our new molybdenum-reduced pterin complexes.

Stoichiometric additions of DCIP to molybdenum complexes of reduced pterins gave the results summarized in Eqs 2-4. [51]

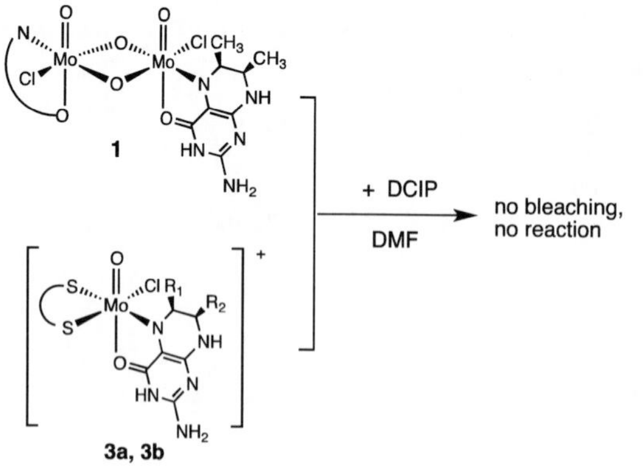

Eq. 2

Eq. 3

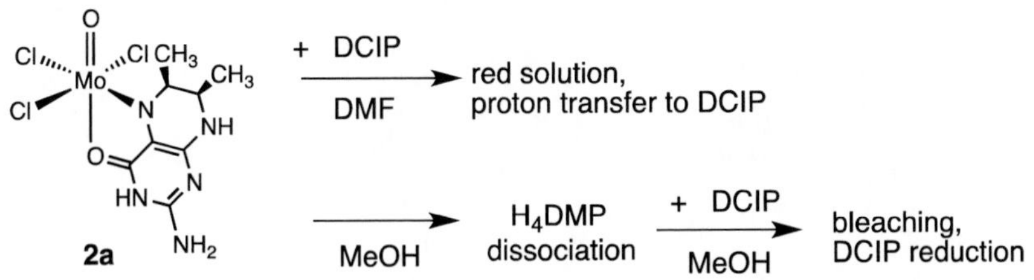

2a

$$+ \text{ DCIP} \xrightarrow{\text{DMF}} \text{red solution, proton transfer to DCIP}$$

$$\xrightarrow{\text{MeOH}} \text{H}_4\text{DMP dissociation} \xrightarrow[\text{MeOH}]{+ \text{ DCIP}} \text{bleaching, DCIP reduction}$$

Eq.4

None of the complexes in dimethylformamide solution reduced DCIP, though proton transfer to DCIP occurred with **2a**. In only one case was DCIP reduction observed, when DCIP was added to $\text{MoOCl}_3(\text{H}_4\text{DMP})$ in methanol solution.

However this observation can be explained as shown in Eq.4 as a consequence of dissociation of free tetrahydropterin from **2a** in methanol solution similar to the reported dissociation of tetrahydropterin from $\text{MoOCl}_3(\text{H}_3\text{biopterin})$ **2b**.

The lack of reactivity of any intact molybdenum complex with DCIP could be explained by several arguments:

a) Coordination of a tetrahydropterinate stabilizes the pterin towards oxidation by DCIP;

b) The coordinated pterin is, in fact, a partially oxidized dihydropterin; or

c) The coordinated pterin is bound as a *partially* oxidized pterin where ownership of the two electrons is *shared* by both the molybdenum and the pterin. Further experimentation (discussed below) showed that option (c) is the most accurate explanation.

2. 1. 3. 3. DMSO Reduction

Model compounds for the molybdenum cofactor are often developed to be capable of mimicking biological activity. [55-57] The ability of synthetic model complexes to demonstrate oxygen atom transfer by reduction of dimethylsulfoxide (DMSO) to dimethyl sulfide (DMS) is a frequently used criterion.

The ambiguity surrounding the molybdenum oxidation state in the pterin complexes **1-3** was also addressed by testing each complex for its ability to reduce DMSO. Different behavior was observed for all of the complexes and is summarized in Eqs. 5-8.

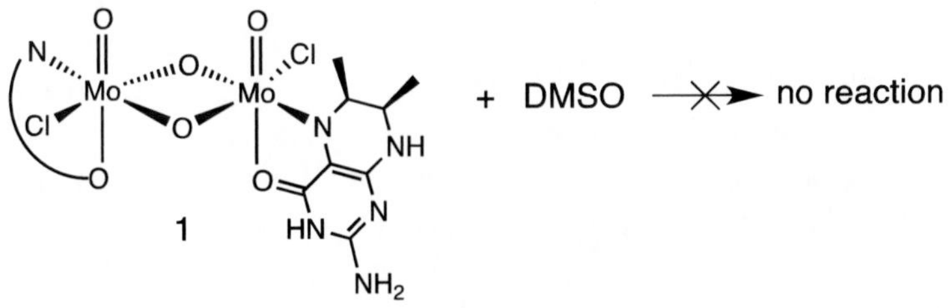

1 $+ \text{ DMSO} \longrightarrow\!\!\!\times\!\!\!\!\rightarrow \text{no reaction}$

Eq. 5

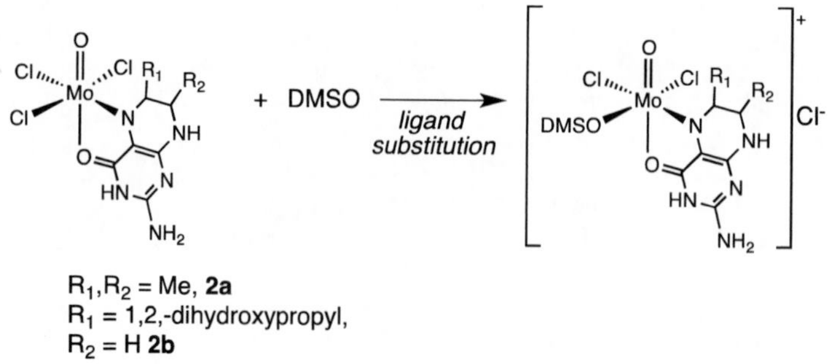
+ DMSO
ligand
substitution
Cl-
R1,R2 = Me, 2a
R1 = 1,2,-dihydroxypropyl,
R2 = H 2b

Eq. 6

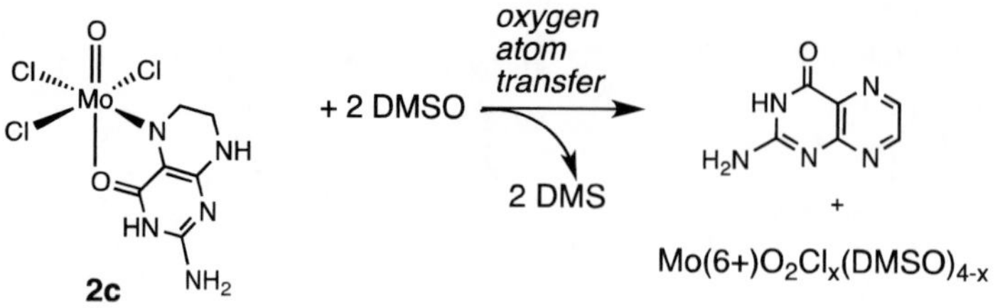
+ 2 DMSO
oxygen
atom
transfer
2 DMS
2c
+
Mo(6+)O2Clx(DMSO)4-x

Eq. 7

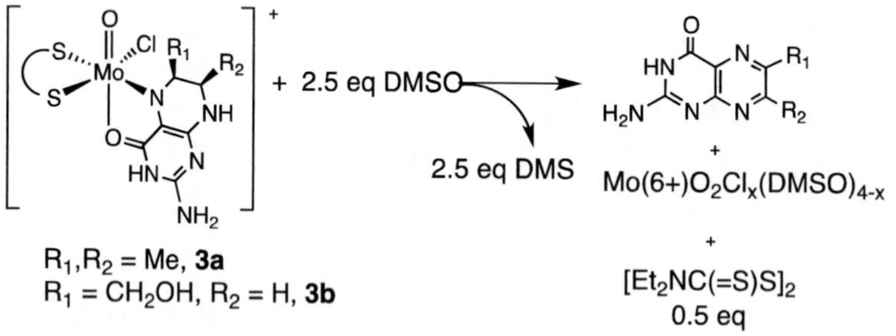
+ 2.5 eq DMSO
2.5 eq DMS
Mo(6+)O2Clx(DMSO)4-x
[Et2NC(=S)S]2
0.5 eq
R1,R2 = Me, 3a
R1 = CH2OH, R2 = H, 3b

Eq. 8

Dimer **1** is unreactive towards DMSO where no change is observed (electronic spectroscopy) after 2 days in DMSO solution (Eq. 5). Complexes **2a** and **2b** undergo ligand substitution with DMSO but not oxygen atom transfer (Eq. 6). In contrast, complex **2c** reduces two equivalents DMSO to yield an oxidized $Mo(+6)(O)_2$ species and fully oxidized pterin (Eq. 7). Complexes **3a** and **3b** react slowly with DMSO (Eq. 8). **3a** consumes 3 equivalents DMSO to produce oxidized pterin, a $Mo(+6)(=O)_2$ core and oxidized dithiocarbamate, $(Et_2NC(=S)S_2)_2$.

The ability of **3a** to reduce DMSO but not complexes **2a, 2b** and **2c** is readily understandable in view of previous studies demonstrating an easier oxidation of Mo(+4) when complexed to sulfur ligands. [56,57] It is likely that the singular reduction effected by **2c**, *but not* **2a** or **2b**, may be related to the much greater insolubility of unsubstituted pterin that drives the reaction forward. There is no apparent difference in the bond distances between **2c** and **2a** or **2b** that would offer a simple solution to the problem.

A mechanism proposed for DMSO reduction by $MoOCl_3(H_4pterin)$ **2c** is shown in Figure 13.

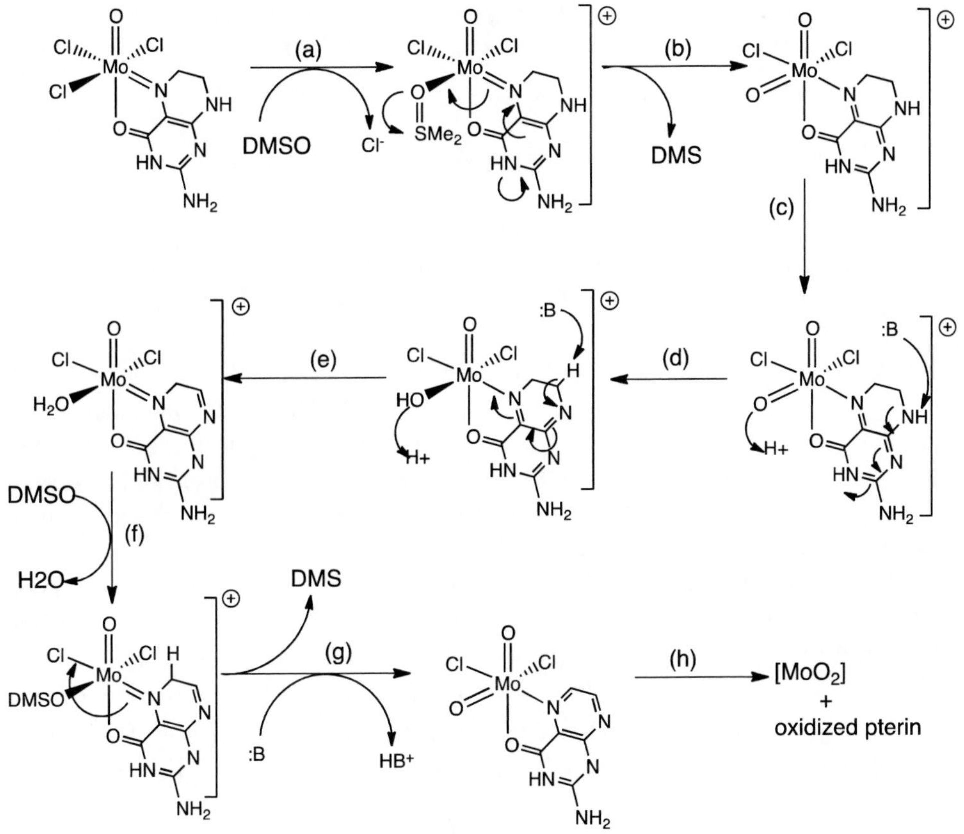

Figure 13. A possible mechanism for the reduction of two molecules of DMSO by one molecule MoOCl₃(H₄pterin) **2c**.

The first step (a), DMSO substitution for chloride, is supported by spectroscopic and conductivity data observed for **3a** and **2a** in DMSO solution. DMSO is introduced into the molybdenum coordination sphere *cis* to the pterin nitrogen N5 based on the X-ray structure of MoOCl₃(H₃DMP) showing that this is the longest, and presumably weakest, Mo-Cl bond. The transfer of an oxygen atom in step (b) from DMSO to Mo may be viewed as the result of a two electron transfer from the Mo=N5 bond to the incipient Mo=O bond; this is the point of formal oxidation of the complex. Prior to further oxidation, the pterin loses at two protons to a base designated: B in Figure 13, c and d. Species capable of proton abstraction are the Mo=O group, as used in Figure 13, or another pterin molecule. The Mo=O group is sequentially converted from an oxo ligand via a hydroxo to an aquo group on Mo(+6) simultaneous with the further oxidation of pterin via electron transfer to molybdenum which regenerates a Mo(4+) oxidation state. Substitution of the water ligand by a second DMSO molecule in step (f) precedes the reduction step (g) of a second DMSO. Overall the reaction is a four-electron oxidation of the molybdenum-pterin complex **2a** coupled to the four electron reduction of two molecules DMSO (h). The six electron oxidation observed for complex **3a** can be imagined to proceed similarly to the reactions (a-h) in Figure 13. However, at some point two dithiocarbamate ligands are oxidized to a disulfide.

To summarize the results of the three chemical reactivity investigations, complexes **1-3** all react with acid or hydroxyquinoline to dissociate free tetrahydropterin, no pterin oxidation reaction occurs between complexes **1-3** with the oxidant DCIP, and complexes **1-3** have variable ability to reduce DMSO to produce DMS, oxidized Mo(6+) and oxidized pterin.

2. 2. Requirements for the Synthesis of Molybdenum Complexes of Reduced Pterins

This section concludes with comments on several aspects of the syntheses that shed light on the conditions necessary to form complexes between tetrahydropterins and molybdenum(+6) reagents.

The electronic structure that emerged for Mo(+6) complexes of H$_4$pterins suggested a high degree of covalency between Mo and pterin, especially through the pyrazine N5 atom. Since the stability of these complexes is closely tied to the formation of a Mo=N5 bond, if reaction conditions prevent formation of the Mo=N bond, no pterin coordination is observed. This requirement is based on several observations. [49] First, we have observed that the syntheses in Figure 9 fail in basic media.

For example, if two equivalents triethylamine are added to the reaction mixture to neutralize the two equivalents HCl associated with each type of pterin, no molybdenum-pterin complexes can be isolated and no pterin coordination is observed spectroscopically. Secondly, when syntheses are attempted in neutral media, a highly reactive MoO$_2$(H$_4$pterin) complex forms that rapidly decomposes in any coordinating solvent. [49,50] Third, we observe formation of a transient MoO$_2$(H$_4$pterin) complex if syntheses using the solubilized pterin are conducted in neutral, aprotic solvents, shown in Eq. 9.

Eq. 9

We conclude from these observations that failure to form a stable monooxo-Mo-(H$_4$pterin) complex from a dioxo-Mo(+6) reagent can be attributed to competition between the two extant Mo=O groups on the molybdenum reagent with the incipient Mo=N5 bond to the pterin. The competition is relieved in protic environments where one oxo ligand is protonated and lost as water.

One may consider that the Mo(=O)(=N5) unit of the molybdenum pterin complexes substitutes for the common Mo(=O)$_2$ core frequently observed in Mo(6+) complexes. [58]

2. 3. Molybdenum Reactions with Oxidized Pterins

We became curious what would result from the pairing of a reduced molybdenum state, Mo(+4), with oxidized pterins. Prior to our investigations, there existed one report of a Mo(+4) flavin complex formed from molybdenum tetrachloride, where flavin is the common name for the isoalloxazine system that contains a pteridine (Eq. 10). [59]

flavin

Mo(+4)OCl₃(flavinH⁺)   Eq 10

In this 1974 report, the molecularity of the product, Mo(+4)OCl₃(flavinH), was determined from spectroscopic and microanalytical data. Infrared spectra revealed characteristic absorptions for the oxo-ligand on molybdenum and for flavin coordination through the N5 and O4 positions. This research was called into question shortly after its publication where an argument was presented for an alternative interpretation of Eq. 10 where the product was formulated as $[flavinH]_2[Mo_2O_3Cl_6]$, a salt containing a protonated flavin cation and a dinuclear Mo(V) anion. [60]

We reinvestigated this Mo(+4) and flavin reaction (Eq. 10) and subsequently verified the accuracy of the flavin coordination as described by the original interpretation. [50] In addition to reproducing the synthesis and the spectroscopic data, the X-ray crystal structure of a related alloxazine complex MoOCl₃(tmazH) **4** (tmaz = tetramethyalloxazine) confirmed the formulation for the molybdenum(+4) complex of protonated flavin. [50]

TMAZ: $R_3 = R_7 = R_8 = R_{10} = CH_3$

Mo(IV)OCl₃(TMAZH⁺)
4   Eq.11

The preparative method for the synthesis of **4** was extended to reactions of MoCl₄(NCMe)₂ with other oxidized pterins (piv-DMP and DMP) (piv-DMP = 2-pivaloyl-6,7-dimethypterin) (Eq. 12). The Mo-pterin products are spectroscopically similar to **4** where they exhibit strong metal-ligand charge transfer (MLCT) absorptions in the UV/vis spectrum and a characteristic pattern of pterin vibrations in the infrared spectrum.

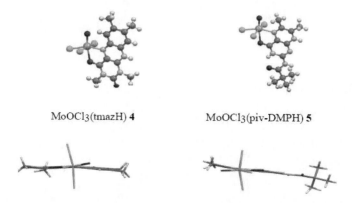

Eq. 12

Two of these, **4** and **5**, were structurally characterized by X-ray diffraction which proved that the isoalloxazine and the pterin chelates were again coordinated through the same O4, N5 chelation site as previously observed for Mo(+6) complexes of reduced pterins (Figure 14). The X-ray structures also showed that these oxidized pteridine ligands were protonated at the coordinated nitrogen atom, in fact as had been deduced for the Mo-flavin complex. [50,59]

MoOCl₃(tmazH) **4**   MoOCl₃(piv-DMPH) **5**

Figure 14. Two views of the X-ray structures of 4 and 5. (top) Ball and stick drawing illustrating the O4,N5 chelate parallel to the Mo=O bond. (bottom) Structures rotated to view non-planarity of pteridine system.

A striking feature of all the Mo(+4)-oxidized pteridine complexes is that pteridine coordination is coupled to pteridine protonation. This protonation is consistent with the notion that Mo(+4) coordination at N5 results in an increase in electron density in the pteridine system, or otherwise stated, that pteridine is effectively reduced by partial oxidation of the metal. The idea that protonation is coupled to electron delocalization from molybdenum onto the pterin is supported by the solution behavior of the molybdenum-flavin and molybdenum-pterin complexes. While the molybdenum complexes produce relatively stable purple solutions in acetonitrile or acetone, dissolution in a more basic solvent like DMF causes an immediate color change to green followed by rapid bleaching. Similar color changes are observed when triethylamine is added to **4** and **5**. This series of reactions is interpreted as pterin or alloxazine deprotonation at site N8 and N10, respectively, to produce an anionic green species [MoOCl₃(pteridine)]⁻ followed by the dissociation of the neutral pteridine, detected by ¹H NMR, as signaled by complete bleaching of the solution (Eq. 13).

Eq.13

The idea that pteridine coordination should be favored under acidic conditions is consistent with studies of ruthenium pterin complexes where pKa values measured for pterin protons at various positions. [61] It was concluded that the site of greatest basicity shifted from N1 to N8 upon coordination of the pterin to the ruthenium. A general conclusion can be made that metal-mediated pterin reduction enables the initial formation of a 5,8-dihydropterin (see below).

The partial pteridine reduction favoring pteridine protonation is further suggested by a structural feature of $MoOCl_3$(tmazH) **4**. A distinct bending of the flavin along the N5-N10 axis is observed in $MoOCl_3$(tmazH) (see Figure 14, bottom views). Flavin bending was also observed in a ruthenium-flavin complex and used as one of the criteria to support the notion that coordinated flavin was partially reduced and that the Ru-flavin complex was best described as a delocalized system of flavinsemiquinone coordinated to ruthenium(+3). [62,63] Applying the same argument to explain the the non-planarity of tmaz in **4** leads to assigned formal oxidation states of Mo(+5) and (tmazH·) radical. As we will see, the Mo(+5) oxidation state is the predicted Mo formal oxidation state consistent with computation and experimental data.

The structures of $MoOCl_3$(piv-DMPH) **5** and $MoOCl_3$(H_3DMP) **2a** offer a unique opportunity to examine the effect of metal coordination on oxidized and reduced tetrahydropterin geometries. The major difference between **5** and **2a** is the length of the Mo-N5 bonds. The shorter Mo-N5 bond in **2a** corresponds to a greater electron transfer from H_4DMP to Mo(+6) as compared to the electron transfer from Mo(+4) to piv-DMP in **5**. Also significant is the longer C4a-C8a bond in **2a**, a result of electron density delocalization from the pterin to Mo and the redistribution of π-electron density towards a structure characteristic of the *p*-quinonoid tautomer of dihydropterin.

2. 4. Theoretical and Experimental Approaches to Determining Formal Oxidation States

With these many examples of molybdenum chelated by pterin in various oxidation states of the metal and the pterin, we sought methods to evaluate the extent of electronic delocalization between molybdenum and pterin and to measure the effective charge on molybdenum. Two computational methods, Extended Huckel molecular orbital (EHMO) calculations and the bond valence sum (BVS) method, [31] and one experimental method, X-ray photoelectron spectroscopy (XPS), [64] was used to investigate the effective charge on molybdenum.

Extended Huckel molecular orbital (EHMO) calculations were performed on 17 molybdenum complexes having a variety of donor atoms ligands including thiolates, tris(pyrazolyl)hydroborates, chlorides and oxo ligands that spanned oxidation states +4 to +6. The calculated Mulliken charge on the metal was compared with Mulliken charges calculated for other oxo-molybdenum complexes for which unambiguous formal oxidation states can be made. These calculated Mullkien charges were compared to those charges calculated for all molybdenum pterin complexes **1, 2b, 3a**, for which crystallographic parameters were available. The bond valence sum (BVS) method was also applied to the same set of 17 'standard' complexes and the three Mo- pterin complexes **1, 2b, 3a**, used for EHMO calculations. The BVS method is based on the observation that as the unit charge on the metal increases, the bond length to ligated atoms decreases. [65] The best illustration of this general trend is in the series of neutral fragments M-OH$_2$, M-OH, M=O where the metal bears no charge, 1+ and 2+ units of charge, respectively, in parallel with decreasing Mo-O distances to the neutral, anionic and dianionic ligands. The empirical BVS method was previously used to estimate oxidation states on metal ions in enzymes. [66,67]

The calculated Mulliken charges of the complexes spanned a range 4.42 – 2.9 where there was little correlation between calculated charge and formal oxidation state. The BVS calculation results were more systematic, where complexes of a formal oxidation were grouped in distinct ranges. The set of Mo(+6) standard complexes had Mo charges calculated by the BVS method in the range 5.99-5.32, whereas the Mo(+5) and the Mo(+4) complexes gave charges in the ranges 5.15 -5.09 and 4.57 – 4.22, respectively. Against these standards, the Mo-pterin complexes **1, 2b, 3a** produced BVS charges in the range matching Mo(+5). Figure 15 presents a graphical display of the BVS results illustrating that compounds conventionally assigned Mo formal charges of 4+, 5+ and 6+ are clustered in well-separated groups while molybdenum pterin data span the range of charges calculated for authentic Mo(5+) compounds.

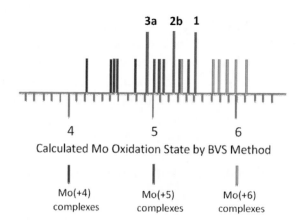

Figure 15. A graphical display of the results of Bond Valence Sum calculations. It is observed that compounds conventionally assigned Mo formal charges of 4+, 5+ and 6+ are clustered in well-separated groups and this is emphasized with different bar shading. The legend identifies the bar shading corresponding to these Mo(6+), Mo(5+) and Mo(4+) complexes used for comparison and the Mo complexes of reduced pterins, **1, 2b** and **3a**.

XPS was used to investigate the effective charge on molybdenum through comparison of Mo 3d binding energies (B.E.) in a series of molybdenum-pterin complexes with B.E. measured in standard molybdenum complexes. [64] Mo-pterin complexes resulting from tetrahydropterin reactions show binding energies that are 1.5-1.8 eV lower than the control Mo(+6) complexes.

This was interpreted as consistent with a Mo(+5)-trihydropterin assignment where one can view the electron pair originating from the tetrahydropterin as covalently shared between Mo and pterin ligands. Complexes prepared from Mo(+4) and fully oxidized pterins show a shift of Mo 3d binding energies to higher values also corresponding to a Mo(+5) oxidation state. Hence, XPS of molybdenum coordinated by oxidized pterins or flavins gave binding energies nearly identical with those observed for the molybdenum complexes coordinated by reduced pterins.

This suggests that oxidized pterin complexes should also be viewed as Mo(+5) species with one-electron reduced pterins. Indeed partial pterin reduction has been proposed to account for the protonated form of the chelated pterins in **4** and **5**. [50]

All three methods, EHMO, BVS and XPS, although different in approach, converge on the same conclusion, shown graphically in Figures 15 and 16: the molybdenum pterin complexes, as a group, have a charge on the molybdenum atom that is most consistent with a formal oxidation state assignment of Mo(5+).

Furthermore, the sum of all the computational and experimental results emphasize that electron flow between molybdenum and pterin is bidirectional and is favored to cause the molybdenum atom to acquire the equivalent of a +5 oxidation state regardless of the oxidation state of the coordinated pterin ligand.

With these results, we now return to the question of how to assign formal oxidation states to the products of Mo(+6) reacted with tetrahydropterins. The limiting oxidation assignments are Mo(+6) bound to deprotonated tetrahydropterin (H_3pterin⁻) and Mo(+4) coordinated by protonated quinoniod dihydropterin (H2pterinH⁺) so as to produce charge balanced neutral compounds. The pterin redox state appropriate to pair with a o(+5) center is the intermediate option between these limiting scenarios, corresponding to a neutral, *trihydropterin radical,* as illustrated in Figure 17. This electronic structure considers the pair of pi electrons donated by the deprotonated H4pterin N5 atom as being delocalized over the Mo-N5 bond and available to either Mo or the pterin, depending on the environment.

The Mo(+5)-trihydropterin radical view accommodates all the experimental data observed for the Mo complexes of reduced pterins. For example, tetrahydropterin ligand dissociation (Figure 17) suggests a heterolytic cleavage of the Mo-N5 bond with the pterin regaining its original lone pair electrons.

The lack of reactivity of molybdenum pterin complexes 1-3 with the mild oxidant DCIP is consistent with a deactivated tetrahydropterin through partial electron delocalization onto the molybdenum.

The variable ability of molybdenum pterin complexes to reduce DMSO can be interpreted as the result of a subtle shift of the electron pair between Mo and N5 in response to changing ligand fields of ancillary ligands on Mo.

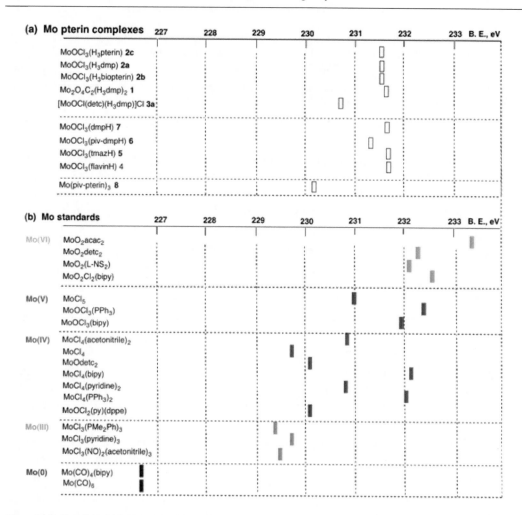

Figure 16. Graphical illustration of binding energies (B.E.) measured by XPS. (a) Molybdenum pterin complexes are listed in the top section. (b) Molybdenum complexes used as standards. The BE values of Mo-pterin complexes correspond most closely to complexes having a formal Mo(+5) oxidation state (red bars).

Mo+6 (H₄pterin⁻)   Mo+5 (H₃pterin·)   Mo+4 (H₂pterin⁺)

preferred structure

Figure 17. Resonance structures for molybdenum coordinated to reduced pterin. Note how the location of the pair of electrons depicted near the Mo-N5 bond shifts in the three structures.

In the case of molybdenum complexes of oxidized pteridine ligands, a similar argument leads to the formulation of these complexes as Mo(+5) bound to a protonated, one electron reduced pteridine radical, or Mo(5+)-(Hpteridine$^{\bullet}$) (Figure 18). This interpretation has precedent from work on Ru(II)-flavin reactions where it was first that suggested radical character on flavin arising from intramolecular, electron transfer. The evidence was structural distortion of flavin observed crystallographically, consistent with partial Ru(III)-flavinsemiquinone character.[99] [100]

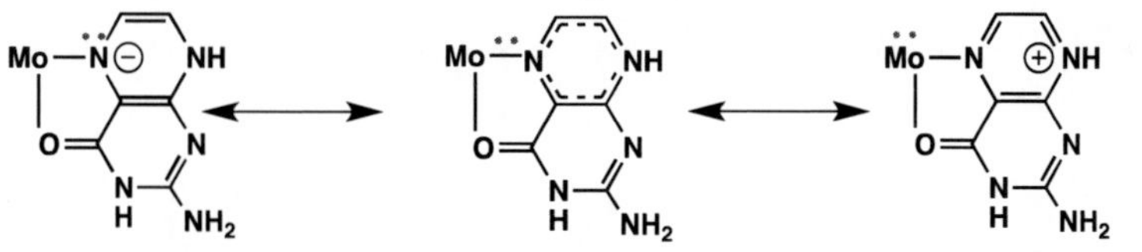

Mo^{+6} (H_2pterin $^-$) Mo^{+5} (Hpterin $^{\bullet}$) Mo^{+4} (Hpterin$^+$)

preferred structure

Figure 18. Resonance structures for molybdenum coordinated to oxidized pterin. Note how the location of the pair of electrons depicted near the Mo-N5 bond shifts in the three structures.

Like the Ru-flavin complex reported by Clarke, the Mo complexes display short M=N5 bonds and bent flavin or pterin planes, consistent with a similar delocalized electronic structure. It should be also noted here that Clarke's group also determined that Ru-pterin complexation shifted a subsequent protonation from N1 (pterin only) to N8, due to electronic delocalization from Ru(II) to the pterin anti-bonding pi system(i.e., back bonding), making the pyrazine more electron rich and basic.

2. 5. The Non-Innocent Nature of Pterin Ligands

Pteridines join several other redox-active ligands that are well-known for their "non-innocent" behavior in coordination chemistry.[68] This category of ligands typically causes difficulties for chemists attempting to fit the complexes into specific oxidation state assignments, hence the redox states of metal and ligand are often ambiguous. All of these non-innocent ligands exhibit the same preferences with respect to matching ligand and metal oxidation states. In general the reduced and electron rich form of the ligand (tetrahydropterin, catechol, dithiolene) reacts most readily with metals in a high oxidation state whereas the oxidized and electron-deficient form of the ligand (pterin, quinone, dithione) reacts with lower valent metals. [69-71] Accordingly, we have described here that Mo(+6), but not Mo(+4), readily reacts with fully reduced tetrahydropterins whereas Mo(0) and Mo(+4) produce complexes of oxidized pterins and Mo(+6) reacts only sluggishly, if at all, with oxidized pterins.

The non-innocent nature of these ligands can be traced to the highly covalent interaction between transition metals and the ligands resulting from well-matched frontier orbital energies and overlap as they seek to attain electroneutrality. The facile electronic flow between metal and ligand is characteristic of ligands that effectively serve as "electronic buffers" and the results presented here corroborate that non-innocent pterin and pteridine ligands also behave as electronic buffers to molybdenum. [72]

The transition metal-pteridine pair exhibits a variety of chemical behaviors and has been previously reviewed. [31] Metal-pterin redox reactions span the gamut of complete transfer of one or more electrons to a partial transfer of electron density producing intermediate redox states for both the metal and pterin. The partial redox has been observed in both directions: metal oxidized with pterin reduction and metal reduction with pterin oxidation. This behavior places metal-pteridine complexes among the growing numbers of metal compounds having non-innocent ligands.

3. 1. Molybdenum Complexes of Pterin-Dithiolenes that Model Moco

There is a long history of synthesis and study of molybdenum complexes to model the molybdenum cofactor. [55,73,74] Much of this body of work aimed to reproduce the inner coordination sphere of Mo, the spectroscopic features of Moco or to provide examples of substrate reactivity and mechanism, but did not attempt to include the pterin component of Moco. Following the identification of the dithiolene tether of molybdopterin on Mo, synthetic analog work was directed at complexes of dithiolenes with simple substituents, such as methyl, [55,75,76] cyanide [77,78] or where dithiolene is part of a ring system (e.g., 1,2-benzenedithiolate, bdt). [79-81] A few labs recognized that a dithiolene chelate substituted by pterin would create additional electronic flexibility including conjugation between the pterin and the dithiolene and proton coupled redox processes. These researchers developed strategies for positioning a pterin on the dithiolene chelate to create a Mo ligand having both essential components of molybdopterin. In this second section of molybdenum and pterin chemistry, the methods developed to synthesize complexes of containing one or more dithiolene chelates substituted by pterin will be reviewed.

3. 1. 1. Synthesis of Pterin-Substituted Dithiolenes

Two synthetic routes to molybdenum pterin-dithiolene complexes have been developed. One approach is to build the entire pterin-dithiolene ligand as a protected dithiocarbonate (Figure 19A). [82] In the presence of appropriate metal reagents, the protecting moiety can be removed under basic conditions allowing the metal center to trap the revealed dithiolene chelate (Eq. 14).

Eq. 14

Several compounds demonstrating the success of this methodology are illustrated in Figure 19 where the molecule A depicts the target pterin precursor, and B and C illustrate specific examples of the subsequent dithiolene ligand formation using cobalt and molybdenum reagents, respectively. [83,84]

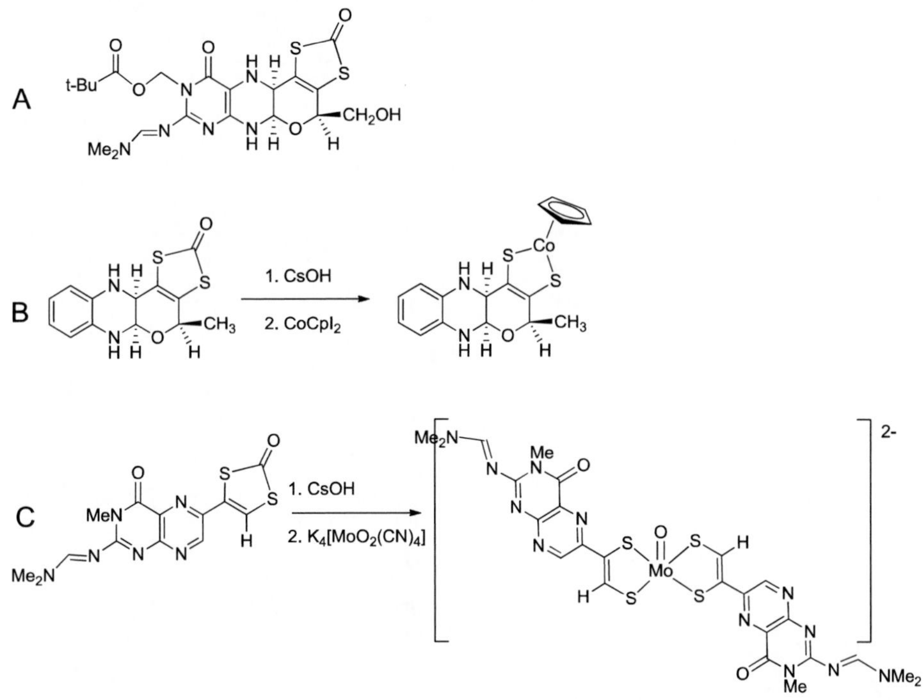

Figure 19. (A) a protected pterin dithiolene used as a precursor to model complexes for Moco; (B) synthetic method demonstrated for a quinoxalyl pterin-dithiolene installed on Cp_2Co (Cp = cyclopentadienide); (C) synthetic method applied to formation of a *bis*-pterinylpterin-dithiolene molybdenum complex.

The second approach to pterin dithiolene complexes uses the well-known ability of certain molybdenum sulfide groups to react with alkynes yielding dithiolene ligands. [85] One particular example, the reaction of molybdenum tetrasulfide unit, $Mo(S_4)$, with alkynes forms dithiolene ligands, particularly if the alkyne is activated by an electron withdrawing substituent (Eq. 15). [86]

Multiple examples have shown that nitrogen heterocycles like quinoxaline and pteridines are sufficiently electron-withdrawing to activate the alkyne for reaction with the tetrasulfide ligand to accomplish dithiolene formation.

The first successful demonstration of this approach to form a pterin dithiolene is shown in reaction path A of Figure 20. [87,88] More recently this method has been used to generate a variety of Mo pterin-dithiolenes on a tris(3,5-dimethylpyrazolyl)hydroborate (Tp*) framework (Figure 20, path B).[89] Notably the Tp*MoO model system allows synthesis of both sulfido and oxo forms of Tp*MoO(pterin-dithiolene) complexes. [89]

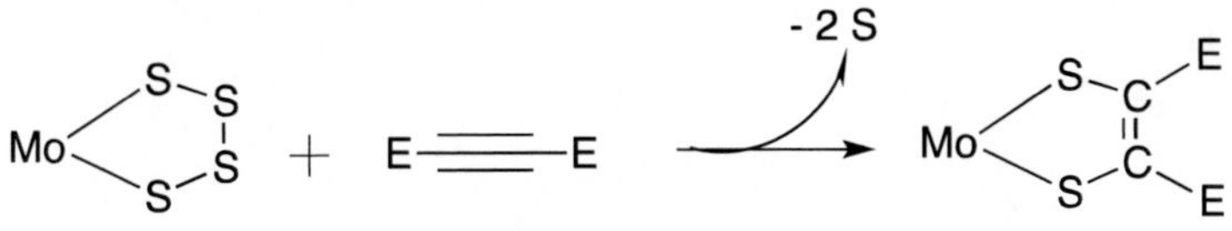

Eq. 15

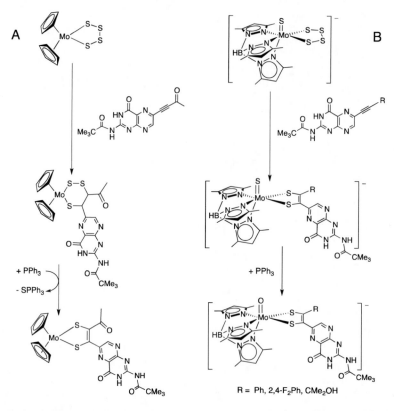

Figure 20. Pterin-dithiolene complexes of molybdenum formed by coupling reactions of pterinyl alkynes and molybdenum tetrasulfide reagents.

A third method for producing quinoxaline and pyridine-dithiolenes proceeds via reactions of *a*-bromo or tosyl N-heterocycles with Mo-(SH$_2$), although this method has not yet been applied to formation of pterin-dithiolenes. [90,91]

It should be noted that during the development of the model systems shown in Figure 20 a common strategy was to begin exploratory reactions using quinoxaline derivatives. Quinoxaline is a N-heterocycle related to the pteridine ring system (Figure 21B) and its derivatives make a convenient starting point due to their considerably easier preparation and greater solubility. A quinoxaline attached via C2 to a dithiolene resembles molybdopterin in positioning a pyrazine ring in conjugation with the dithiolene (Figure 21B). This approach has been valuable not only as a synthetic stepping stone to pterin dithiolenes but also in providing useful information about how the heterocycle can modulate the electronic structure of the metal-dithiolene unit and alter its chemistry.

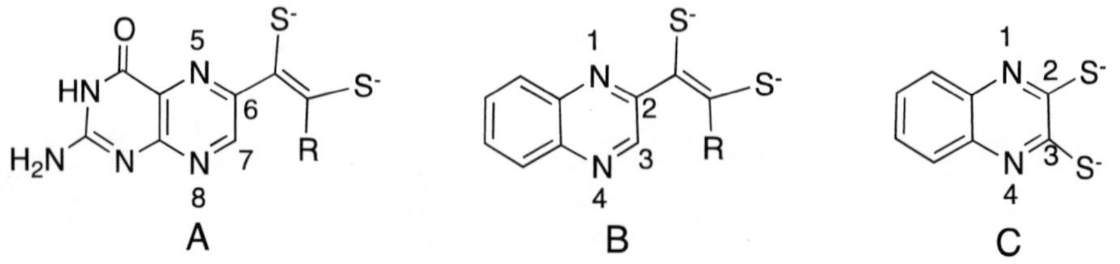

Figure 21. A: pterin-6-ene-dithiolate, B: quinoxaline-2-enedithiolate, C: quinoxaline-2,3-dithiolate.

3. 2. Consequences of Pterin and N-Heterocycle Substitution on Dithiolene

The chief motivation for accomplishing the long synthetic path to an isolable Mo pterin-dithiolene complex is for investigating how differently a Mo-dithiolene unit behaves when a pterin substituent is present. The most significant differences are highlighted next where the effect of a pterin (or quinoxaline) on a dithiolene molybdenum complex has been studied through spectroscopic methods (EPR, cyclic voltammetry, electronic spectroscopy, including magnetic circular dichroism), studies of their chemical reactivity and probed through molecular orbital computations.

The Mo(+5) complexes of both model systems shown in Figure 20, Cp_2Mo(pterin-dithiolene) (A) and $Tp*MoO$(pterin-dithiolene) (B) were produced by oxidation of the initial Mo(4+) product with ferrocenium or iodine. [88,89] These Mo(5+) species allowed spectroscopic analysis by EPR [88,89] and magnetic circular dichroism (MCD) [89]. EPR data obtained from the $Tp*MoO$(pterin-dithiolene) model complexes have [95,97]Mo hyperfine A values considerably larger (A_{ave} = 37 G) than observed for Cp_2Mo(pterin-dithiolene) (A_{ave} = 11 G). The smaller [95,97]Mo A value in Cp_2Mo(pterin-dithiolene) has been interpreted as reflecting the composition of the HOMO being based on the C and S atoms producing substantial spin density delocalized onto the dithiolene ligands. A surprising result from detailed spectroscopic analysis was that the EPR and MCD parameters for $Tp*MoO$(pterin-dithiolene) model complexes were nearly identical to those exhibited by $Tp*MoO$(bdt) (bdt= 1,2-benzenethiolate) suggesting the electronic effect of the pterin on the Mo atom was minimal.

The electrochemical technique of cyclic volammetry (CV) as a probe of the effect of pterin and quinoxaline on the Mo(+5/+4) reduction potential told another story whose message is summarized diagrammatically by Figure 22. Within a series of $Tp*MoO$(dithiolenes), it was concluded that the most significant effect of pterin (or quinoxaline) substitution was to shift the Mo(+5/+4) redox potential to significantly more positive values compared to simpler dithiolenes like benzenedithiolate (bdt) or ethanedithiolate (edt). [89,92,93] Cyclic voltammetry was also a good reporter of a significant electronic effect produced by N-heterocycles cyclized with the dithiolene, as described more detail below.

The introduction of pterin- and quinoxaline-substituents on dithiolenes induces reactivity at the pyrazine N atoms. In both Cp_2Mo(quinoxaline-dithiolene) and $Tp*MoO$(N-cycle-dithiolene) (N-cycle is pterin or quinoxaline) complexes, electrophilic attack at atom N1 of the pyrazine ring results in an intramolecular cyclization producing a pyrrole-like ring (Figure 23). [88,92,93] While this cyclization does not, on the surface, appear to have any relevance to the possible roles of pterin in Moco, the X-ray structures and an analysis of the electronic structure of this type of ligand provide evidence of tautomers such as depicted in Figure 24. In both cyclized products in Figure 23, the dithiolene chelate is asymmetrically bound, exhibiting asymmetric Mo-S and S-C bond lengths. Resonance Raman, EPR and Density Functional Theory (DFT) calculations on the product in Figure 23B are consistent with a admixture of a thione-thiolate structure which can be considered to result from electron density distributed into the quinoxaline structure from partial thiolate to thione oxidation (Figure 24). [92,93]

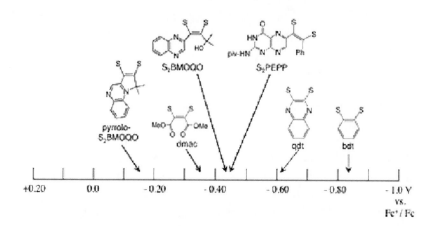

Figure 22. Comparison of Mo(+5/+4) reduction potentials in a series of Tp*MoO(dithiolene) complexes where the specific dithiolene is shown on the plot. Potentials were measured by CV and are shown vs the ferrocenium/ferrocene couple.

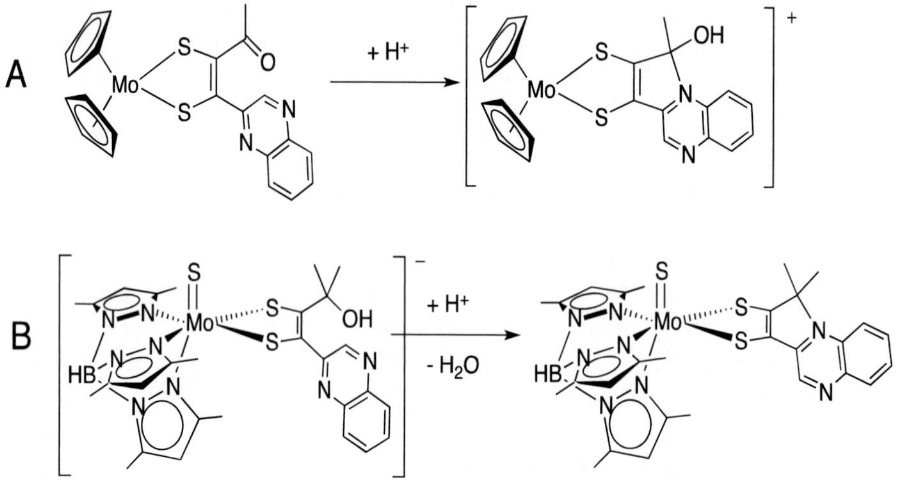

Figure 23. Electrophilic reactions of quinoxalyl-dithiolenes cause intramolecular cyclization.

This electronic delocalization into the quinoxaline system makes structure B (Figure 24) significantly electron-withdrawing as compared to the structure on the left and has the effect of stabilizing the Mo(+4) state. A stabilized Mo(+4) is indicated by a 300 mV positive shift in the Mo(+5/+4) reduction potential, as shown in Figure 22. Both of the cyclized quinoxaline dithiolene complexes in Figure 23 are characterized by intense absorption in the visible electronic spectrum that have been assigned to intramolecular ligand charge transfer transitions.

Several studies explored the effects of N-heterocyclic protonation on the electronic structure of molybdenum dithiolene. The first report concerned Mo(+5,+4) tris-dithiolene complexes of 2,3-quinoxalyldithiolate (qdt). [94] These were structurally characterized by X-ray crystallography prior to studying how the Mo(5+,4+) reduction potentials and ligand redox processes monitored using cyclic voltammetry were affected by N-protonation. The affect of N-heterocycle protonation on the electronic structure of dithiolene was later revisited in a number of studies of Mo dithiolenes substituted with quinoxaline, pyrazine and pyridines. [90,91,95] The key findings of all these studies were that protonation at quinoxaline made reduction processes more favorable and induces a reorganization of electron density throughout the heterocycle in conjugation with the dithiolene consistent with the scheme shown in Figure 25. In certain cases the one electron reduced species were best described as quinoxalyl dithiolene radicals.

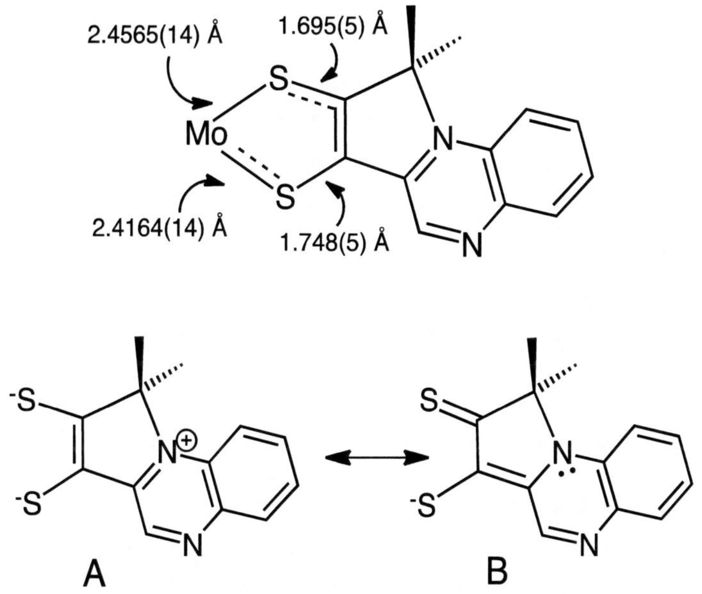

Figure 24. The asymmetry of the quinoxaline-dithiolene complexes in Figure 23 can be explained by a including a resonance contribution from the thione-thiolate (structure B) to the dithiolene (structure A).

Tautomers B and C in Figure 25 illustrate one of the most significant consequences of a pterin or quinoxaline substiuent on a dithiolene. Protonating a ring N atom induces a subtle shift of electron density from either the S atom in tautomer B or the Mo atom in tautomer C resulting in two thione-thiolate chelates oxidized compared to the dithiolene (or ene-dithiolate) in tautomer A. A detailed electrochemical study of $Cp_2Co(S_2C_2H(quin))$ (Cp = cyclopendienide; quin = 2-quinoxaline) provided evidence for multiple tautomers of protonated quinoxaline N atoms. [96] The electronic reorganization depicted in Figure 24 in addition to the example illustrated in Figure 25 hints at the rich chemistry possible when a N-heterocycle is appended to a dithiolene on a redox active metal.

Other investigations of $Cp_2Mo(S_2C_2H(N\text{-cycle}))$ have shown that the pKa values for protonated N-cycles (N-cycle is either quinoxaline or pyridine) on dithiolene chelated to Mo and Pt increase by 1-3 units as compared to the free heterocycles due to the resonance stabilization by the metallo-1,2-enedithiolate. [90] N-heterocycle protonation also has a strong effect on electronic transitions in these complexes where the relative energies of d-based and ligand-based unoccupied orbitals can be switched, accessing luminescent emissive Inter Ligand Charge Transfer (ILCT) excited states. [95] Similar effects can be expected for complexes of pterin-dithiolenes, though parallel studies have not yet been accomplished.

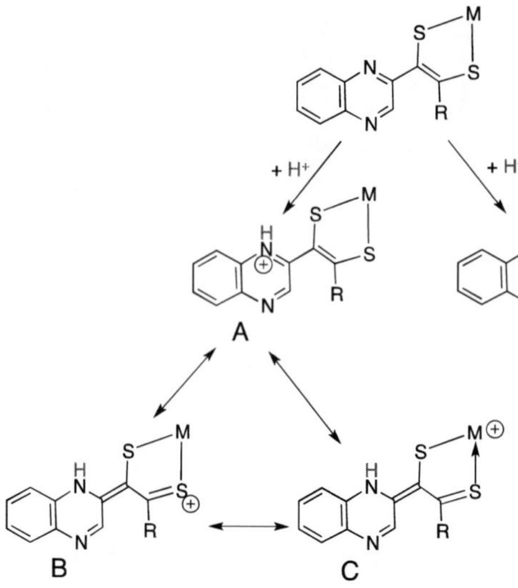

Figure 25. Quinoxaline protonation can access other resonance forms including thiolate, thione chelates on Mo.

Computation methods have been pursued to complement experimental efforts to delineate the effect of pterins or N-hetercycles on the Mo-dithiolene unit. Molecular orbital calculations using density functional theory (DFT) evaluated the importance of including the entire pterin ring system in computational studies of the molybdenum cofactor. [97] Comparing structural details (bond lengths, angles, dihedral fold angles), charge distribution and redox potentials for increasingly complex MoO(dithiolene)$_2$ structures (Figure 26), the researchers concluded that the simplest enedithiolate (a) was insufficient to accurately describe the molecular properties while including the full pterin-dithiolene structure (b) of molybdopterin made a significant difference. However, including only the pyrazine ring (c) of the pterin (not the pyrimidine) did reproduce rather closely the values obtained using the full molybdopterin ligand.

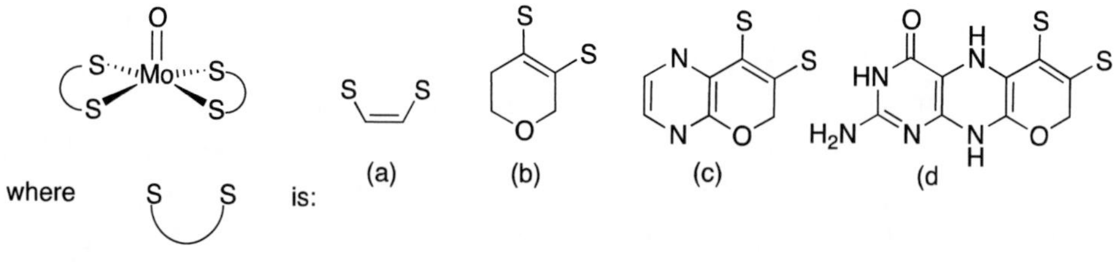

Figure 26. The series of pterin-dithiolene ligands used in DFT calculations of [MoO(pterin-dithiolene)$_2$] complexes to investigate the importance of fusing pyran, pyranopyrazine and pyranopterin systems to the pterin-dithiolene chelate.

The enhanced reactivity in pterin dithiolene complexes is further illustrated by the next example. Dechelation of one S atom of a dithiolene chelate can lead to S attack on a pyrazine carbon and cyclization to form thiophenes fused to quinoxaline and pterin (Figure 27 A and B). [98] This observation was an early confirmation of the correctness of the proposed pterin-dithiolene in Moco before X-ray protein structure were available since a natural metabolite of

Moco, urothione, had previously been identified as a pterinylthiophene (Figure 29C). [2,28,99]

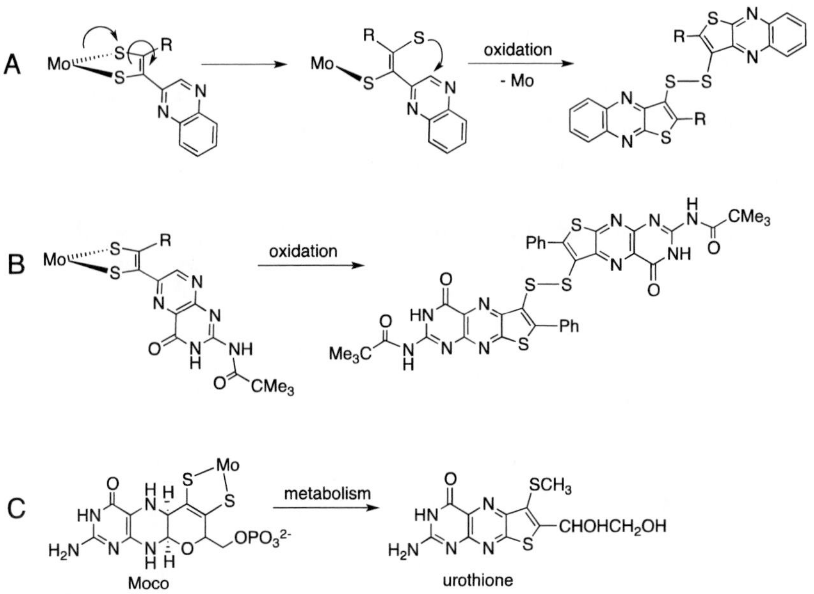

Figure 27. Oxidative products of quinoxaline and pterin pterin-dithiolene originating from dechelation of the metal and the metabolic product of the cofactor degradation.

4. LESSONS LEARNED FROM MOLYBDENUM-PTERIN MODEL STUDIES THAT APPLY TO THE PYRANOPTERIN DITHIOLENE IN MOLYBDENUM ENZYMES

The "molybdenum cofactor", i.e., the molybdenum coordinated by one or more pyranopterin dithiolene ligands, is now recognized to be the most redox rich cofactor in all of biology. [92,93] In addition to the participation of molybdenum in oxidation states +4 through +6, the dithiolene chelate can access oxidized thione forms and the pterin has a plethora of tautomers for semi-reduced forms available as well as several fully saturated, reduced forms. Examples of redox interplay between all three of these components—molybdenum, pterin, and dithiolene—have been discussed in this chapter.

A redox role for the pyranopterin in the molybdenum enzymes is clear from the intimate interactions through H-bonds between the pterin and other electron carriers that will conduct the electron flow to or from the ultimate acceptor or donor. Two examples are illustrated in Figure 28 where dissimilatory nitrate reductase (diss. NRase) has a clear electron transfer chain of multiple FeS clusters that lead from the terminal hemes to the Mo center via the pterin. [100] Likewise an example from carbon monoxide dehydrogenase (CODH) shows two Fe_2S_2 clusters in H-bonding distance from the pterin. [101] Certainly in this regard the pterin is functioning as part of the "circuit" to deliver electrons to and from the metal. This pterin-mediated electron flow was predicted from the results of both the Mo(+6) - H_4pterin studies and the pterin-dithiolene complexes of molybdenum. The mechanism by which enzymes might use this redox capability of the pterin-dithiolene is still an area of study in several research groups. One question concerns how the Mo atom communicates electronically with the pterin terminus that interacts with the FeS redox centers. Electronic communication between molybdenum and pterin via the pi-conjugation of the pterin-dithiolene unit is blocked by the saturated region of the bridgehead carbons in the pyranopterin (Eq. 16, left). Possibly the cyclized pyranopterin structure represents a protected resting state and a different electronic description is accessed during substrate turnover. Several possibilities were presented earlier in Figure 5. Eqs. 16 and 17 shown two different possibilities following pyran ring scission where Eq. 16 produces a 5,6-dihydropterin tautomer while Eq. 17 shows a 5,8-dihydropterin, an intriguing structure that maintains pi-conjugation throughout the pterin.

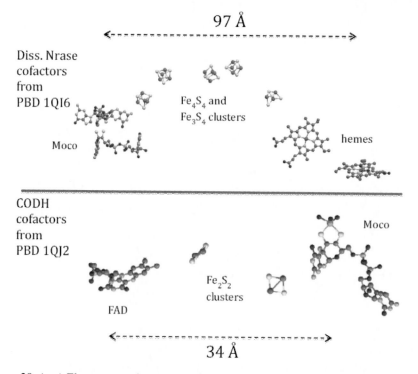

Figure 28. (top) Electron transfer chain in dissimilatory nitrase reductase (diss. NRase) using structural data from the Protein Data Bank #1QI6. The dashed arrow indicates the approximate 97 Å separation between Moco and the most remote heme redox partner. (bottom) Electron transfer chain in carbon monoxide dehydrogenase (CODH) using structural data from the Protein Data Bank #1QJ2. Here the dashed arrow shows 34 Å separation between Moco and the FAD redox partner.

cyclized molybdopterin
(pyrano-molybdopterin)   5,6-dihydropterin

Eq. 16

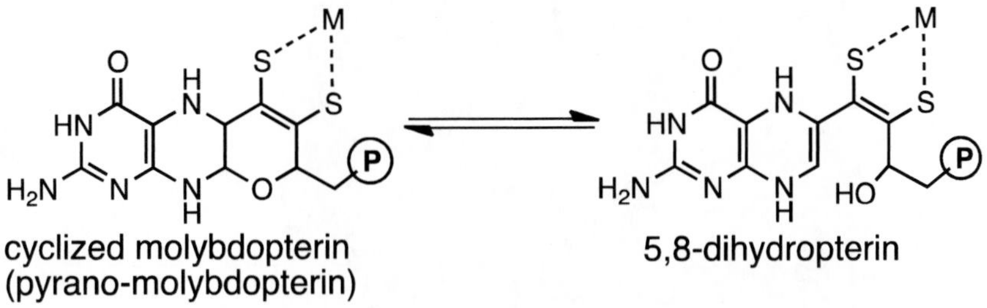

cyclized molybdopterin
(pyrano-molybdopterin)

5,8-dihydropterin

Eq. 17

A functional role for the pyran ring opening depicted in Eqs. 16 and 17 seems likely given three recent reports of several molybdoenzymes where Moco contains *both* a pyranopterin and a ring opened, non-cyclized pterin. [100,102,103]

It is expected that the flexibility of the conjugation and multiple H-donor and H-acceptor sites in the pterin system might be exploited by different protein structures to tune the pyranopterin for the specific redox role required by that enzyme.

The pterin-dithiolene binding site observed in all the X-ray structures is securely tethered to the protein chain by extensive hydrogen bonding between every heteroatom in the pterin system and amino acid residues (Figure 29).

This indicates that another job of the pterin system is to anchor Moco into the proper site by constraining the pterin via a complex hydrogen bonding network. This H-bonding network may have another role, that of adjusting the pterin environment to tune the redox potential of the pterin through H-donor and –acceptors that conformation.

The studies on pyranopterin redox behavior discussed in this chapter prove that pyranopterin possesses distinctive redox chemistry unlike that of the simple pterin system, a result that may be critical to its use as part of the molybdopterin ligand for molybdenum and tungsten in enzymes.

Current experiments in the author's labs are focused on understanding reversible ring scission and cyclization processes such as Eqs. 16 and 17 using the model pterin dithiolene in Eq. 18.

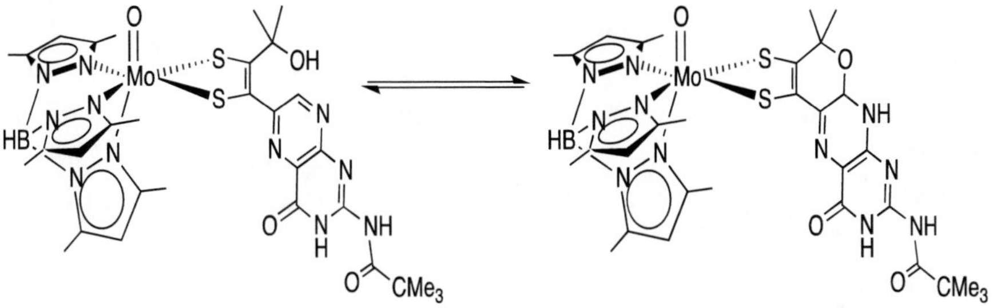

Eq. 18

Answers to many of the remaining mysteries regarding the function of the pyranopterin dithiolene in Moco will be obtained through higher resolution X-ray structures and with model complexes.

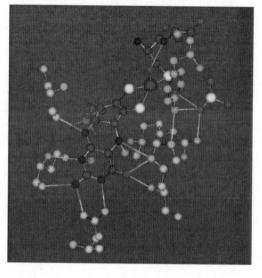

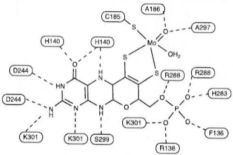

Figure 29. (top) The extensive hydrogen bonding around Moco in chicken liver sulfite oxidase [104] is shown in the top illustration where the protein residues are depicted as faded ball and stick structures. (bottom) Specific residues involved in H-bonds to the pterin and the Mo sites are labeled in the diagram below.

CONCLUSION

This chapter has presented the breadth of molybdenum-pterin chemistry where the theme of the chemistry occurring between these two partners is an electronically flexible interaction. Molybdenum-pterin compounds have defied traditional categorization by formal oxidation number and have challenged the chemist to formulate fresh interpretations for what may first seem like deceptively ordinary complexes. From their roles in biology to their chemical behavior in organic and inorganic systems, it should be clear that a pterin is never a spectator group, but that it contributes to the chemistry of the system. Pterins are most often involved in redox processes so it is likely the same will be true of the pterin part of the molybdenum cofactor. It has already been noted that Moco stands as the most redox rich biological cofactor since it has three redox active units: the Mo center, the pterin-dithiolene and the pterin. The pterin is likely to work in concert with the dithiolene and the molybdenum center to create the unique reactivity of Moco.

REFERENCES

[1]   Zhang, Y.; Rump, S.; Gladyshev, V. N., *Coord. Chem. Rev.* 2011, 255, 1206.

[2]   Leimkühler, S.; Wuebbens, M. M.; Rajagopalan, K. V. *Coord. Chem. Rev.* 2011, 255, 1129.

[3]   Rajagopalan, K. V. in *Advances in Enzymology and Related Areas of Molecular Biology,* Vol. 64, Wiley, New York, 1991, 215.

[4]   Magalon, A.; Fedor, J. G.; Walburger, A.; Weiner, J. H. *Coord. Chem. Rev.* 2011, 255, 1159.

[5]   Hille, R.; Nishino, T.; Bittner, F. *Coord. Chem. Rev.* 2011, 255, 1179.

[6]   Hille, R.; Mendel, R. R. *Coord. Chem. Rev.* 2011, 255, 991.

[7]   Dobbek, H. *Coord. Chem. Rev.* 2011, 255, 1104.

[8]   Newton, W. E. *this volume.*

[9]   Tunney, J. M.; McMaster, J.; Garner, C. D. in *Comprehensive Coordination Chemistry II* 2003, 8, 459.

[10] Johnson, M. K.; Rees, D. C.; Adams, M. W. W. *Chem. Rev.* 1996, 2817.

[11] Kletzin, A.; Adams, M. W. W., *F. E. M. S. Microbiol. Rev.*1996, 18, 5.

[12] Schlesinger, W. H. in *Biogeochemistry*, Academic Press, San Diego, 1997, 166-223.

[13] Stiefel, E. I. *Science* 1996, 272, 1599.

[14] Schlesinger, W. H. in *Biogeochemistry*, Academic Press, San Diego, 1997, 402-414.

[15] Mendel, R. R. *Planta* 1997, 203, 399.

[16] Mendel, R. R.; Schwarz, G. *Coord. Chem. Rev.* 2011, 255, 1145-1158.

[17] Cartron, M. L.; Roldán, M. D.; Ferguson, S. J.; Berks, B. C.; Richardson, D. J. *Biochem. J.* 2002, 368, 425.

[18] Hille, R. *Chem. Rev.* 1996, 96, 2757.

[19] Jankielewicz, A.; Klimmek, O.; Kroger, A., *Biochim. Biophys. Acta,* 1995, 1231, 157.

[20] Méjean, V.; Iobbi-Nivol, C.; Lepelletier, M.; Giordano, G.; Chippaux, M.; Pascal, M. C., *Mol. Microbiol.* 1994, 11, 1169.

[21] Bilous, P. T.; Weiner, J. H. *J. Bacteriol.* 1985, 163, 369.

[22] McCrindle, S. L.; Kappler, U.; McEwan, A. G. *Adv. Microb. Physiol.* 2005, 50, 147.

[23] Enroth, C.; Eger, B. T.; Okamoto, K.; Nishino, T.; Pai, E. F. *Proc. Natl. Acad. Sci. US.* 2000, 97, 10723.

[24] Burgmayer, S. J. N.; Stiefel, E. I. *J. Chem. Ed.* 1985, 62, 934.

[25] Pilato, R. S.; Stiefel, E. I. in *Bioinorganic Catalysis*, J. Reedijk and E. Bouwman, Eds., Marcel Dekker, New York, 1993, 131.

[26] Pilato, R. S.; Stiefel, E. I. in *Bioinorganic Catalysis*, J. Reedijk and E. Bouwman, Eds., Marcel Dekker, New York, 1999, pp. 81.

[27] Chan, M. K.; Mukund, S.; Kletzin, A.; Adams, M. W. W.; Rees, D. C. *Science* 1995, 267, 1463.

[28] Johnson, J. L.; Rajagopalan, K. V. *Proc. Natl. Acad. Sci. US* 1982, 79, 6856.

[29] Stiefel, E. I. in *Molybdenum and Molybdenum Enzymes*, M. Coughlan, Ed., Pergamon Press, New York, 1980, 43.

[30] Pfleiderer, W. *J. Heterocycl. Chem.* 1992, 29, 583.

[31] Burgmayer, S. J. N. in *Struct. Bonding,* M. J. Clarke, Ed., Springer, Berlin, 1998, Vol. 92, 67.

[32] Dryhurst, G; Raghavan, R.; Ege-Serpkenci, D.; Karber, L. in *Electrochemical and Spectrochemical Studies of Biological Redox Components, Adv. Chem. Ser.*, Kadish, K., Ed, American Chemical Society, Washington, D. C., 1982, 457.

[33] Karber, L. G.; Dryhurst, G. *J. Electroanal. Chem. Interfacial Electrochem.* 1984, 160, 141.

[34] D. Ege-Serpkenci, R. Raghavan, Dryhurst, G. *Bioelectrochem. Bioenerg,* 1983, 10, 357.

[35] L. G. Karber, Dryhurst, G. *J. Electroanal. Chem. Interfacial Electrochem.* 1982, 136, 271.

[36] D. Ege-Serpkenci, Dryhurst, G. *Bioelectrochem. Bioenerg.* 1982, 9, 175-195.

[37] R. Raghavan, Dryhurst, G. *J. Electroanal. Chem. Interfacial Electrochem.* 1981, 129,189.

[38] Diculescu, V. C.; Militaru, A.; Shah, A.; Qureshi, R.; Dryhurst, G. *J. Electroanal. Chem. Interfacial Electrochem.* 2010, 647, 1.

[39] Elliott, S. J.; Hoke, K. R.; Heffron, K.; Palak, M.; Rothery, R. A.; Weiner, J. H.; Armstrong, F. A. *Biochemistry* 2003, 43, 799.

[40] Gardlik, S.; Rajagopalan, K. V. *J. Biol. Chem.* 1990, 265, 1304.

[41] Gardlik, S.; Barber, M. J.; Rajagopalan, K. V. *Arch. Biochem Biophys.* 1987, 259, 363.

[42] Schircks, B.; Bieri, J. H.; Viscontini, M. *Helv. Chim. Acta,* 1985, 68,1639.

[43] R. Soyka, W. Pfleiderer, R. Prewo, *Helv. Chim. Acta* 1990, 73, 808.

[44] R. Soyka, W. Pfleiderer, *Pteridines* 1990, 2, 63.

[45] Burgmayer, S. J. N.; Pearsall, D. L.; Blaney, S. M.; Moore, E. M.; Sauk-Schubert, C. *J. Biol. Inorg. Chem.* 2004, 9, 59.

[46] Vonderschmitt, D. J.; Scrimgeour, K. G. *Biochem. Biophys. Res. Commun.,* 1967, 28, 302.

[47] Burgmayer, S. J. N.; Stiefel, E. I., *J. Am. Chem. Soc.* 1986, 108, 8310.

[48] Burgmayer, S. J. N.; Baruch, A., Kerr, K.; Yoon, K. *J. Am. Chem. Soc.* 1989, 111, 4982.

[49] Kaufmann, H. L.; Liable-Sands, L.; Rheingold, A. L.; Burgmayer, S. J. N. *Inorg. Chem.* 1999, 38, 2592.

[50] Kaufmann, H. L.; Carroll, P. J.; Burgmayer, S. J. N. *Inorg. Chem.* 1999, 38, 2600.

[51] Burgmayer, S. J. N.; Arkin, M. R.; Bostick, L.; Dempster, S.; Everett, K. M.; Layton, H. L.; Paul, K. E.; Rogge, C.; Rheingold, A. L. *J. Am. Chem. Soc.* 1995, 117, 5812.

[52] Fischer, B.; Straehle, J.; Viscontini, M. *Helv. Chim. Acta* 1991, 74, 1544.

[53] Wieghardt, K.; Hahn, M.; Swiridoff, W.; Weiss, J. *Inorg. Chem.* 1984, 23, 94.

[54] Kaufman, S. *J. Biol. Chem.* 1961, 236, 804.

[55] Holm, R. H. Solomon, E. I.; Majumdar, A.; Tenderholt, A. *Coord. Chem. Rev.* 2011, 255, 993.

[56] Holm, R. H. *Coord. Chem. Rev.* 1990, 100, 183.

[57] Holm, R. H. *Chem. Rev.* 1987, 87, 1401

[58] Stiefel, E. I. in *Progress in Inorganic Chemistry* , Lippard, S. J., Ed. 1977, Vol. 22, 3.

[59] Selbin, J.; Sherrill, J.; Bigger, C. H. *Inorg. Chem.* 1974, 13, 2544.

[60] Sawyer, D. T.; Doub, W. H. *Inorg. Chem.* 1975, 14, 1736.

[61] Abelleira, A.; Galang, R.; Clarke, M. J. *Inorg. Chem.* 1990, 29, 633.

[62] Clarke, M. J.; Dowling, M. G.; Garafalo, A. R.; Brennan, T. F. *J. Biol. Chem.* 1980, 255, 4372.

[63] Clarke, M. J.; Dowling, M. G. *Inorg. Chem.* 1981, 20, 3506.

[64] Burgmayer, S. J. N.; Kaufmann, H. L.; Carroll, P. J.; Fortunato, G.; Hug, P.; Fischer, B. *Inorg. Chem.* 1999, 38, 2607.

[65] Brown, I. D.; Altermatt, D. *Acta. Crystallogr.* 1985, B41, 244.

[66] Liu, W.; Thorp, H. H. *Inorg. Chem.* 1993, 32, 4102.

[67] Thorp, H. H. *Inorg. Chem.* 1992, 31, 1585.

[68] Chirik, P. J. *Inorg. Chem.* 2011, 50, 9737.

[69] Pierpont, C. *Inorg. Chem.* 2011, 50, 9766.

[70] Jüstel, T.; Bendix, J.; Metzler-Nolte, N.; Weyhermuller, T.; Nuber,B.; Wieghardt, K. *Inorg. Chem.* 1998, 37, 35.

[71] Eisenberg, R.; Gray, H. B., *Inorg. Chem.* 2011, 50, 9741.

[72] Westcott, B.; Gruhn, N. E.; Enemark, J. H. *J. Am. Chem. Soc.* 1998,120, 3382.

[73] Enemark, J. H.; Cooney, J. J. A.; Wang, J.-J.; Holm, R. H. *Chem. Rev.* 2004, 104, 1175.

[74] Fischer, B.; Burgmayer, S. J. N. in: *Metal Ions in Biology,* Sigel, A. (Ed.), Marcel Dekker, New York, 2002, 265.

[75] Lim, B. S.; Willer, M. W.; Miao, M.; Holm, R. H. *J. Am. Chem. Soc.* 2001, 123, 8343.

[76] Lim, B. S.; Holm, R. H. *J. Am. Chem. Soc.* 2001, 123, 1920.

[77] Majumdar, A.; Pal, K.; Sarkar, S. *Dalton Trans.* 2009, 1927.

[78] Majumdar, A.; Pal, K.; Sarkar, S. *Inorg. Chem.* 2008, 47, 3393.

[79] Kirk, M. L.; K. Peariso, K. *Polyhedron* 2004, 23, 499.

[80] McNaughton, R. L.; Helton, M. E.; Rubie, N. D.; Kirk, M. L. *Inorg. Chem.* 2000, 39, 4386.

[81] Helton, M. E.; Gruhn, N. E.; McNaughton, R. L.; Kirk, M. L. *Inorg. Chem.* 2000, 39, 2273.

[82] B. Bradshaw, A. Dinsmore, W. Ajana, D. Collison, C. D. Garner, J. A. Joule, *J. Chem. Soc., Perkin Trans.* 2001, 3239.

[83] Dinsmore, A.; Birks, J. H.; Garner, C. D.; Joule, J. A. *J. Chem. Soc., Perkin Trans.* 1997, 801.

[84] Davies, E. S.; Beddoes, R. L.; Collison, D.; Dinsmore, A.; Docrat, A.; Joule, J. A.; Wilson, C. R.; Garner, C. D. *J. Chem. Soc., Dalton Trans.* 1997, 3985.

[85] Young, C. G. *J. Inorg. Biochem.* 2007, 101, 1562.

[86] Sproules, S. A.; Morgan, H. T.; Doonan, C. J.; White, J. M.; Young, C. G. *Dalt. Trans.* 2005, 3552.

[87] Pilato, R. S., K. Eriksen, M. A. Greaney, Y. Gea, E. C. Taylor, S. Goswami, L. Kilpatrick, T. G. Spiro, A. L. Rheingold, E. I. Stiefel, *J. Am. Chem. Soc.* 1991, 116, 9372.

[88] Pilato, R. S.; Eriksen, K.; Greaney, M. A.; Gea, Y.; Taylor, E. C.; Goswami, S.; Kilpatrick, Spiro; T. G.; Rheingold; A. L.; Stiefel; E. I. *A. C. S. Symp. Ser.* 1993, 535, 83.

[89] Burgmayer, S. J. N.; Kim, M.; Petit, R.; Rothkopf, A.; Kim, A.; BelHamdounia, S.; Hou, Y.; Somogyi, A.; Habel-Rodriguez, D.; Williams, A.; Kirk, M. L. *J. Inorg. Biochem.* 2007, 101,1601.

[90] Hsu, J. K.; Bonangolino, C. J.; Kaiwar, S. P.; Boggs, C. M.; Fettinger, J. C.; Pilato, R. S. *Inorg. Chem.* 1996, 35, 4743.

[91] Van Houten, K. A.; Boggs, C. M.; Pilato, R. S. *Tetrahedron* 1998, 54, 10973.

[92] Matz, K. G.; Mtei, R. P.; Leung, B.; Burgmayer, S. J. N.; Kirk, M. L. *J. Am. Chem. Soc.* 2010, 132, 7830.

[93]   Matz, K. G.; Mtei, R. P.; Rothstein, R.; Kirk, M. L.; Burgmayer, S. J. N.; *Inorg. Chem.* 2011, 50, 9804.

[94]   Boyde, S.; Garner, C. D.; *J. Chem. Soc., Dalt. Trans.* 1991, 713.

[95]   Kaiwar, S. P.; Vodacek, A.; Blough, N. V.; Pilato, R. S. *J. Am. Chem. Soc.* 1997, 119, 9211.

[96]   Armstrong, E. M.; Austerberry, M. S.; Birks, J. H.; Beddoes, R. L.; Helliwell, M.; Joule, J. A.; Garner, C. D. *Heterocycles* 1993, 35, 563.

[97]   Ryde, U.; Schulzke, C.; Starke, K.; *J. Biol. Inorg. Chem.* 2009, 14, 1053.

[98]   Soricelli, C. L.; Szalai, V. A.; Burgmayer, S. J. N. *J. Am. Chem. Soc.* 1991, 113, 9877.

[99]   Koschara, W. *Hoppe-Seyler's Z. Physiol. Chem.* 1940, 263, 78.

[100] Bertero, M. G.; Rothery, R. A.; Palak, M.; Hou, C.; Lim, D., Blasco, F.; Weiner, J. H.; Strynadka, N. C. *J. Nat. Struct. Biol.* 2003, 10, 681.

[101] Dobbek, H.; Gremer, L.; Kiefersauer, R.; Huber, R.; Meyer, O. *Proc. Natl. Acad. Sci. US* 2002, 99, 15971.

[102] Jormakka, M.; Richardson, D.; Byrne, B.; Iwata, S. *Structure* 2004, 12, 95.

[103] Kloer, D. P.; Hagel, C.; Heider, J.; Schulz, G. E. *Structure* 2006, 14, 1377.

[104] Kisker, C.; Schindelin, H.; Pacheco, A.; Wehbi, W.; Garrett, R. M.; Rajagopalan, K. V.; Enemark, J. H.; Rees, D. C. *Cell*, 1997, 91, 973.

In: Molybdenum
Editor: Alvin A. Holder

ISBN: 978-1-62417-272-4
© 2013 Nova Science Publishers, Inc.

Chapter 10

MOLYBDENUM-NITROGENASE AND RELATED ENZYMES

*William E. Newton**

Virginia Polytechnic Institute and State University, Blacksburg, VA 24061, US

ABSTRACT

Biological nitrogen fixation is the major contributor of assimilable nitrogen to world agriculture. This chapter opens with a comprehensive comparative account of the composition and the catalytic and spectroscopic properties of the classical molybdenum-based nitrogense and Mo-based variant enzymes produced by directed mutagenesis techniques. These properties are then compared with those of the closely related vanadium-nitrogenase and the iron-nitrogenase with special emphasis placed on the differences among them. The individual structures of both component proteins, the Fe protein and the MoFe protein, of wild-type and variant Mo-nitrogenases are presented, plus structures of the stabilized 2:1 complexes of wild-type Mo-nitrogenase. However, no x-ray-derived three-dimensional structures are as yet available for the V-nitrogenase and the Fe-nitrogenase. Then, the current understanding of the mechanism of action is described emphisizing the role of MgATP, where substrates and inhibitors likely bind and how electrons and protons are delivered to bound substrate. A brief description of the unique *Streptomyces thermoautotrophicus* nitrogenase is then given, followed by some thoughts on the current barriers to a wider dissemination of the biological nitrogen fixation and how they might be overcome.

INTRODUCTION

The biogeochemical nitrogen cycle inter-converts the inert atmospheric N_2 pool and the usable terrestrial/marine fixed-nitrogen pool. Within this cycle, biological nitrogen fixation drives the reductive conversion of atmospheric N_2 to ammonia, [1-7] whereas the processes of

---

* Department of Biochemistry, Virginia Polytechnic Institute and State University, Blacksburg, VA 24061, US. E-mail: *wenewton@vt.edu*.

nitrification and denitrification oxidize and so return the fixed-nitrogen forms to the atmosphere as N_2 through intermediates, such as nitrite, nitrate and nitrogen oxides. [8] Both the evolution of life as we know it and its continuing survival depend on sources of fixed nitrogen for production of the basic molecules of life, namely DNA, RNA and proteins.

In the modern world, fixed nitrogen is produced by several processes, both biological and abiological. The two most important processes are industrial ammonia production through the Haber-Bosch process and biological nitrogen fixation, which together account for about 90% of the total annual fixation. [9-10] Without the invention and refinement of the Haber-Bosch process, today's global demand for fixed-nitrogen, which is almost always the limiting nutrient in agriculture, could not possibly be satisfied. Mankind's requirements have outstripped the capacity of biological nitrogen-fixing systems. Even so, it is sobering to realize that only some of the smallest living things, *i.e.*, bacteria and archaea, can perform biological nitrogen fixation and, furthermore, that this process was invented only twice (at most) during evolution as shown by the two distinct types of nitrogenase extant in nature!

TYPES OF NITROGENASE

Two very different types of nitrogenase are known. The first type is the classical nitrogenase group of three closely related, but genetically distinct, enzymes. These are the well-studied molybdenum-based enzyme (Mo-nitrogenase), a vanadium-based enzyme (V-nitrogenase), and an enzyme that contains neither hetero-metal but relies on iron alone (Fe-nitrogenase). Even though each enzyme contains a prosthetic group that is based on a different metal atom (Mo, V, or Fe), they are otherwise so similar that they must have arisen from a common ancestor. [11-12] In contrast, the second type of nitrogenase is so different that it may well be an evolutionary independent invention and be completely unrelated to the classical nitrogenases. [13]

THE CLASSICAL NITROGENASES

With the single exception involving the second type of nitrogenase (see later), all nitrogen-fixing organisms have the classical Mo-nitrogenase, but the distribution of the V-nitrogenase and the Fe-nitrogenase appears completely random. Some organisms, *e.g.*, the free-living *Klebsiella pneumonia* and the rhizobacteria that form nodules on the roots of legumes, have only Mo-nitrogenase, whereas others, *e.g.*, *Azotobacter vinelandii*, have all three enzymes. Other combinations also exist, *e.g.*, *A. chroococcum* has the Mo- and V-nitrogenases, whereas *Rhodobacter capsulatus* has the Mo- and Fe-nitrogenases. [14]

Which of these nitrogenases is expressed depends on the availability of the metal ions (either Mo or V) in the growth environment. [15] Whenever Mo is available, expression of the Mo-nitrogenase genes is stimulated and the expression of the genes for the other two nitrogenases is repressed. Similarly, when V is available and Mo is absent, expression of only the V-nitrogenase genes occurs. If both metals are absent, then just the Fe-nitrogenase is produced. This control by metal availability is physiologically reasonable because Mo-nitrogenase is the most efficient N_2-reduction catalyst and Fe-nitrogenase the least efficient.

Relationships among the Classical Nitrogenases

All three classical nitrogenases consist of two component metalloproteins, [1] which can be separately purified, but which have no individual N_2-fixation activity (see below). When isolated from the same organism, *e.g.*, *A. vinelandii*, either component protein from Mo-nitrogenase forms an active hybrid nitrogenase when it is mixed with the complementary component protein from V-nitrogenase. However, neither component protein from the Fe-nitrogenase forms an active hybrid with the complementary protein from either the Mo- or V-nitrogenase. [14]

Furthermore, even mixtures of the Mo-nitrogenase component proteins isolated from different organisms may not result in an active hybrid nitrogenase. [15] A notable example is the Mo-nitrogenase components from the strict anaerobe, *Clostridium pasteurianum*.

Very little is known about both the origin and evolution of the nitrogen-fixation genes and proteins and the mechanisms involved in shaping the process itself. [12] Similarly, how the ability to fix N_2 was distributed among the relatively few genera of bacteria and archaea that do so is also a matter of some controversy. Its apparent haphazard distribution among microbes might be a common ancestral property that was lost randomly during divergent evolution, so indicating a very ancient origin. In contrast, the nitrogen-fixation genes could be of more recent origin and are being spread laterally, like antibiotic resistance, among diverse prokaryotic genera. In fact, some gene sequences appear to support an ancient origin, whereas others suggest more recent lateral gene transfer. As more and more genomes are sequenced, it appears that a combination of both multiple losses and multiple transfers of the nitrogen-fixation genes has occurred. Whatever the case, the genetic relatedness of the classical nitrogenases, including even the order in which the genes are found in genomes, supports a common ancient ancestry. [17]

So, which of the classical nitrogenases evolved first? One suggestion cites a primal nitrogenase from which the three classical nitrogenases developed. This suggestion finds support in that, although genetically distinct, the three sets of structural genes, which encode the polypeptide subunits of the proteins, were likely formed by gene iteration. [12] Other support for this suggestion includes:

(i) The products of certain nitrogen-fixation-specific genes support all three nitrogenases;

(ii) The heterometal-containing prosthetic groups are transferable among all three nitrogenases; and

(iii) All have similar catalytic properties.

Mo-Nitrogenase

The individual component proteins of Mo-nitrogenase are called the Fe protein (sometimes component 2 or dinitrogenase reductase) and the MoFe protein (sometimes component 1 or dinitrogenase). The trivial names for these proteins are derived from their metal compositions. Often, especially when using hybrid mixtures, each component protein is identified by a two-letter abbreviation for the organism of its origin together with the number 1 or 2. For example, the Fe protein of *A. vinelandii* Mo-nitrogenase would be labeled as Av2.

The Mo-nitrogenases from a variety of bacterial genera exhibit a high level of primary (amino acid) sequence identity. The sequence conservation is particularly high in the regions of the MgATP- and metallocluster-binding sites.

The Fe protein is a homodimer with a molecular mass of about 64 kDa. Both subunits are encoded by the *nifH* gene. It contains a single [4Fe-4S] cluster that bridges the two identical subunits. Each subunit has its own MgATP/MgADP-binding site. The Fe protein is a specific reductant for the MoFe protein (but see later). The MoFe protein is an $\alpha_2\beta_2$ heterotetramer with a molecular mass of about 230 kDa. As a mechanistic simplification, it is often assumed that each $\alpha\beta$ pair of subunits of the MoFe protein operates independently of the other $\alpha\beta$ pair, although long-range interactions between the two $\alpha\beta$ pairs have been detected. [18] Each $\alpha\beta$ pair contains one copy of each of two different prosthetic groups; these are the P-cluster and the iron-molybdenum cofactor (or FeMo-cofactor or the M-center), which serves as the site of substrate binding and reduction. [19] Unlike the P-cluster, which is disrupted when removed from the MoFe protein, the FeMo-cofactor can be extracted essentially intact into a variety of organic solvents. [20] The isolated prosthetic group is then referred to as FeMoco. Three-dimensional structures of the individual component proteins from both wild-type and mutant bacterial strains and their complex have been completed (see below).

Each of the component proteins of Mo-nitrogenase exhibits an electron paramagnetic resonance (EPR) spectrum when isolated in the presence of sodium dithionite, their so-called "resting state". The resting state of the [4Fe-4S] cluster of the Fe protein exhibits signals from a mixture of $S=1/2$ and $S=3/2$ spin states (Figure 1 B). The rhombic EPR signal around $g = 2$ (ca. 330 mT), which arises from the $S=1/2$ spin state, is much sharper than the EPR signal at about $g = 4$ (ca. 160 mT) from the $S=3/2$ spin state. In the presence of MgATP, the shape of the $S=1/2$ EPR spectrum becomes more nearly axial.

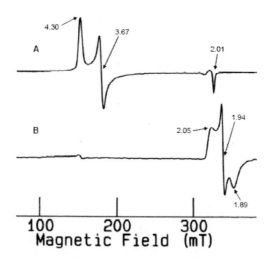

Figure 1. The X-band electron paramagnetic resonance (EPR) spectra of the as-isolated dithionite-reduced resting state of both component proteins of Mo-nitrogenase in frozen solution at about 10 K. (A) the $S=3/2$ spectrum of the MoFe protein and (B) the $S=1/2$ spectrum of the Fe protein in the absence of MgATP. The relevant g values are noted on the spectra.

The resting state of the MoFe protein exhibits a rhombic $S=3/2$ EPR signal with two g values around 4 ($g = 4.3$ and 3.7) and one at $g = 2.01$ (Figure 1 A), which is essentially unaffected by added MgATP. This EPR signal arises from the FeMo-cofactor within the MoFe protein. Both EPR signals have been instrumental in determining the direction of electron flow between the component proteins [21] and in monitoring many of their catalyzed reactions. During turnover of a mixture of the two proteins in the presence of MgATP and sodium dithionite as reductant, the $S=3/2$ MoFe protein-based EPR loses about 90% of its intensity and a mixture of the rhombic and axial Fe protein-based $S=1/2$ EPR signals appears. These observations indicate that the MoFe protein has been reduced by electron transfer from the Fe protein.

The physiologically important nitrogen-fixation reaction (equation [1]) is usually described as involving the delivery of eight electrons, six of which reduce N_2 to two ammonia molecules with the remaining two electrons producing one H_2 molecule, and the hydrolysis of 16 MgATP molecules. The evolution of one H_2 for each N_2 reduced may be either a mandatory step in the mechanism [22] or an as yet unexplained kinetic phenomenon.

$$N_2 + 8\,H^+ + 8\,e^- + 16\,MgATP \rightarrow 2\,NH_3 + H_2 + 16\,MgADP + 16\,P_i \qquad [1]$$

In vivo, Mo-nitrogenase uses either a ferredoxin or flavodoxin as the reductant of the Fe protein, whereas *in vitro*, the artificial reductant, sodium dithionite ($Na_2S_2O_4$), is most often used. With sodium dithionite as reductant, the Fe protein accepts only a single electron, which it then transfers to the MoFe protein with the concomitant hydrolysis of two molecules of MgATP. Both the rate of electron transfer (the flux) and this ratio of electrons transferred-to-MgATP hydrolyzed is independent of the substrate (see below) being reduced. Other reductants, e.g., Ti(III) and flavodoxin, used *in vitro* may transfer two electrons to the Fe protein. With both electrons being transferred in a single step to the MoFe protein and with still only two molecules of MgATP being hydrolyzed, the MgATP-consumption rate is halved. [23] It remains to be seen if both one-electron and two-electron transfers occur *in vivo*. Wild-type Mo-nitrogenase also catalyzes the reduction of many other small-molecule "alternative" substrates in addition to N_2 and H^+. All such substrates have the same requirements as N_2 reduction, namely a supply of MgATP, a low-potential reductant, and an anaerobic environment. [1,24] The most often used of these is acetylene, which is reduced by two electrons to ethylene, in a reaction that accounts for about 95% of the electron flux under a 10% C_2H_2 atmosphere with the remainder going to H_2 production. Other "alternative substrates" are shown in Figure 2 together with carbon monoxide (CO), which is a potent non-competitive inhibitor of all wild-type Mo-nitrogenase-catalyzed substrate reductions except for proton reduction to H_2. [1,25]. When no other substrate is present, all electron flux is used for proton reduction to H_2.

H_2 has other unique involvements with N_2 reduction catalyzed by Mo-nitrogenase. First, H_2 can provide reducing equivalents for Mo-nitrogenase, *via* the action of hydrogenase. Second, H_2 is a specific inhibitor of N_2 reduction, affecting neither the reduction of any other substrate nor its own evolution. Third, under a mixed atmosphere of N_2 and D_2, HD is formed in a reaction that has all the requirements of a nitrogenase-catalyzed reaction and is also inhibited by CO. [1,24-25]

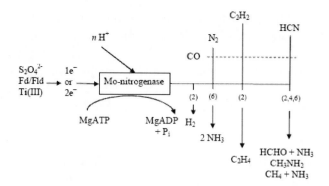

Figure 2. Electron donors, some substrates, and their products for wild-type Mo-nitrogenase catalysis. CO is a potent reversible inhibitor of all wild-type Mo-nitrogenase-catalyzed substrate reductions except for that of protons to H_2. Fld is flavodoxin and Fd is ferredoxin, both of which are reductants for Mo-nitrogenase, as is Ti(III). The number of electrons (e^-) and protons (H^+) transferred to each substrate is shown in parentheses.

V-Nitrogenase and Fe-Nitrogenase

These so-called "alternative" nitrogenases also consist of two protein components. [1,14,26] Each nitrogenase has its specific Fe-protein component. The larger component protein of the V-nitrogenase contains a VFe-cofactor, with a vanadium atom replacing the Mo atom of the Mo-nitrogenase. Thus, the genetically distinct VFe protein from *A. vinelandii* is sometimes designated as Av1*. Similarly, the Fe-only nitrogenase has a cofactor in which the Mo atom is replaced by Fe to produce a FeFe-cofactor in a FeFe protein.

The high level of primary sequence identity recognized among the Mo-nitrogenases also extends to the V- and Fe-only nitrogenases. This identity strongly suggests that all nitrogenases share common structural features and have mechanistic similarities. A major difference, however, is that the VFe protein and FeFe protein have additional δ subunits. Initially, their subunit composition was reported as $\alpha_2\beta_2\delta_2$ [26-27] rather than $\alpha_2\beta_2$ as found for the MoFe protein. More recently, using affinity chromatography and His-tagging, the VFe protein was purified as an $\alpha_2\beta_2\delta_4$ octamer. [28] The δ subunits apparently bind to the apo-protein during biosynthesis of both the VFe and FeFe proteins and remain bound thereafter. In contrast, the equivalent of the δ subunit for the MoFe protein (encoded by the *nifY* gene) is lost in the late stages of its maturation.

The Fe-protein component of both alternative nitrogenases, when reduced with sodium dithionite, exhibits a rhombic EPR spectrum essentially identical to that of the Fe protein from the Mo-nitrogenase; both change shape to axial with added MgATP.

However, the dithionite-reduced VFe protein exhibits an EPR spectrum that is considerably more complex than that of the MoFe protein. [27-28] The EPR signal has $S=5/2$, $S=3/2$ and $S=1/2$ components (Figure 3) with the rhombic $S=3/2$ component assigned to the presence of a FeV-cofactor. [26] The origin and physiological relevance of the $S=1/2$ and $S=5/2$ components of this EPR signal are still somewhat uncertain, but recent studies suggest that both likely arise from the P cluster rather than the FeV-cofactor. [28]

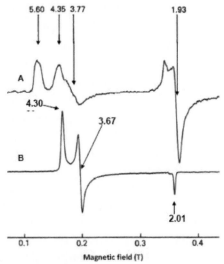

Figure 3. The X-band EPR spectrum of the as-isolated dithionite-reduced resting state of the VFe protein (A) from *Azotobacter chroococcum* compared with that of the MoFe protein (B) in frozen solution at about 10 K. The relevant g values are noted on the spectra. In contrast to the $S=3/2$ EPR spectrum of the MoFe protein, the VFe protein spectrum is a mixture of $S=5/2$, $S=3/2$ and $S=1/2$ components. The figure was adapted from ref. 26. Reproduced with permission, from R. R. Eady, R. L. Robson, T. H. Richardson, R. W. Miller and M. Hawkins (1987) *Biochemical Journal,* **244,** 197-207. © the Biochemical Society.

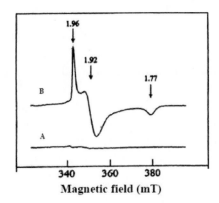

Figure 4. The X-band EPR spectrum of the FeFe protein from *Rhodobacter capsulatus* in frozen solution at about 10 K. As isolated in the presence of dithionite, the reduced resting state of the FeFe protein is EPR-silent (A), but when reduced, it exhibits a rhombic $S=1/2$ EPR spectrum (B). The relevant g values are noted on the spectra. [29] Adapted with permission, from K. Schneider, U. Gollan, M. Dröttbroom, S. Selsemeier-Voigt, and A. Müller, 1997, *Eur. J. Biochem.,* **244,** 789-800. Copyright (1997) John Wiley & Sons - Journals.

In contrast, no EPR signal is observed from the purified resting-state FeFe protein. [29] Consistent with this observation, Mössbauer spectroscopy indicates that both prosthetic groups are present but are diamagnetic in the resting state FeFe protein. [30] However, under turnover conditions, the FeFe protein develops a rhombic $S=1/2$ EPR signal (Figure 4) suggesting that it too is reduced by electron transfer from its Fe-protein partner. [29]

The catalytic properties of the V-nitrogenase also differ from those of Mo-nitrogenase. Most noticeably, only about 50% of the electron flux is used to produce NH_3 under 100% N_2 compared to about 75% for Mo-nitrogenase, plus a very small amount of N_2H_4, which is not observed with Mo-nitrogenase. [31] The Fe-nitrogenase is even less efficient with only about 30% of electron flux reducing N_2. [29] V-nitrogenase is also less effective for C_2H_2 reduction with only about 40% of the flux producing C_2H_4, but with an additional about 5% producing C_2H_6, under a 10% C_2H_2 atmosphere. In comparison, Mo-nitrogenase uses about 95% of the electron flux for C_2H_4 production with no C_2H_6 formed. [32] The Fe-nitrogenase is exceptionally poor as a C_2H_2-reducing catalyst with only about 15% of the electron flux used to produce C_2H_4 plus some C_2H_6. [29]

As observed for wild-type Mo-nitrogenase, 10% carbon monoxide (CO) is a non-competitive inhibitor of the V-nitrogenase-catalyzed reduction of all substrates except that of the proton, however, its inhibitory effect is much less. [32] Another significant difference is that, above 10% CO, catalyzed proton reduction is inhibited by 35% or more, [28] which is consistent with the recently discovered ability of V-nitrogenase to catalyze CO reduction to a variety of C_1-to-C_4 hydrocarbon products. [33-34]

Since this discovery, exceedingly small quantities of similar CO-reduction products have been detected with wild-type Mo-nitrogenase [34] and, with somewhat higher yields, from a variant Mo-nitrogenase. [35] A similar range of concatenated hydrocarbon products was previously observed from Mo-nitrogenase-catalyzed isocyanide reduction. [36] The physiological significance of this discovery is yet to be determined.

Structures of the Nitrogenase Component Proteins and their Complexes

X-ray-based three-dimensional structures of the wild-type Fe protein, the wild-type MoFe protein, complexes of the two proteins, and several variant MoFe proteins isolated from mutant bacterial strains are all known. No three-dimensional structures are available for either the V-nitrogenase or the Fe-nitrogenase components, however both Mössbauer [30,37] and x-ray absorption spectroscopies [30,38-39] indicate that these nitrogenases share many structural similarities with the Mo-nitrogenase components. [1]

The Fe Protein

The Fe protein is a homodimer of subunits and its x-ray-derived structure reveals that each subunit is composed of a single domain, which involves an eight-stranded β-sheet that is flanked by nine α-helices (see Figure 7). Its single [4Fe-4S] cluster is bridged symmetrically between the two subunits. Each subunit provides two cysteinyl (numbered 97 and 132 in the *A. vinelandii* primary sequence) ligands to the [4Fe-4S] cluster, which occupies a solvent-exposed position at one end of the dimer interface. Each subunit has a nucleotide-binding site, which is located in the channel between the subunits. These sites were first recognized by the presence of two consensus amino acid sequences that are common to other nucleotide-binding proteins.

The original Fe-protein structure [40] showed only partial and unusual occupancy of these sites by MgADP, but a later structure, which involved crystallization in the presence of excess MgADP (PDB code: 1FP6), [41] showed full occupancy. The orientation of both nucleotides in the later structure was parallel to the subunit-subunit interface. The same parallel nucleotide orientation was found in a structure of the 2:1 complex of the Fe protein with the MoFe protein (see Figure). [42] This complex was stabilized as a "transition-state" analogue by adding MgADP plus tetrafluoroaluminate (AlF_4^-) as a surrogate for ATP. This structure had two MgADP•AlF_4^- entities bound to each Fe protein with one nucleotide associated primarily with each Fe-protein subunit.

Nucleotide binding to the Fe protein is cooperative and changes several properties of the [4Fe-4S] cluster, including its redox potential, which goes from ca. −300 mV to ca. −400 mV, and the shape of its EPR spectrum. [25,43] Even with the available structures, it is still unclear exactly how these changes are achieved.

Although the nucleotide does not contact the [4Fe-4S] cluster directly, the various structures show that a region of the Fe-protein backbone undergoes a significant structural change when nucleotide binds. This region, called switch II by analogy to the nomenclature used with G proteins, starts with the aspartate-125 residue, which interacts with the nucleotide-bound Mg^{2+}, and ends at the cysteine-132 residue, which is a ligand to the [4Fe-4S] cluster. The effects of nucleotide binding appear to be propagated through this region to produce a conformational change at the cluster and changes in its electronic and redox properties. [43]

A similar mechanism, called switch I, might also allow communication between the nucleotide-binding site and the part of the Fe-protein surface that interacts with the MoFe protein during complex formation. This switch involves the region from the aspartate-39 residue to a loop region of the Fe protein composed of residues 59-68, which also undergoes a nucleotide-dependent structural change. This loop may communicate to the nucleotide-binding site that contact has occurred with the MoFe-protein surface. Such contact could indicate electron transfer to the MoFe protein, which could initiate MgATP hydrolysis and then dissociation of the Fe protein from the MoFe protein.

The MoFe Protein

This $\alpha_2\beta_2$ heterotetramer is encoded by the *nifDK* genes. Early spectroscopic, x-ray anomalous scattering, and cluster-extrusion studies of the MoFe protein showed that the MoFe protein contained two types of prosthetic group, neither of which had been previously recognized. Each of these unique cluster types contains about 50% of both the Fe and S^{2-} content of the MoFe protein. They are called the P cluster and the FeMo-cofactor (or M center). The exact composition and distribution of these clusters within the protein was firmly established only after x-ray techniques had revealed the structures of both cluster types within the MoFe protein from both *A. vinelandii* and *K. pneumoniae* (PDB codes: 1QGU, 1QH1 and 1QH8). [44-46] These prosthetic groups are distributed in pairs; one pair of prosthetic groups resides within each pair of $\alpha\beta$-subunits. The prosthetic-group pairs are separated from one another by about 70Å and each pair includes one FeMo-cofactor, which is a [Mo-Fe_7-S_9] cluster with a central carbide and a Mo-attached *R*-homocitrate molecule (Figure 5), and one P cluster, which has a [Fe_8-S_7] composition (Figure).

The interface between the two $\alpha\beta$-dimers is primarily through interactions of helices in the two β-subunits. An 8Å-wide channel, which contains a two-fold rotation axis, passes through the center of the tetramer. The α- and β-subunits have similar polypeptide folds with three domains composed of α-helices and parallel β-sheets. In the α-subunit, the three domains meet to form a shallow cleft within which the FeMo-cofactor resides about 10Å below the protein's surface. It is covalently bound by only two amino-acid residues (cysteinyl-275 and histidinyl-442, using the *Azotobacter vinelandii* numbering scheme) from the α-subunit and it has no close involvement with the β-subunit. In contrast, the P cluster is located at the interface of the α- and β-subunits with each subunit providing three ligating cysteinyl residues. Each P cluster is bisected by a pseudo-twofold axis that relates the α-and β-subunits (see Figure 7).

The FeMo-Cofactor Prosthetic Group

The FeMo-cofactor (or M-center) can be extruded intact from the MoFe protein into one of several organic solvents. [20,47] After its isolation, it is recalcitrant to crystallization. FeMoco retains the $S=3/2$ EPR signal, although significantly broadened, but cannot catalyze N_2 reduction.

A definitive description of the FeMo-cofactor's composition and structure came from the high-resolution MoFe-protein structure. The FeMo-cofactor consists of two sub-clusters, one [Mo-Fe$_3$-S$_3$] and one [Fe$_4$-S$_3$]; each sub-cluster may be visualized as missing one sulfide from either a [Mo-Fe$_3$-S$_4$] or a [Fe$_4$-S$_4$] cubane cluster, respectively. The original structure showed that the two sub-clusters were bridged to one another by three sulfides. [48-49] As a result, only one of the Fe atoms (the terminal one) had tetrahedral geometry and the other six (central) Fe atoms had apparent trigonal geometry. However, a more recent, very high resolution structure [50] provided evidence for a single light atom, now shown to be carbide (C^{4-}) within the central cavity of the FeMo-cofactor and equidistant to all six of the central Fe atoms (Figure 5). [51-52]

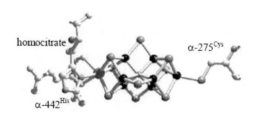

Figure 5. The structure of the FeMo-cofactor of *Azotobacter vinelandii* nitrogenase MoFe protein with its α-subunit-based ligating amino-acid residues (αCys-275 and αHis-442) and homocitrate. The seven darkest spheres are the Fe atoms, the eight lighter-gray spheres are the S atoms, and the largest sphere (to the left) is the Mo atom. The identity of the central atom has now been assigned as C^{4-}. The figure was drawn from coordinates available at *PDB code: 1M1N*.

It is uncertain whether this light atom has a mechanistic or a structural role or both. The Mo atom has octahedral geometry provided by the imidazole δ-N of α-histidinyl-442, three cubane μ$_3$-sulfides, and by ligation from both the 2-hydroxyl and 2-carboxyl groups of *R*-homocitrate. The α-cysteinyl-275-Fe apex of the FeMo-cofactor has no associated water molecules, whereas the homocitrate-Mo apex is surrounded by water molecules. Moreover, the homocitrate is positioned between the FeMo-cofactor and the P cluster and may be a component of the electron/proton-transfer pathway to bound substrate (see later).

There are also many important hydrogen-bonding interactions between the FeMo-cofactor and the surrounding amino-acid residues. For example, the side chains of both α-glutaminyl-191 and α-glutaminyl-440 hydrogen bond to the homocitrate (one to each of homocitrate's terminal carboxyl groups), whereas the α-histidinyl-195, α-argininyl-96 and α-argininyl-359 residues hydrogen bond to various sulfides of the cluster.

The P Cluster Prosthetic Group

The P cluster also has a biologically unique structure. Both its location at the α/β-subunit interface and its formulation as a Fe-S cluster containing eight Fe atoms were only confirmed by the original x-ray crystal structure of the MoFe protein.

Each P cluster is ligated by six cysteinyl residues, three from each subunit. The P cluster consists of a [4Fe-4S] sub-cluster that shares one of its sulfides with a [4Fe-3S] partial cube. This shared sulfide is bound to the six central Fe atoms, a very unusual situation for sulfide. The [4Fe-4S] sub-cluster is terminally ligated by the γ-S of both α-cysteinyl-62 and α-cysteinyl-154, whereas the [4Fe-3S] partial cube has terminal ligation from the equivalent residues of the β-subunit, namely, the γ-S of both β-cysteinyl-70 and β-cysteinyl-153 as terminal ligands. In addition, two other cysteinyl residues, α-cysteinyl-88 and β-cysteinyl-95, form μ$_2$-sulfide bridges between the sub-clusters (Figure 6 B).

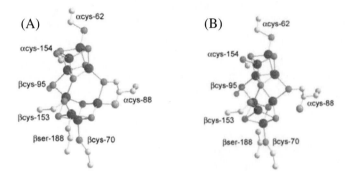

Figure 6. The structure of the P cluster of *Azotobacter vinelandii* nitrogenase MoFe protein in its (A) oxidized (POX) and (B) dithionite-reduced (PN) states, together with its ligating amino-acid residues (αCys-62, αCys-88, αCys-154, βCys-70, βCys-95, βCys-153, and βSer-188), which are provided by both the α- and β-subunits. The Fe atoms are the larger darker spheres. [53] Reproduced with permission, from J. W. Peters, M. H. B. Stowell, S. M. Soltis, M. G. Finnegan, M. K. Johnson and D. C. Rees, 1997, *Biochemistry*, **36**, 1181-1187. Copyright (1997) American Chemical Society.

On oxidation by redox-active dyes, the P cluster structurally rearranges to a more open structure. Two of the four Fe atoms located in the [4Fe-3S] partial cube lose contact with the central hexacoordinated sulfide and change ligation. One Fe atom becomes ligated by the γ-O of β-serinyl-188 and the other Fe atom bonds to the deprotonated backbone amide-N of the already bound and bridging α-cysteinyl-88 (Figure 6 A). Because both of these latter ligands are protonated in the unbound state and deprotonated in the bound state, these redox-induced ligand changes raise the possibility that a two-electron oxidation of the P cluster during catalysis will also release two protons from the P cluster. [53]

Variant MoFe Proteins

The crystal structures of four variant MoFe proteins have been solved; two are of proteins with single amino-acid substitutions and two have more substantial changes. The variant

MoFe protein, which has its α-histidinyl-195 residue replaced by glutaminyl (*PDB code: 1FP4*) is compromised in its ability to catalyze N_2 reduction, [54] but otherwise hardly affected. Its structure was virtually identical to that of the wild-type MoFe protein with the single exception that the >NH→S hydrogen bond between a central μ_2-sulfide of the FeMo-cofactor and the ε-N of the imidazole side chain of αHis195 is replaced by a similar bond with the amide-N of glutamine. [55] The other structure had the α-valinyl-70 residue, which is also close to the FeMo-cofactor, replaced by isoleucinyl (*PDB code: 3K1A*). [56] This variant is hampered in its ability to catalyze both N_2 and C_2H_2 reduction, but not proton reduction, which could be caused by the longer isoleucinyl side chain blocking access to the substrate-binding site. Again, its structure is virtually identical to that of the wild-type MoFe protein with the single exception that the longer isoleucinyl side chain more closely approaches the Fe6 atom of the FeMo-cofactor. Both structures confirm that the substitutions introduced in these variant MoFe proteins have only a local and not a global effect.

The first of the two other rather different structures is the variant MoFe protein from a *nifV⁻* mutant that had, therefore, lost the ability to biosynthesize homocitrate (*PDB code: 1H1L*). [57] Again, the structure was essentially identical to that of the wild-type protein, except that citrate replaced homocitrate, but only partially, as a ligand to the Mo atom. The second of these structures is of a FeMo-cofactor-deficient form of the MoFe protein (*PDB code: 1L5H*). [58] Not surprisingly, only one of the three domains of the α-subunit shows significant structural changes, which create a funnel that leads to the FeMo-cofactor-binding site within the α-subunit. This funnel is lined with positively-charged residues from its entrance to α-histidinyl-442, which likely serves both as the initial docking point for the negatively-charged FeMo-cofactor and as the trigger to close the funnel and bury the FeMo-cofactor within the α-subunit.

The MoFe Protein-Fe Protein Complex

The primary structure of the Fe protein is quite similar to those of "nucleotide switch" proteins, like ATPases and GTPases, and so similar trapping techniques, using AlF_4^- together with ADP, were used with the nitrogenase components.

The result was a stable complex of two Fe-protein molecules with one MoFe-protein molecule. The 3Å-resolution crystal structure of this complex (Figure 7), which may approximate the transition state for inter-component electron transfer, showed a significant conformational change for the Fe protein, but only little change for the MoFe protein (*PDB code: 1N2C*). [42] Each of the four Fe-protein subunits in the complex has an associated Mg^{2+}-ADP•AlF_4^- moiety, which are bound parallel to the interface between the subunits as found for the MgATP molecules bound to the Fe protein alone. The conformational change of the Fe protein results from a 13° rotation of both subunits, resulting in a more compact structure. Interestingly, small-angle x-ray scattering data indicate that this 2:1 complex maintains this structure in solution. [59]

Docking of the two proteins occurs along the Fe protein's two-fold symmetry axis, which bisects its single [4Fe-4S] cluster, and the pseudosymmetric αβ-interface of the MoFe protein. This more compact conformation results in the Fe protein's [4Fe-4S] cluster becoming buried in the protein-protein interface and approaching to within ~14Å of the MoFe protein's P-cluster, which is now situated equidistant between the Fe protein's [4Fe-4S] cluster and the FeMo-cofactor. This arrangement has been interpreted as indicating the electron-transfer pathway by which electrons move from the [4Fe-4S] cluster through the P-cluster to the FeMo-cofactor, where substrate reduction occurs.

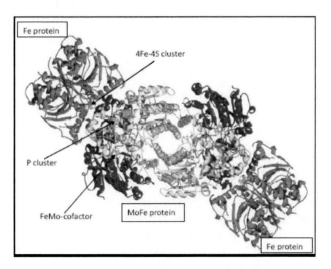

Figure 7. The structure of the 2:1 Fe protein-MoFe protein complex of the *Azotobacter vinelandii* Mo-nitrogenase stabilized by MgADP plus AlF_4^-. The Fe protein molecules are located at 4 o'clock and 10 o'clock with respect to the centrally located MoFe protein. Each Fe-protein docks over a MoFe-protein α/β-subunit interface to juxtapose its 4Fe-4S cluster with a P cluster. All three types of prosthetic group are indicated. The figure was drawn from coordinates available at *PDB code: 1N2C*.

About 20 intimate contacts occur between the amino-acid residues of the Fe protein adjacent to the [4Fe-4S] cluster and stretches of both the α- and β-main chains of the MoFe protein. A significant interaction involves the argininyl-100 residues of the Fe protein. In some bacteria, this residue is modified in a facile, reversible manner to regulate nitrogenase activity. [60] These argininyl-100 residues are part of the first turn in a pair of helices that extend symmetrically on both sides of the [4Fe-4S] cluster and their side chain protrudes into a small depression in the surface of the MoFe protein. Here, the side chain interacts with the side chains of glutaminyl residues from both subunits of the MoFe protein. Modification of these argininyl-100 residues introduces steric hindrance to the protein-protein interface, prevents complex formation, suppresses activity, and regulates the enzyme.

Two other structures of the 2:1 Fe protein/MoFe protein complex have been solved. The first structure involved a variant Fe protein (L127Δ), which has leucinyl-127 deleted from the switch-II region (see above). The effect of this deletion is to mimic the binding of nucleotide and it causes the Fe protein to be permanently in the equivalent of an MgATP-bound state. As such, the L127Δ Fe protein forms a tightly bound, but inactive 2:1 complex with the MoFe protein (*PDB code: 1G20 and 1G21* for the structures with or without MgATP). [61] This structure closely resembles that of the MgATP-AlF$_4^-$-stabilized complex except for one significant difference, which is the more open conformation adopted by the complexed L127Δ Fe protein. This conformation resembles that of the uncomplexed nucleotide-free, rather than the complexed nucleotide-bound, wild-type Fe protein.

The wild-type Fe protein in the second 2:1 complex structure, which results from chemical cross-linking the two wild-type component proteins through glutamatyl-112 of the Fe protein and β-lysinyl-400 of the MoFe protein, adopts a structure that is even more open than when it is uncomplexed (*PDB code: 1M1Y*). [62] Again, the structure of the MoFe-protein component protein is effectively unchanged. However, the relative orientation of the two components is changed and results in a completely different interface area. It's possible that the cross-linked complex represents an "initial encounter" state that then proceeds through a series of conformational changes on the Fe protein to reorient the Fe protein in the "electron-transfer competent" state, which is likely represented by the $MgADP \cdot AlF_4^-$-stabilized complex.

Mechanism of Nitrogenase Action

Using sodium dithionite as the reductant *in vitro*, the one-electron-reduced Fe protein is alternately oxidized and re-reduced as it delivers its single electron to the MoFe protein in a process that couples MgATP binding and hydrolysis to the association and dissociation of the two component proteins and concomitant intra-complex electron transfer. The Fe protein alone is capable of binding MgATP, but both component proteins are required for MgATP hydrolysis. Neither component protein alone, with or without MgATP and/or reductant, will reduce substrate under the usual assay conditions (but see below).

The catalytic process occurs in four steps. First, the reduced MgATP-bound Fe protein associates with the MoFe protein. Second, an electron is transferred from the [4Fe-4S] cluster of the Fe protein likely through the P cluster to the FeMo-cofactor of the MoFe protein within this complex. Third, MgATP is hydrolyzed and the complex dissociates and releases phosphate. Fourth, the now oxidized Fe protein-$(MgADP)_2$ is re-reduced, exchanges the MgADP for MgATP, and is ready for the next round of association/electron transfer with the MoFe protein. However, one or more of these steps could change when either Ti(III) or the *in vivo* reductant, flavodoxin, is used as reductant. [63]

It is still unclear how, when, and where the eight electrons necessary for the reduction of each N_2 (accompanied by one H_2) are accommodated within the MoFe protein and how the required protons are delivered. This situation has been simplified by the assertion that that the metal core of the FeMo-cofactor has only two accessible oxidation levels, the EPR-active resting state (called M^N; with no electrons received from the Fe protein) and the one-electron-reduced EPR-silent state (called M^R; with one electron received from the Fe protein). [64] All other electrons delivered from the Fe protein must, therefore, reside either on partially reduced substrates (or inhibitors) or on the P cluster.

The Lowe-Thorneley Model

This computational model was developed to describe the process by which electrons, initially derived from dithionite, and protons are sequentially delivered to the MoFe protein and then to substrate. [65] This model treats the MoFe protein as a dimer of $\alpha\beta$-dimers with each $\alpha\beta$-dimer operating independently and being serviced by Fe protein. The actual situation is more complicated because the Fe protein appears to service each of $\alpha\beta$-dimer either alternately or cooperatively. [66-67] The model involves two interconnecting processes, called the Fe-protein cycle (Figure 8; left side) and the MoFe-protein cycle (Figure 8; right side). The Fe-protein cycle describes the reactions that allow the Fe protein's [4Fe-4S] cluster to cycle between its 2+ (oxidized) and 1+ (reduced) redox states. The MoFe-protein cycle is necessarily more complex because it involves the progressive reduction of the MoFe protein (plus bound substrate) by up to eight electrons for N_2 binding and reduction, which therefore requires eight turns of the Fe-protein cycle.

Figure 8 (right side) shows a highly abbreviated version of the MoFe-protein cycle. Partially reduced nitrogen intermediates must remain on the enzyme until the reduction cycle is finished because NH_3 as the only product of catalyzed N_2 reduction by Mo-nitrogenase.

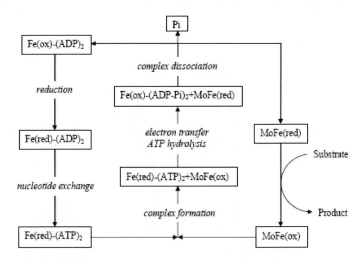

Figure 8. A modified Lowe-Thorneley kinetic scheme for nitrogenase catalysis. The Fe-protein cycle involves both the nucleotide-bound and MoFe-protein-complexed states of the Fe protein. It describes the one-electron redox reactions of the Fe protein's [4Fe-4S] cluster, nucleotide exchange, and complex formation with and electron transfer to the MoFe protein. Here, Fe represents the Fe protein in its oxidized (ox) or one-electron reduced (red) states; MoFe represents the MoFe protein. Each turn of the cycle adds one electron to the MoFe protein-substrate complex. Because each turn of the Fe-protein cycle transfers only one electron, the MoFe protein-substrate complex is treated as going through a succession of increasingly reduced states until sufficient electrons (and accompanying protons) are accumulated to effect substrate reduction.

This model proposes that N_2 is bound to the active site only after three and up to four electrons have been accumulated within the MoFe protein. If only one of the three electrons can be accommodated by the FeMo-cofactor, which would then become EPR-silent, where do the other two electrons reside before N_2 binds? They most likely reside on a hydride that subsequently either becomes H_2 or is used to partially reduce N_2. Similarly, the four-electron-reduced MoFe protein would equate to an oxidized EPR-active FeMo-cofactor with two bound hydrides. In fact, this latter conclusion has been experimentally demonstrated with both hydrides proposed as bridges between Fe atoms on FeMo-cofactor. [68]

Of course, other substrates or inhibitors may be bound before three electrons have been accepted. For example, the CO complexes of Mo-nitrogenase (see-below) only appear after two electrons have arrived at the MoFe protein. Because they are EPR-active ($S=1/2$), both electrons must reside either on the CO ligands, maybe as formyl, or as a hydride. Rapid-freezing experiments, using Mo-nitrogenase turning over under a N_2, C_2H_2 or argon atmosphere, produced a new $S=3/2$ EPR-active enzyme form that was common to all three substrates. Time-course simulations of its appearance suggested a three-electron-reduced intermediate had been formed rather than a two (or four) electron-reduced form as might be predicted for an EPR-active oxidized form of the FeMo-cofactor. [69] So, even the early stages of substrate binding and reduction retain some aspects of mystery!

Why Is MgATP Needed?

The overall reduction of N_2 to yield two molecules of NH_3 is thermodynamically favorable. So, if MgATP binding and hydrolysis during nitrogenase catalysis is not a thermodynamic requirement, it must be for kinetic purposes. Most likely, MgATP hydrolysis serves to drive electron transfer towards substrate reduction and to ensure the irreversibility of the reaction by preventing the back flow of electrons to the Fe protein, a so-called "gating" mechanism. [43-44]

When MgATP binds to the Fe protein, the resulting conformational change allows the Fe protein to complex with the MoFe protein. A substantial decrease of ca. −200 mV in the redox potential of the Fe protein's [4Fe-4S] cluster also occurs and this might be due to limiting water accessibility to the cluster. Similarly on complex formation, the redox potential of the P cluster is also decreased but by only ca. -100 mV. So, complexation of the MgATP-bound Fe protein with the MoFe protein increases the driving force (by increasing the difference in redox potential of the donor and acceptor) for electron transfer from the Fe protein's [4Fe-4S] cluster to the P cluster of the MoFe protein. Complex formation, however, has no effect on the redox potential of the FeMo-cofactor. [70] In addition to promoting electron transfer, complex formation triggers MgATP hydrolysis, although it is not clear whether hydrolysis occurs shortly before, concomitantly with, or shortly after electron transfer or whether the timing varies depending on other factors. But it is clear that phosphate release, which is usually when energy transduction occurs in other systems, from the complex follows electron transfer and that phosphate release does *not* drive the dissociation of this complex into its component proteins. [71] The exchange of the bound MgADP for MgATP on the Fe protein causes the conformational change to relax and the Fe protein dissociates from the complex, thus preventing any back-flow of electrons to the Fe protein.

Complex dissociation is the rate-limiting step in nitrogenase catalysis, using dithionite as reductant. [65] In this way, multiple electrons are accumulated within the MoFe protein and its bound substrate.

Where Are the Binding Sites for Substrates and Inhibitors?

Because the substrates and inhibitors of nitrogenase are invariably small multiple-bonded molecules, like N_2 and CO, it has always been assumed that binding and any subsequent reduction occur at one or more metal atoms. However, direct evidence to support this assumption has been hard to come by. The major problem is that neither component protein alone binds either substrates or inhibitors. Both of the component proteins, plus reductant and MgATP, must be present for substrate binding, but then enzymatic turnover occurs immediately! If no added substrate is present, *e.g.*, under an argon atmosphere, then the enzyme turns over by reducing protons to H_2 gas.

Early circumstantial evidence for a role for the FeMo-cofactor in substrate binding came from mutant organisms and their variant nitrogenases. First, mutant strains, which are unable to biosynthesize the FeMo-cofactor, are also unable to catalyze nitrogen fixation. However, when isolated FeMoco is added to crude extracts of these mutants, the ability to fix N_2 is restored. Second, when citrate replaces homocitrate as the organic constituent of an altered FeMo-cofactor, it changes the reactivity. Third, amino-acid substitutions within the FeMo-cofactor's polypeptide environment produce variant MoFe proteins that have altered FeMo-cofactor-based spectroscopic properties and different catalytic activities. [19,25]

This situation is complicated by a variety of observations that indicate the existence of multiple binding sites for some substrates and inhibitors. For example, two C_2H_2-binding sites have been detected by detailed kinetic analyses, [72-75] both of which can be occupied in the presence of CO and so are distinct from at least one of the two CO-binding sites. [73] By the judicious use of combinations of substrates and inhibitors, the high affinity ($K_m \sim 0.1\%$) C_2H_2-binding site, called site 2, has been implicated with N_2 binding and reduction and, therefore, is the physiologically relevant site. [75] Furthermore, based on studies with a variant enzyme, [74] these two C_2H_2-binding sites were proposed in to be in close proximity to one another with both sites being able to bind CO. These observations raise two questions immediately. First, is the non-competitive inhibitory effect of CO on substrate reduction a result of its preferred binding at low p(CO) to the non-physiologically relevant C_2H_2-binding site 1 or to a third distinct site? Second, at high p(CO), does CO bind at the physiological relevant C_2H_2-binding site 2, where it can now be reduced to a variety of hydrocarbons as recently demonstrated? [34,76]

Theoretical calculations are now coming to grips with the physical size, the chemical nature, the total-spin state, and the oxidation states of the constituent metal atoms of the FeMo-cofactor during catalysis. Earlier calculations for N_2 binding tended to favor modes that bridge either two or four of its central Fe atoms. [77] All of the proposed metal-N_2 interactions resulted in a small N_2-binding energy and, therefore, a weak bond. Further, direct N_2 cleavage to metal-nitrides is unfavored, suggesting that protonation of bound N_2 must occur. But many of these calculations were performed before the discovery of the central light atom within the FeMo-cofactor. More recently, [78-79] this central light atom (initially assumed to be nitride, but now known to be carbide) has been included in the calculations. The major consequence is that all of the various combinations of either two or four of the six central Fe atoms are less able to accommodate bridging Fe-N_2-Fe interactions, so much so that N_2 binding at a Fe_4 face appears very much less likely than binding at either an Fe_2 edge or a single Fe atom. [80-81] Currently, the interaction of substrates and inhibitors with the FeMo-cofactor is under intense study and some combination of the centrally located Fe atoms appears to be the preferred site(s) for substrate and inhibitor binding, [82-83] although the Mo atom retains its proponents. [84]

The binding of substrates and inhibitors to Mo-nitrogenase only occurs under turnover conditions. The first real insights into where and how these small molecules bind to the protein came from studies using CO, which is a potent inhibitor of the reduction of all substrates, except the proton. Because it is not reduced to any significant extent while Mo-nitrogenase is catalyzing the production of H_2 from protons, its bound forms should be present in relatively high concentration, so making it a good probe. When wild-type Mo-nitrogenase turns over under CO, the $S=3/2$ EPR signal arising from the resting-state FeMo-cofactor within the MoFe protein disappears and one of two $S=1/2$ EPR signals appear (Figure 9). A rhombic signal appears at low CO concentrations (p(CO) <10 kPa), whereas an axial signal results at higher CO concentration (p(CO) >50 kPa). [72,85] In both instances, however, the $S=1/2$ EPR intensity accounts for only up to 50% of the total enzyme present, which indicates a substantial concentration of undetected EPR-silent enzyme-based species.

Using [13]CO and [57]FeMo-cofactor, electron nuclear double resonance (ENDOR) indicated that, at low p(CO), only one CO was bound in the rhombic-EPR species called lo-CO, most likely as a bridge between two Fe atoms of the FeMo-cofactor. At the higher p(CO), two CO molecules were detected in the axial-EPR species called hi-CO and both were suggested to be terminally bound, most likely to different Fe atoms. [86] Furthermore, the two $S=1/2$ EPR signals could be inter-converted by either increasing or decreasing the p(CO), which suggested that the single bridging CO present in lo-CO converts to a terminal CO in hi-CO. [85-87] A third CO-bound species, with a $S=5/2$ EPR signal and called hi(5)-CO, has also been detected under higher p(CO) and has been suggested to have two bridging CO molecules bound. [85]

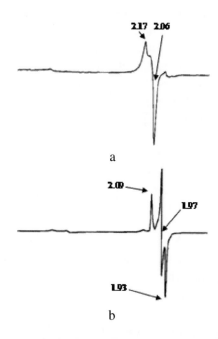

Figure 9. The X-band EPR spectra obtained at about 10 K after turnover of Mo-nitrogenase under a carbon monoxide (CO) atmosphere. (A) The "hi-CO" axial $S=1/2$ spectrum obtained under 100% (1 atm) CO that has two CO molecules bound to the FeMo-cofactor; (B) the "lo-CO" rhombic $S=1/2$ spectrum obtained under <10% (0.1 atm) CO that has only one CO molecule bound to the FeMo-cofactor. The relevant g values are noted on the spectra. [85] Adapted with permission, from L. M. Cameron and B. J. Hales, 1998, *Biochemistry*, **37**, 9449-9456. Copyright (1998) American Chemical Society.

More recent CO-photolysis-based studies of the Mo-nitrogenase-CO system, however, indicate that the first bound CO molecule (in lo-CO) retains its bridging mode even when the second terminal CO is bound to give hi-CO. Moreover, only the terminally bound CO can be photolyzed off the hi-CO species. Most importantly, these studies clearly show the presence of CO-bound species that do not correlate with any of the EPR/ENDOR-detectable species. [88] These results are consistent with stopped-flow FT-infrared studies of wild-type Mo-nitrogenase turning over under CO, where one intense CO vibration (plus two considerably weaker) from a terminally bound CO molecule was produced under high p(CO), whereas under low p(CO), an initially formed terminal-CO band rapidly decayed to a bridging-CO band. [89-90] Together, these studies suggest that the CO bound under low p(CO) is the primary agent of inhibition of catalyzed substrate reduction.

In sharp contrast to Mo-nitrogenase, no EPR-active species have been observed for V-nitrogenase turning over under a CO atmosphere, [91] even though CO binding must occur because CO is an effective reversible inhibitor of V-nitrogenase-catalyzed substrate reduction. [32] The resulting complexes await investigation by a suitable probe.

Similar EPR/ENDOR studies, under turnover conditions, have shown that C_2HR (where R = –H or –CH_2OH) and CN^- can each interact with the FeMo-cofactor of variant MoFe proteins, in particular, those where the α-valinyl-70 residues have been replaced by, for example, alaninyl and glycinyl. [92-93] The same freeze-trapping technique was then used to produce FeMo-factor-bound intermediates from turnover under labeled N_2 (Figure 10), methyldiazene, or hydrazine. [94-95]

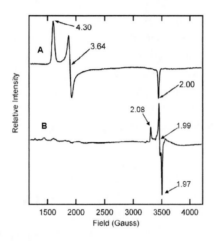

Figure 10. The X-band EPR spectrum obtained at about 5 K after turnover of Mo-nitrogenase under one atmosphere of N_2. The EPR spectrum of the dithionite-reduced resting state of the MoFe protein is shown (A) for comparison with the rhombic $S=1/2$ spectrum (B) that results from the freeze-trapping at 77 K of the MoFe protein within about 10 sec after initiating turnover. The relevant g values are noted on the spectra. [95] Adapted with permission, from B. M. Barney, D. Lukoyanov, R. Y. Igarashi, M. Laryukhin, T.-C. Yang, D. R. Dean, B. M. Hoffman and L. C. Seefeldt, 2009, *Biochemistry*, **48**, 9094-9102. Copyright (2009) American Chemical Society.

The chemical nature of most of the trapped intermediates was well characterized spectroscopically, although that of the N_2-based intermediate is the least clear. In addition to confirming the FeMo-cofactor as the site of substrate binding and reduction, these trapped intermediates represent a major step toward understanding the intimate details of N_2 binding and reduction. [83]

How Are Electrons and Protons Delivered?

The current dogma is that electrons are delivered by the Fe protein to the P cluster, then through the protein matrix to the FeMo-cofactor, and finally to bound substrate. However, two early spectroscopic observations are inconsistent with this proposed role for the P clusters. First, electrons transferred to the MoFe protein from the Fe protein are quickly relocated to the FeMo-cofactor as shown by the rapid loss of intensity of the S = 3/2 EPR signal. Second, no change occurs in the [57]Fe Mössbauer spectrum of the P clusters during nitrogenase turnover. [14]

In contrast, the structure of the Mo-nitrogenase complex shows the P cluster located midway between the [4Fe-4S] cluster of the Fe protein and the FeMo-cofactor. Although this arrangement could be coincidental, the redox-driven structural rearrangement of the P cluster supports an electron-transfer role. [53] Other support comes from substituting the β-cysteinyl-153 ligand of the P cluster with serinyl (see Figure 6). The resulting β-serinyl-153 MoFe protein has a normal FeMo-cofactor, gives normal substrate-reduction products, and interacts normally with the Fe protein. It cannot, however, match the wild-type's maximum rate of substrate reduction and so it is likely that intra-MoFe protein electron transfer has been compromised. [96] In addition, substitution of α-serinyl-188 by cysteine results in an additional $S=1/2$ signal in the EPR spectrum of the isolated variant MoFe proteins. This signal disappears, when Fe protein, MgATP and reductant are added, indicating that the P-cluster oxidation state could change during turnover. [97]

A more recent freeze-trapping Mössbauer study indicates that the P clusters do not obviously change their redox state during turnover under low electron-flux conditions, even though the FeMo-cofactor is receiving electrons. [98] So, under some conditions at least, electrons from the Fe protein may by-pass the P cluster and be directly transferred to the FeMo-cofactor. Possibly, more than one electron-transfer pathway may exist within the MoFe protein and, if so, the P clusters could have a N_2 reduction-specific role in catalysis and, only at the highest electron-flux rates, provide the assistance necessary to commit bound N_2 to the irreversible reduction pathway.

An alternative explanation of these observations, based on stopped-flow measurements, is that electron transfer from the [4Fe-4S] cluster of the Fe protein to the P cluster is so much faster than electron transfer from the P cluster to the FeMo-cofactor that the oxidized P cluster is never observable. [99] So, if the P cluster is involved in intra-MoFe protein electron transfer, is there only one or are there several electron-transfer pathways? And which substrates are serviced by which pathway?

Three likely proton-transfer routes have been identified. [92,100] The first is a water-filled interstitial channel that runs between the α- and β-subunits. It stretches from the surface of the MoFe protein to the pool of water molecules around the homocitrate-Mo end of the FeMo-cofactor. This water-filled channel could rapidly deliver protons to bound substrate and might also provide a pathway for substrates and products to diffuse into and out of their reduction site.

Extensive theoretical studies of the hydrogen-related chemistry of the FeMo-cofactor use this same interstitial channel to deliver protons. [80] Once electrons are delivered to the FeMo-cofactor, its sulfur atoms become more basic which, in turn, makes them attractive sites for protonation by water molecules in the interstitial pool. These protons are then reduced to hydrogen atoms that can then migrate across the FeMo-cofactor structure to other Fe and S atoms and become involved in substrate reduction. [81]

The first of the other two potential proton-relay systems involves the hydrogen bond between the imidazole side-chain of α-histidinyl-195 and a central μ_2-sulfide of the FeMo-cofactor. This strictly conserved residue is known to play an essential role in N_2 reduction. [54] This same imidazole ring forms a hydrogen bond through an intervening water molecule to the –OH group of α-tyrosinyl-281, which is close to the protein's surface and flanked by two potential proton-capturing histidines, α-histidinyl-196 and α-histidinyl-383. This relay system could provide protons as demanded by the redox state of the enzyme-substrate complex. The second of these potential proton relays is more complicated and involves a hydrogen-bonded series of three water molecules and three histidinyl residues, one of which (α-histidinyl-362) is on the surface and may capture protons for this relay. This path terminates in a different central bridging sulfide of FeMo-cofactor.

These proton-relay systems may play a role in substrate reduction but they probably cannot deliver the multiple protons required to complete substrate reduction. Proton delivery would require the relay to switch to an alternative hydrogen-bonding network as each proton is delivered and then realign itself to deliver the next proton. This operation would be much more difficult for the histidine residues than for the water molecules in the interstitial channel, suggesting that the interstitial channel may be the primary route of protons to be delivered to substrates.

STREPTOMYCES THERMOAUTOTROPHICUS NITROGENASE

The unique nitrogenase isolated from the thermophile, *Streptomyces thermoautotrophicus,* bears no similarity to the classical Mo-nitrogenase except that it consists of two component proteins, the larger of which contains Mo, Fe, and S. [13,101] This αβγ Mo-Fe-S-containing heterotrimer has the site for N_2 binding and reduction. The smaller component protein is not an Fe-S protein but rather a manganese-containing superoxide oxidoreductase that oxidizes superoxide ($O_2^{•-}$) to dioxygen (O_2) and transfers the electron to the larger heterotrimeric protein component. Moreover, the electron donor is a Mo-containing carbon monoxide dehydrogenase, which couples the oxidation of CO to the reduction of O_2 to produce the superoxide ($O_2^{•-}$).

The catalyzed eight-electron reduction of N_2 to two molecules of NH_3 includes the electron pair used to produce the accompanying one molecule of H_2 in a reaction that appears to be more efficient in its use of MgATP than that by the classical Mo-nitrogenase.

The *S. thermoautotrophicus* nitrogenase exhibits several functional features that are also unique. It is completely insensitive to the presence of O_2, CO and H_2, all of which are potent inhibitors of nitrogen fixation in the "classical" Mo-nitrogenase system, and it does not catalyze the reduction of acetylene to ethylene. It is so different that it may well constitute an independent invention during evolution. This unique enzyme and its unusual structural and mechanistic properties hold promise of new insights into the problem and possibly new ways of extending the benefits of biological nitrogen fixation in agricultural systems.

CONCLUSION

Although tremendous progress has been made, many mysteries remain concerning biological nitrogen fixation, especially with the intimate details of substrate binding and reduction. The requirements for N_2 binding and reduction are likely to be so stringent that they are satisfied by only a single site on the MoFe protein. However, many of the alternative more-easily-reduced substrates have more than one binding and reduction site. Sorting out these different sites and their possible relevance to the overall chemistry conducted by the enzyme should prove very insightful. Some variant Mo-nitrogenases have been constructed that bind but do not reduce N_2, which now acts as a reversible inhibitor of electron flow through the enzyme that is manifested in a decreased H_2-evolution rate. Wouldn't it be exciting if we constructed a variant nitrogenase where N_2 binds as an irreversible inhibitor of electron flux?

But other mechanistic challenges and questions remain too! These include the following inter-connected questions:

(i)   Are both component proteins and their complexation required for activity?
(ii) Is the Fe protein the obligate electron donor? and
(iii) Is MgATP hydrolysis required?

The answer to all three questions is "yes", when wild-type Mo-nitrogenase uses sodium dithionite as the reductant *in vitro*. Here, the Fe protein must be released from its complex with the MoFe protein before it can be re-reduced by dithionite and then must reform the catalytic complex to transfer the next electron to the MoFe protein. However, when reduced flavodoxin, a physiological reductant, is used *in vitro* (and maybe *in vivo*) to support substrate reduction, the MoFe protein/Fe protein complex remains associated. [102] Moreover, some variant Fe proteins (e.g., L127Δ) not only do not dissociate from the MoFe protein, but they allow intra-complex electron transfer without MgATP hydrolysis. [103] Furthermore, when a low-potential Eu(II)-based reductant is supplied, the variant β-histidinyl-98 MoFe protein catalyzes the reduction of hydrazine to ammonia without the Fe protein and MgATP. [104]

Another important result is the Mo-nitrogenase-catalyzed photo-reduction of both protons and acetylene during a light-driven process using eosin as the photo-sensitizer with NADH as the sacrificial electron donor. [105] Here, a non-dissociating 1:1 nitrogenase complex was suggested to catalyze a process that was more effective than the usual system with dithionite as electron donor, but still required MgATP.

Photo-reduction has since been taken one level further by using light and a surface-tethered ruthenium photo-sensitizer, which uses dithionite as the sacrificial electron donor. [106] In the absence of both Fe protein and MgATP, the photo-sensitized MoFe-protein catalyzed both proton and acetylene photo-reduction. The overall conclusion from these observations must be that neither Fe protein nor MgATP is absolutely essential for Mo-nitrogenase-catalyzed substrate reduction, which opens many possibilities for the future.

Finally, why do prokaryotes have the alternative nitrogenases, especially when it appears that there are few, if any, areas of the World where molybdenum concentrations are limiting? Do they serve some purpose other than nitrogen fixation? And will it be possible to apply what we learn about nitrogenase to either enhance the nitrogen-fixation capabilities of microorganisms or endow new organisms and plants with this ability or to develop new commercial nitrogen-fertilizer production systems? These questions await answers that can only come from insightful research progress.

On the applications side, the ever-increasing demand for food by the ever-increasing population has, so far, been met by intensive cultivation of the available arable land. The high-yielding plant varieties that have been bred to respond to this challenge require high application rates of commercial nitrogen fertilizer. Because much of this fixed nitrogen never reaches the crop plant, excessive amounts are often applied, which results in considerable losses (as ammonia and nitrogen oxides) either to the atmosphere, which can impact the health of our forests, or by leaching from soils to contaminate natural waterways and even drinking water supplies. But, even with its environmental and health risks and fossil-fuel demands, there is no doubt that agriculture productivity would decline significantly without the production and application of commercial nitrogen fertilizer. [9-11]

This is only a shorter-term solution to the problem of growing sufficient food, however, because already arable land is becoming limiting in many places. So, how do we maximize the benefits while minimizing the negative consequences of nitrogen fertilization? Long-term solutions to the global-food-supply problem must lie in other directions for providing fixed nitrogen. There are not many options and the most obvious choice is biological nitrogen fixation. With appropriate effort and support, biological nitrogen fixation could become a major factor in the delicate balance needed among environmental concerns and sufficient food production for the future.

REFERENCES

[1]   Smith, B. E.; Richards, R. L.; Newton, W. E., Eds. *Catalysts for Nitrogen Fixation*; Kluwer/Springer: Dordrecht, The Netherlands, 2004.

[2]   Klipp, W.; Masepohl, B.; Gallon, J. R.; Newton, W. E., Eds. *Genetics and Regulation of Nitrogen Fixation in Free-Living Bacteria*; Kluwer/Springer: Dordrecht, The Netherlands, 2004.

[3]   Palacios, R.; Newton, W. E., Eds. *Genomes and Genomics of Nitrogen–fixing Organisms*; Springer: Dordrecht, The Netherlands, 2005.

[4]   Werner, D.; Newton, W. E., Eds. *Nitrogen Fixation in Agriculture, Forestry, Ecology and the Environment*; Springer: Dordrecht, The Netherlands, 2005.

[5]   Elmerich, C.; Newton, W. E., Eds. *Associative and Endophytic Nitrogen-fixing Bacteria and Cyanobacterial Associations*: Springer: Dordrecht, The Netherlands, 2007.

[6]   Pawlowski, K.; Newton, W. E., Eds. *Nitrogen-fixing Actinorhizal Symbioses*; Springer: Dordrecht, The Netherlands, 2008.

[7]   Dilworth, M. J.; James, E. K.; Sprent, J. I.; Newton, W. E., Eds. *Nitrogen-fixing Leguminous Symbioses*: Springer: Dordrecht, The Netherlands, 2008.

[8]   Bothe, H.; Ferguson, S. J.; Newton, W. E., Eds. *Biology of the Nitrogen Cycle*; Elsevier: Amsterdam, The Netherlands, 2007.

[9]   Smil, V. *Enriching the Earth: Fritz Haber, Carl Bosch, and the Transformation of World Food Production*; M. I. T. Press: Cambridge, M. A., 2001.

[10]   Smil, V. In *Land, Shops and Kitchens: Technology and the Food Chain in Twentieth-Century Europe*; Scholliers, P., Van Molle, L., Sarasua, C., Eds.; Brepohls Publishers: Turnhout, 2005; pp. 110-119.

[11]   Leigh, G. J. *The World's Greatest Fix: A History of Nitrogen and Agriculture*; Oxford University Press: New York, NY, 2004.

[12]   Fani, R.; Gallo, R.; Lio, P. *J. Mol. Evol.* 2000, *51*, 1-11.

[13]   Ribbe, M.; Gadkari, D.; Meyer, O. *J. Biol. Chem.* 1997, 272, 26627-26633.

[14]   Newton, W. E. In *New Horizons in Nitrogen Fixation*; Palacios, R., Mora, J., Newton, W. E., Eds.; Kluwer Academic: Dordrecht, 1993; pp. 5-18.

[15] Pau, R. N. In *Advances in Inorganic Biochemistry*; Eichhorn, G. L., Marzilli, L. G., Eds.; P. T. R. Prentice Hall: N. J., 1994; Vol. 10, pp. 49-70.

[16] Emerich, D. W.; Burris, R. H., *J. Bacteriol.* 1978, 134, 936-943.

[17] Young, J. P. W. In ref. 3, pp. 221-241.

[18] Maritano, S.; Fairhurst, S. A.; Eady, R. R., *J. Biol. Inorg. Chem.* 2001, 6, 590-600.

[19] Scott, D. J.; May, H. D.; Newton, W. E.; Brigle, K. E.; Dean, D. R. *Nature* 1990, 343, 188-190.

[20] Wink, D. A.; MacLean, P. A.; Hickman, A. B.; Orme-Johnson, W. H. *Biochemistry* 1989, 28, 9407-9412.

[21] Orme-Johnson, W. H.; Hamilton, W. D.; Ljones, T.; Tso, M.-Y. W.; Burris, R. H.; Shah, V. K.; Brill, W. J. *Proc. Nat. Acad. Sci. US* 1972, 69, 3142-3145.

[22] Simpson, F. B.; Burris, R. H. *Science* 1984, 224, 1095-1097.

[23] Lowery, T. J.; Wilson, P. E.; Zhang, B.; Bunker, J.; Harrison, R. G.; Nyborg, A. C.; Thiriot, D.; Watt, G. D. *Proc. Natl. Acad. Sci. US* 2006, 103, 17131-17136.

[24] Newton, W. E.; Dilworth, M. J. In *Nitrogen Fixation: Methods and Protocols*; Ribbe, M. W., Ed.; Humana Press: New York, N. Y., 2011; pp. 105-127.

[25] Burgess, B. K.; Lowe, D. J. *Chem. Rev.* 1996, 96, 2983-3011.

[26] Eady, R. R.; Robson, R. L.; Richardson, T. H.; Miller, R. W.; Hawkins, M. *Biochem. J.* 1987, 244, 197-207.

[27] Blanchard, C. Z.; Hales, B. J. *Biochemistry* 1996, 36, 472-478.

[28] Lee, C. C.; Hu, Y.; Ribbe, M. *Proc. Natl. Acad. Sci. US* 2009, 106, 9209-9214.

[29] Schneider, K.; Gollan, U.; Dröttbroom, M.; Selsemeier-Voigt, S.; Müller, A. *Eur. J. Biochem.* 1997, 244, 789-800.

[30] Krahn, E.; Weiss, B. J. R.; Kröckel, M.; Groppe, J.; Henkel, G.; Cramer, S. P.; Trautwein, A. X.; Schneider, K.; Müller, A. *J. Biol. Inorg. Chem.* 2002, 7, 37-45.

[31] Dilworth, M. J.; Eady, R. R. *Biochem. J.* 1991, 277, 465-468.

[32] Dilworth, M. J.; Eady, R. R.; Eldridge, M. *Biochem. J.* 1988, 249, 745-751.

[33] Lee, C. C.; Hu, Y.; Ribbe, M. *Science* 2010, 329, 642.

[34] Hu, Y.; Lee, C. C.; Ribbe, M. *Science* 2011, 333, 753-755.

[35] Yang, Z. Y.; Dean, D. R.; Seefeldt, L. C. *J. Biol. Chem.* 2011, 286, 19417-19421.

[36] Kelly, M. *Biochem. J.* 1968, 107, 1-6.

[37] Ravi, N.; Moore, V.; Lloyd, S.; Hales, B. J.; Huynh, B. H. *J. Biol. Chem.* 1994, 269, 20920-20924.

[38] George, G. N.; Coyle, C. L.; Hales, B. J.; Cramer, S. P. *J. Am. Chem. Soc.* 1988, 110, 4057-4059.

[39] Chen, J.; Christiansen, J.; Tittsworth, R. C.; Hales, B. J.; George, S. J.; Coucouvanis, D.; Cramer, S. P. *J. Am. Chem. Soc.* 1993, 115, 5509-5515.

[40] Georgiadis, M. M.; Komiya, H.; Chakrabarti, P.; Woo, D.; Kornuc, J. J.; Rees, D. C. *Science* 1992 257, 1653-1659.

[41] Jang, S. B.; Seefeldt, L. C.; Peters, J. W. *Biochemistry* 2000, 39, 14745-14752.

[42] Schindelin, H.; Kisker, C.; Schlessman, J. L.; Howard, J. B.; Rees, D. C. *Nature* 1997, 387, 370-376.

[43] Seefeldt, L. C.; Dean, D. R. *Acc. Chem. Res.* 1997, 30, 260-266.

[44] Howard, J. B.; Rees, D. C. *Chem. Rev.* 1996, 96, 2965-2982.

[45] Kim, C.; Rees, D. C. *Nature*, 1992, 360, 553-560.

[46] Mayer, S. M.; Lawson, D. M.; Gormal, C. A.; Roe, S. M.; Smith, B. E. *J. Mol. Biol.* 1999, 292, 871-891.

[47] Shah, V. K.; Brill, W. J. *Proc. Natl. Acad. Sci. US* 1977, 74, 3249-3253.

[48] Kim, C.; Rees, D. C. *Science* 1992, 257, 1677-1682.

[49] Chan, M. K.; Kim, J.; Rees, D. C. *Science* 1993, 260, 792-794.

[50] Einsle, O.; Tezcan, A.; Andrade, S. L. A.; Schmid, B.; Yoshida, M.; Howard, J. B.; Rees, D. C. *Science* 2002, 297, 1696-1700.

[51] Spatzel, T.; Aksoyoglu, M.; Zhang, L.; Andrade, S. L. A.; Schleicher, E.; Weber, S.; Rees, D. C.; Einsle, O. *Science* 2011, 334, 940.

[52] Wiig, J. A.; Hu, Y.; Lee, C. C.; Ribbe, M. W. *Science* 2012, 337, 1672-1675.

[53] Peters, J. W.; Stowell, M. H. B.; Soltis, S. M.; Finnegan, M. G.; Johnson, M. K.; Rees, D. C. *Biochemistry* 1997, 36, 1181-1187.

[54] Dilworth, M. J.; Fisher, K.; Kim, C.-H.; Newton, W. E. *Biochemistry* 1998, 37, 17495-17505.

[55] Sørlie, M.; Christiansen, J.; Lemon, B. J.; Peters, J. W.; Dean, D. R.; Hales, B. J. *Biochemistry* 2001, 40, 1540-1549.

[56] Sarma, R.; Barney, B. M.; Keable, S.; Dean, D. R.; Seefeldt, L. C.; Peters, J. W. *J. Inorg. Biochem.* 2010, 104, 385-389.

[57] Mayer, S. M.; Gormal, C. A.; Smith, B. E.; Lawson, D. M. *J. Biol. Chem.* 2002, 277, 35263-35266.

[58] Schmid, B.; Ribbe, M. W.; Einsle, O.; Yoshida, M.; Thomas, L. M.; Dean, D. R.; Rees, D. C.; Burgess, B. K. *Science* 2002, 296, 352-356.

[59] Grossman J. G.; Hasnain, S. S.; Yousafzai, F. K.; Smith, B. E.; Eady, R. R.; Schindelin, H.; Kisker, C.; Howard, J. B.; Tsuruta, H.; Muller, J.; Rees, D. C. *Acta Cryst.* 1999, D55, 727-728.

[60] Pope, M. R.; Murrell, S. A.; Ludden, P. W. *Proc. Natl. Acad. Sci. US* 1985, 82, 3173-3177.

[61] Chiu, H.-J.; Peters, J. W.; Lanzilotta, W. N.; Ryle, M. J.; Seefeldt, L. C.; Howard, J. B.; Rees, D. C. *Biochemistry* 2001, 40, 641-650.

[62] Schmid, B.; Einsle, O.; Chiu, H.-J.; Willing, A.; Yoshida, M.; Howard, J. B.; Rees, D. C. *Biochemistry* 2002, 41, 15557-15565.

[63] Erickson, J. A.; Nyborg, A. C.; Johnson, J. L.; Truscott, S. M.; Gunn, A.; Nordmeyer, F. R.; Watt, G. D. *Biochemistry* 1999, 38, 14279-14285.

[64] Doan, P. E.; Telser, J.; Barney, B. M.; Igarashi, R. Y.; Dean, D. R.; Seefeldt, L. C.; Hoffman, B. M. *J. Am. Chem. Soc.* 2011, 133, 17329-17340.

[65] Lowe, D. J.; Thorneley, R. N. F. *Biochem. J.* 1984, 224, 877-909.

[66] Clarke, T. A.; Maritano, S.; Eady, R. R. *Biochemistry* 2000, 39, 11434-11440.

[67] Johnson, J. L.; Nyborg, A. C.; Wilson, P. E.; Tolley, A. M.; Nordmeyer, F. R.; Watt, G. D. *Biochim. Biophys. Acta* 2000, 1543, 24-46.

[68] Igarashi, R. Y.; Laryukhin, M.; Dos Santos, P. C.; Lee, H.-I.; Dean, D. R.; Seefeldt, L. C.; Hoffman, B. M. *J. Am. Chem. Soc.* 2005, 127, 6231-6241.

[69] Fisher, K.; Newton, W. E.; Lowe, D. J. *Biochemistry* 2001, 40, 3333-3339.

[70] Lanzilotta, W. N.; Seefeldt, L. C. *Biochemistry* 1997, 36, 12976-12983.

[71] Lowe, D. J.; Ashby, G. A.; Brune, M.; Knights, H.; Webb, M. R.; Thorneley, R. N. F. In *Nitrogen Fixation: Fundamentals and Applications*; Tikhonoich, I. A., Provorov, N.

A., Romanov, V. I., Newton, W. E., Eds.; Kluwer Academic: Dordrecht, 1995; pp. 103-108.

[72] Davis, L. C.; Henzl, M. T.; Burris, R. H.; Orme-Johnson, W. H. *Biochemistry* 1979, 18, 4860-4869.

[73] Shen, J.; Dean, D. R.; Newton, W. E. *Biochemistry* 1997, 36, 4884-4894.

[74] Christiansen, J.; Seefeldt, L. C.; Dean, D. R. *J. Biol. Chem.* 2000, 275, 36104-36107.

[75] Han, J.; Newton, W. E. *Biochemistry* 2004, 43, 2947-29556.

[76] Hu, Y.; Lee, C. C.; Ribbe, M. *Dalton Trans.* 2012, 41, 1118-1127.

[77] Dance, I. *Aust. J. Chem.* 1994, 47, 979-990.

[78] Dance, I. *Chem. Commun.* 2003, 324-325.

[79] Lovell, T.; Liu, T.; Case, D. A.; Noodleman, L. *J. Am. Chem. Soc.* 2003, 125, 8377-8383.

[80] Dance, I. *J. Am. Chem. Soc.* 2005, 127, 10925-10942.

[81] Dance, I. *Biochemistry* 2006, 45, 6328-6340.

[82] Dance, I. *Dalton Trans.* 2011, 40, 6480-6489.

[83] Hoffman, B. M.; Dean, D. R.; Seefeldt, L. C. *Acc. Chem. Res.* 2009, 42, 609-619.

[84] Durrant, M. *Biochemistry* 2002, 41, 13934-13945.

[85] Cameron, L. M.; Hales, B. J. *Biochemistry* 1998, 37, 9449-9456.

[86] Lee, H.-I.; Cameron, L. M.; Hales, B. J.; Hoffman, B. M. *J. Am. Chem. Soc.* 1997, 119, 10121-10126.

[87] Maskos, Z.; Hales, B. J. *J. Inorg. Biochem.* 2003, 93, 11-17.

[88] Yan, L.; Dapper, C. H.; George, S. J.; Wang, H.; Mitra, D.; Dong, W.; Newton, W. E.; Cramer, S. P. *Eur. J. Inorg. Chem.* 2011, 2064-2074.

[89] George, S. J.; Ashby, G. A.; Wharton, C. W.; Thorneley, R. N. F. *J. Am. Chem. Soc.* 1997, 119, 6450-6451.

[90] Thorneley, R. N. F.; Ashby, G. A.; George, S. J. In *Nitrogen Fixation: From Molecules to Crop Productivity*; Pedrosa, F. O., Hungria, M., Yates, M. G., Newton, W. E., Eds.; Kluwer Academic: Dordrecht, 2000; pp. 39-40.

[91] Moore, V. G.; Tittsworth, R. C.; Hales, B. J. *J. Am. Chem. Soc.* 1994, 116, 12101-12102.

[92] Igarashi, R. Y.; Seefeldt, L. C. *Crit. Rev. Biochem. Mol. Biol.* 2003, 38, 351-384.

[93] Dos Santos, P. C.; Igarashi, R. Y.; Lee, H.-I.; Hoffman, B. M.; Seefeldt, L. C.; Dean, D. R. *Acc. Chem. Res.* 2005, 38, 208-214.

[94] Barney, B. M.; Yang, T.-C.; Igarashi, R. Y.; Dos Santos, P. C.; Laryukhin, M.; Lee, H.-I.; Hoffman, B. M.; Dean, D. R.; Seefeldt, L. C. *J. Am. Chem. Soc.* 2005, 127, 14960-14961.

[95] Barney, B. M.; Lukoyanov, D.; Igarashi, R. Y.; Laryukhin, M.; Yang, T.-C.; Dean, D. R.; Hoffman, B. M.; Seefeldt, L. C. *Biochemistry* 2009, 48, 9094-9102.

[96] May, H. D.; Dean, D. R.; Newton, W. E. *Biochem. J.* 1991, 277, 457-464.

[97] Chan, J. M.; Christiansen, J.; Dean, D. R.; Seefeldt, L. C. *Biochemistry* 1999, 38, 5779-5785.

[98] Fisher, K.; Lowe, D. J.; Tavares, P.; Pereira, A. S.; Huynh, B.-H.; Edmondson, D.; Newton, W. E. *J. Inorg. Biochem.* 2007, 101, 1649-1656.

[99] Danyal, K.; Dean, D. R.; Hoffman, B. M.; Seefeldt, L. C. *Biochemistry* 2011, 50, 9255-9263.

[100] Durrant, M. C. *Biochem. J.* 2001, 355, 569-576.

[101] Gadkari, D. In ref. 1, pp. 309-332.

[102] Duyvis, M. G.; Wassink, H.; Haaker, H. *Biochemistry* 1998, 37, 17345-17354.

[103] Lanzilotta, W. N.; Fisher, K.; Seefeldt, L. C. *Biochemistry* 1996, 35, 7188-7196.

[104] Danyal, K.; Inglet, B. S.; Vincent, K. A.; Barney, B. M.; Hoffman, B. M.; Armstrong, F. A.; Dean, D. R.; Seefeldt, L. C. *J. Am. Chem. Soc.* 2010, 132, 13197-13199.

[105] Druzhinin, S. Yu.; Syrtsova, L. A.; Uzenskaja, A. M.; Likhtenstein, G. I. *Biochem. J.* 1993, 290, 627-631.

[106] Roth, L. E.; Nguyen, J. C.; Tezcan, F. A. *J. Am. Chem. Soc.* 2010, 132, 13672-13974.

In: Molybdenum
Editor: Alvin A. Holder
ISBN: 978-1-62417-272-4
© 2013 Nova Science Publishers, Inc.

Chapter 11

THE MOLYBDENUM HYDROXYLASES: XANTHINE OXIDASE AND RELATED ENZYMES

Russ Hille
Department of Biochemistry, University of California, Riverside, CA, US

ABSTRACT

An account is provided of our present understanding of the xanthine oxidase family of enzymes, focusing on the relationship of structure to function in this diverse and broadly distributed family of enzymes. More recent studies of xanthine- and aldehyde-oxidizing enzymes are considered first, and the structures and function of several other crystallographically characterized members of this family of enzymes are subsequently compared and contrasted.

INTRODUCTION

In 1974, Ed Stiefel moved from The Department of Chemistry at SUNY Stony Brook to the Charles F. Kettering Research Laboratory in Yellow Springs, Ohio, intent upon pursuing his interests at the interface of inorganic chemistry and biology. At that time, the Laboratory had begun a research emphasis in bioinorganic chemistry including, among other things, the molybdenum- and iron-containing nitrogenase. That same year, I began my graduate studies at Rice University, studying the O_2 transporter hemoglobin under the direction of John S. Olson. In the adjacent laboratory, Graham Palmer was pursuing mechanistic studies of several metalloenzymes, including cytochrome bc_1, cytochrome c oxidase from the mitochondrial respiratory chain and the molybdenum-containing enzyme xanthine oxidase. Students in the Palmer laboratory, especially Mike Davis and Arturo Porras, introduced me to the intricacies of this last enzyme at a critical time when my own interests in enzymology and metallobiochemistry were forming.

Ed's and my paths would not cross for another seven years, at the 1982 International Conference on the Chemistry and Uses of Molybdenum organized by the Climax Molybdenum Company in Golden, CO. At that point I was studying xanthine oxidase myself as a post-doctoral scholar in the laboratory of Vincent Massey at the University of Michigan. The meeting was one of the first I attended and was memorable for two reasons. First, it underscored to me just how primitive our understanding of the active site structures and reaction mechanisms of molybdenum-containing enzymes really was at the time (I recall several talks at the meeting about μ-oxo bridged Mo(V) dimers, with claims of biological relevance based on there being two equivalents of molybdenum in the enzyme... this despite it being known even then that the enzyme was a dimer with two independent mononuclear molybdenum centers). The second thing was the incredible enthusiasm of the group, the keen interest in biological aspects of molybdenum by the chemists and the sense that new experimental approaches would provide key insight into understanding both the structures of enzyme active sites and the chemical course of the reactions catalyzed. Ed was an important part of this enthusiasm and interest, and reported at the meeting a comparison of model compounds and the enzymes xanthine dehydrogenase, sulfite oxidase and nitrogenase using the quite new method of X-ray absorption spectroscopy (XAS)[1]. This work, done in collaboration with Keith Hodgson at Stanford, showed that the molybdenum coordination spheres of both sulfite oxidase and xanthine dehydrogenase were dominated by thiolate and terminal oxo ligands[2,3]. Subsequent XAS work would demonstrate that one important distinction between the active sites of these two enzymes was the replacement of one of two Mo=O groups in the metal's coordination sphere with a catalytically essential Mo=S[4,5]. From this point on, things really began to get interesting.

In 1982, there were precisely five known molybdenum-containing enzymes: xanthine oxidase/dehydrogenase from various sources, the closely related aldehyde oxidase from vertebrates, sulfite oxidase (also from vertebrates), the plant (and algal) assimilatory nitrate oxidase and of course nitrogenase. Today there are nearly 100 enzymes known to contain molybdenum, with those possessing mononuclear centers in their active sites falling into three distinct and non-overlapping families: those epitomized by the enzymes xanthine oxidase, sulfite oxidase and DMSO reductase[6]. At present, there are some 50 known unique members of the xanthine oxidase family alone, enzymes that usually (but not always, as will be seen) catalyze the hydroxylation of a carbon center, and which usually (but again not always) have mononuclear molybdenum centers in their active sites. The range of substrates that are acted upon by these enzymes is considerable, including not only a wide range of aromatic heterocyles but also aldehydes and even carbon monoxide.

What follows is an account of our present understanding of this extended family of enzymes, focusing on the relationship of structure to function in those enzymes for which a crystal structure is known. For the "canonical" xanthine- and aldehyde-utilizing enzymes, the focus is on progress in the past decade, and the reader is referred to other reviews for a consideration of earlier work[6,7]. Included are several other enzymes that, while clearly *bona fide* members of the xanthine oxidase family of enzymes on the basis of their amino acid sequences and overall protein structures, are non-canonical either in the structure of the molybdenum center in their active sites, or in the reaction that they catalyze. Ed Stiefel, himself a bit of an iconoclast, was delighted with the discoveries of these latter enzymes.

XANTHINE OXIDASE AND DEHYDROGENASE

Certainly the best understood of the enzymes considered here is that known historically as xanthine oxidase. The enzyme from mammalian sources is more properly referred to as xanthine oxidoreductase, as it exists in two distinct forms: one an oxidase capable of utilizing only O_2 as oxidizing substrate, and the other a dehydrogenase that utilizes NAD^+ as oxidant (although it retains the ability to react with O_2). The X-ray crystal structures of both oxidase and dehydrogenase forms of the bovine enzyme have been determined[8], it being shown that the loss of reactivity toward NAD^+ in the oxidase form is due to the rearrangement of a peptide loop into a position that obstructs the NAD^+ binding site. The protein is expressed under normal conditions as the dehydrogenase, but various physiological stresses can induce conversion to the oxidase form, either by (reversible) oxidation of cysteines to cystine, or by (irreversible) proteolytic nicking[9]. The so-called dehydrogenase-to-oxidase (or D/O) conversion has been proposed to play a role in the tissue damage observed upon reperfusion of ischemic tissue (in, *e.g.*, stroke or cardiac infarct), but the precise role played by the enzyme in this pathophysiological process remains undetermined[10,11]. Only the enzyme from mammalian sources is predisposed to this D/O conversion – in other organisms, ranging from chicken to bacteria such as *Rhodobacter capsulatus*, the enzyme exists strictly as a dehydrogenase.

As shown in Figure 1, the active site of the bovine enzyme (like that of the *D. gigas* aldehyde:ferredoxin oxidoreductase whose crystal had been determined previously[12,13]) consists of an $LMo^{VI}OS(OH)$ core, where L is a pyranopterin cofactor (also called molybdopterin in the literature) coordinated to the molybdenum via an enedithiolate side chain. The coordination geometry is square-pyramidal, with the Mo=O occupying the apical position[14,15]. The reaction mechanism whereby xanthine is oxidized to uric acid is now generally understood to involve the base-assisted nucleophilic attack of the equatorial Mo-OH, which projects toward the substrate binding site in the crystal structure, on the C-8 position that is to become hydroxylated; subsequent (or concomitant) hydride transfer to the Mo=S yields formal reduction of the molybdenum center (Figure 1). The key $LMo^{IV}O(SH)(OR)$ intermediate thus generated (with OR representing product urate coordinated to the molybdenum via the catalytically introduced oxygen) breaks down by displacement of product by HO^- from the molybdenum coordination sphere and oxidation of the molybdenum center in sequential one-electron steps, with the specific sequence of events dependent upon the reaction conditions and specific substrate used. When oxidation precedes product dissociation, a paramagnetic $LMo^{V}OS(OR)$ species forms that gives rise to the long-studied "very rapid" EPR signal (for a review, see[16]). This mechanism is supported by: (1) the observed pH-dependence of both the steady-state parameter k_{cat}/K_m and the rapid-reaction parameter k_{red}/K_d (both obtained from the substrate concentration dependence of the steady-state v_{obs}, or k_{obs} from the reduction of enzyme by substrate under anaerobic conditions), which indicates that the reaction requires an active site base[17]; (2) the observation that while the oxygen incorporated into product is ultimately derived from solvent[18], there is a catalytically labile oxygen site on the enzyme that is the proximal donor of oxygen to substrate[19] and that this catalytically labile oxygen was the equatorial Mo-OH of the active site[20]; and (3) the ENDOR[21] and X-ray crystallographic evidence[22] that product in the "very rapid" species was bound to molybdenum in a simple end-on fashion.

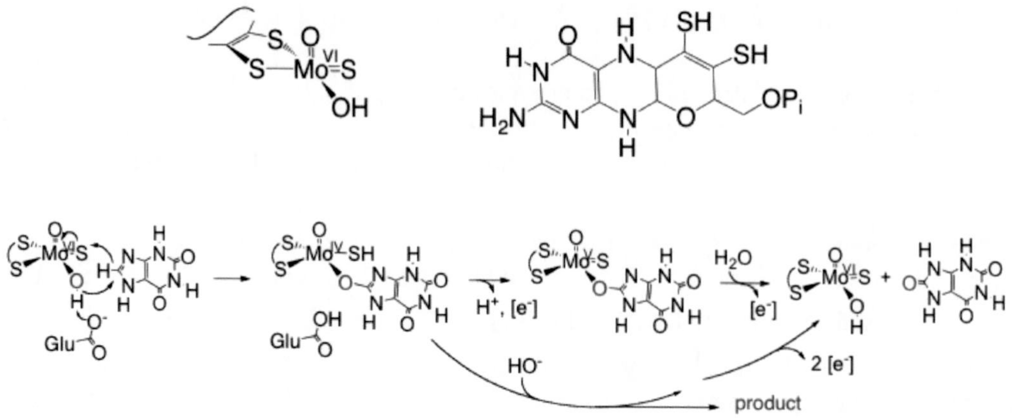

Figure 1. The active site of bovine xanthine oxidoreductase. *Top*, a schematic of the ligand coordination geometry of the molybdenum center and the structure of the bidentate pyranopterin ligand to the molybdenum. *Bottom*, the reaction mechanism of xanthine oxidase as described in the text, with Glu 1261/730 acting as a general base to initiate catalysis.

The roles of several highly conserved active site residues have been examined by site-directed mutagenesis studies of the *R. capsulatus* xanthine dehydrogenase, which bears strong structural homology to the bovine enzyme, and has a virtually identical active site[23]. These include Glu 730 (equivalent to Glu 1261 in the bovine enzyme), Glu 232 (Glu 802), Gln 197 (Gln 767) and Arg 310 (Arg 880), as shown in Figure 2. The substrate binding site is further comprised of Phe 344 and 459 (Phe 914 and 1009 in the bovine enzyme), which constrain substrate to a plane parallel to the apical Mo=O bond. With the molybdenum center oriented as shown in Figure 2, Glu 232/802 sits above substrate, Glu 730/1261 below it, within hydrogen-bonding distance of the Mo-OH, and Arg 310/880 on the opposite side of the substrate binding site from the molybdenum center. Gln 197/767 does not interact with substrate, but sits above the molybdenum center at a distance appropriate for hydrogen-bonding to the apical Mo=O. Mutation of Glu 730 in the *R. capsulatus* enzyme to Ala reduces the limiting rate constant for reduction by xanthine by at least seven orders of magnitude[24], corresponding to at least 10 kcal/mol of compromised transition state stabilization: while wild-type enzyme is reduced to completion within 30 ms at 100 μM xanthine (pH 7.8, 25 °C), the E730A mutant is not perceptibly reduced by substrate in an overnight anaerobic incubation. That Glu 730 in the *R. capsulatus* enzyme is functioning specifically as a base in initiating catalysis is supported by the observation that at pH 10 (where XAS evidence suggests the Mo-OH spontaneously deprotonates[25]). Furthermore, the E730A mutant does become reduced slowly by substrate, albeit on a tens of minutes time scale (Ibdah and Hille, unpublished).

Mutation of Glu 232 to Ala results in a more modest twelve-fold decrease in k_{red} in reductive half-reaction studies, as well as a twelve-fold increase in $K_d{}^{24}$. Assuming there is no change in rate-limiting step (but see below), these results indicate that approximately half of the ~3 kcal/mol in free energy associated with the interaction of Glu 232 with substrate is used to stabilize the transition state and accelerate reaction rate, with the remainder contributing to substrate affinity. Mutation of Gln 197 to Ala has a similarly modest seven-fold decrease in k_{red}, and as expected the Q197A mutant has the same 34 μM K_d as wild-type enzyme[24]. Given that this residue interacts directly with the molybdenum center, its mutation presumably modulates the intrinsic reactivity of the molybdenum center via its hydrogen bond to the apical Mo=O group.

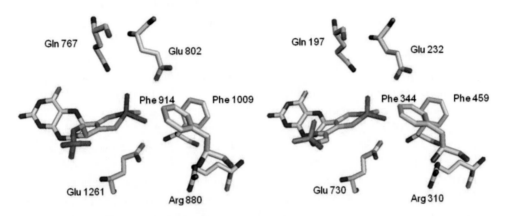

Figure 2. The X-ray crystal structures of the active sites for bovine xanthine dehydrogenase (PDB file 1FO4, ref. [8]; *left*) and *R. capsulatus* xanthine dehydrogenase (PDB 1JRO, ref. [23]; *right*). Conserved amino acid residues thought to be important in catalysis are indicated, illustrating the fundamental similarity of the two active sites.

Mutation of Arg 310 to the approximately isosteric Met is interesting. This residue is positioned on the opposite side of the substrate binding site from the molybdenum center, and is some 8 Å from the Mo-OH oxygen and the site of the hydroxylation chemistry. One might have expected the principal effect of the mutation to be compromised affinity for substrate, but instead it is a 10^4-fold decrease in k_{red} with xanthine as substrate[26]. The corresponding mutation in rat xanthine dehydrogenase leads to at least a 100-fold decrease in the steady-state V_{max}[27]. The interaction of Arg 310 with substrate thus provides approximately 5.5 kcal/mol in transition state stabilization, and the question arises as to how this is accomplished given the relatively remote position of the residue. An important clue is provided by an examination of the reactivity of several other purine substrates, all hydroxylated at the C-8 position, with the wild-type and R310M mutant. These substrates fall into two groups: a first consisting of good substrates that react rapidly with wild-type enzyme and which are significantly affected by mutation of Arg 310, and a second consisting of poor substrates for the wild-type enzyme but which are only negligibly affected by the mutation[26]. These results have been interpreted as reflecting two alternate orientations for substrate bound in the active site, one "right side up" with C6=O (or C6=S) of substrate positioned adjacent to Arg 310 so that negative charge accumulating on the heterocycle in the course of nucleophilic attack can be stabilized by the positive charge of the quanidinium group, and the other "upside down" such that Arg 310 is unable to make such a stabilizing interaction. What distinguishes good substrates from poor ones then is their orientation in the active site (see below). Poor substrates bind in such a way that they cannot make use of Arg 310 (thus accounting for their low reactivity), but are therefore insensitive to the mutation.

The effect of the above mutations in all likelihood underestimates the actual effect on the chemical step of the reaction, since with wild-type enzyme the rate-limiting step in the reductive half-reaction (and in overall catalysis) is thought to be product release rather than the chemical step of the reaction (*i.e.*, formation of the $LMo^{IV}O(SH)(OR)$ intermediate). In the case of the bovine and chicken enzymes, it has been shown that the chemical step of the reaction is some 75-fold faster than product release[28]. Making the (likely) assumption that the chemical step has become rate-limiting in the E730A, R310M and E232A mutants, one must correct the observed effect of a given mutation on the kinetics of enzyme reduction for an additional two orders of magnitude (and ~2.8 kcal/mol in transition state stabilization). The precise extent to which product release is rate-limiting in the *R. capsulatus* enzyme remains to be determined.

Several crystal structures have subsequently been reported of the bovine enzyme with various substrates bound in the active site that have substantiated the above suggestion that substrate orientation is important to catalysis and the specific catalytic roles proposed for Glu 232/802 and Arg 310/880. In the structure of the enzyme with 2-hydroxy-6-methylpurine (a poor substrate) discussed above, the purine is bound in the "upside down" orientation. By contrast, the complex of enzyme that has been inactivated by reaction with cyanide (thus removing the catalytically essential Mo=S group[29]) with xanthine (a good substrate) shows the purine oriented "right side up" in both the bovine[30] and *R. capsulatus*[31] enzymes, as is lumazine (the pterin homolog to xanthine)[30]. The representative structures of enzyme in complex with xanthine and 2-hydroxy-6-methylpurine are shown in Figure 3.

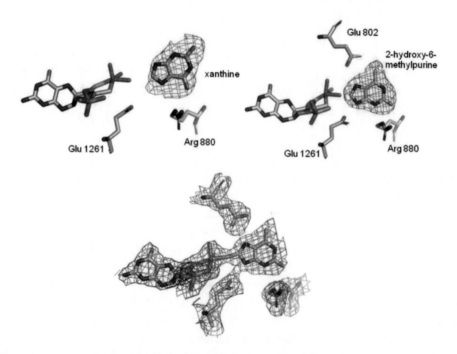

Figure 3. *Top left,* the 2.6Å-resolution structure of xanthine complexed to desulfo xanthine oxidase (PDB 3EUB, ref. [30]). The F_0-F_c map was contoured to 3σ and shows the clear asymmetry of the electron density attributable to the bound xanthine, making assignment of orientation unambiguous. *Top right,* The 2.3Å-resolution structure of 2-hydroxy-6-methylpurine complexed to the functional enzyme (PDB 3B9J, ref. [22]). The F_0-F_c map was contoured to 2.5σ and again shows clear asymmetry allowing unambiguous assignment of substrate orientation. *Bottom,* the structure of the 2-hydroxy-6-methylpurine complex with the 2F_0-F_c electron density map contoured at 1.0σ. Note the bridging electron density between the molybdenum and heterocycle, reflecting the predicted Mo-O-R structure of the initial catalytic intermediate of the reaction.

The above proposal regarding the role of substrate orientation has recently been called into question, based in part on the argument that at the resolutions reported, 1.8-2.4 Å (2.6-3.4 Å in the case of the *R. capsulatus* enzyme), it is impossible to definitively assign substrate orientation[32]. This criticism ignores the fact that at such resolutions it is generally possible to distinguish specific amino acid residues from one another, and in fact crystal structures reported at such resolutions have on occasion corrected mistakes in amino acid sequences inferred from incorrect gene sequences. At these resolutions it is frequently possible to distinguish between, say, leucine and isoleucine at a given position in the polypeptide chain. The question is not simply the resolution of the crystal structure, but also the inherent degree of asymmetry in the electron density attributable to the structure of interest. The degree of asymmetry evident in the electron density attributable to bound xanthine as illustrated in Figure 3 (*left*) is sufficient to clearly indicate a single preferred orientation for xanthine.

Further complicating the issue of substrate orientation is a report by Nishino and coworkers of a 1.1 Å resolution structure of a D428A mutant of rat xanthine dehydrogenase in complex with uric acid, but in an apo form lacking the molybdenum center altogether[33]. The uric acid is found in what would be considered the "upside down" orientation in the context of the above discussion, with the C-2 carbonyl of the bound uric acid oriented toward Arg 803 (in the rat protein). This is virtually the identical position relative to the polypeptide as the inhibitor alloxanthine complexed with reduced enzyme[31], an inhibitor that directly coordinates the molybdenum via its N2 ring nitrogen (a position equivalent to the C-8 of purines), displacing the equatorial Mo-OH. In order to accommodate the Mo-OH, however, substrate must necessarily lie further away from the molybdenum by at least the 2.0 Å of the Mo-O bond. This being the case, it is likely that the C-6 rather than C-2 carbonyl group is more appropriately positioned to interact with the active site arginine. The relative positions of the several heterocycles for which crystal structures exist are shown in Figure 4.

The issue of substrate orientation in the active site is important in understanding the catalytic roles of different active site residues. With xanthine oriented as shown in Figure 3, Glu 802 is positioned properly to facilitate tautomerization of the heterocycle in the course of nucleophilic attack, facilitating proton translocation from N3 to N7. This tautomerization has been proposed to play an important role in catalysis, and constitute the basis for transition state stabilization by this residue[34]. This can be the case, however, only if xanthine is oriented as shown in Figure 3. If it instead binds in the opposite orientation then Glu 802 must be involved in transition state stabilization in some other, unspecified way. Similarly for Arg 880, if it interacts with the carbonyl at C-2 rather than C-6 it cannot be involved in stabilization of negative charge at the latter position of substrate. Again, no alternative role for transition state stabilization for Arg 880 has been proposed. Clearly, additional work is required to definitively establish the way in which substrate orients in the active site, and how the amino acid residues interacting with it contribute to transition state stabilization and the rate acceleration that ensues.

Another crystal structure has recently been reported of urate complexed with enzyme that had been pre-reduced by Ti(II)•citrate. In this structure, there is finite electron density intervening between the heterocycle and molybdenum, indicating that urate has displaced the equatorial Mo-OH ligand of the molybdenum coordination sphere[33]. Interestingly, the structure strongly suggests that the C-8 carbon is sp^3 rather than sp^2 hybridized, implying that the structure represents a position along the reaction coordinate subsequent to nucleophilic attack and formation of the C-O bond of product, but prior to hydride transfer (which cannot occur in the crystal as prepared, since the molybdenum center is already reduced). The stability of this species suggests that nucleophilic attack and hydride transfer occur sequentially rather than concomitantly in leading to the LMo^{IV}O(SH)(OR) intermediate (but see below).

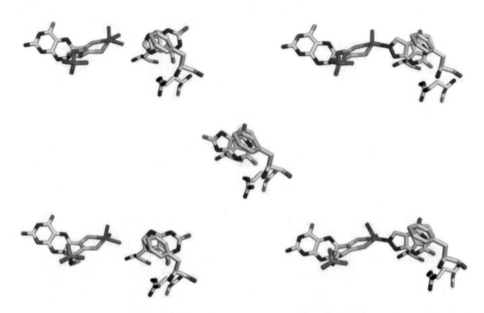

Figure 4. The structures of: *Top left*, xanthine bound to the desulfo from of bovine xanthine oxidase (3EUB, ref. [30];*bottom left*, xanthine bound to *R. capsulatus* xanthine dehydrogenase (PDB 2W3S, ref. [31]; *upper right*, alloxanthine complexed to reduced bovine xanthine dehydrogenase (PDB 3BDJ, ref. [32]; *lower right*, alloxanthine complexed to reduced *R. capsulatus* xanthine dehydrogenase (PDB 1JRP, ref. [31]; and *center,*, uric acid bound to the *apo* form of rat liver xanthine dehydrogenase (PDB 3AN1, ref. [33]).

The reaction mechanism of xanthine oxidase has also been examined computationally. Although an initial study[35] assumed formation of an intermediate in the course of reaction of an LMoOS(OH) model with acetaldehyde having a direct Mo-C bond, more recent work has provided strong support for the reaction proceeding essentially as shown in Figure 1. Voityuk *et al.*[36] were the first to examine this reaction explicitly, and found evidence for discrete steps involving nucleophilic attack on substrate (formaldehyde) and subsequent hydride transfer, with formation of a tetrahedral intermediate. No such tetrahedral intermediate was seen using formamide as substrate[37] (formamide was known to give rise to a "very rapid"-like EPR signal on reaction with the enzyme[38]), and subsequent work with formamide as substrate substantiated the need for the equatorial Mo=S of the molybdenum coordination sphere for catalytic activity: substitution of this sulfur with oxygen raised the activation barrier for hydride transfer substantially (12-17 kcal/mol[39,40]) while substitution of S for Se actually resulted in a slight lowering of the barrier[40]. Explicit comparison of one-step versus two-step mechanism[41,42], using both formamide and acetaldehyde among other substrates, indicates that a concerted mechanism to be more energetically favorable, by some 6 kcal/mol, than one forming a stable tetrahedral intermediate. This seems to be the case even when xanthine rather than formamide is used as substrate in the calculations[43]. Consistent with a reaction mechanism initiated by base-catalyzed abstraction of the Mo-OH, beginning with the ionized rather than protonated model results in a much more facile reaction[42]. An examination of the reaction with xanthine rather than formamide has also led to the conclusion that the reaction proceeds in a concerted fashion with the physiological substrate[43]. It has been further concluded that Glu 1261, having abstracted the proton from the Mo-OH, subsequently protonated substrate and this (rather than substrate tautomerization) contributed further to transition state stabilization. Such a role for Glu 1261 has previously been suggested[27], but unfortunately the absence of Arg 880 in the calculations seriously biases the results in favor of substrate protonation (as opposed to stabilizing the negative charge accumulating on substrate in the course of nucleophilic attack by charge compensation with the arginine) and raises concerns about this conclusion.

In addition to the above computational studies utilizing density functional theory, the reaction of xanthine oxidase has been examined using a quantum mechanical/molecular mechanical (QM/MM) approach[44,45]. Starting with a model that includes both Glu 1261 and Glu 802 (the former ionized and the latter protonated) as well as the LMoOS(OH) model and with xanthine rather than formamide as substrate, Pathways starting with substrate oriented in each of the two orientations shown in Figure 3 were specifically considered. It was concluded that xanthine preferentially bound in the orientation seen crystallographically (Figure 3) but that the reaction proceeded with lower overall activation barrier from the inverted orientation, through a complicated series of substrate tautomerization and proton transfers to and from the heterocycle. The lower activation barrier reported for the inverted orientation of substrate, however, did not include the free energy necessary to populate the less favorable orientation and it can be argued that this should be added in to compare the two orientations on a level playing field; to not do so essentially determines the barrier from an arbitrary point already part way up it. Further, the calculations began with a protonated Glu 802, requiring that its pK_a lie well above 8.0, possibly biasing the relative activation barriers in favor of that for the inverted orientation. It remains for future studies incorporating Arg 880 explicitly in DFT and QM/MM calculations such as these to clarify the relative roles of substrate protonation and tautomomerization in contributing to transition state stabilization.

The reaction considered above accounts for only the reductive half of the catalytic cycle of xanthine oxidase/dehydrogenase, yielding uric acid and reduced enzyme. Completion of the catalytic cycle involves electron transfer out of the molybdenum center, via a pair of [2Fe-2S] iron-sulfur clusters to the FAD, where again reducing equivalents are removed by reaction with O_2 or NAD^+ depending on the enzyme form. The reductive and oxidative halves of the catalytic cycle are thus physically separated in these enzymes and electron transfer from molybdenum to FAD is thus an obligatory part of catalysis. These processes have been shown to be rapid compared to the rate of reaction at the molybdenum center[47-50] and are not rate-limiting under normal circumstances. It is interesting to note that electron transfer from the second iron-sulfur center to the FAD, over a distance no greater than 7 Å, is the slowest of the electron transfer events, with a k_{et} of 150-300 s^{-1}, depending on the pH[47,48]. This relatively slow rate has been attributed to the involvement of protonation/deprotonation of the FAD concomitant with electron transfer, consistent with the large solvent kinetic isotope effects seen on electron transfer[49]. This electron transfer step in xanthine oxidase thus constitutes an example of coupled proton/electron transfer, a process now recognized to be a general one seen in many chemical and biological systems[51,52].

ALDEHYDE OXIDASES

The enzymes described above that utilize xanthine as reducing substrate are very similar in eukaryotes and prokaryotes, and the eukaryotic aldehyde oxidases are very similar to these in cofactor constitution. The same cannot be said for the aldehyde-utilizing enzymes from bacteria. In prokaryotes the molybdenum centers often possess a dinucleotide form of the pyranopterin cofactor, typically that of cytosine, although this is not thought to significantly influence the chemistry of the reductive half-reaction. More importantly, however, the prokaryotic enzymes often lack an FAD-containing domain/subunit, and in these cases are thought to be reoxidized after reaction with aldehydes by ferredoxin.

The best characterized bacterial aldehyde oxidoreductase is that from *Desulfovibrio gigas*, which was in fact the first molybdenum hydroxylase to be characterized crystallographically[12]. The structure of one monomer of this dimeric enzyme is shown in Figure 5, along with that for a monomer of the (again dimeric) dehydrogenase form of the bovine enzyme. It can be seen that the polypeptide folds of the iron-sulfur- and molybdenum-containing portions of the two enzymes are extremely similar. It is interesting to note how, in the context of the bacterial structure, the FAD-binding domain has been inserted in creating the eukaryotic form of the enzyme. Although portions of the two stretches of polypeptide that connect the C-terminus of the second iron-sulfur center to the N-terminus of FAD domain, and the C-terminus of the FAD domain to the N-terminus of the molybdenum binding portion of the protein are not fully resolved in the structure of the bovine enzyme, it is nevertheless evident that the first of these connectors (*green*) passes in front of the iron-sulfur domains (*dark red* and *light red*, respectively) as shown in Figure 5 and, after tracing out the entirety of the FAD domain (*yellow*) the second connector loops behind the iron-sulfur domains and completes a fifth strand of β sheet in the second of the two molybdenum domains (*blue*)

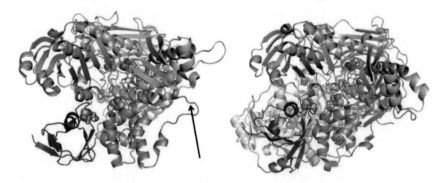

Figure 5. The overall protein folds and disposition of redox-active centers in, *left*, aldehyde oxidoreductase from *Desulfovibrio gigas* (PDB 1VLB, ref. [12]) and *right*, bovine xanthine dehydrogenase (PDB 1FO4, ref. [8]). The domains containing the several redox-active centers are color-coded as follows: [2Fe-2S], *red* (dark and light for the first and second centers, respectively); FAD, *yellow*; Mo N-terminal domain, *gray,* and C-terminal domain, *blue*. The two linker strands connecting the second iron-sulfur domain to the FAD domain (*green*) and the FAD domain to the molybdenum-binding portion of the protein (*gray*) in the case of xanthine dehydrogenase are also indicated in *green*, as is the vestigial linker in the . The *arrow* in the aldehyde oxidoreductase structure at left show the approximate point in the bacterial enzyme's structure at which the FAD domain of the eukaryotic enzyme is inserted.

before adjoining the amino terminus of the first of the two molybdenum domains (*gray*). The two stretches of connecting polypeptide pass close to one another immediately behind and to the right of the second iron-sulfur domain in Figure 5. In the prokaryotic enzyme, there is only a single polypeptide stretch connecting the C-terminus of the second iron-sulfur domain with the first molybdenum domain. The apparent point at which the FAD is inserted is approximately in the middle of the connector in the prokaryotic enzyme, as indicated by the arrow in Figure 5.

The eu- and prokaryotic aldehyde oxidases are thus sufficiently distinct that they will be considered separately here, taking the eukaryotic version first. The vertebrate aldehyde oxidases are very closely related to the xanthine oxidoreductases described above, with extensively overlapping substrate specificities and the requirement for a catalytically essential Mo=S group in the molybdenum coordination sphere. Xanthine oxidoreductase is the product of a single-copy gene, but the copy number for genes encoding aldehyde oxidases (AOX) and aldehyde oxidase homologs (AOH) varies considerably among vertebrates. Humans have a single *Aox1* gene and no homologs, while most rodent genomes have one *Aox1* gene and three genes for homologs, *Aoh1-3*. These four genes have a high degree of sequence homology, and their intron/exon structures are highly conserved[53].

Mammalian aldehyde oxidases hydroxylate and inactivate a variety of drugs, including many aromatic heterocycles, but the physiological substrate(s) remain unknown. It has been suggested to play a role in retinoic acid biosynthesis[54], but in humans individuals with a genetic lesion in the molecular apparatus that sulfurates xanthine oxidase and the aldehyde oxidases have relatively minor clinical symptoms and no evident developmental abnormalities[53,55-57], indicating that systemic biosynthesis of retinoic acid (a major signaling molecule in vertebrate limb development) is not impaired. On the other hand, a mouse knockout for the *Aoh2* gene has been described[58], and while these mice develop normally retinoid metabolism in specific tissues (most notably the skin) is disrupted and retinoid-dependent genes generally underexpressed, suggesting that AOH2 is involved in the local biosynthesis and biodistribution of retinoic acid in the affected tissues.

The recombinantly expressed AOX1 from mouse has been characterized, and the roles of several amino acid residues in the active site examined by mutagenesis, including Glu 1265, Val 806 and Met 884 (at positions corresponding to Glu 1261, Glu 802 and Arg 880 in the bovine enzyme)[59]. Interestingly, mutation of Val 806 to Glu and Met 884 to Arg, the residues found in the xanthine-utilizing enzymes, abolish aldehyde oxidase activity but does not impart xanthine oxidase activity.

The determinants of substrate specificity are thus apparently more subtle than might have been suspected, and involve as-yet undefined structural factors in addition to these specific residues.

Higher plants typically possess two to four genes encoding aldehyde oxidases[53], including those for the enzymes that catalyze the final step in the biosynthesis of the plant hormones abscissic acid and indole-3-acetic acid. Both reactions involve the oxidative hydroxylation of the respective aldehyde to the carboxylic acid hormone. *A. thaliana* has four aldehyde oxidase genes, AOX1-4[60,61], with AOX3 specifically involved in abscissic acid biosynthesis in leaves (but not seeds)[60,62]. Similarly, *Pisum sativum* has three genes encoding aldehyde oxidases, *Psaox1-3*, the last appearing to encode a stress-specific abscissic aldehyde oxidase[63].

None of the plant enzymes have been studied in great detail at a biochemical level, but by analogy to other enzymes of this family considerable overlap in substrate specificity among the plant aldehyde oxidases is to be expected. It is likely that the specific physiological roles of the gene products is due more to the manner in which gene expression is regulated in different plant tissues under different physiological conditions rather than to the intrinsic substrate specificity of the proteins encoded.

No crystal structure has yet been reported for a eukaryotic aldehyde oxidase. Nevertheless, a comparison of the amino acid sequences of bovine, murine and human aldehyde oxidase genes with the bovine, murine and human xanthine oxidoreductases does allow some general statements to be made[58]. The following amino acid residues (Figure 2) are conserved between the mammalian xanthine- and aldehyde-utilizing enzymes: Gln 767, Phe 914 and Glu 1261. Glu 802 of xanthine oxidoreductase is a valine in the aldehyde oxidases (except in murine AOH1, where it is Ala). Phe 1009 of xanthine oxidoreductase is conserved in murine AOH1 and 3, but is an aliphatic residue (Leu, Ile or Val) in the other four aldehyde oxidases.

Finally, Arg 880 in xanthine oxidoreductase is a Met in the proper aldehyde oxidases, or Phe/Tyr in the murine AOHs. Given the specific catalytic roles in xanthine hydroxylation discussed above for Glu 802 and Arg 880, their lack of conservation in the aldehyde oxidases is to be expected. Again, however, additional undefined factors are involved in determining substrate specificity.

As indicated above, the first member of the molybdenum hydroxylase family to be characterized crystallographically was the aldehyde:ferredoxin oxidoreductase from $D.$ $gigas$[12]. It was for this enzyme that the highly conserved active site glutamate was first proposed to function as an active site base[13] and the overall coordination geometry of the molybdenum center established to be square pyramidal. Still, additional work was required to establish that the catalytically essential Mo=S group occupied an equatorial rather than apical position[14,15] and that the equatorial oxygen was a Mo-OH rather than $Mo-OH_2$[25]. Other work with the $D.$ $gigas$ enzyme[64], as well as with the recombinant rat protein[65], permitted the assignment of the two distinct iron-sulfur EPR signals exhibited by the enzyme to the specific [2Fe-2S] centers seen crystallographically. Interestingly, the EPR signal with the more typical g-values and temperature dependence (that designated Fe/S I) was found to arise from the [2Fe-2S] cluster in the domain with the unusual α-helical fold, and that with the more unusual g-values and temperature dependence (that designated Fe/S II) to the cluster in the more spinach ferredoxin-like domain.

These assignments were consistent with the long-known observation that Fe/S I was spin-coupled to the molybdenum center when the latter was in the Mo(V) oxidation state[66], as the [2Fe-2S] cluster in the helical domain lies closer to the molybdenum center (one of it's coordinating cysteine residues is in fact very near, and possibly within hydrogen-bonding distance of, the distal amino group of the pyranopterin cofactor of the molybdenum center[12]). [2Fe-2S] clusters are spin-localized, meaning that only one of the two Fe^{III} ions of the oxidized cluster is redox-active, and in an elegant single-crystal EPR study with the $D.$ $gigas$ enzyme[67], the specific redox-active iron in each [2Fe-2S] cluster has been identified (Figure 6). It is likely that this assignment can be generalized to all members of the xanthine oxidase family of enzymes.

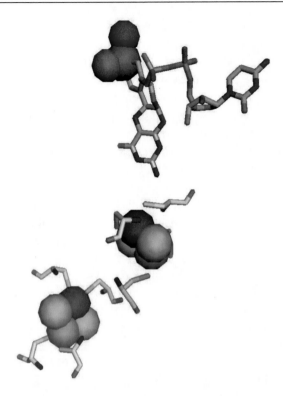

Figure 6. The disposition of the redox-active centers in the *D. gigas* aldehyde oxidoreductase, with the redox-active iron atoms in each of the two [2Fe-2S] centers indicated in *red*. The distal amino group of the pyranopterin cofactor is within hydrogen-bonding distance of Cys 139 of the proximal iron-sulfur center (designated Fe/S I).

It has recently been suggested that the *D. gigas* enzyme is active in the absence of the Mo=S group that in other enzymes of this family is known to be catalytically essential, based on steady-state assays and the inhibition patterns seen with classic inhibitors of this family of enzymes (*e.g.*, cyanide and ethylene glycol)[68]. While it is true that aldehydes are in general more susceptible to nucleophilic attack than the heterocycles acted on by many molybdenum hydroxylases, and the Mo=S might therefore not be required, it is well known (and confirmed recently in the author's laboratory) that the ability of bovine xanthine oxidase to oxidize aldehydes is strictly dependent on the Mo=S being present. The crystal structure of the desulfo *D. gigas* enzyme in complex with the classic inhibitor arsenite has recently been reported[68], with the inhibitor found coordinated to the molybdenum at the equatorial position normally occupied by the catalytically labile Mo-OH. By contrast, the structure of the (sulfurated) bovine xanthine oxidase in complex with arsenite has also been reported recently[69], with the inhibitor found bound to the reduced enzyme in a distinctly different bidentate fashion, with two bridging ligands in the equatorial plane of the molybdenum, one oxygen the other sulfur. Interestingly, in the oxidized enzyme the arsenic itself was found to have a coordination geometry suggesting that it had become oxidized to arsenate (presumably in the X-ray beam). It appears that if the *D. gigas* enzyme is indeed active in a desulfo form, then it is not possible to make generalizations about the family of enzymes based on its characteristics.

In addition to a xanthine dehydrogenase, the *E. coli* genome encodes an aldehyde:ferredoxin oxidoreductase in the *yagTSRQ* operon[70]. The enzyme has a pair of [2Fe-2S] cluster in YagT, FAD in YagS and a molybdenum center in YagR; YagQ is homologous to XdhC from *R. capsulatus*, which is known to be involved in the sulfuration of the nascent molybdenum center and its subsequent insertion into apoprotein[71,72]. YagTSR is unusual in several respects: first, it exists as an $\alpha\beta\gamma$ trimer rather than the expected $(\alpha\beta\gamma)_2$ hexamer; second, it possesses the FAD domain/subunit seen in the eukaryotic forms of the enzyme while retaining ferredoxin as oxidizing substrate; and it is unique among *E. coli* enzymes in utilizing the cytosine dinucleotide of the pyranopterin cofactor (the *D. gigas* aldehyde:ferredoxin aldehyde oxidoreductase also utilizes this form). YagTSR is able to oxidize a variety of aldehydes[70], but is particularly effective with aromatic aldehydes (such as cinnamaldehyde, vanillin and benzaldehyde, all exhibiting k_{cat}/K_m ~10^6 M^{-1} s^{-1}). Interestingly, deletion mutants of *E. coli* do not grow in the presence of cinnamaldehyde, suggesting that the enzyme plays a role in detoxification.

The reaction mechanism for both eu- and prokaryotic aldehyde oxidases is thought to involve the same base-assisted proton abstraction from the equatorial Mo-OH group to initiate catalysis as seen with the xanthine-utilizing enzymes[13]. Computational studies[73] suggest that this is followed by nucleophilic attack on the carbonyl carbon of substrate with concomitant hydride transfer to the Mo=S group, through a tetrahedral transition state in which the C-O bond of product is ~90% formed and the C-H bond of substrate ~80% broken in the transition state. Although the reaction is thought to involve nucleophilic attack on the highly activated carbonyl carbon and proceed through the same type of $LMo^{IV}O(SH)(OR)$ intermediate as seen with xanthine oxidase, no EPR signal equivalent to the "very rapid" EPR signal seen with xanthine oxidase has been seen with any aldehyde oxidase (see, *e.g.*, ref. 74).

Human aldehyde oxidase oxidizes a spectrum of aromatic heterocycles in addition to aldehydes, as mentioned above, and many of these are therapeutically important – a DFT approach to understanding reactivity of the enzyme, in the context of a reaction initiated by nucleophilic attack on substrate, has successfully accounted for the experimentally observed regioselectivity of substrate hydroxylation for a number of aromatic heterocycles[75]. Recently, human aldehyde oxidase has been cloned and heterologously expressed in *E. coli*, and while expression levels were modest it proved possible to obtain sufficient protein to undertake steady-state kinetic studies[76]. Enzyme activity on a series of substituted quinazoline substrates analogous to that used previously with xanthine oxidase[77], yield the same general trend in reactivity (with the notable exception of the nitro derivative, which was found not to be an effective substrate for aldehyde oxidase).

CO DEHYDROGENASE

The xanthine and aldehyde-utilizing enzymes discussed above include some of the longest studied members of the xanthine oxidase family of enzymes, and the *D. gigas* enzyme has pride of place in being the first to have its X-ray crystal structure determined. What follows now is a discussion of several members of this family of enzyme, each of which has also been characterized crystallographically, that are non-canonical either in the structure of the molybdenum center or the reaction catalyzed. We begin with CO dehydrogenase, which is heterodox both in the nature of its active site and in the reaction catalyzed, then consider nicotinate dehydrogenase, quinoline-2-oxidoreductase and 4-hydroxybenzoate hydroxylase. Carboxydotrophic bacteria (*e.g.*, *Oligotropha carboxidovorans*) are able to grow using CO as sole source of both carbon and energy[78]. A molybdenum-containing CO dehydrogenase[79] catalyzes the critical first step in this process, the oxidation of CO to CO_2. The reducing equivalents thus obtained are passed on to the ubiquinone pool and finally to a CO-insensitive terminal oxidase, cytochrome b_{563} that pumps protons while reducing O_2 to water; CO_2 is subsequently fixed non-photosynthetically via the reductive pentose phosphate cycle, utilizing ribulose bisphosphate carboxylase and phosphoribulokinase[79]. Aerobic organisms such as *O. carboxidovorans* are responsible for the annual clearance of ~2 x 10^8 metric tons of CO from the environment[80,81], a very impressive degree of bioremediation.

The Mo-containing CO dehydrogenase from *O. carboxidovorans* is distinct from the highly O_2-sensitive Ni/Fe-containing CO dehydrogenase from obligate anaerobes such as the acetogen *Clostridum thermoaceticum* or the methanogen *Methanosarcina barkerii*[82]. It is an $(\alpha\beta\gamma)_2$ hexamer, and the enzymes from both *O. carboxidovorans*[83] and *Hydrogenophaga pseudoflava*[84] have been crystallographically characterized. In both cases, the enzyme consists of a small subunit (CoxS; 18 kDa) that has two [2Fe-2S] iron-sulfur clusters, a medium subunit (CoxM; 30 kDa) that possesses FAD, and a large subunit (CoxL; 89 kDa) that has the active site molybdenum center (Figure 7). Each subunit bears considerable sequence homology and virtually identical structural homology with the corresponding portion of bovine xanthine oxidoreductase (although there is no overlapping substrate specificity between the two enzymes). In *O. carboxidovorans,* CO dehydrogenase is encoded by the megaplasmid-localized *coxBCMSLDEFGHIK* gene cluster[85,86], and on the basis of the operon's structure it appears that CO dehydrogenase (with separately encoded subunits) represents an early evolutionary intermediate in the gene duplication/fusion process by which the vertebrate molybdenum hydroxylases presumably arose.

Remarkably, the active site of the *O. carboxidovorans* CO dehydrogenase is not a mononuclear molybdenum center but rather a binuclear Mo/Cu center having the structure shown in Figure 8[87,88]. The molybdenum has the typical square-pyramidal coordination geometry of other members of this enzyme family, with an apical Mo=O and an equatorial plane consisting of two sulfurs from the pyranopterin cofactor and a second Mo=O occupying the position of the catalytically labile Mo-OH of xanthine oxidoreductase; the final equatorial molybdenum ligand position is a catalytically essential sulfur that is μ-bridged to a Cu(I) ion, which in turn possesses a second thiolate ligand contributed by Cys 388. The observed rate constant for the reduction of CO dehydrogenase by excess CO under anaerobic conditions is independent of CO concentration, with $k_{red} = 51$ s^{-1} at 25°C[89]. Nominally, this means that K_d is smaller than the ~30 μM lower limit of [CO] that is experimentally accessible. k_{red} is also approximately independent of pH, indicating that there is no acid-base catalysis involved in the reaction going forward from the E_{ox}•CO complex (this despite the fact that Glu 763, equivalent to the active site base Glu 1261 in the bovine enzyme, is conserved in CO dehydrogenase).

In the course of reaction with CO, an EPR signal clearly attributable to the Mo/Cu binuclear center accumulates[90], with $g_{1,2,3} = 2.0010, 1.9604, 1.9549$ and extremely large hyperfine coupling to the naturally abundant [63,65] Cu nuclei (I = 3/2), with $A_{1,2,3} = 117,$ 164 and 132 MHz (Figure 9)[89]. The strength of the copper hyperfine coupling indicates that the singly-occupied molecular orbital possesses significant Cu s orbital character, a point that is likely of mechanistic significance (see below). This EPR signal is not changed on preparation of the sample in D_2O, but lines do broaden slightly when [13] CO is used as substrate. The signal-giving species appears to represent an enzyme•substrate complex in which the molybdenum has been partially reduced by reaction with a prior equivalent of substrate and as such represents a paramagnetic analog of the Michaelis complex. The species is thought to have the structure shown in Figure 9, where CO has bound to the active-site copper, with the molybdenum in the Mo(V) oxidation state. Binding of CO to the Cu would be expected to activate it for nucleophilic attack, and the pre-binding of CO prior to initiation of the oxidative chemistry would account for the observed [CO]-independent rapid reaction kinetics.

A very high-resolution (1.1-Å) structure of CO dehydrogenase in complex with the inhibitor *n*-butylisonitrile has been reported[87], in which the bridging sulfur bond to the copper is clearly seen to have been cleaved and the inhibitor inserted between the Mo and Cu, as shown in Figure 10. A mechanism has been proposed in which CO similarly cleaves the sulfido bridge of the binuclear center in the course of the reaction, as shown in Figure 11, *top*. In this mechanism, the insertion leads to a bridging thiocarbamate moiety and reduction of the molybdenum to Mo(IV). The thiocarbamate is subsequently hydrolyzed by solvent, with regeneration of the sulfur bridge. It is surprising, however, that the (labile) sulfur bridge might be cleaved in the course of the catalytic cycle. An alternate mechanism, based on the structure of the paramagnetic species described above, involves nucleophilic attack on an initial Cu•CO complex, with subsequent formation of CO_2 and reduction of the binuclear cluster (Figure 11, *bottom*). The initial nucleophilic attack may occur using either the

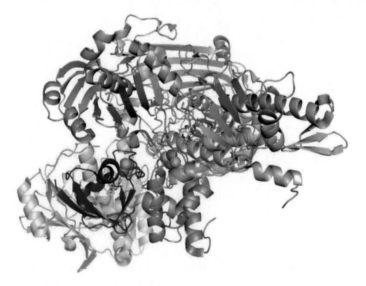

Figure 7. The 1.5Å-resolution crystal structure of CO dehydrogenase from *O. carboxidovorans* (PDB 1QJ2, ref. [83]). The separate subunits containing the two [2Fe-2S] clusters (*red*), FAD (*yellow*) and molybdenum (*gray* and *blue*) are indicated.

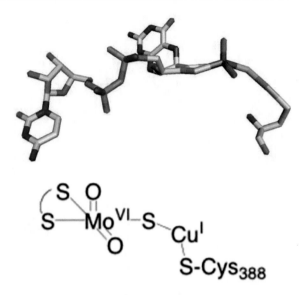

Figure 8. The (oxidized) active site binuclear Mo/Cu center of *O. carboxidovorans* CO dehydrogenase (PDB 1N5W, ref. [84]). The molybdenum is at left, and the copper at right.

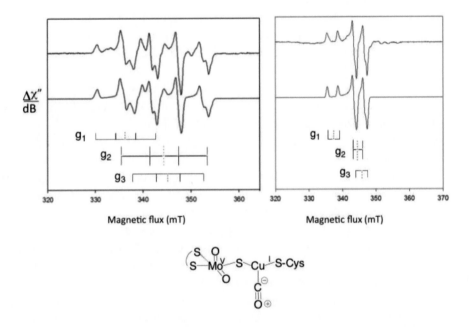

Figure 9. EPR signals manifested by the binuclear center of CO-reduced CO dehydrogenase. *Left*, the signal seen with the naturally occurring enzyme, and *right* that seen with enzyme in which the copper ion of the active site has been substituted with silver. The line representations shown illustrate the strong hyperfine interaction seen for copper ([63,65]Cu I=3/2) and silver ([103,105]Ag I=1/2). Also shown is the structure of the presumed signal-giving species, which appears to be a paramagnetic analog of the Michaelis complex for the enzyme.

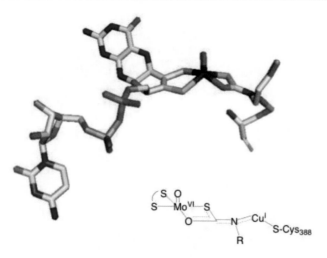

Figure 10. Structure of the complex of CO dehydrogenase with *n*-butylisonitrile (PDB 1N62, ref. [84]).

equatorial Mo=O (which, already being deprotonated, would not require base-assisted catalysis) or a solvent water/hydroxide (which presumably would require Glu 763, raising the question why its ionization is not observed in the pH profile of k_{red}).

Regardless of the source of the oxygen incorporated in the initial event into product, the final step of this alternate mechanism deserves further comment, as reducing equivalents nominally enter the (predominantly Mo-based) redox-active orbital via the copper. Gourlay *et al.*[91] have recently considered a model for the binuclear active site of CO dehydrogenase that possesses many (but not all) of the salient structural features of the enzyme's active site and, critically, very similar EPR characteristics to that exhibited by the enzyme, including the extremely strong Cu superhyperfine. Their analysis of the paramagnetic species indicates a redox-active (singly occupied) molecular orbital with some 25% S p character and 21% Cu d_{z^2}/d_{xy} character (along with an undefined amount of Cu s character). The significance of this work is that the copper and bridging sulfur act essentially to extend the redox-active orbital spatially a considerable distance from the molybdenum, making it possible for the molybdenum to become reduced in the final step depicted in Figure 11 *bottom*. The binuclear cluster, with its sulfur bridge to copper, thus appears to be constructed so as to (1) create a substrate binding site adjacent to the molybdenum that activates CO for nucleophilic attack, and (2) at the same time "extend" the redox-active Mo d_{xy} orbital such that it can accept an electron pair in the course of the reaction at the more remote site.

Like the Mo=S of xanthine oxidase, the bridging sulfur of CO dehydrogenase can be removed by reaction with cyanide, which in the latter case results in loss of the copper as well. A reconstitution protocol has been developed by Meyer and coworkers[90] that utilizes Cu(I)•thiourea as source of copper. When the silver salt is used instead, activity is partially recovered [92]. The enzyme thus reactivated reacts with CO under anaerobic conditions with a rate constant of 8.1 s^{-1} (as compared with 51 s^{-1} for the as-isolated enzyme[89]); the extent of the spectral change indicates *ca.* 75% of the enzyme was successfully reconstituted and became reduced, comparable to the extent of reactivation seen when copper is used rather than silver in the reconstitution. Importantly, the EPR signal seen upon partial reduction of the enzyme by CO shows the doublets expected for substitution of Ag for Cu (I = ½ for the naturally-occurring ^{103,105}Ag), as shown in Figure 9, with $g_{1,2,3}$ = 2.043, 1.9595, 1.9540 (very similar the values seen with the as-isolated enzyme) and $A_{1,2,3}$ = 82.0, 78.9, 81.9 MHz.

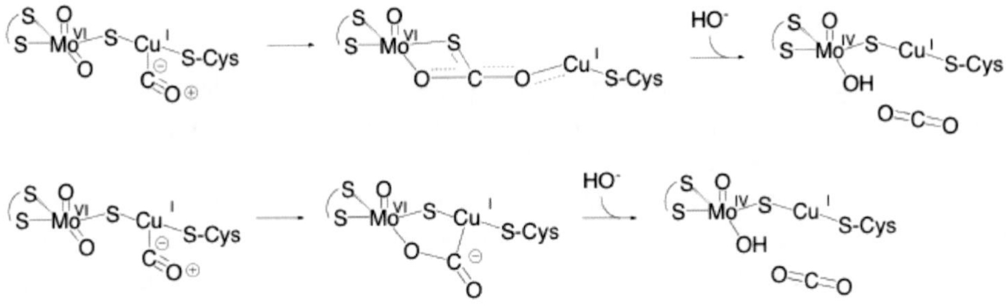

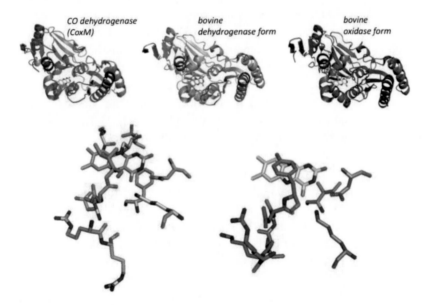

Figure 11. Alternative reaction mechanisms for the reaction of CO dehydrogenase. *Top*, that proposed by Dobbek *et al.* [89], with an intermediate having a structure analogous to that seen in the *n*-butylisonitrile complex shown in Figure 10. *Bottom*, an alternative mechanism in which the reaction proceeds by reduction of molybdenum via the highly delocalized redox-active orbital described by Gourley *et al.* [91].

Figure 12. A comparison of the FAD-binding portions of CO dehydrogenase with bovine xanthine dehydrogenase and xanthine oxidase. *Top*, the overall folds of CO dehydrogenase (*left*) more closely resembles that of the dehydrogenase (*middle*) than the oxidase (*right*) form of the mammalian enzyme (note the position of the loop indicated in *red*). *Bottom*, a close-up of the environment of the flavin in CO dehydrogenase (*left*) and xanthine dehydrogenase (*right*), illustrating the differences between the two sites.

It has recently been shown that the physiological oxidant for CO dehydrogenase is most likely ubiquinone, it having been demonstrated that any of several quinone species effectively reoxidize the reduced enzyme[93]. Reoxidation occurs at the FAD site, as expected. The overall fold of the FAD-containing domain resembles that of the dehydrogenase form of the bovine enzyme, where a specific loop of the polypeptide on the *si* side of the FAD occupies a position that leaves the flavin more exposed than would otherwise be the case (Figure 12). In the oxidase form of the bovine enzyme, this loop occupies a different position and obstructs NAD^+ binding. The fold observed in CO dehydrogenase is in fact the more typical one seen in other members of this family of enzymes, but these react with pyridine nucleotides rather than quinones.

A closer examination of the environment of the FAD of CO dehydrogenase indicates that, while there are similarities with the bovine dehydrogenase, there are also differences (Figure 12). The Lys-Asp pair near the pyrimidine subnucleus is preserved, but the positions of the Ile and aromatic residues are reversed, with the Ile on the *re* side and Tyr (a Phe in the bovine enzyme) on the *si* side of the isoalloxazine ring. The two Asps and Arg near the dimethylbenzene ring are conserved, but the Lys residue seen in CO dehydrogenase occupies a position rather closer to the flavin than the cognate Arg in the bovine dehydrogenase.

NICOTINATE DEHYDROGENASE, QUINOLINE-2-OXIDOREDUCTASE AND 4-HYDROXYBENZOYLCOA REDUCTASE

Next considered are three enzymes which, while considerably less well-understood than the enzymes discussed above from a mechanistic standpoint, have nevertheless been characterized crystallographically: nicotinate dehydrogenase, quinoline-2-oxidoreductase and 4-hydroxy benzoylCoA reductase (Figure 13). Nicotinate dehydrogenase is significant in requiring an equatorial Mo=Se rather than Mo=S in the molybdenum coordination sphere, quinoline 2-oxidoreductase important in having been the first molybdenum hydroxylase to have the Mo=S assigned to an equatorial rather than apical position, and 4-hydroxbenzoylCoA reductase interesting in that it catalyzes the _de_hydroxylation rather than hydroxylation of its substrate.

The anaerobic soil bacterium *E. barkeri* is able to ferment nicotinate to propionate, acetate, carbon dioxide and ammonia utilizing a pathway that is initiated by the hydroxylation of nicotinate to 6-hydroxynicotinate. This reaction is catalyzed by a molybdenum- and selenium-dependent nicotinate dehydrogenase[94-96]. Indeed, several molybdenum-containing enzymes are known to contain selenium[97,98], and a recent genomics analysis has shown that selenium and molybdenum utilization are highly correlated in biology[99]. Selenium is most commonly found as selenocysteine (*e.g.*, in the molybdenum-containing formate dehydrogenase H from *Escherichia coli*, a member of the DMSO reductase family of enzymes, where it coordinates the active site molybdenum, at least in the oxidized state of the enzyme[101,102]) or in an acid-labile form (in members of the xanthine oxidase family of molybdenum enzymes, *e.g.* nicotinate dehydrogenase from *E. barkeri*[103] and the xanthine oxidoreductases from *Clostridium purinolyticum*[103], *C. acidiurici*[104] and *E. barkeri*[105] and the purine hydroxylase from *C. purinolyticum*[103]). In each of these latter enzymes the selenium is essential for activity[106]. The *E. barkeri* nicotinate dehydrogenase utilizes $NADP^+$ as oxidizing substrate and like CO dehydrogenase has an $(\alpha\beta\gamma\delta)_2$ composition with two [2Fe-2S] clusters, FAD and a molybdenum center in separate subunits; the pyranopterin cofactor of the molybdenum center is present as the dinucleotide of cytosine[106,107].

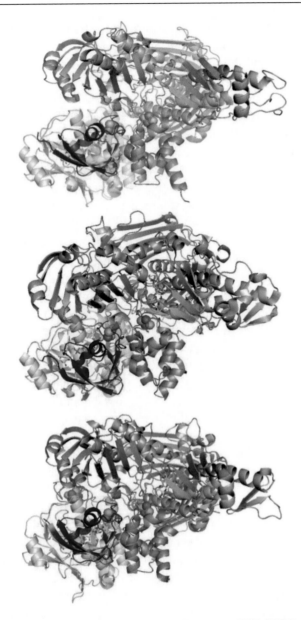

Figure 13. The x-ray crystal structures for nicotinate dehydrogenase (PDB 3HRD, *top*; ref. [40]), quinoline-2-oxidoreductase (PDB 1T3Q, *center*; ref. [15]) and 4-hydroxybenzoylCoA reductase (PDB 1RM6, *bottom*; ref. [113]). The [2Fe-2S], FAD and molybdenum-binding subunits are indicated in red, yellow and gray/blue, respectively. The additional [4Fe-4S] cluster of 4-hydroxybenzoylCoA reductase is shown in green.

The genes encoding nicotinate dehydrogenase occur in the transcriptional order *ndhFSLM* and are part of a 23.3 kb gene cluster dedicated to the fermentation of nicotinate[107]. The NdhF subunit (33 kDa) carries one FAD molecule and the NdhS subunit (23 kDa) contains two [2Fe-2S] clusters. By contrast to the structures of all other molybdenum hydroxylases, the molybdenum-binding portion of the protein is split into two separate subunits, NdhL (50 kDa) and NdhM (37 kDa). The crystal structure of nicotinate dehydrogenase shows that the selenium is present as a terminal Mo=Se ligand and that it occupies the same equatorial position of the terminal sulfido ligand in other molybdenum hydroxylases[40]. The reaction mechanism of nicotinate likely resembles that of xanthine oxidase described above, and the role of selenium in catalysis has been assessed by density functional calculations indicating that the transition state for the critical hydride transfer from substrate to the molybdenum center is stabilized by an additional 3 kcal/mol with selenium rather than sulfur in the molybdenum coordination sphere[40]. Incorporation of selenium into the active site this accounts for more than two orders of magnitude of additional rate acceleration of the chemical step of the reaction.

Pseudomonas putida 86 is capable of growth on quinoline as sole source of both carbon and energy, and the first step in the degradative pathway is a hydroxylation catalyzed by the molybdenum-containing quinoline 2-oxidoreductase[108]. The hydroxylated product subsequently spontaneously tautomerizes to 2-oxo-1,2-dihydroquinoline prior to subsequent degradation[109]. Quinoline 2-oxidoreductase is an $(\alpha\beta\gamma)_2$ hexamer with small, medium and large subunits possessing its pair of [2Fe-2S] centers, FAD and a molybdenum center[110]. The overall organization closely resembles that of CO dehydrogenase discussed above, including the presence of the pyranopterin cofactor as the dinucleotide of cytosine and the organization of the three structural genes in the order MSL in the operon encoding the polypeptides, but the active site is a mononuclear molybdenum center rather than a binuclear Mo/Cu center as seen in CO dehydrogenase.

Quinoline 2-oxidoreductase exhibits UV/visible and EPR characteristics very closely resembling bovine xanthine oxidase[108]. Its molybdenum center closely resembles that of xanthine oxidase described above with an $LMo^{VI}OS(OH)$ coordination sphere, and again was the first enzyme in which the catalytically labile Mo=S was correctly assigned to be in the equatorial rather than apical position in the molybdenum coordination sphere[110]. In the active site, Glu 743 and Gln 224 occupy positions equivalent to Glu1261 and Gln 787 in the bovine enzyme discussed above, but the position of Glu 802 in the bovine enzyme is occupied by Ala 259 in quinoline 2-oxidoreductase, and that of Arg 880 by Val 339. As with the *R. capsulatus* xanthine dehydrogenase, mutation of Glu 743 to valine dramatically reduces catalytic activity[110]. Both sides of the substrate binding site of quinoline 2-oxidoreductase are constrained by loops of polypeptide rather than by Phe residues as seen in the bovine enzyme. The substrate binding site of quinoline 2-oxidoreductase is capped by Trp 331, which has no homolog in the bovine or *R. capsulatus* structures.

4-hydroxybenzoyl-CoA reductase from *Thauera aromatica* and related organisms is a critical enzyme in the metabolism of phenolic compounds in anaerobes, which lack the O_2-utilizing mono- and dioxygenases utilized by aerobes to break open the aromatic ring[111]. The enzyme catalyzes the reductive dehydroxylation of substrate to the key intermediate benzoyl-CoA, which is then reductively dearomatized by benzoyl-CoA reductase prior to subsequent degradation. The reducing equivalents required for the reaction come from a 2x[4Fe-4S] bacterial ferredoxin[112]. Like many of the other bacterial molybdenum hydroxylases, 4-hydroxybenzoyl-CoA reductase is an $(\alpha\beta\gamma)_2$ hexamer, with separate molybdenum-, FAD- and iron-sulfur- containing subunits, and an overall protein fold that closely resembles that of other members of this enzyme family[113]. Again, the pyranopterin cofactor of the molybdenum center is present as the dinucleotide of cytosine. Uniquely in 4-hydroxybenzoyl-CoA reductase, however, the FAD subunit has a 41-amino acid insert that contains an additional [4Fe-4S] cluster that is the presumed point of entry of reducing equivalents from ferredoxin[113].

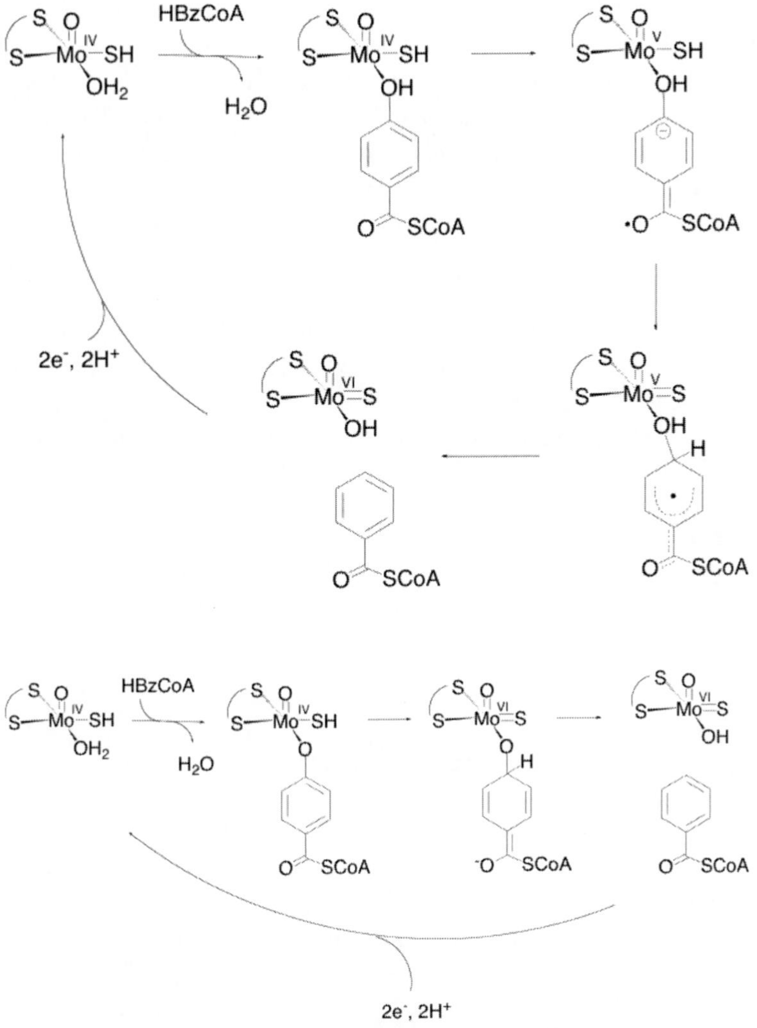

Figure 14. The proposed Birch reduction-like mechanism for 4-hydroxybenzoyl-CoA reductase [114].

The reduction potentials of the several redox-active centers of 4-hydroxybenzoyl-CoA reductase have been determined[114], with unusually low potentials for the FAD ($\Delta E_{FAD/FADH\cdot} = -250$ mV, $\Delta E_{FADH\cdot/FADH_2} = -470$ mV) and molybdenum center ($\Delta E_{Mo}{}^{VI/V} = -380$ mV, $\Delta E_{Mo}{}^{V/IV} = -500$ mV), and substantially higher reduction potentials for the two [2Fe-2S] centers (-205 mV and -255 mV for Fe/S I and II, respectively); the [4Fe-4S] cluster also possesses a low potential (-465 mV). Electron flow is in the reverse direction of that seen in other members of this family, but is thermodynamically favorable overall given the extremely low reduction potential of the ferredoxin. The [4Fe-4S] cluster is unusually far from the isoalloxazine ring of the FAD, 16.5 Å, but this is compensated for by an unusually high peptide packing density in the intervening region and an essentially direct covalent link from Cys 122 (coordinating one of the iron atoms of the cluster) through Arg 121 to Phe 233, which π-stacks onto the *si* face of the isoalloxazine ring[113]. Owing to these structural considerations, electron-transfer to the FAD is likely to be sufficiently fast as to not be rate-limiting to turnover.

The reaction mechanism of 4-hydroxybenzoyl-CoA reductase has been proposed to resemble that of a Birch reduction[114], in which a first reducing equivalent is added to substrate, followed by protonation at C-4 of substrate and addition of a second reducing equivalent, which leads to dehydroxylation and rearomatization, as shown in Figure 14, *top*. This chemistry has been incorporated into a reaction mechanism in which substrate first coordinates to the reduced molybdenum center by displacing an equatorial water, followed by sequential one-electron transfers such as described above to cleave the C-O bond of substrate, leaving the oxygen coordinated to the now-reoxidized molybdenum center as hydroxide in the equatorial position. A plausible variation on this mechanism would involve re-reduction of the molybdenum center from Mo^V to Mo^{IV} prior to the second electron transfer to substrate, so that both would be introduced from the lower-potential couple of the molybdenum center. At present, however, it is not possible to exclude the possibility that the reaction in fact runs simply in the reverse of the hydroxylation pathway for xanthine oxidase, with hydride transfer from an equatorial Mo-SH to C-4 of molybdenum-coordinated substrate, followed directly by dehydroxylation and rearomatization (Figure 14, *bottom*). Indeed, it is known that the xanthine oxidase reaction involves obligatory two-electron chemistry[115], and that the enzyme can catalyze the dehydroxylation of uric acid to xanthine under strongly reducing conditions[116]. It remains for future work to distinguish among these mechanistic possibilities.

CONCLUSION

The manner in which biological systems utilize molybdenum was near and dear to Ed Stiefel's heart, and he would undoubtedly be pleased with the current state of affairs. Impressive advances have been made in our understanding of how molybdenum-containing enzymes work, and at the same time fascinating new ones continue to be discovered. In this regard, a recent report in which the "metallome" of a single organism, *Pyrococcus furiosus*, has been exhaustively analyzed is noteworthy[117]. Proteins were analyzed for their ability to bind a large number of metals (including Fe, Zn, W, Ni, Co, Mo, Mn and V, as well as outliers Pb and U), and the analysis of those found to bind molybdenum quite telling. 35 proteins were identified using ICP: 19 had amino acid sequences (as determined by MS/MS) homologous to one or another known molybdenum enzyme, but a remarkable 18 had no homology to any known molybdenum-containing enzyme – and this in a hyperthermophilic archaeon not previously thought to utilize molybdenum at all! Clearly, there is much more to be discovered (possibly including enzymes that possess molybdenum but do not utilize the pyranopterin cofactor, for example), and this would have thrilled Ed.

REFERENCES

[1] Stiefel, E.I. The bioinorganic and coordination chemistry of molybdenum-sulfur systems. In *Proceedings of the Fourth International Conference on the Chemistry and Uses of Molybdenum* (H.F. Barry and P.C.H. Mitchell, eds.), Climax Molybdenum Company, 1982, Ann Arbor, MI, pp. 56-66.

[2] Berg, J.M.; Hodgson, K.O.; Cramer, S.P.; Corbin, J.L.; Elsberry, A.; Pariyadath, N.; Stiefel, E.I., *J. Am. Chem. Soc.* 1979, *101*, 2774-2776.

[3] Tullius, T. D.; Kurtz, D. M., Jr.; Conradson, S. D.; Hodgson, K. O., *J. Am. Chem. Soc.* 1979, *101*, 2776–2779.

[4] Bordas, J.; Bray, R. C.; Garner, C. D.; Gutteridge, S.; Hasnain, S. S., *Biochem. J.* 1980, *1980*, 499–508.

[5] Cramer, S. P.; Wahl, R.; Rajagopalan, K. V., *J. Am. Chem. Soc.* 1981, *103*, 7721–7727.

[6] Hille, R., *Chem. Rev.* 1996, *96*, 2757-2816.

[7] Hille, R., *Trends Biochem. Sci.* 2002, *27*, 360-367.

[8] Enroth, C.; Eger, B.T.; Okamoto, K.; Nishino, T.; Nishino, T.; Pai, E.F., *Proc. Natl. Acad. Sci. USA* 2000, *97*, 10723-10728.

[9] Nishino, T.; Okamoto, K.; Kawaguchi, Y.; Hori, H.; Matsumura, T.; Eger, B.T.; Pai, E.F.; Nishino, T., *J. Biol. Chem.* 2005, *280*, 24888-24894.

[10] McCord, J.M., *N. Engl. J. Med.* 1985, *312*, 159-163.

[11] Hille, R.; Nishino, T., *FASEB J.* 1995, *9*, 995-1003.

[12] Romão, M.J.; Archer, M.; Moura, I.; Moura, J.J.G.; LeGall, J.; Engh, R.; Schneider, M.; Hof, P.; Huber R., *Science* 1995, *270*, 1170-1176.

[13] Huber, R.; Hof, P.; Duarte, R.O.; Moura, J.J.G.; Moura, I.; LeGall, J.; Hille, R.; Archer, M.; Romão, M., *Proc. Natl. Acad. Sci. USA* 1996, *93*, 8846-8851.

[14] Jones, R.M.; Inscore, F.E.; Hille, R.; Kirk, M.L., *Inorg. Chem.* 1999, *38*, 4963-4970.

[15] Bonin, I.; Martins, B.M.; Purvanov, V.; Fetzner, S.; Huber, R.; Dobbek, H., *Structure* 2004, *12*, 1425-1435.

[16] Hille, R., EPR studies of xanthine oxidoreductase and other molybdenum-containing hydroxylases Ch. 5. in *Biological Magnetic Resonance* vol. 29, Metals in Biology: Applications of High-Resolution EPR to Metalloenzymes. (G. Hanson and L. Berliner, Jr., eds.), 2010, Springer, Berlin, pp. 91-121.

[17] Kim, J.H.; Ryan, M.G.; Knaut, H.; Hille, R., *J. Biol. Chem.* 1996, *271*, 6771-6780.

[18] Murray, K.N.; Watson, J.G.; Chaykin, S., *J. Biol. Chem.* 1966, *241*, 4798-4801.

[19] Hille, R.; Sprecher, H., *J. Biol. Chem.* 1987, *262*, 10914-10917.

[20] Xia, M.; Dempski, R.; Hille, R., *J. Biol. Chem.* 1999, *274*, 3323-3330.

[21] Manikandan, P.; Choi, E.-Y.; Hille, R.; Hoffman, B.M., *J. Am. Chem. Soc* 2001, *123*, 2658-2663.

[22] Pauff, J.M.; Zhang, J.; Bell, C.E.; Hille, R., *J. Biol. Chem.* 2008, *283*, 4818-4824.

[23] Truglio, J.J.; Theis, K.; Leimkühler, S.; Rappa, R.; Rajagopalan, K.V.; Kisker, C., *Structure* 2002, *10*, 115-125.

[24] Leimkühler, S.; Stockert, A.L.; Igarashi, K.; Nishino, T.; Hille, R., *J. Biol. Chem.* 2004, *279*, 40437-40444.

[25] Doonan, C.J.; Stockert, A.L.; Hille, R.; George, G.N., *J. Am. Chem. Soc.* 2005, *127*, 4518-4522.

[26] Pauff, J.L.; Hemann, C.F.; Leimkühler, S.; Hille, R., *J. Biol. Chem,* 2007, *282,* 12785-12790.

[27] Yamaguchi, Y.; Matsumura, T.; Ichida, K.; Okamoto, K.; Nishino, T., *J. Biochem.* 2007, *141,* 513-524.

[28] D'Ardenne, S.C.; Edmondson, D.E., *Biochemistry* 1990, *29,* 9046-9052

[29] Massey, V.; Edmondson, D., *J. Biol. Chem.* 1970, *245,* 6595-6598.

[30] Pauff, J.M.; Cao, H.; Hille, R., *J. Biol. Chem.* 2009, *284,* 8751 - 8758.

[31] Dietzel, U.; Kuper, J.; Doebbler, J.; Schulte, A.; Truglio, J.; Leimkühler, S.; Kisker, C., *J. Biol. Chem.* 2009, *284,* 8768-8776

[32] NishinoT.; Okamoto, K.; Eger, B.T.; Pai, E.F.; Nishino, T., *FEBS J.* 2008, *275,* 3278-3289.

[33] Okamoto, K.; Kawaguchi, Y.; Eger, B.T.; Pai, E.F.; Nishino, T., *J. Am. Chem. Soc.* 2010, *132,* 17080-17083.

[34] Ilich, P.; Hille, R., *Inorg. Chim. Acta* 1997, *263,* 87-94.

[35] Bray, M.R.; Deeth, R.J., *J. Chem. Soc. Dalton Trans.* 1997, 1267-1268.

[36] Voityuk, A.A.; Albert, K.; Romão, M.J.; Huber, R.; Rösch, N., *Inorg. Chem.* 1998, *37,* 176-180.

[37] Ilich, P.; Hille, R., *J. Phys. Chem.(B)* 1999, *103,* 5406-5412.

[38] Morpeth, F.F.; George, G.N.; Bray, R.C., *Biochem. J.* 1984, *220,* 235-242.

[39] Ilich, P.; Hille, R. *J. Am. Chem. Soc.* 2002, *124,* 6796-6797.

[40] Wagener, N.; Pierik, A.; Ibdah, A.; Hille, R.; Dobbek, H., *Proc. Natl. Acad. Sci. USA,* 2009, *106,* 11055-11060

[41] Zhang, X.-H.; Wu, Y.-D., *Inorg. Chem.* 2005, *44,* 1466-1471.

[42] Amano, T.; Ochi, N.; Sato, H.; Sakaki, S., *J. Am. Chem. Soc.* 2007, *129,* 8131-8138.

[43] Bayse, C.A., *Dalton Trans.,* 2009, 2306-2314.

[44] Metz, S.; Thiel, W., *J. Am. Chem. Soc.* 2009, *131,* 14885-14902.

[45] Metz, S.; Thiel, W., *J. Phys. Chem. B* 2110, *114,* 1506-1517.

[46] Metz, S.; Thiel, W. *Coord. Chem. Rev.* 2011, *255,* 1085-1103.

[47] Hille, R.; Massey, V. *J. Biol. Chem.* 1986, *261,* 1241-1247.

[48] Hille, R.; Anderson, R.F., *J. Biol. Chem.* 1991, *266,* 5608-5615.

[49] Hille, R., *Biochemistry* 1991, *30,* 8522-8529.

[50] Hille, R.; Anderson, R.F., *J. Biol. Chem.* 2001, *276,* 31193-31201.

[51] Reese, S.Y.; Nocera, D.G., *Annu. Rev. Biochem.* 2009, *78,* 673-699.

[52] Stubbe, J.; Novera, D.G.; Yee, C.S.; Chang, M.C.Y., *Chem. Rev.* 2003, *103,* 2167-2201.

[53] Garattini, E.; Fratelli, M.; Terao, M., *Cell. Mol. Life Sci.* 2008, *65,*1019-1048.

[54] Terao, M.; Kurosaki, M.; Barzago, M.M.; Fratelli,M.; Bagnati, R.; Bastone, A.; Guidici, C.; Scanziani, E.; Mancuso, A.; Tiveron, C.; Garattini, E., *Mol. Cell. Biol.* 2009, *29,* 357-377.

[55] Ichida, K.; Matsumura, T.; Sakuma, R.; Hosoya, T.; Nishino, T., *Biochem. Biophys. Res. Commun.* 2001, *285,* 1194-200.

[56] Yamamoto, T.; Moriwaki, Y.; Takahashi, S.; Tsutsumi, Z.; Tuneyoshi, K.; Matsui, K.; Cheng, J.D.; Hada, T., *Metabolism* 2003, *52,* 1501-1504.

[57] Peretz, H.; Naamati, M.S.; Levartowsky, D.; Lagziel, A.; Shani, E.; Horn, I.; Shalev, H.; Landau, D., *Mol. Genet. Metab.* 2007, *91,* 23-29.

[58] Kurosaki, M.; Terao, M.; Barzago, M.M.; Bastone, A.; Bernardinello, D.; Salmona, M.; Garattini, E., *J. Biol. Chem.* 2004, *279,* 50482-50498.

[59] Schumann, S.; Terao, M.; Garattini, E.; Saggu, M.; Lendzian, F.; Hildebrandt, P.; Leimkühler, S., *PloS One*, 2009, *4*, 1-9.

[60] Seo, M.; Peeters, A.J.M.; Koiwai, H.; Oritani, T.; Marion-Poll, A.; Zeevart, J.A.D.; Koornneef, M.; Kamiya, Y.; Koshiba, T., *Proc. Natl. Acad. Sci. USA* 2000, *97*, 12908-12913.

[61] Hoff, T.; Frandsen, G.I.; Rocher, A.; Mundy, J., *Biochim. Biophys. Acta* 1998, *1398*, 397-402.

[62] Seo, M.; Aoki, H.; Koiwai, H.; Kamiya, T.Y.; Nambara, E.; Koshiba, T., *Plant Cell Physiol.* 2004, *45*, 1694-1703.

[63] Zdunek-Zastocka, E., *Plant Physiol. Biochem.* 2008, *46*, 19-28.

[64] Andrade, S.L.A.; Brondino, C.; Feio, M.J.; Moura, I.; Moura, J.J.G., *Eur. J. Biochem.* 2000, *267*, 2054-2061.

[65] Iwasaki, T.; Okamoto, K.; Nishino, T.; Mizushima, J.; Hori, H.; Nishino, T., *J. Biochem.* 2000, *127*, 771-778.

[66] Lowe, D.J.; Bray, R.C., *Biochem J.* 1978, *169*, 471-479.

[67] More, C.; Asso, M.; Roger, G.; Guigliarelli, B.; Caldiera, J.; Moura, J.J.G.; Bertrand, P., *Biochemistry* 2005, *44*, 11628-11635.

[68] Boer, D.R.; Thapper, A.; Brondino, C.D.; Romão, M.J.; Moura J.J.G., *J. Am. Chem. Soc.* 2004, *126*, 8614-8615.

[69] Cao, H.; Hall, J.; Hille, R., *J. Am. Chem. Soc.* 2011, *133*, 12414-12417.

[70] Neumann, M.; Mittelstädt, G.; Iobi-Nivol, C.; Saggu, M.; Lendzian, F.; Hildebrandt, P.; Leimkühler, S., *FEBS J.* 2009, *276*, 2762-2774.

[71] Leimkühler, S.; Klipp, W., *J. Bacteriol.* 1999, *181*, 2745-2751.

[72] Neumann, M.; Schulte, M.; Jünemann, N.; Stöcklein, W.; Leimkühler, S., *J. Biol. Chem.* 2006, *281*, 15701-15708.

[73] Alfaro, J.F.; J.P. Jones, *J. Org. Chem.* 2008, *23*, 9469-9473.

[74] Turner, N.A.; Doyle, W.A.; Ventom, A.M.; Bray, R.C., *Eur. J. Biochem.* 1995, *232*, 646-657.

[75] Torres, R.A.; Korzekwa, K.R.; McMasters, D.R.; Fandozzi, C.M.; Jones, J.P., *J. Med. Chem.* 2007, *50*, 4642-4647.

[76] Alfaro, J.F.; Joswing-Jones, C.A.; Ouyang, W.; Nicols, J.; Crouch, G.J.; Jones, J.P., *Drug Metab. Disposition* 2009, *37*, 2393-2398.

[77] Skibo, E.B.; Gilchrist, J.H.; Lee, C.-H., *Biochemistry* 1987, *26*, 3032-3037.

[78] Meyer, O.; Frunzke, K.; Mördorf, G., Biochemistry of the aerobic utilization of carbon monoxide. in *Microbial Growth on C1 Compounds* (J.C. Murrell and D.P. Kelly, eds.) Intercept Ltd., 1993, Andover, UK, pp. 433-459.

[79] Kraut, M.; Hugendieck, I.; Herwig, S.; Meyer, O., *Arch. Microbiol.* 1989, *152*, 335-341.

[80] Moxley, J. M.; Smith, K. A., *Soil Biol. Biochem.* 1998, *30*, 65-79

[81] Mörsdorf, G.; Frunzke, K.; Gadkari, D.; Meyer, O., *Biodegradation* 1992, *3*, 61-82

[82] Ragsdale, S.; Kumar, M., *Chem. Rev.* 1996, *96*, 2515-2539.

[83] Dobbek, H.; Gremer, L.; Meyer, O.; Huber, R., *Proc. Natl. Acad. Sci. USA* 1999, *96*, 8884-8889.

[84] Hänzelmann, P.; Dobbek, H.; Gremer, L.; Huber, R.; Meyer, O., *J. Mol. Biol.* 2000, *301*, 1221-1235.

[85] Kang, B.S.; Kim, Y.M., *J. Bacteriol.* 1999, *181*, 5581-5590.

[86]   Santiago, B.; Schübel, U.; Egelseer, C.; Meyer, O., *Gene* 1999, *236*, 115-124.

[87]   Dobbek H.; Gremer L.; Kiefersauer R.; Huber R.; Meyer O., *Proc. Natl. Acad. Sci. USA* 2002, *99*, 15971-15976.

[88]   Meyer-Klaucke, W.; Gnida, M.; Ferner, R.; Gremer, L.; Meyer, O., *J. Inorg. Biochem.* 2001, *86*, 339-339.

[89]   Zhang, B.; Hemann, C.F.; Hille, R., *J. Biol. Chem.*, 2010, *285*, 12571-12578.

[90]   Resch, M.; Dobbek, H.; Meyer, O., *J. Biol. Inorg. Chem.* 2005, *10*, 518-528.

[91]   Gourlay, C.; Nielsen, D.J.; White, J.M.; Knottenbelt, S.Z.; Kirk, M.L.; Young, C.G., *J. Am. Chem. Soc.* 2006, *128*, 2164-2165.

[92]   Wilcoxen, J.; Snider, S.; Hille, R., *J. Am. Chem. Soc.*, 2011, *133*, 12934-12936.

[93]   Wilcoxen, J.; Zhang, B.; Hille, R., *Biochemistry* 2011, *50*, 1910-1916.

[94]   Holcenberg, J.S.; Stadtman, E.R. *J. Biol. Chem.* 1969, *244*, 1194-1203.

[95]   Imhoff, D.; Andreesen, J.R., *FEMS Microbiol. Lett.* 1979, *5*, 155-158.

[96]   Dilworth, G.L., *Arch. Biochem. Biophys.* 1982, *219*, 30-38.

[97]   Stadtman, T.C., *Annu. Rev. Biochem* 1990, *59*, 111-127.

[98]   Gladyshev, V.N., *Metal Ions Biol. Systs.* 2002, *39*, 655-672.

[99]   Chang, Y.; Gladyshev, V.N., *J. Mol. Biol.* 2008, *379*, 881-899

[100] Gladyshev, V.N.; Khangulov, S.V.; Axley, M.J.; Stadtman, T.C., *Proc. Natl. Acad. Sci. USA* 1994, *91*, 7708-7711.

[101] Boyington, J.C.; Gladyshev, V.N.; Khangulov, S.V.; Stadtman, T.C.; Sun, P., *Science* 1997, *275*, 1305-1308.

[102] Raaijmakers, H.C.; Romao, M.J., *J. Biol. Inorg. Chem.* 2006, *11*, 849-854.

[103] Self, W.T.; Stadtman, T.C., *Proc. Natl. Acad. Sci. USA* 2000, *97*, 7208-7213.

[104] Wagner, R.; Cammack, R.; Andreesen, J.R., *Biochim. Biophys. Acta* 1984, *791*, 63-74.

[105] Schrader, T.; Rienhofer, A.; Andreesen, J.R., *Eur. J. Biochem.* 1999, *264*, 862-871.

[106] Gladyshev, V.N.; Khangulov, S.V.; Stadtman, T.C., *Proc. Natl. Acad. Sci. USA* 94, *91*, 232-236.

[107] Gladyshev, V.N.; Lecchi, P., *Biofactors* 1995, *5*, 93-97.

[108] Tshisuaka, B.; Kappl, R.; Hüttermann, J.; Lingens, F., *Biochemistry* 1993, *32*, 12928-12934.

[109] Frerichs-Deeken, U.; Goldenstedt, B.; Gahl-Janssen, R.; Kappl, R.; Hüttermann, J.; Fetzner, S., *Eur. J. Biochem.* 2003, *270*, 1567-1577.

[110] Bonin, I.; Martins, B.M.; Purvanov, V.; Huber, R.; Dobbek, H., *Structure* 2004, *12*, 1425-1435.

[111] Gibson, J.; Dispensa, M.; Harwood, C.S., *J. Bacteriol.* 1997, *179*, 634-642.

[112] Boll, M.; Fuchs, G., *Eur. J. Biochem.* 1998, *251*, 946-954.

[113] Unciuleac, M.; Warkentin, E.; Page, C.C.; Boll, M.; Ermler, U., *Structure* 2004, *12*, 2249-2256.

[114] Boll, M.; Fuchs, G.; Meier, C.; Trautwein, A.; El Kasmi, A.; Ragsdale, S.W.; Buchanan, G.; Lowe, D.J., *J. Biol. Chem.* 2001, *276*, 47853-47862.

[115] Stockert, A.L.; Shinde, S.; Anderson, R.F.; Hille, R., *J. Am. Chem. Soc.* 2002, *124*, 14554-14555.

[116] Bergmann, F.; Dikstein, S., *J. Biol. Chem.* 1956, *223*, 765-780.

[117] Cvetkovic, A.; Menon, A.L.; Thorgersen, M.P.; Scott, J.W.; Poole, F.L. II; Jenney, F.E. Jr.; Lancaster, W.A.; Praissman, J.L.; Shanmukh, S.; Vaccaro, B.J.; Trauger, S.A.;

Kalisiak, E.; Apon, J.V.; Siuzdak, G.; Yannone, S.M.; Tainer, J.A.; Adams, M.W.W., *Nature* 2010, *466*, 779-784.

In: Molybdenum
Editor: Alvin A. Holder

ISBN: 978-1-62417-272-4
© 2013 Nova Science Publishers, Inc.

Chapter 12

ORGANOMETALLIC MOLYBDENUM COMPLEXES AS ANTICANCER AGENTS

*Enrique Meléndez**

University of Puerto Rico Department of Chemistry, Mayagüez, Puerto Rico

ABSTRACT

The pioneer work of Köpf-Maeir and Köpf in the late 1970s established for the first time the potential application of metallocene complexes as anticancer drugs. As a consequence of their leading experiments, a new field of research emerged in the 1980s, Bioorganometallic Chemistry. Bioorganometallic chemistry has developed rapidly in the last thirty years leading to application of organometallic species into diagnostic, sensors, immunoassays and anticancer research among others. This chapter focuses on the bioorganometallic chemistry of molybdenum as metal-based anticancer drugs. The anticancer properties of molybdenocene dichloride, its derivatives and Mo(II) organometallic complexes are described as well as the mechanism of action, aqueous and coordination chemistry, and molybdenum-biomolecule interactions.

1. INTRODUCTION

In the last century, metals have been used as anticancer, anti-fungus, anti-arthritis, anti-ulcer along with other conditions. Among these metals, molybdenum has attracted the attention of many investigators due to its importance as cofactor in enzymes (in sulfur containing proteins), as an essential element in human nutrition and as a metal-based drug. [1-3] Molybdenum coordination compounds have been reported to possess antidiabetic and anticancer properties, however, this is out of the scope of this chapter. We will focus on biologically active organometallic molybdenum complexes, in particular as metal-based anticancer drugs.

---

* University of Puerto Rico Department of Chemistry, PO Box 9019, Mayagüez, Puerto Rico 00681, Telephone: 787-832-4040 ext. 2524, Fax: 787-265-3849, E-mail: *enrique.melendez@upr.edu*.

The discovery of metallocene-based organometallic anticancer agent, Cp_2TiCl_2 in 1979 by Köpf and Köpf-Maier [4] and in subsequent years other metallocenes of general formula Cp_2MX_2, I (Cp = cyclopentadienyl, M = Ti, V, Nb, Mo; X = halides and pseudo-halides), Cp_2Fe^+X (ferrocenium), main group $(C_5R_5)_2M$ (M = Sn, Ge; R = H, CH_3), stimulated much interest to investigate other non-platinum complexes with different mechanism of antineoplastic activity. [4-14] From their initial experiments, Köpf-Maeir and Köpf found that titanocene dichloride, Cp_2TiCl_2, was the most active metallocene *in vitro*, but its low hydrolytic stability hindered it to be studied in more details. In contrast to titanocene dichloride, Cp_2Mo^{2+} possesses good hydrolytic stability at physiological pH while Cp_2Ti^{2+} hydrolyzes extensively. [20] Thus, this stability is an attractive property of Cp_2MoCl_2 and provides an excellent model to study its aqueous chemistry under physiological conditions and understand which species are likely to reach the target places in the cell. Inspired by this findings, several research groups have been working on organometallic molybdenum complexes, in particular with Mo(IV) and in less extent with Mo(II) species. Since the most studied and characterized complexes as potential metal-based drugs are molybdenocene dichloride and its derivatives, we start discussing their aqueous and coordination chemistry.

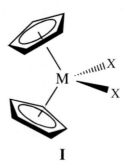

I

2. MOLYBDENOCENE DICHLORIDE, CP_2MOCL_2: AQUEOUS STABILITY AND COORDINATION CHEMISTRY WITH DNA, OLIGONUCLEOTIDES AND PROTEIN AND THE IMPLICATION IN THE MECHANISM OF ACTION

2. 1. Aqueous and Coordination Chemistry of Cp_2MoCl_2

Bis(cyclopentadienyl)molybdenum dichloride, Cp_2MoCl_2, is an organometallic complex that belongs to the sandwich complex category. It contains two planar aromatic five-membered rings and two chlorides coordinated to Mo(IV). Molybdenocene dichloride was prepared by Cooper and Green, and single crystal X-ray structure revealed two molecules in the unit cell, in which one molecule the Mo(IV) is π-bonded to two staggered Cp rings and two chlorides and the second molecule contains two eclipsed Cp rings, both in a pseudo-tetrahedral coordination geometry or better described as an clamshell geometry with two ancillary chloride ligands on the open edge. [21,22]

The chemistry of Cp_2MoCl_2 in aqueous solution: hydrolysis of Cl^-, M-Cp stability and coordination chemistry of "Cp_2Mo^{2+}" with DNA components have been initially investigated by Marks and coworkers and later by Meléndez's and Harding's groups. [20,23-36] According to Marks and coworkers report, the chloride loss from Cp_2MoCl_2 in water (unbuffered) at 37^0C occurs very rapid during the complex dissolution. The first chloride is lost during the dissolution process, followed by the loss of the second chloride within 1 hr (equations 1 and 2). Increasing the ionic strength with KNO_3 to 0.318 M did not affect the chloride hydrolysis. [20]

$$Cp_2MoCl_2 + H_2O \leftrightarrow Cp_2Mo(H_2O)Cl^+ + Cl^- \tag{1}$$

$$Cp_2Mo(H_2O)Cl^+ + H_2O \leftrightarrow Cp_2Mo(H_2O)_2{}^{2+} + Cl^- \tag{2}$$

At pH 7.4, one of the aqua ligand gets deprotonated and the principal species is the monocation, $Cp_2Mo(H_2O)(OH)^+$, which exist in equilibrium with the dimeric species $[Cp_2Mo(\mu-OH)_2MoCp_2]^{2+}$. [23]

$$2\ Cp_2Mo(H_2O)(OH)^+ \leftrightarrow [Cp_2Mo(\mu-OH)_2MoCp_2]^{2+} + 2\ H_2O \tag{3}$$

The coordination chemistry of Cp_2MoCl_2 with nucleobases and nucleotides was also investigated by Marks and coworkers. [20] In aqueous solution, at physiological pH, molybdenocene dichloride gets engaged in N(3), N(4) coordination, for N-methylcytosine, forming a four-membered chelate while for N-methyladenine, N(1), N(6) (four-membered chelate) and N(7), NH(6) (five-membered chelate) coordination modes are observed, Figure 1. In the solid state for the N-methyladenine, only the N(1), N(6), coordination mode is observed, Figure 2.

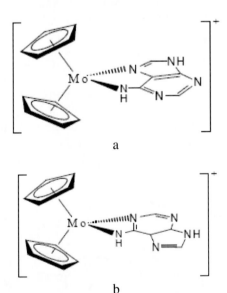

a

b

Figure 1. (Continued) .

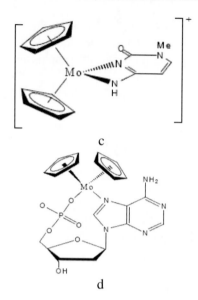

Figure 1. Coordination modes between Cp$_2$MoCl$_2$ and nucleobases and nucleotide. a) N(7), NH(6) chelation b) N(1), NH(6) chelation, c) N(3), NH(4) chelation d) N(7), O(phosphate) chelation.

As mentioned above, see Figure 2, the Cp$_2$Mo^{2+} adopts the clamshell geometry and a Cp(centroid)-Mo-Cp(centroid) bent angle of 135.3°, similar to other Cp$_2$MoX$_2$ complexes. In the case of the deoxynucleotides, guanosine (5'-dGMP) and adenosine (5'-dAMP), N(7)-O(phosphate) coordination prevails whereas for cytosine (5'-dCMP) and thymidine (5'-dTMP), N(3), O(phosphate) coordination mode is observed.[20] Solid state X-ray diffraction structure, Figure 3, revealed that 5'-dMGP forms a dimeric species where Cp$_2$Mo^{2+} is σ-bonded to N(7) and O(phosphate) from the adjacent 5'-dMGP. [20]

Binding studies between Cp$_2$MoCl$_2$ and DNA and oligonucleotides were investigated by Harding's, Meléndez's and Marks' groups. Binding studies, by Harding's group, between Cp$_2$MoCl$_2$ and calf-thymus DNA revealed that Cp$_2$Mo^{2+} binds the terminal phosphates of DNA. [24] However, the fact that DNA has no terminal phosphates and that such coordination was observed must likely by fragmentation of the DNA after sonication, they performed an additional study between Cp$_2$MoCl$_2$ and oligonuclotides in saline unbuffered solution at pH 7.0. [25] They reported that Cp$_2$MoCl$_2$ does not get engaged in any type of bonding with oligonucleotides, disregarding this type of interaction. [25]

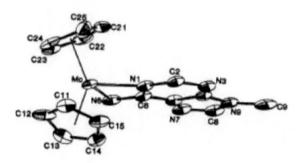

Figure 2. Solid state structure of [Cp$_2$Mo(9-methyladenyl)]PF$_6$. Reproduced with permission of the American Chemical Society.

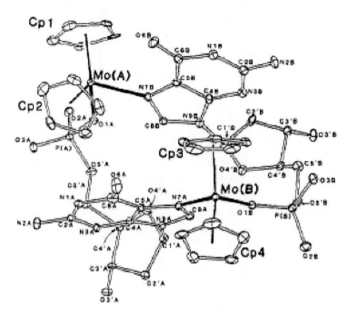

Figure 3. Ortep diagram of [Cp2Mo(5'-dGMP)]2 showing the dimeric molybdenum coordination and the 24-membered chelate ring. Thirteen molecules of water are surrounding the dimer are omitted. Reproduced with permission of the American Chemical Society.

Marks' group studied the interaction of Cp_2MoCl_2 with self-complementary oligonucleotide d(ApGpGpCpCpT) and the 5'-phosphorylated analog d(pApGpGpCpCpT) by NMR spectroscopy at pH = 7.0. [26] The interaction of Cp_2MoCl_2 with d(ApGpGpCpCpT) showed minor changes on the ^{1}H NMR spectrum suggesting a weak interaction of Cp_2Mo^{2+} to the oligonucleotide, whereas the spectrum of d(pApGpGpCpCpT) exhibited significant changes at the 5' end. Two signals corresponding to the nonequivalent Cp rings and the upfield shifts for H2 and H8 signals observed in the ^{1}H NMR spectrum, together with the downfield displacement for the 5'-terminal phosphate in the ^{31}P NMR spectrum suggest the coordination of Cp_2Mo^{2+} to N(7) and O(phosphate) positions at this terminal. [26]

Conversely, Meléndez's group performed several studies in order to unravel mechanistic information about the molybdenocene coordination properties with biologically important molecules. Inductive Coupled Plasma Emission Spectroscopy (ICPES) studies between calf-thymus DNA (pH 7.0 and buffer conditions) and Cp_2MCl_2 (M = Ti, Mo) showed that molybdenocene binds DNA in about 5-10%, while titanocene is bound in 90-95%. [27,28] In addition, similar studies were pursued using electrochemistry (cyclic voltammerty) and 1D and 2D NMR spectroscopy. [29-31] In similar manner as in the ICPES study, cyclic voltammetry experiments corroborated that molybdenocene dichloride and its derivatives bind calf-thymus DNA in 5-12%. [29,30]

To identify which type of interactions and what nucleobases are involved, Melendez's group pursued molybdenocene-oligonucleotide binding studies at physiological and buffered conditions using 1D and 2D NOESY ^{1}H NMR spectroscopy and cyclic voltammetry. [31] The self-complimentary oligonucleotide CGCATATATGCG with 5'- and 3'-OH terminals was used as a model to establish binding interactions with C_2MoCl_2. This oligonucleotide was selected because it does not possess terminal phosphate, thus the Ti-O(phosphate) coordination can be ruled out. Meléndez's group determined that molybdenoecene gets engaged in a weak N(7) coordination with purine bases only and almost negligible phosphate ester coordination was observed by ^{31}P NMR spectroscopy. [31] Even though the sensitivity of the NMR techniques is much lower than ICPES and electrochemistry, we estimated about a 5-10% of interaction using NMR data. [31] Additionally, cyclic voltammetry experiments demonstrated and corroborated that molybdenocene-oligonucletide interaction is about 5%. [31]

The above results are to some extent opposite to Harding's findings. [25] Nevertheless, our studies were performed under physiological conditions while they used saline solution (NaCl) perhaps inhibiting the chloride hydrolysis of Cp_2MoCl_2 and subsequent interaction with the nucleotides. Furthermore, on an independent study, Kuo and collaborators found that Cp_2MoCl_2 promotes phosphoester bond cleavage. [32] Therefore, a weak interaction of Cp_2MoCl_2 with N(7) followed by phosphoester bond cleavage could explain our findings, in particular under the acidic conditions encountered in the cancer cells, but it has not been investigated in further details.

2. 2. Mechanism of Action of Cp_2MoCl_2

The mechanism of action of Cp_2MoCl_2 at cellular levels is not well understood and continues being a subject of debate. The investigations on the biochemical aspects of molybdenocene dichloride by several research groups have provided insights and hypotheses about the possible mechanism of action of molybdenocene dichloride as explained below. [26,33-37]

Marks and coworkers investigated the interaction of Cp_2MCl_2 (M = V, Mo) with DNA-processing enzymes. This study revealed that these metallocenes have no effect on the DNA electrophoretic mobility, endonuclease, ligase or polymerase activity. [26] On the other hand, Cp_2MoCl_2 demonstrated to inhibit protein kinase C (PKC), an enzyme that regulates cellular proliferation. [26] Thus, this could be one target for Cp_2MoCl_2 to elicit its anticancer activity. Other hypotheses were tested regarding antitumor activity of Cp_2MoCl_2. For instance, Harding and coworkers have shown that glutathione (GSH), an intracellular tripeptide responsible for reacting with electrophilic cytotoxic drugs, forms stable adducts with molybdenocene dichloride and it is likely that GSH plays an important role in the mechanism of action of Cp_2MoCl_2. [33] But titanocene and niobocene dichlorides failed to be recognized (coordinated) by glutathione thus, this tripeptide is apparently only specific for molybdenocene. [33]

Competition experiments with nucleic acid components (dAMP, ribose monophosphate), and aminoacids (histidine, lysine, alanine and cysteine) were performed by ^{1}H NMR spectroscopy. [34] First, the coordination of lysine and alanine to Cp_2MoCl_2 either by the carboxylate or amino groups was not observed by ^{1}H NMR spectroscopy. For histidine, coordination of the imidazole ring to molybdenum was observed by the presence of new aromatic signals in the spectrum. The addition of cysteine to this mixture showed that histidine is replaced forming the $Cp_2Mo(Cys)_2$. Additional experiments were performed with dAMP and ribose monophosphate, see Figure 4. Addition of cysteine to the dAMP and ribose monophosphate molybdenocene complexes yields new NMR signals corresponding to the $Cp_2Mo(Cys)_2$. Moreover, addition of dAMP and ribose monophosphate to the $Cp_2Mo(Cys)_2$ solution produced no change in the NMR spectrum, indicating the cysteine cannot be replaced by nucleic acid components. Also, Cp_2MoCl_2 showed strong coordination to the glutathione. While these experiments suggest that GSH may be involved in the mechanism of action, additional experiments shown that the coordination of glutathione to Cp_2MoCl_2 at physiological pH leads to significant deactivation of molybdenocene dichloride antitumor activity. [34,35] Thus, at least for molybdenocene dichloride, glutathione serves as a deactivating molecule rather than metal carrier agent inside the cell. [34,35]

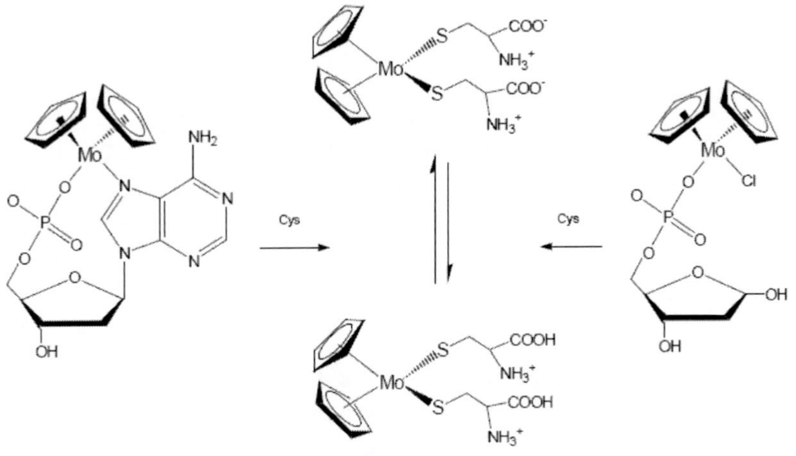

Figure 4. Reactions representing competition experiments.

A distribution study of the transition metal in Chinese hamster lung cells treated with Cp_2MCl_2 (M = Ti, V, Nb, Mo) was published in 2005 by Harding and collaborators. [36] In particular for Cp_2MoCl_2, molybdenum is dispersed throughout the cell not in a particular organelle, although there is some evidence for accumulation near the center of the cell (in the nuclear region). Since, according to the authors, the DNA binding by molybdenocene is very unlikely, it seems that molybdenocene is targeting thiol containing nuclear proteins. [36] With this in mind, binding studies of radioactive (radiotracer) $Cp_2{}^{99}MoCl_2$ with a thiol containing protein, human serum albumin (HSA), were pursued by monitoring ^{99}Mo gamma emission. These studies demonstrated that Cp_2MoCl_2 binds HSA in a ratio of 9.4 to 1. [37] In 2008, Meléndez and co-workers reported an electrochemical methodology to determine the Cp_2MoCl_2-HSA interaction, using the change in current as the molar fraction of HSA increases.[38] Using this methodology, it was determined that about 30% of the Cp_2MoCl_2 binds HSA, but the interaction is mainly hydrophobic and weak to be measured by spectral changes in UV-Vis and NMR spectroscopy.[39-41]

Harding and coworkers published an *in vitro* study using V79 Chinese hamster lung cells and provided additional information regarding the mechanism of action of Cp_2MoCl_2. [42] V79 Chinese hamster lung cells were treated with Cp_2MoCl_2 (ranging from 100 to 400 μM,) and studied using micronucleus assay and transmission electron microscopy to elucidate the genotoxic effect induced by the molybdenocene. [42] These studies demonstrated an increase in frequency of micronuclei (chromosome breaks and/or loss) as the dose increases in comparison to the control cells (untreated cells). In addition, transmission electron microscopy of the treated V79 Chinese hamster lung cells displayed high incidence of polynucleation with high predominance of cells containing three to five nuclei as well as enlargement in the cell diameter by 1-2 μM in contrast to the control cells. Also, the treated cells exhibited increased chromatin condensation and damaged mitochondria in the cytoplasm. These features are in marked contrast to the untreated control V79 cells, which are characterized by a single commonly well shape nucleus, containing a single, well defined nucleolus and a granular cytoplasm sparingly filled with organelles. With this experimental data the authors propose that tubulin, a thiol rich protein with 20 cysteine residues located in the spindle apparatus, might be involved in coordination of Cp_2Mo^{2+} to the Cys residues, deactivating the spindle apparatus and producing the observed micronuclei. [42]

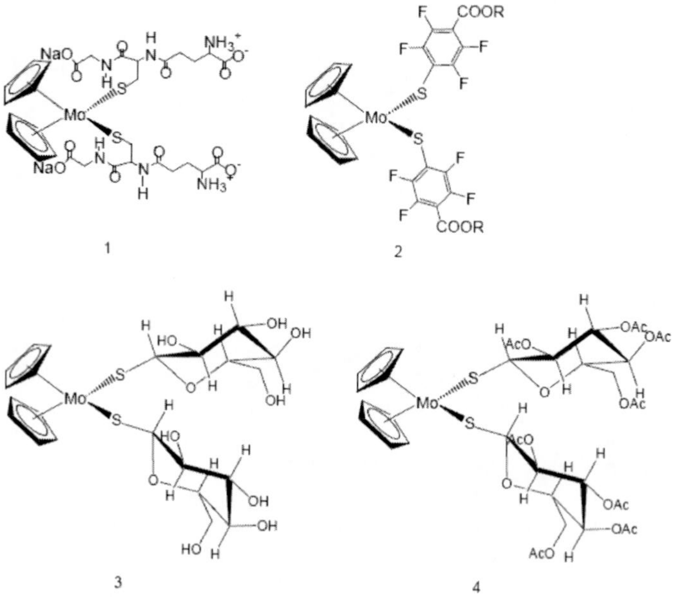

Figure 5. Structures of thiol derivatives of molybdenocene dichloride.

With the mechanistic studies presented above, it is clear that molybdenocene dichloride could have various targets and its mechanism of action is far from being well understood. The fact that Cp_2MoCl_2 forms stable species at physiological pH, $Cp_2Mo(H_2O)(OH)^+/Cp_2Mo(\mu\text{-}OH)_2MoCp_2$, and the coordination affinity for sulfur and phosphates (Mo-S and Mo-O(PO$_3$) ligations) makes it difficult to hypothesize just one mechanism of action. It is very likely that the mechanism of action of Cp_2MoCl_2 is a complex one, involving more than one target place.

3. MOLYBDENOCENE DERIVATIVES

Following the initial investigations on molybdenocene dichloride and its binding capability to biomolecules, several research groups have been working in the structure modification of molybdenocene complex to increase its anticancer activity and to obtain structure-activity relationship (SAR). The main goal is, using structure-activity relationship, the rational design of more efficient and potent antineoplastic agents. To accomplish this, two strategies have been pursued: replacement of halides with ancillary ligands to modulate solubility-stability and biological activity in aqueous solution, and functionalization of cyclopentadienyl to improve biological activity and make them target specific antineoplastic agents. The first studies on molybdenocene dichloride were directed to the replacement of the chloride with ancillary ligand that can lead to a better and less toxic drug. [35] Four thiol derivatives of molybdenocene (1-4, Figure 5) were synthesized varying their size, charge and lipophilicity. In marked contrast to Cp_2MoCl_2, these thiolate derivatives do not undergo ligand hydrolysis at pH 7.0, demonstrating the robustness of these species at neutral pH.

The cytotoxic activities (IC_{50}) of 1-4 were determined. [35] The IC_{50} is the concentration required to inhibit the 50% of cell growth. The cytotoxic and cellular uptake studies of molybdenum in V79 Chinese hamster lung cells demonstrated that there is no correlation between the cell uptake and cytotoxicity, since the complex that showed the highest intracellular content of Mo is not the most cytotoxic, see Table I. Additionally, the thiolate coordination to molybdenocene inactivate the resulting complex due to the inert character of the Mo-S bond which makes the ligand hydrolysis less accessible to form the vacant coordination site for subsequent reaction with the target biomolecule. [35]

In contrast to the above results, it was found that not always the Mo-S coordination renders detrimental to the cytotoxic activity of the resulting modified molybdenocenes. A series of water soluble molydenocene thiolate complexes have been synthesized in water at pH 7.0, in presence of thionucleobases and thionucleosides ligands, demonstrating high aqueous stability and robustness at physiological pH. [43] The goal of this study was to elucidate the role of the ancillary ligands on molybdenocene and the outcoming anticancer properties. The new water soluble and robust species, $[(\eta^5-C_5H_5)_2Mo(L)]Cl$ (L= 6-mercaptopurine, 2-amino-6-mercaptopurine, (-)-2-amino-6-mercaptopurine ribose and 6-mercaptopurine ribose), were characterized by spectroscopic methods. NMR spectroscopic data on $[(\eta^5-C_5H_5)_2Mo(6-mercaptopurine)]Cl$, in D_2O, showed the presence of two coordination isomers, S(6), N(7), A and S(6), N(1), B, Figure 6. In general, all four complexes exhibited two coordination isomers, S(6), N(7), A and S(6), N(1), B, in aqueous solution but only $[(\eta^5-C_5H_5)_2Mo(6-mercaptopurine ribose)]Cl$ showed two coordination modes in DMSO-d_6. [43] Of these two possible coordination isomers, we believe, based on thermodynamic considerations, that the 5-membered chelate, S(6),N(7) thionucleobase coordination (A) is the most stable. [43]

The $[(\eta^5-C_5H_5)_2Mo(L)]Cl$ complexes are stable at pH 7.4 for extended period of time. Based on the aqueous stability of the $[(\eta^5-C_5H_5)_2Mo(L)]Cl$ complexes and long term stability under physiological pH, their antiproliferative activities in HT-29 colon cancer and MCF-7 breast cancer cell lines were investigated, see Table 2. The cytotoxic data showed that the coordination of the thionucleobases and thionucleosides to Cp_2Mo^{2+} apparently enhances its antiproliferative activity on HT-29 and MCF-7 cell lines, but the thionucleobase/thionucleoside ligands have their own activity. In this regard, the authors mentioned that since the thionucleobases/thionucleosides have antiproliferative properties on these cell lines, the cytotoxic data can be explained the other way around. That is, the inclusion of molybdenocene moiety into the thionucleobases/thionucleosides reduces their cytotoxic activities. [43]

In any event, the unique properties of these complexes are expressed on MCF-7 cell line. The cytotoxic data of $[Cp_2Mo(L)]Cl$ complexes in MCF-7 breast cancer cell line was more intriguing and different from that of HT-29 cell line, as MCF-7 cell line expresses higher amount of estrogen receptor. Cp_2MoCl_2 possesses proliferative activity on MCF-7 breast cancer cells since it acts as an estrogen-like agonist on the estrogen receptor. [44-46]

Additionally, 6-mercaptopurine and 2-amino-6-mercaptopurine have low antiproliferative activity in MCF-7 cell line ($IC_{50} \gg 100\mu M$). Interestingly, $[(\eta^5\text{-}C_5H_5)_2Mo(6\text{-}mercaptopurine)]Cl$ ($IC_{50} = 203(\pm45\ \mu M)$ and $[(\eta^5\text{-}C_5H_5)_2Mo(2\text{-}amino\text{-}6\text{-}mercaptopurine)]Cl$ ($IC_{50} = 16\ (\pm2\ \mu M)$ have cytotoxic activities exceeding those of the thionucleobase and Cp_2MoCl_2. It is very likely that this enhancement in cytotoxicity comes from two sources: the increase in lipophilicity as result of incorporating Cp_2Mo^{2+} into the thionucleobase, increasing the permeability across the lipophilic cell membrane, and synergism between the two anticancer moieties. [43]

Table 1. Cytotoxicities of molybdenocenes in V79 Chinese Hamster Lung cell line using MTT assay and cellular uptake of Mo. *Relative values standardized to Cp_2MoCl_2

Complex	IC_{50} (μM), 24 h	Cell uptake*
Cp_2MoCl_2	820	1.0
1	2230	0.15-0.20
2	2900	
3	>500	3.5-5.0

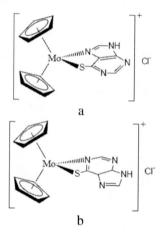

Figure 6. Proposed structures of $[Cp_2Mo(6\text{-}mercaptopurine)]Cl$. a) S(6), N(7) and b) S(6), N(1) coordination modes.

Table 2. Cytotoxicities of $[Cp_2Mo(L)]Cl$ complexes studied on HT-29 colon cancer and MCF-7 breast cancer cell lines at 72 h, as determined by MTT assay. IC values are the average of four independent measurements with their standard deviations ( ). n/a = not active under the concentrations studied

Complex	IC_{50} (μM), HT-29	IC_{50} (μM), MCF-7
$[Cp_2Mo(6\text{-}mercaptopurine)]Cl.$	180(±8)	203(±45)
6-mercaptopurine.	10.1($\pm.3$)	750(±30)
$[Cp_2Mo(6\text{-}mercaptopurine\ ribose)]Cl.$	201(±45)	n/a
6-mercaptopurine ribose.	15.7($\pm.8$)	100(±7)
$[Cp_2Mo(2\text{-}amino\text{-}6\text{-}mercaptopurine)]Cl.$	15(±2)	16 (±2)
2-amino-6-mercaptopurine.	7.1($\pm.4$)	239(±33)
$[Cp_2Mo((-)\text{-}2\text{-}amino\text{-}6\text{-}mercaptopurine\ ribose)]Cl.$	277(±25)	n/a
(-)-2-amino-6-mercaptopurine ribose.	31.8($\pm.1$)	100(±4)
$Cp_2MoCl_2.$	2600(±300)	Proliferative effect

The cytotoxic activity of [Cp$_2$Mo(thionucleobase)]Cl complexes deserves additional explanation. The cytotoxic activity of these [Cp$_2$Mo(thionucleobase)]Cl complexes differs markedly from the Cp$_2$Mo(L)$_2$ complexes (L = glutathione, S-4-thio-2,3,4,6-tetrafluorobenzoic acid, S-1-thio-β-D-glucose and S-1-thio-2,3,4,5-tetracaetic β-D-glucose) presented above for the following rationale. The Cp$_2$Mo(L)$_2$ derivatives have two Mo-S bonds, whereas, the [Cp$_2$Mo(thionucleobase)]Cl complexes contain one Mo-S and one Mo-N bonds in the ancillary positions. The Mo(IV)-S bond is more inert than Mo(IV)-N bond. [47] Since in the Cp$_2$Mo(L)$_2$ complexes (L = glutathione, S-4-thio-2,3,4,6-tetrafluorobenzoic acid, S-1-thio-β-D-glucose and S-1-thio-2,3,4,5-tetracaetic β-D-glucose) both ancillary ligands involve thiolate coordination, the availability of vacant coordination sites at this position is unlikely. In the [Cp$_2$Mo(thionucleobase)]Cl complexes, the Mo(IV)-N bond is more labile than Mo(IV)-S bond [47] and the hydrolysis of this bond allow one vacant site on the Mo(IV) center to further react with important biomolecules and express antiproliferative activity.

The role of oxygen containing chelating ligands was also investigated. While based on thermodynamic considerations, the Mo(IV)-O bond strength in Cp$_2$Mo^{2+} is stronger than Mo(IV)-S [48,49], the Mo(IV)-O bond is more labile [47]. Thus, the objective of these two compounds (Cp$_2$Mo(malonate) and [Cp$_2$Mo(maltolato)]Cl) was also to elucidate the role of the oxygen chelating ligands, the aqueous stability and charge on the molybdenocene cytotoxic activity.

The syntheses of water soluble Cp$_2$Mo(malonate) and [Cp$_2$Mo(maltolato)]Cl were carried out by reacting Cp$_2$MoCl$_2$ with sodium malonate or maltol in a 1:1 ratio in water, Figure 7. [38] These species were characterized chemically, electrochemically and biochemically. First, these species are stable at pH of 7.4 for several days without decomposition. The NMR data provided evidence that the chelating ligands are located in the horizontal plane, making the structures very symmetric and the Cp rings become magnetically equivalents, as shown in Figure 7.

The electrochemical characterization of Cp$_2$Mo(malonate) and [Cp$_2$Mo(maltolato)]Cl was performed using cyclic voltammetry (cv), in order to study the redox behavior of the molybdenocene complexes in aqueous environment. This data is important because there are many redox processes involved in the cell that could result in damages to biological molecules and because these species are known to be genotoxic due to their redox behavior. Furthermore, not only Mo(IV) but also Mo(VI) has shown to possess anti-cancer properties. [50] The cyclic voltammograms (Figure 8) of the Cp$_2$MoCl$_2$, Cp$_2$Mo(malonate) and [Cp$_2$Mo(maltolato)]Cl showed that all molybdenum (IV) species exhibit irreversible electrochemical behaviors under physiological conditions. The oxidation potentials for Cp$_2$Mo(malonate), 790 mV and [Cp$_2$Mo(maltolato)]Cl, 800 mV, are higher than the oxidation potential of Cp$_2$MoCl$_2$, 700 mV, which indicate higher stability in aqueous solution under physiological conditions than molybdenocene dichloride, as expected due to the stability imparted by a chelating ligand. The irreversible oxidation potentials of Cp$_2$MoCl$_2$, Cp$_2$Mo(malonate) and [Cp$_2$Mo(maltolato)]Cl have been attributed to the formation of electrodeficient and reactive Mo(V) species, or the formation of a stable Mo(V)-oxo complex, that prevents the reverse reduction. Additionally, the effect on the charge on the molybdenocene complexes (Cp$_2$Mo(malonate), 790 mV and [Cp$_2$Mo(maltolato)]Cl, 800 mV) is negligible based on the oxidation potentials. [38]

As mentioned in the previous section, human serum albumin (HSA) has been proposed to be responsible for carrying/stabilizing molybdenocene species into the target places in the cell. [37] Therefore, the binding interactions between Cp_2MoCl_2, Cp_2Mo(malonate) and [Cp_2Mo(maltolato)]Cl complexes and human serum albumin (HSA) under physiological conditions were investigated using cyclic voltammetry, see Table 3 below. [38] Since the molybdenocene-HSA interaction is mainly hydrophobic and there is no change in coordination about the Mo(IV) center, a change in current was monitored in the titration since it could be associated to a change in the diffusion as a result of molybdenocene incorporating in the hydrophobic pocket of HSA. This binding study revealed that Cp_2MoCl_2 has higher affinity to HSA than Cp_2Mo(malonate) and [Cp_2Mo(maltolato)]Cl complexes. [38]

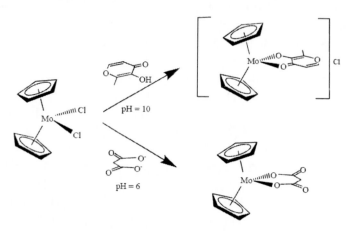

Figure 7. Synthesis and structures of molybdenocene derivatives.

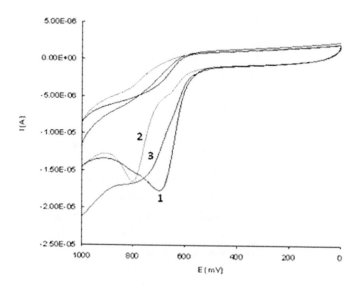

Figure 8. Cyclic voltammograms of Cp_2MoCl_2, 1, Cp_2Mo(malonate), 2 and [Cp_2Mo(maltolato)]Cl, 3 complexes, at a scan rate of 100 mV/s and in 100mM Tris/ 10mM NaCl pH 7.4, as supporting electrolyte. [M] = 5.0 x 10-4 M.

Table 3. Binding interactions of molybdenocene complexes with HSA in 100 mM Tris/ 10 mM NaCl buffer solution monitored by cv at a scan rate of 100 mV/s and cytotoxic activity on HT-29 colon cancer cell line at 72 h

Complex	Mo-HSA interaction % ΔI (± sd)	IC_{50} (mM) HT-29 (± sd)
Cp_2MoCl_2	32(7)	2.6 (0.3)
Cp_2Mo(malonate)	21(5)	1.31 (0.02)
[Cp_2Mo(maltolato)]Cl	15(4)	1.9 (0.3)

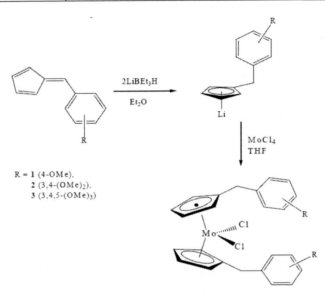

R = 1 (4-OMe),
    2 (3,4-(OMe)$_2$),
    3 (3,4,5-(OMe)$_3$)

Figure 9. Reaction sequence for the synthesis of benzyl-substituted molybdenocene dichlorides.

To further investigate the role of the chelating ancillary ligands on molydenocene complex and correlate it with Mo(IV)-HSA binding and biological activity, cytotoxic studies on HT-29 colon cancer and MCF-7 breast cancer cell lines were pursued. Both species, Cp_2Mo(malonate) and [Cp_2Mo(maltolato)]Cl complexes, are more cytotoxic on HT-29 colon cancer cells than Cp_2MoCl_2, nevertheless the enhancement is not very noteworthy (Table 3). Particularly important is that the less cytotoxic complex, Cp_2MoCl_2, is the one with higher HSA binding affinity. Therefore, the authors concluded that there is no correlation between molybdenocene-HSA binding affinity and cytotoxic activity of the complexes in HT-29 cells. [38] By contrast, in hormone dependent MCF-7 breast cancer cell line, none of the molybdenum complexes exhibit antiproliferative effects, instead they showed proliferative effects. In fact, incorporation of maltolate and malonate ligands on molybdenocene yields complexes with higher proliferative effects on MCF-7 than Cp_2MoCl_2. Thus, this proliferative activity has been attributed to the estrogen-like effects of the molybdenocene species on hormone dependent cancer cell line with possible coordination interactions with cysteines of the estrogen receptor. [44-46] Recently, Tacke and coworkers have pursued the functionalization of molybdenocene dichloride incorporating pendant groups on the cyclopentadienyl ligands to improve its anticancer activity. [51] In this regard, benzyl-substituted molybdenocene dichlorides were synthesized by reacting the corresponding methoxy substituted fulvane and LiBEt$_3$H, forming the lithium salt of the cyclopentadienide and subsequent reaction with MoCl$_4$, according to the reaction below, Figure 9. [51] The *in vitro* cytotoxic studies on human renal cell line Caki-1 at 48 h revealed that 2 and 3, both displayed the same low cytotoxicity IC$_{50}$ values of 290 µM while substantial improvement was observed for molybdenocene 1, with IC$_{50}$ of 84 µM. Cp$_2$MoCl$_2$ has IC$_{50}$ activities > 290 µM. [51] In comparison with isostructural metallocenes of Ti and V, (IC$_{50}$ 21 µM and 3.0 µM), molybdenocene 1 does not reach the same level of cytotoxicity. Nevertheless, this study highlights the importance of the p-methoxyphenyl substituent on the Cp ring since the di- and tri-substituted Cp rings yield molybdenocenes with low cytotoxic. [51] This provides some fertile grounds to further explore structure-activity studies on molybdenocenes and it is clear that it is an unexplored area of research.

4. ORGANOMETALLIC MO(II) COMPLEXES

The antitumor properties of low valent organo-molybdenum complexes are recently receiving more attention and new families of Mo(II) cytotoxic agents are currently being developed. Calhorda and co-workers prepared a series of molybdenum(II) η^3-allyldicarbonyl complexes with a variety of pyridil and pyridine ligands 2-(2'-pyridyl)imidazole, 2-(2'-pyridyl)benzimidazole,   N,N'-bis(2'-pyridinecarboxamido)-1,2-ethane,   and   2,2'-bisimidazole), 1-5, see Figure 10. [52] The molecular structure determined by X-ray diffraction, Figure 11, showed that 1 is a binuclear complex with the N,N'-bis(2'-pyridinecarboxamido)-1,2-ethane ligand bridging two Mo(η^3-C$_3$H$_5$)Br(CO)$_2$ moieties. Each metal center is in a pseudo-octahedral coordination environmernt. [Mo(η^3-C$_3$H$_5$)Br(CO)$_2$(µ-N,N'-bis(2'pyridinecarboxamido)-1,2-ethane] displays a two fold symmetry bisecting the bridging ligand and N-H binding groups are hydrogen bonded to bromine atoms. [52] The solid state structure of 5 was also determined by single crystal X-ray diffraction, Figure 12. The complex is in a pseudo-octahedral coordination environment and it is self assembled with two hydrogen bonds between the triflates (O) and the N-H of pyridylbenzimidazole ligands with a N-H···O distance of 2.02 Å. [52]

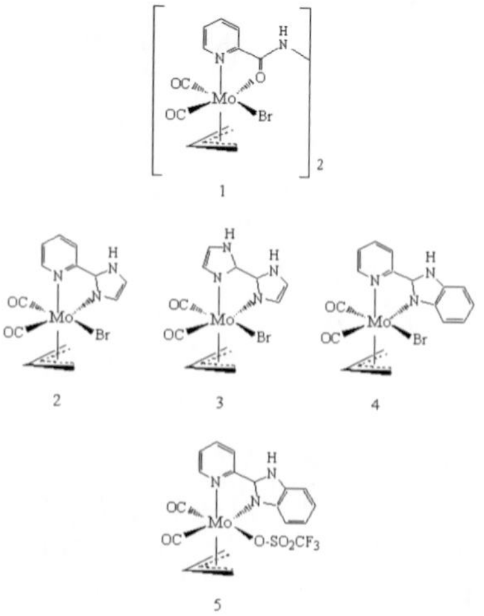

Figure 10. Structures of pyridil and pyridine molybdenum(II) complexes.

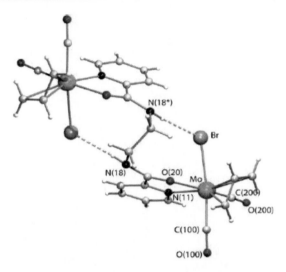

Figure 11. Molecular structure of 1, [Mo(η3-C3H5)Br(CO)₂(μ-N,N'-bis(2'pyridinecarboxamido)-1,2-ethane]. Reproduced with permission of Elsevier, J. Organometallic Chemistry.

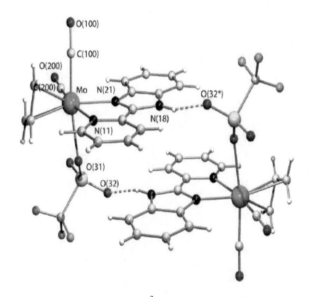

Figure 12. Molecular structure of 5, [Mo(η³-C₃H₅)(CF₃SO₃(CO)₂(2-(2'-pyridyl)benzimidazole)]. Reproduced with permission of Elsevier, J. Organometallic Chemistry.

Table 4. Cytotoxic studies of complexes 1-5 on HeLa cervical cancer cell line at 48 h

Complex	IC_{50} (μM)
1	>300
2	118
3	100
4	15
5	12

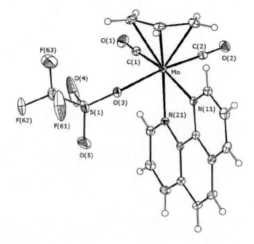

Figure 13. Structures of $[Mo(\eta^3\text{-allyl})(CO)_2(N\text{-}N)X]$ complexes. N-N = 1,10-phenantroline and bipyridil; X = Br, CF$_3$SO$_3$.

Figure 14. Molecular structure of a, $[Mo(\eta^3\text{-allyl})(CO)_2(1,10\text{-phenantroline})X]$. Reproduced with permission of Elsevier, J. Inorganic Biochemistry.

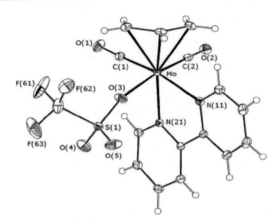

Figure 15. Molecular structure of **c**, $[Mo(\eta^3\text{-allyl})(CO)_2(2,2'\text{-bipyridil})(CF_3SO_3)]$. Reproduced with permission of Elsevier, J. Inorganic Biochemistry.

These pseudo-octahedral complexes were initially tested as catalyst precursors for olefin epoxidation exhibiting moderate catalytic activity. In contrast, they showed good cytotoxic activity in HeLa cervical carcinoma cell line with IC_{50} values in the low micromolar range, in particular for complexes 4 and 5, Table 4. [52]

The same research group also synthesized a series of trinuclear molybdenum(II) η^3-allyldicarbonyl complexes, $[Mo(\eta^3\text{-allyl})(CO)_2(L_2)Br]$, where L = ferrocenoyl benzimidazole and ferrocenoyl imidazole, and examined their cytotoxic activity. [53] While the addition of ferrocenyl moiety may enhance the biological activity of the Mo(II) complexes since ferrocene/ferrocenium is active in cancer cell lines, the outcome complexes rendered detrimental as the trinuclear species showed no cytotoxic activity on MCF-7 breast cancer and HeLa cervical cancer cell lines. [53]

A series of biologically active Mo(II) complexes have been reported recently with apparently different mechanism action of molybdenocene.dichloride. The series of complexes, $[Mo(\eta^3\text{-allyl})(CO)_2(N\text{-}N)X]$ (N-N = 1,10-phenanthroline and 2,2'-bipyridil; X = Br, CF_3SO_3), with structures a-d in Figure 13, have been fully characterized by NMR spectroscopy and X-ray diffraction methods. [54] The crystal structures of a and c (molybdenum(II) η^3-allyldicarbonyl derivatives), Figures 14 and 15, showed both complexes have pseudo-octahedral coordination with two nitrogen donors of the chelating ligands occupying axial and equatorial positions. The second axial position is occupied by the centroid of the allyl ligand. The allyl and carbonyl ligands are in a *fac* configuration consistent with the solution NMR studies. On the other hand, solution NMR studies showed that the bromide analogs b and d exist as equatorial isomers, where the nitrogens of 1,10-phenantroline and bipyridil occupy two equatorial positions. [54]

The cell uptake, lipophilicity, and antitumor properties of these species were thoroughly investigated. The intracellular content of Mo with b and c complexes on HeLa cell line showed that the cells treated with the bromide derivative of molybdenum(II) η^3-allyldicarbonyl, b, have higher content of Mo than the triflate species c. To support this, octanol/water partition coefficients were determined to predict the capability of these complexes to cross the cell membrane. [54] Complex b, $[Mo(\eta^3\text{-allyl})(CO)_2(phen)Br]$, showed lipophilic behavior that is consistent with the levels of intracellular Mo determined in the cell uptake studies, whereas **c** complex ([Mo(η^3-allyl)(CO)$_2$(bipy)CF$_3$SO$_3$]) presented very low lipophilicity.

But cytotoxic assays on cervical HeLa, breast MCF-7 and neuroblastoma N1E-115 cancer cell lines, Table 5, demonstrated that a, [Mo(η^3-allyl)(CO)$_2$(phen) CF$_3$SO$_3$], and b, [Mo(η^3-allyl)(CO)$_2$(phen)Br], are the most potent antitumoral drugs, being a, the triflate derivative the most active. Also b complex ([Mo(η^3-allyl)(CO)$_2$(phen)Br]) is more cytotoxic and more hydrophobic than c. This difference in structure between b and c may explain the difference in antitumor properties between b and c. The 1,10-phenantroline ligand has better capability to interact with DNA, as explained below, enhancing the cytotoxic activity of its complexes. [54]

To gain insights about the mechanism of action of these Mo(II) species, DNA-drug binding studies were performed by electronic absorption spectroscopy (UV-Vis). The DNA binding studies support the hypothesis that these species elicit cytotoxic activity via intercalation according to the spectral behavior of DNA. [54] The binding constants determined for b and c, 2.08 x 10^5 M^{-1} and 3.68 x 10^5 M^{-1} (at 37^{0}C), respectively, suggest that the Mo(II) complexes with phenanthroline chelating ligand are more cytotoxic than the corresponding one with bipyridine due to its ability to intercalate between the DNA strands.

Non-steroidal anti-inflammatory drugs such as aspirin (ASS) have demonstrated activity in the prevention of colon cancer. ASS mechanism of action involves the inhibition of cyclooxygenase enzymes COX-1 and COX-2, affecting more COX-1 variant than COX-2, but without cytotoxic effects. [55] Pharmacological inhibition of COX can provide relief from the symptoms of *inflammation* and *pain*. To improve the biological activity of ASS for the treatment of cancer, a metal moiety has been attached to ASS. This metal moiety, in principle, should enhance the anticancer activity of aspirin since it has a redox active metal center. In this regard, molybdenum complexes containing the non-steroidal anti-inflammatory drug aspirin (ASS) as pendant group on the cyclopentadienyl ring have been synthesized, ASS-Cp-Mo and ASS-Cp-Mo-I, see Figure 16, below.

The cytotoxic effects of ASS-Cp-Mo and ASS-Cp-Mo-I were investigated in HT-29 colon cancer, MDA-MB-231 and MCF-7 breast cancer cell lines, Table 6. The selection of MDA-MB-231 and MCF-7 breast cancer cells was based on the following properties. MCF-7 cell line has a basal level of COX-1 and small and transient amount of COX-2 whereas MDA-MB-231 cells have low concentration of COX-1 and high concentration of COX-2. [55]

The study demonstrated that the three metallic species were more active than the ASS. The replacement of Tl for Mo-carbonyls slightly reduces the activity on MCF-7 cells. Additionally, these complexes were less cytotoxic in MDA-MB-231 cells than in MCF-7. In HT-29 cells, all the species have very similar cytotoxicities. [55]

Table 5. *In vitro* cytotoxicity assays of [Mo(η^3-allyl)(CO)$_2$(N-N)X] complexes on HeLa, MCF-7 and N1E-115 cell lines at 48 h of drug exposure

Complex	IC$_{50}$ (µM), HeLa	IC$_{50}$ (µM), MCF-7	IC$_{50}$ (µM),NiE-115
A	2.9 ± 0.004	13.4 ± 0.7	3.5 ± 1.0
B	5.1 ± 1.0	8.9 ± 0.5	32.5 ± 1.3
C	23.7 ± 0.005	44.5 ± 0.7	60.0 ± 0.4
D	38.9 ± 7.9	30.6 ± 10.0	--

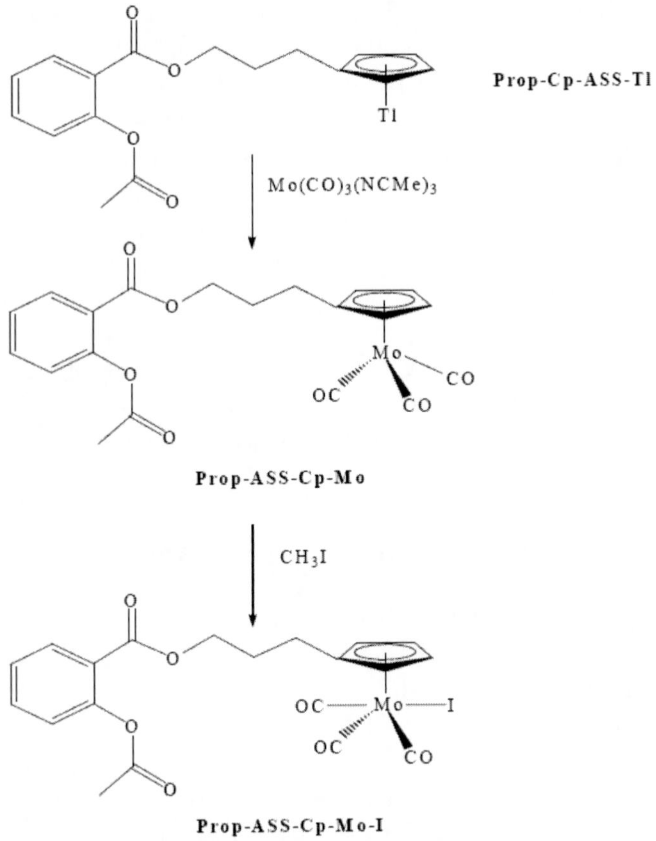

Figure 16. Synthetic route and structures of [cyclopentadienyl]molybdenumtricarbonyl complexes of acetylsalicyclic acid.

Table 6. Cytotoxic effects of Prop-Cp-ASS-metal compounds on cancer cell lines

Complex	IC_{50} (μM), MCF-7	IC_{50} (μM), MDA-MB-231	IC_{50} (μM), HT-29
ASS	>50	>50	>50
Prop-Cp-ASS-Mo	14.0(3.6)	26.1(0.2)	13.8(2.6)
Prop-Cp-ASS-Mo-I	13.7(2.4)	31.3(2.6)	12.0(1.6)
Prop-Cp-ASS-Tl	7.3(2)	11.7(.9)	12.1(2.3)

Table 7. COX inhibition assay of metallic species

Complex	COX-1 inhibition	COX-2 inhibition
ASS	29.2%	1%
Prop-Cp-ASS-Mo	27%	24%
Prop-Cp-ASS-Mo-I	11.7%	26%
Prop-Cp-ASS-Tl	27.6%	42.3%

COX inhibitory effects were determined on these species since aspirin mediates its pharmacological effects via inhibition of COX-1 and COX-2 enzymes.

ASS inhibits COX-1 enzyme by 29% while it has no inhibitory effects on COX-2. Prop-Cp-ASS-Tl and Prop-Cp-ASS-Mo have inhibitory effects on COX-1 very similar to aspirin, whereas, Prop-Cp-ASS-Mo-I is less active than ASS (Table 7). In contrast, Cp-ASS-Tl, Prop-Cp-ASS-Mo and Prop-Cp-ASS-Mo-I were more active on COX-2 than aspirin. Given the fact that these species inhibit COX-2 more strongly than COX-1 but they are less antiproliferative in MDA-MB-231 cells, which express more COX-2 than in MCF-7, demonstrated that the COX inhibitory effects of these Prop-Cp-ASS-M (M = Tl, Mo(CO)$_3$, Mo(CO)$_3$I) species do not correlate with the cytotoxicity against MDA-MB-231 and MCF-7 cells. These results also suggest that the interference of these metallic species in the arachidonic acid cascade (responsible for the production of cyclooxygenases) is not the principal mechanism of action.

The authors conclude that these organometallic species functionalized with ASS exhibit complex pathways in which both, COX-mediated and non-COX-mediated mechanisms, may be present but pharmacological studies are needed to propose a mechanism. [55]

5. INCLUSION COMPLEXES

Inclusion complexes of molybdenocene dichloride with macrocyclic molecules such as cyclodextrins and cucurbiturils have been reported. [56-58] These macrocyclic molecules have been investigated as drug delivery systems. Cyclodextrins (CDs) are cyclic oligosaccharides that have α-1,4 linked D-glucose units forming a toroid structure. In particular β-CD which contains seven glucose units have been used to encapsulate Cp2MoCl2. Cyclodextrins act as molecular hosts to a variety of guest species: ions, metal complexes, polar and non-polar organic molecules. These inclusion complexes have found applications in the formulation of drugs due to the increased aqueous solubility and stability of the drugs and better oral absorption. Host-guest inclusion complexes between Cp$_2$MoCl$_2$ and β-CD, heptakis-2,3,6-tri-O-methyl-β-CD (TRIMEB-β-CD) and 2-hydroypropyl-β-CD (HP-β-CD) (Figure 17) have been characterized structurally and their cytotoxic properties explored. [56,57] According to the solid state structural characterization combined with ab initio calculations, Cp$_2$MoCl$_2$ is encapsulated inside the β-CD and HP-β-CD cavities. These adducts exhibit strong host-guest interactions and penetration of one or both Cp rings inside the cavity are possible inclusion geometries. The Cp$_2$MoCl$_2$·TRIMEB-β-CD adduct showed weak host-guest interaction. [57]

In vitro study of the inclusion species on HeLa cervical cancer and healthy cell lines (BJ fibroblast) was pursued. From this study it was concluded the following. First, cyclodextrins can enhance the antitumor activity of Cp$_2$MoCl$_2$. Second, the Cp$_2$MoCl$_2$·TRIMEB-β-CD showed the highest cytotoxic activity toward HeLa cervical cancer cell line at 72 h. Third, Cp$_2$MoCl$_2$ and Cp$_2$MoCl$_2$·β-CD have higher toxicity toward healthy cells than Cp2MoCl2·TRIMEB-β-CD and Cp2MoCl2·HP-β-CD. The antiproliferative and cytotoxic effects of Cp$_2$MoCl$_2$·TRIMEB-β-CD and Cp$_2$MoCl$_2$·HP-β-CD are reversible by 75-80% in HeLa cells and 85-90% for healthy cell line (fibroblast). The Cp$_2$MoCl$_2$·TRIMEB-β-CD adduct displayed the highest antitumor activity and the lowest toxicity toward non-neoplastic cells. [57] Another type of macrocyclic molecule studied as possible drug delivery systems is the cucurbit[n]urils, Cucurbit[n]urils (CB[n]s) are pumkin-like *macrocyclic molecules* made of *glycoluril* [=C$_4$H$_2$N$_4$O$_2$=] monomers linked by *methylene* groups, Figure 18. [59]

Cucurbit[n]urils have two hydrophilic carbonyls lined portals, capping the inner hydrophobic cavity. Their cavity size depends on the number (n) of glycoluril units. CB[7] and CB[8] have portal widths of 5.4 and 6.9 Å and cavity widths of 7.3 and 8.8 Å respectively. CB[n]s have very similar host-guest interactions as the cyclodetrins. [59]

The inclusion complexes of molybdenocene dichloride with cucurbit[n]urils, n = 7, 8, and their cytotoxic activities on MCF-7 breast cancer and 2008 (human ovary carcinoma) cell lines were investigated [58]. NMR experiments, under rigorous exclusion of oxygen, showed that CB[7] can encapsulate $Cp_2Mo(OH)(H_2O)^+$ at pD 7.0 and at pD 2.0 forming a 1:1 host-guest complex. Molecular modeling studies for $CB[7]-Cp_2Mo(OH)(H2O)^+$ suggests that the metallocene is encapsulated deep inside the cavity. The presence of oxygen promotes the catalytic degradation of CB[7] by the encapsulated Mo(IV) species. The encapsulation of $Cp_2Mo(OH)(H_2O)^+$ in CB[8] was not detected by spectroscopic methods but, NMR experiments showed that the presence of oxygen in the sample solution promoted CB[8] degradation as well. [58] In vitro studies on MCF-7 breast cancer cell and 2008 cell (derived from human ovary carcinoma) lines were performed on $CB[7]-Cp_2Mo(OH)(H_2O)^+$ and showed that the encapsulated species has improved antiproliferative activity on both cell lines than Cp_2MoCl_2, most likely as a result of the improved solubility and membrane permeability. [58]

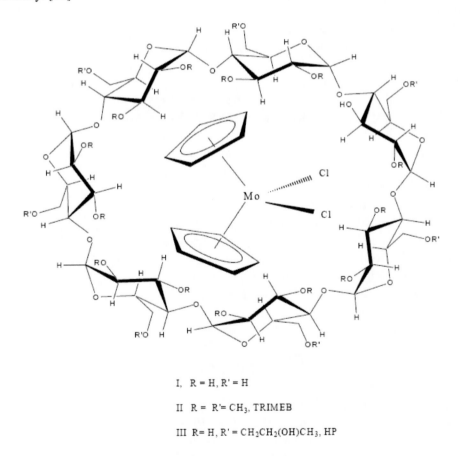

I, R = H, R' = H

II R = R'= CH₃, TRIMEB

III R= H, R' = CH₂CH₂(OH)CH₃, HP

Figure 17. Representation of β-CD- Cp₂MoCl₂ inclusion complex.

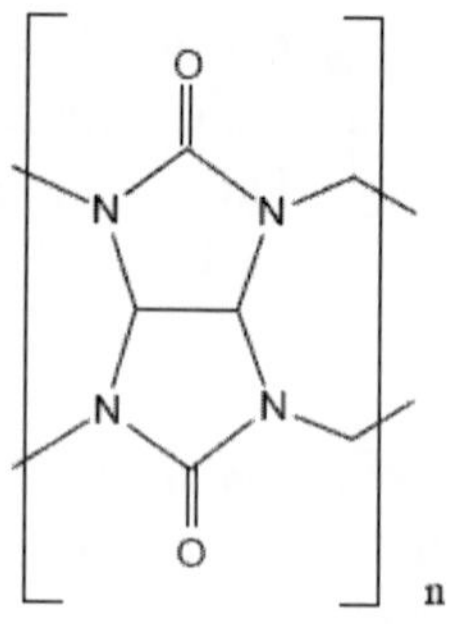

Figure 18. General chemical structure of cucurbit[n]uril, where n = 5, 6, 7, 8, 10.

CONCLUSION

The contribution of the organometallic chemistry of molybdenum in the development of metal-based anticancer agents was clearly demonstrated with molybdenocene dichloride, its derivatives and Mo(II) species, but it is an area of research that is largely unexplored. It is clear that organometallic molybdenum complexes provide versatile scaffold for metal-based drug design. In this chapter, we have illustrated two types of organometallic molybdenum complexes in two oxidation states: Mo(IV) and Mo(II).

For molybdenocene dichloride, from the mechanistic point of view, inhibition of protein kinase C (PKC), coordination of Cp_2Mo^{2+} to the Cys residues in tubulin, the interaction of Cp_2MoCl_2 into the hydrophobic pocket of HSA and weak DNA coordination leading to phosphoester bond cleavage are possible target places to be considered to explain the antineoplastic activity. The replacement of the chlorides by other ancillary ligands has provided insights in terms of aqueous stability and antitumor activity and demonstrated that molybdenocene species needs at least one coordination vacant site to remain active as anticancer agent. For Mo(II) species, little information is available regarding the mechanism of action but DNA seems to be the target place.

In the future, we expect more synthetic routes to be developed and new functionalized molybdenocenes (on Cp rings and ancillary ligands) and new Mo(II) species will appear to increase/enhance its anticancer activity and perhaps with different mechanism of actions as those proposed currently. It is evident that there are many possibilities for structure modifications and drug design, and we can expect to see new organometallic molybdenum complexes becoming candidate for clinical trials as anticancer drugs, with molybdenum in different oxidation states.

REFERENCES

[1]   Kisker, C.; Schindelin, H.; Rees, D. C. Molybdenum-Cofactor–Containing Enzymes: Structure and Mechanism, *Ann. Rev Biochem.* 1997, 66: 233.

[2]   Dietary Reference Intake, National Academy Press, Washington D. C. 2002.

[3]   a. Jaouen, G. (Ed.) *Bioorganometallics*, Wiley-VCH Verlag GmbH and Co. KGaA, Weinheim 2006.

b. Jaouen, G.; Meztler-Nolte, N. (Eds.) *Medicinal Organometallic Chemistry*, Springer Heidelberg Dordrecht, London, N. Y. 2010.

[4]   Köpf, H.; Köpf-Maier, P. *Angew. Chem. Int. Ed. Engl.* 1979, 18, 477.

[5]   Köpf-Maier, P. *Eur. J. Clin. Pharmacol.* 1994, 47, 1.

[6]   Köpf-Maier, P.; Köpf, H. *Structure and Bonding* 1988, 70, 103.

[7]   Köpf-Maier, P.; Köpf, H. *Chem. Rev.* 1987, 87, 1137.

[8]   a. Köpf-Maier, P.; Köpf, H. in: Fricker, S. P. (Ed.), *Metal Compounds in Cancer Therapy, Organometallic Titanium, Vanadium, Niobium, Molybdenum and Rhenium Complexes - Early Transition Metal Antitumor Drugs*, Chapman and Hall, London, 1994, pp. 109-146.

        b. Köpf-Maier, P. in Keppler B.K. (Ed.) *Metal complexes in cancer chemotherapy-Antitumor Bis(cyclopentadienyl)metal Complexes*, Weinheim, New York, V. C. H. 1993, pp. 260-296.

[9]   Harding, M. M; Mokdsi, G. *Current Medicinal Chemistry* 2000, 7, 1289.

[10]   Meléndez, E. *Critical Review in Oncology and Hematology*, 2002, 47, 309.

[11]   Köpf-Maier, P.; Köpf, H. *Z. Naturforscher* 1979, 34b, 805.

[12]   Köpf-Maier, P.; Leitener, M.; Voitländer, R.; Köpf, H. *Z. Naturforscher* 1979, 34C, 1174.

[13]   Köpf-Maier, P.; Köpf, H. *Naturwissenschaften* 1980, 67, 415.

[14]   Köpf-Maier, P.; Hesse, B.; Voigtlander, R.; Köpf, H. *J. Cancer Res. Clin. Oncol.* 1980, 97, 31.

[15]   Köpf-Maier, P.; Leitner, M.; Köpf, H. *J. Inorg. Nucl. Chem.* 1980, 42, 1789.

[16]   Kurbacher, C. M.; Bruckner, H. W.; Andreotti, G.; Kurbacher, P. E.; Saβ, J. A.; Krebs, D., In vitro activity of titanocenedichloride versus cisplatin in four ovarian carcinoma cell lines evaluated by a microtiter plate A. T. P. bioluminescence assay, *Anti-Cancer Drugs* 1995, 6, 697.

[17]   Kurbacher, C. M. Mallmann,P. Kurbacher, J. A. Saβ, G. Andreotti, P. E. Rahmun, A. Hübner, H and Krebs, D. *Anti-Cancer. Research* 1994, 14, 1961.

[18]   Villena-Heisen, C.; Friedich, M.; Ertan, A. K.; Farnhammer, C.; Schmidt, W. *Anti-Cancer Drugs* 1998, 9, 557.

[19]   Christodoulou, C. V.; Ferry, D. R.; Fyfe, D. W.; Young, A.; Doran, J.; Sheehan, T. M. T.; Eliopoulos, A.; Hale, K.; Baumgart, J.; Sass, G.; Kerr, D. J. *J. Clin. Oncol* 1998, 16, 2761.

[20]   Kuo, L. Y.; Kanatzidis, M. G.; Sabat, M.; Tipton, A. L.; Marks, T. J. Metallocene Antitumor Agents. Solution and Solid-State Molybdenocene Coordination of D. N. A. Constituents, *J. Am. Chem. Soc.* 1991, 113, 9027.

[21]   Cooper, R. L.; Green, M. L. H. *J. Chem. Soc.* A, 1967, 1155.

[22]   Prout, K.; Cameron, T. S.; Forder, R. A.; Critchley, S. R.; Denton, B.; Rees, G. V. *Acta Cryst.* 1974. B30, 2290.

[23]   Waern, J. B.; Harding, M. M. *J. Organometal. Chem.* 2004, 689, 4655.

[24]   Harding, M. M.; Harden, G. J.; Field, L. D. *F. E. B. S.* 1993, 322, 291.

[25]   Harding, M. M.; Mokdsi, G.; Mackay, J. P.; Prodigalidad, M.; Lucas, S. W. *Inorg. Chem.* 1998, 37, 2432.

[26] L. Y. Kuo, A. H. Liu, T. J. Marks, in: A. Sigel, H. Sigel, (Eds.), Metal Ions in Biological Systems, vol. 33, Metallocene Interactions with D. N. A. and D. N. A. - Processing Enzymes, M. Dekker, New York (1996) 53-85.

[27] Vera, J. L.; Román, F. R.; Meléndez, E. *Anal. Bioanal. Chem.* 2004, 379, 399.

[28] Rodríguez, M. I.; Chávez-Gil, T. E.; Colón, Y.; Díaz, N.; Meléndez, E. *J. Electroanal. Chem.* 2005, 576, 315.

[29] Chavez-Gil, T. E.; Vega, C. A.; López, V.; Meléndez, E. *Biochemistry* 2001, 40, 8650.

[30] López-Ramos, V.; Vega, C. A.; Cádiz, M.; Meléndez, E. *J. Electroanal. Chem.* 2004, 565, 77.

[31] Vera, J. L; Román, F. R.; Meléndez, E. *Biorg. Med. Chem.* 2006 14, 8683.

[32] Kuo, L.; Kuhn, S.; Ly, D. *Inorg. Chem.* 1995, 34, 5341.

[33] Mokdsi, G.; Harding, M. M. *J. Inorg. Biochem.* 2001, 86, 61.

[34] Waern, J. B.; Harding M. M. *Inorg. Chem.* 2004, 43, 206.

[35] Waern, J. B.; Dillon, C. T.; Harding, M. M. *J. Med. Chem.* 2005, 48, 2093.

[36] Waern, J. B.; Harris, H. H; Lai, B.; Cai, Z.; Harding, M. M.; Dillon, C. T. *J. Biol. Inorg. Chem.* 2005, 10, 443.

[37] Campell K. S.: Dillon C. T.: Smith S. V., Harding M. M. *Polyhedron* 2007 26, 456.

[38] Feliciano, I.; Matta, J.; Meléndez, E. *J. Biol. Inorg. Chem.* 2009, 14, 1109.

[39] Tinoco A. D., Eames E. V., Valentine A. M. Reconsideration of serum Ti(IV) transport: albumin and transferrin trafficking of Ti(IV) and its complexes, *J. Am. Chem. Soc.* 2008, 130, 2262.

[40] Ravera, M.; Gabano, E.; Baracco, S.; Osella, D. *Inorg. Chim. Acta* 2009, 362, 1303.

[41] Pavlaki M., Debeli K., Triantaphyllidou I.-E., Klouras N., Giannopoulou E., Aletras A. J. *J. Biol. Inorg. Chem.* 2009, 14, 947.

[42] Campbell, K. S.; Foster, A. J., Dillon, C. T.; Harding, M. M. *J. Inorg. Biochem.* 2006, 100, 1194.

[43] Acevedo-Acevedo, D.; Matta, J.; Meléndez, E. *J. Organometal. Chem.* 2011, 696, 1032.

[44] Vessières, A.; Top, S.; Beck, W.; Hillard, E.; Jaouen, G. *Dalton Trans.* 2006, 529.

[45] Vessières, A.; Plamont, M.-A.; Cabestaing, C.; Claffey, J. ; Dieckmann, S., ; Hogan, M.; Müller-Bunz, H.; Strohfeldt, K.; Tacke, M., *J. Organomet. Chem.* 2009, 694, 874.

[46] Jaouen, G.; Top, S.; Vessières, A.; Leclercq, G.; McGlinchey, M. J. *Curr. Med. Chem.*, 2004, 11, 2505.

[47] Zimmermann, H.; Hegetschweiler, K.; Keller, T.; Gramlich, V.; Schmalle, H. W.; Peter, W.; Schneider, W. *Inorg. Chem.* 1991, 30, 4336.

[48] Calhorda, M. J.; de C. T. Carrondo, M. A. A. F.; Dias, A. R.; Domingos, A. M. T. S.; Simões, J. A.; Teixeira, C. *Organometallics* 1986, 5, 660.

[49] Johnson, A. R.; Davis, W. M.; Cummins, C. C.; Serron, S.; Nolan, S. P.; Morokuma, K. *J. Am. Chem. Soc.* 1998, 120, 2071.

[50] Köpf-Maier, P.; Klapötke, T. *J. Cancer Res. Clin. Oncol.* 1992, 118, 216.

[51] Gleeson, B.; Claffey, J,; Deally, A.; Hogan, M.; Menéndez Méndez, L. M.; Müller-Bunz, H.; Patil, S.; Tacke, M. *Inorg. Chim. Acta* 2010, 363, 1831.

[52] Saraiva, M. S.; Quintal, S.; Portugal, F. C. M.; lopes, T. A.; Félix, V.; Nogueira, J. M. F.; Meireles, M.; Drew, M. G. B.; Calhorda, M. J. *J. Organometal. Chem.* 2008, 693, 3411.

[53] Quintal, S.; Matos, J.; Fonseca, I.; Félix, V.; Drew, M. G. B.; Trindade, N.; Meireles, M.; Calhorda, M. J. *Inorg. Chim. Acta* 2008, 361, 1584.

[54] Bandara, D.; Lopes, M.; Lopes, T.; Almeida, J.; Saraiva, M. S.; Vasconcellos-Dias, M.; Nunes, C. D.; Félix, V.; Brandaoã, P.; Vaz, P. D.; Meireles, M.; Calhorda, M. J. *J. Inorg. Biochem.* 2010, 104, 1171.

[55] Rubner, G.; Bensdorf, K. Wellner, A.; Bergemann, S.; Ott, I.; Gust, R. *Eur. J. Med. Chem.* 2010, 45, 5157.

[56] Braga, S. S; Goncalves, I. S.; Pillinger, M.; Claro-Ribeiro, P.; Teixeira-Dias, J. J. C. *J. Organometal. Chem.* 2001, 632, 11.

[57] Braga, S. S; Marques M. P. M; SoUS, J. B.; Pillinger, M.; Teixeira-Dias, J. J. C.; Goncalves, I. S. *J. Organometal. Chem.* 2005, 690, 2905.

[58] Buck, D. P.; Abeysinghe, P. M.; Cullinane, C.; Day, A. I.; Collins, J. G.; Harding, M. M. *Dalton Trans.*, 2008, 2328.

[59] Wheate, N. J. J. *Inorg. Biochem.* 2008, 102, 2060.

INDEX

hormone(s), 281, 313
host, 111, 205, 320, 321
human, vii, 15, 41, 282, 284, 301, 307, 311, 314, 321
human body, 15
human health, vii
husband, 2
hybrid(s), 18, 38, 54, 111, 113, 115, 245, 257
hydrazine, 28, 95, 98, 261, 264
hydrocarbons, 259
hydrocracking, 12
hydrogen, 11, 12, 19, 38, 39, 40, 90, 91, 100, 110,
    111, 115, 122, 132, 142, 190, 191, 237, 238, 252,
    254, 262, 263, 274, 275, 282, 283, 314
hydrogen atoms, 262
hydrogen bonds, 90, 110, 111, 314
hydrogen peroxide, 190, 191
hydrogen sulfide, 11
hydrogenase, 247
hydrogenation, 130
hydrolysis, 22, 23, 39, 81, 87, 88, 89, 96, 113, 191,
    247, 251, 256, 258, 264, 302, 306, 309, 311
hydrolytic stability, 302
hydrosilylation, 194
hydrothermal process, 38
hydroxide, 31, 288, 294
hydroxyl, 28, 252
hyperfine interaction, 287
hypothesis, 146, 148, 155, 318

I

ID, 91
identification, 148, 161, 228
identity, 150, 246, 248, 252
impotence, 41
impurities, 11
in transition, 275, 276, 277
in vitro, 247, 256, 264, 302, 307, 314
in vivo, 247, 256, 264
incidence, 307
independence, 62
India, 3, 175
individuals, 281
industry, 130
infants, 15
inflammation, 318
infrared spectroscopy, 23
ingestion, 15
inhibition, 260, 283, 318, 319, 322
inhibitor, 247, 248, 250, 259, 261, 264, 277, 283,
    286
initiation, 286
inositol, 106, 112

insertion, 284, 286
integrity, 37, 204
intellect, 4
Inter-American Development Bank, ix, 6
interface, 250, 251, 253, 254, 255, 256, 271
interference, 320
intron, 281
inversion, 114, 170, 171
iodine, 231
ion-exchange, 75, 95
ionization, 288
ions, 17, 18, 21, 23, 30, 36, 57, 58, 60, 61, 66, 73,
    74, 75, 78, 79, 80, 81, 86, 88, 91, 93, 99, 100,
    109, 111, 115, 120, 121, 215, 282, 320
Iowa, 3
IR spectroscopy, 24
iridium, 184
iron, 3, 11, 12, 14, 39, 40, 118, 127, 243, 244, 246,
    271, 279, 280, 281, 282, 283, 285, 292, 293
irradiation, 38, 39
Islam, 49
isolation, 111, 122, 129, 212, 252
isoleucine, 277
isomerization, 97, 124, 126, 166, 196, 199, 215
isomers, 38, 61, 110, 112, 121, 130, 164, 181, 309,
    317
isotope, 13, 85, 279
issues, 13
iteration, 245

J

Jamaica, ix, 6, 9, 22, 45
Japan, 2, 6, 13, 135, 138
Japanese women, 15
Jordan, 45

K

K^+, 77
ketones, 187, 195
kidneys, 41
kinetic parameters, 157
kinetic studies, 81, 88, 89, 94, 99, 284
kinetics, 15, 21, 23, 27, 39, 77, 89, 99, 100, 126, 148,
    151, 152, 276, 286
Korea, 6, 141
Kuwait, 6

L

labeling, 60, 81, 85, 91

Q

R

T

U